£12-40

THIOPHENE
and Its Derivatives

This is the third volume published in the series
THE CHEMISTRY OF HETEROCYCLIC COMPOUNDS

THE CHEMISTRY OF HETEROCYLIC COMPOUNDS

A SERIES OF MONOGRAPHS

ARNOLD WEISSBERGER, *Consulting Editor*

THIOPHENE
and Its Derivatives

HOWARD D. HARTOUGH

Socony-Vacuum Laboratories
Paulsboro, New Jersey

With Special Chapters by
F. P. HOCHGESANG
Socony-Vacuum Laboratories, Paulsboro, New Jersey

and F. F. BLICKE
University of Michigan, Ann Arbor, Michigan

1952

INTERSCIENCE PUBLISHERS, INC., NEW YORK

INTERSCIENCE PUBLISHERS LTD., LONDON

LIBRARY OF CONGRESS CATALOG CARD NUMBER 51-13781

INTERSCIENCE PUBLISHERS, INC., 250 Fifth Ave., New York 1, N. Y.

For Great Britain and Northern Ireland:
Interscience Publishers Ltd., 2a Southampton Row, London W. C. 1

PRINTED IN THE UNITED STATES OF AMERICA BY MACK PRINTING CO., EASTON, PA.

INTRODUCTION TO THE SERIES

The Chemistry of Heterocyclic Compounds

The chemistry of heterocyclic compounds is one of the most complex branches of organic chemistry. It is equally interesting for its theoretical implications, for the diversity of its synthetic procedures, and for the physiological and industrial significance of heterocyclic compounds.

A field of such importance and intrinsic difficulty should be made as readily accessible as possible, and the lack of a modern detailed and comprehensive presentation of heterocyclic chemistry is therefore keenly felt. It is the intention of the present series to fill this gap by expert presentations of the various branches of heterocyclic chemistry. The subdivisions have been designed to cover the field in its entirety by monographs which reflect the importance and the interrelations of the various compounds, and accommodate the specific interests of the authors.

Research Laboratories
Eastman Kodak Company
Rochester, New York

ARNOLD WEISSBERGER

Preface

Since thiophene was discovered in 1882 by Victor Meyer its importance has increased at an accelerating rate. Although there has not been a year from 1883 to the present without publications concerning thiophene or its derivatives, there are three main periods in which the greater proportions of the publications were issued. The first of these was the Victor Meyer period of 1883 to 1888, which culminated in Victor Meyer's book *Die Thiophengruppe* (Braunschweig, 1888). The second period, which should be classified as the Steinkopf period, began in 1918 and continued until 1941. Again the work was summarized in a book by Wilhelm Steinkopf, *Die Chemie des Thiophens* (Verlag von Theodor Steinkopff, Dresden, 1941). The present period of accelerated research, initiated by the commercial availability of thiophene, began in 1945 and promises to continue into the next decade.

The rapid strides in thiophene chemistry between 1944 and 1950 have created the need for the present volume. For example, the subject matter of Chapter IX, one of the longest in the book, is covered in less than a page in *Die Chemie des Thiophens*. I once commented before an American Chemical Society meeting that thiophene chemistry was merely in its infancy, since there were still so many problems to be undertaken and solved before we could know its true character. The remark came back from the floor that, while this was probably true, thiophene chemistry was certainly enjoying a robust and healthy childhood.

The present book was begun in 1947 but so many references appeared in 1947 and 1948 that it was necessary to rewrite most of the chapters as many as three times. The text originally included references up to January 1, 1949. Several hundred references appearing in *Chemical Abstracts* between January 1 and October 1, 1949, were inserted into the completed text but in a number of cases it was not possible to handle these later references in detail. Since October 1, 1949, about four hundred additional articles and patents have been published.

The treatise was designed to cover critically all phases of thiophene chemistry and to point out some of the existing problems yet to be solved. In order to achieve this goal, Dr. F. F. Blicke, Head of the Pharmacy School, University of Michigan, contributed Chapter II on toxicological and pharmacological properties of thiophene, and Mr. F. P. Hochgesang of the Physics Division of the Socony-Vacuum Laboratories reviewed the spectrochemical and related properties of thiophene. In addition,

Chapter IV includes a complete summary of the unpublished data obtained in the Socony-Vacuum Laboratories. These data should be of particular value to petroleum chemists, as well as to organic chemists, in identifying natural-source thiophenes and synthetic thiophenes. The literature was reviewed with the intention of including every significant reference and every derivative of thiophene. It will be appreciated that this is a rather formidable task, and I shall be most grateful to those users of the book who will bring to my attention deficiencies of which they become aware.

In addition to the contributions mentioned above, I am deeply indebted to Drs. A. A. O'Kelly and D. E. Badertscher for their encouragement during the writing period. Dr. S. L. Meisel and Dr. E. M. Crane were especially helpful in proofreading the manuscript and in offering critical comments. Great credit goes to Dr. W. P. Hawthorne for his painstaking proofreading and critical review of the contents of this volume which have immeasurably improved its quality and organization. Special thanks are due to Dr. R. Bulkley, Dr. L. A. Hamilton, and Mr. J. J. Dickert, Jr., who graciously volunteered to help in the tedious task of checking references.

The writing of this book was greatly facilitated by private communications to the author from friends in this country and abroad. Sincere thanks are due Dr. Robert Levine of the University of Pittsburgh, Dr. C. D. Hurd of Northwestern University, Dr. F. F. Nord of Fordham University, and many others. Dr. Otto Dann of the University of Erlangen, Germany, was instrumental in maintaining contact for the author with Dr. Steinkopf and in supplying biographical data about Dr. Steinkopf. He also transmitted information concerning his own work in thiophene chemistry. Dr. Frederick Challenger of the University of Leeds, England, has been helpful in forwarding copies of his articles submitted for publication in English journals many months prior to their availability in this country.

Originally this volume was to include fused ring systems containing thiophene rings such as thianaphthene and dibenzothiophene. To expedite publication of thiophene data, the data on condensed ring systems containing thiophene rings are now scheduled for publication in a separate volume by the present author and Dr. S. L. Meisel which should appear in 1952 or 1953.

Hercules Experiment Station   H. D. H.
Wilmington, Delaware
August, 1951

Contents

CHAPTER I

General Discussion

I. History of Thiophene

The history of thiophene does not actually begin with the discovery and isolation of thiophene in 1882. It begins in 1844 with the synthesis of thionessal (tetraphenylthiophene) by Laurent, although the structure of that compound was not proved until many years later. Dibenzothiophene was discovered in 1870 by Stenhouse, but here again the structure was not fully established until a later date.

Three years before the discovery of thiophene Claisen found that coal tar benzene produced a violet color with phenylglyoxylic acid when concentrated sulfuric acid was added. This was later found by Victor Meyer to be due to the presence of thiophene. In a similar manner, the "indophenine test" for aromatic compounds had been developed by von Baeyer. This test had been accepted for some time as characteristic for aromatic hydrocarbons and was directly responsible for the series of events that led to the discovery of thiophene.

The actual discovery of thiophene by Victor Meyer at Zürich followed from a series of events well worthy of relating again. In 1882 Meyer's good friend, Prof. Wilhelm Weith, died. Meyer was called upon that autumn to present the special series of lectures on aromatic chemistry at Zürich, previously given by Weith. Victor Meyer's generous use of demonstrations in his brilliant lectures called for the use of von Baeyer's indophenine test with "pure benzene" from coal tar. This test consisted of treating benzene and a trace of isatin with a little sulfuric acid, whereby the blue color of indophenine developed. However, at this particular lecture, T. Sandmeyer, Meyer's assistant, preparing the lecture table, substituted synthetic benzene from the dry distillation of calcium benzoate. This material, to Victor Meyer's consternation, failed to give the characteristic test. Sandmeyer called Meyer's attention to the fact that synthetic benzene had been used. In Meyer's own words[1]: "However, the riddle was not completely resolved thereby, and, while I disclosed the

---

[1] V. Meyer, *Die Thiophengruppe*. Braunschweig, 1888, pp. 1–2.

striking phenomenon to my class room, I added the observation that here lay a problem whose experimental solution would certainly yield important information." Victor Meyer set out the same day to investigate this phenomenon and taking the purest commercial benzene available (sold under the name of *Benzol purissim. crystallisatum*) treated it with sulfuric acid and found the "indophenine test," *i.e.*, the test with isatin and sulfuric acid, to be much weaker than with the unpurified product. He then prepared an extract of the commercial benzene by regenerating from the sulfonic acid that was called "activated benzene," since it gave a greatly intensified indophenine test. At this point Meyer surmised that two forms of benzene existed—an "active form" and an "inactive form" in regard to the indophenine test. He also considered that the sulfonic acid of this "active form" of benzene was undergoing the color transformation with isatin and began work on that basis.

Further treatment of ten liters of commercial benzene by "extraction" with sulfuric acid followed by dry distillation of the lead salt of the sulfonic acid contained in the sulfuric acid layer gave Victor Meyer a "single cubic centimeter of a light, water-clear, mobile liquid, that boiled at about 83°, that appeared similar to benzene, yet did not solidify in ice-water and showed very considerable sulfur content." This material gave the most intense indophenine test obtained so far and Meyer then abandoned his theory of an "activated benzene" in favor of a reaction of isatin with a sulfur compound.

At that time a study of the chemistry of dyes such as indophenine and bromoindophenine was being undertaken in von Baeyer's laboratories in an intensive manner and Victor Meyer received considerable encouragement from that source. Von Baeyer sent Meyer samples of indophenine and bromoindophenine and Meyer was able to point out to von Baeyer that they contained sulfur and were formed from the reaction of isatin and thiophene in the presence of sulfuric acid.

Through friends, R. Bindschedler and R. Gnehm, Victor Meyer was able to persuade the Farbenfabrik Bindschedler, Busch and Co. to extract some 250 liters of benzene with 25 liters of concentrated sulfuric acid. The "black-acid" received by this process was converted to the lead salt and dry distillation of this salt with ammonium chloride gave a "crude thiophene." The thiophene received by this treatment, 140 g. from a 2660 g. portion of the lead salt, was found to boil at 84° and contain about 28% sulfur (the sample was about 70% thiophene and 30% benzene). A portion, 70 g., was brominated and a dibromo derivative, which analyzed as $C_4H_2Br_2S$, was obtained. Victor Meyer then could surmise that the original material, before bromination, was C_4H_4S. The dibromothiophene resisted dehydrobromination in boiling alcoholic

potassium hydroxide and the bromo groups could not be removed by
reduction. Its properties were similar to those of the bromobenzenes
and Victor Meyer quickly grasped its aromatic nature. The history of
the naming of the C_4H_4S compound is described by Thorpe.[2] He states
that Meyer's first inclination was to use the name *thianthren*, then *thiophan*,
next *thiol*, and finally *thiophen*, to denote that it was a sulfur-containing
compound giving derivatives analogous to those of the phenyl series.

With the cooperation of the Fabrik Griesheim Co. at Frankfurt am
Main and the Anilinfarbenfabrik Gans und Co., some 2000 kg. of pure,
half-degree benzene was treated with 100 kg. of concentrated sulfuric
acid, and 1944 g. of pure thiophene of sulfur content 38.02% (38.1% is
the theoretical) was obtained. Victor Meyer then set out to determine
the chemistry of thiophene. Its structure was established by a ring-
closure synthesis from the reaction of succinaldehyde or succinic acid
with phosphorus pentasulfide.

After the process for the extraction of thiophene from benzene was
announced, the Schuchardt Co. in Görlitz made thiophene available at
130 marks per kilogram. Victor Meyer indicates that after obtaining
1 kg. from that source he abandoned it in favor of his own synthetic
methods by ring closure.

The methylthiophenes were isolated from coal tar toluene in much
the same manner and were eventually synthesized by ring closure of
levulinic acid (2-methylthiophene) and methylsuccinic acid (3-methyl-
thiophene).

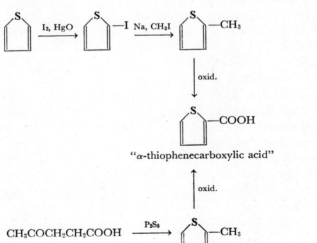

(1)

"α-thiophenecarboxylic acid"

---

[2] Thorpe, *J. Chem. Soc.*, **77**, 169 (1900). British Chemical Society's Victor Meyer
Memorial Lecture.

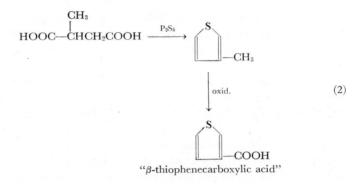

$$\text{(2)}$$

"β-thiophenecarboxylic acid"

Orientation in the thiophene series was carried out with the methylthiophenes as shown in equations (1) and (2) above.

In *Die Thiophengruppe*,[1] Meyer summarizes the approach he and his students took to the problem. The conclusions reached at that time concerning the structure of thiophene have not changed to the present day. In 1888, when Victor Meyer completed his book after five years of active research, 106 publications on thiophene chemistry had been released from his laboratories at the Universities of Zürich (1882–1885) and Göttingen (1885–1888). Only 25 publications appeared from other laboratories during that period.

From the time of publication of *Die Thiophengruppe* until the Victor Meyer Memorial Lecture was given by Thorpe[2] in 1900, an additional 50 articles appeared in the literature. This attests to the interest aroused by the new chemistry of thiophene.

In 1910 Dr. Wilhelm Steinkopf at Karlsruhe University (later at the Dresden Technical Academy) began what developed into a lifetime study of thiophene chemistry. He published consistently during the thirty years until his retirement in 1940, primarily in *Liebig's Annalen*. Approximately 65 lengthy articles have appeared under his name that have greatly advanced the chemistry of thiophene. His book *Die Chemie des Thiophens*[3] published in 1941 summarized the chemistry of thiophene up to that date. Steinkopf used synthetic thiophene as his starting material and describes in his book the apparatus in which almost daily runs were made with phosphorus sulfides and disodium succinate. To say that Steinkopf centered his work on any one branch of thiophene chemistry would be an understatement, since reference to his work will be found in nearly all of the chapters of this book. He contributed prolifically to the mercuration of thiophene, the halogenation of thiophene, and the synthesis of many new thiophene derivatives. His work

[3] Steinkopf, *Die Chemie des Thiophens*. Steinkopff, Leipzig, 1941. Lithoprinted by Edward Brothers, Ann Arbor, Mich.

was primarily involved with syntheses rather than theoretical aspects of thiophene chemistry, although contributions in the latter field are not lacking.

Wilhelm Steinkopf was born in Stassfurt on June 28, 1879. He attended grammar school there and in Bernburg where the family moved after his mother's early death. He matriculated at Heidelberg where he attended lectures of Curtius. After three semesters at Heidelberg, he transferred to Karlsruhe and studied under Engler, Bunte, LeBlanc, Haber, Scholl, and the physician, O. Lehmann. He received his Dr.-Ing. degree in 1909 and upon graduation became a member of the staff at Karlsruhe. During World War I, 1915 to 1918, he worked at the Kaiser Wilhelm Institute for Physical and Electro-chemistry. He returned briefly to Karlsruhe and then was called to the Institute for Organic Chemistry at the Dresden Technical Academy. In 1934 he became director, and in 1940 retired as *professor emeritus*. Until his death on March 12, 1949, Dr. Steinkopf had lived in Niebelsbach, Swabia, near the Black Forest in Germany.

The present commercial process for the synthesis of thiophene, developed in the Socony-Vacuum Laboratories in the early 1940's, adds another case of serendipity to the history of thiophene. A. N. Sachanen, R. C. Hansford, and H. E. Rasmussen, in studying methods of dehydro-genating butane to butadiene, examined the dehydrogenation of butane with sulfur and discovered that thiophene was being formed in the process. After suitable modifications of the sulfur-butane feed streams, it was found that a feasible process for the production of thiophene was at hand. At that time no practical uses of thiophene were apparent. In 1943, J. H. McCracken prepared a literature survey of the field of thio-phene chemistry. Although this failed to uncover potential commercial uses, the survey was used as the basis of the literature search made by the present author. Almost at the time of completion of McCracken's survey, Steinkopf's book, which had been unavailable due to the war, was obtained.[3] This also failed to disclose any practical commercial uses for thiophene. For that reason, some preliminary studies of the alkylation of thiophene were undertaken very early in these Laboratories. The author's connection with this project began in 1944 and active work was continued for a little more than three years.

Sample distribution of thiophene began late in 1944 and the response of the drug industry, resin industry, dye industry, chemical industry, and the universities in this country and abroad led the Socony-Vacuum Oil Co., Inc., to plan to market thiophene on a modest scale. Initially, samples were supplied from a 100-pound-per-day unit which began production in September, 1945, and later demands required the con-struction of a 1000-pound-per-day unit which was put into operation in 1947. During 1946 and 1947 approximately 100 derivatives of thiophene were distributed by Socony-Vacuum to several hundreds of interested parties to facilitate their research. These samples ranged in quantity from one gram to several pounds. 2-Acetylthiophene, *tert*-butylthiophene, di-*tert*-butylthiophene, and 2-benzoylthiophene, as well as 2- and 3-methylthiophenes, have been available in pilot plant scale.

At the present writing, the only commercial use for the thiophenes is in the form of intermediates for the production of antihistaminic drugs (see Chapters II and IX for more specific details). Their use in the dye industry is being considered seriously, but production has not yet started. Thiophene has been considered as a dewaxing solvent, paint remover, intermediate in phenol-formaldehyde plastics, resin intermediate, and as an intermediate in preparation of antispasmodic drugs. Fundamentally, thiophene looks quite promising in the resin industry because of its difunctional characteristics due to the extreme activity of positions 2 and 5, but until the present time this work has been discouraging due to light instability of the thiophene unit in the resins. It is possible that this color instability can be overcome, but no study of the subject has been made.

II. Nomenclature of Thiophene Compounds

The *Ring Index*, system 114, refers to C_4H_4S as *thiophene*, thiofuran, thiole, thiofurfuran, thiotetrole, and divinylene sulfide. Its tetrahydro form, C_4H_4S, is named *thiolane*, tetramethylene sulfide, and thiacyclopentane. No name is assigned to the dihydro form, C_4H_6S. *Chemical Abstracts* uses *thiophene* for C_4H_4S, tetrahydrothiophene for C_4H_8S, and dihydrothiophene for C_4H_6S. Since the di- and tetrahydrothiophene names are cumbersome to use, the American Chemical Society Subcommittee for Heterocyclic Nomenclature has accepted tentatively the author's suggestion that the three proper names of thiophene and its hydrogenated forms shall be as follows:

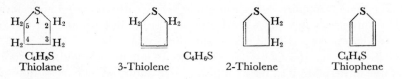

This same Subcommittee has not yet recommended any major changes in thiophene nomenclature over that now in current use by *Chemical Abstracts*. The nomenclature used by *Chemical Abstracts* is not always the most convenient nor the most accurate and the author has taken some liberties in this book in order to render a more usable form.

Unfortunately, there are no hard and fast rules for thiophene nomenclature, and thiophene takes on peculiar root and prefix forms that are rather foreign to the basic name thiophene and their origin is subject to practically no rules of nomenclature. It is to be hoped that the nomenclature can be systematized and adhered to more closely than in the past. In general, the following roots can be used systematically applying standard nomenclature rules:

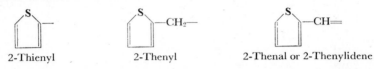

| 2-Thienyl | 2-Thenyl | 2-Thenal or 2-Thenylidene |

Table I-1 lists the nomenclature as it appears in *Chemical Abstracts*, as found in this book, and less common terms which have been used, in some instances, incorrectly.

Thiophene nomenclature has undergone a number of changes. Originally, Victor Meyer labeled the sulfur atom as the α-position and the other positions β, γ, β', γ' as follows:

A few years later this was changed to the α, β, α', β' nomenclature used for many years, *i.e.*, the 2,5-positions were designated as α,α' and the 3,4-positions became β,β':

This type of positional designation is now obsolete.

A recent communication to the author from S. S. Kurtz, Jr., Chairman of the Nomenclature Committee, Division of Petroleum Chemistry regarding nomenclature to be used in A. P. I. Project #48 reports states in part: "Compounds containing the thiophene ring shall be named in such a manner that 'thiophene' forms the base of the name. Thus benzothiophene rather than thianaphthene. Radical names such as thenyl and thienyl shall be recognized. Fully or partially hydrogenated thiophenes as well as any other sulfur-containing cyclic compounds, other than those containing thiophene, shall be named using the thia system." This last portion on hydrogenated thiophenes is not in accord with the recommendations of the A. C. S. Subcommittee on Heterocyclic Nomenclature and it further serves to point out the need for a standard, systematic nomenclature.

TABLE I-1. Nomenclature of Thiophene Compounds

Compound	Chemical Abstracts	This book	Other nomenclature
(thiophene)—COOH	2-Thiophenecarboxylic acid	2-Thiophenecarboxylic acid	α-Thienylcarboxylic acid 2-Thenoic acid 2-Thiophenoic acid
(thiophene)—OH	Thiophene-2-ol	2-Hydroxythiophene	2-Thienol
CH₃—(thiophene)—OH	5-Methylthiophene-2-ol	5-Methyl-2-hydroxythiophene	Thiotenol
(thiophene)—CHO	2-Thiophenecarboxaldehyde	2-Thiophenealdehyde	α-Thiophenealdehyde 2-Thenaldehyde
(thiophene)—NH₂	3-Aminothiophene	3-Aminothiophene	3-Thiophenine
(thiophene)—CH₂NH₂	2-Thenylamine	2-Thenylamine	2-Aminomethylthiophene 2-Thienylmethylamine
(thiophene)—CH₂CH₂NH₂	β-(2-Thienyl)ethylamine	2-(2-Thienyl)ethylamine	2-Aminoethylthiophene
(thiophene)—COCH₃	2-Thienyl methyl ketone 2-Acetylthiophene	2-Acetylthiophene	2-Acetothienone α-Acetothienone

Compound	Chemical Abstracts	This book	Other Nomenclature
$CO(CH_2)_7CH_3$	2-Thienyl octyl ketone	2-Nonanoylthiophene	2-Pelargonothienone
$CO(CH_2)_4COOH$	ϵ-Oxo-2-thiophenecaproic acid	5-(2-Thenoyl)pentanoic acid	—
$CH=CHCOOH$	2-Thienylacrylic acid	2-Thienylacrylic acid	—
$HgCl$, CH_3	5-Methyl-2-thiophenemercuri-chloride	5-Methyl-2-thiophenemercuri-chloride	—
CN	2-Thiophenecarbonitrile	2-Thiophenenitrile	α-Cyanothiophene
SH	3-Thiophenethiol	3-Thiophenethiol	—
SH, HS	3,4-Thiophenedithiol	3,4-Thiophenedithiol	—
H_2, H_2, S, S		3,4-Thiolanedithione	—
Se	Selenophene	Selenophene	Selenofuran

Table continued

TABLE I-1 (*Continued*)

Compound	Chemical Abstracts	This book	Other nomenclature
	Tellurophene	Tellurophene	Tellurofuran
	Thieno[2,3-b]thiophene	Thieno-[2,3-b]thiophene	Thiophthene (liquid)
	Thieno[3,2-b]thiophene	Thieno-[3,2-b]thiophene	Thiophthene (solid)
		Thieno-[3,4-b]thiophene	—
	2,2'-Bithiophene	2,2'-Dithienyl	α-Dithienyl
	2,2'-5',2''-Terthiophene	2,2'-5',2''-Terthienyl	α-Terthienyl

III. Occurrence of Thiophene Compounds in Nature

There is no definite proof that thiophene compounds actually exist, as such, in natural products. They apparently are the end products of thermal or catalytic treatment of carbonaceous deposits. Victor Meyer's discovery of thiophenes in coal tar in 1882 and 1883 has led to a variety of investigations which have shown that a great number of thiophene homologs exist in products derived from natural sources. The source of these products is normally in carbonaceous deposits of lignite, peat, shale, coal, and crude oil. Naturally, the amount of sulfur-bearing products varies with the source, but, usually, the thiophenes represent a portion of the sulfur-containing constituents of any of the light oils from carbonaceous deposits. Whenever thiophene is found, its homologs are present in higher fractions of the distillable oils. It is open to question if thiophene compounds actually exist in crude oils or whether they are formed by refining processes such as high temperature distillation or catalytic cracking (where they may be formed by dehydrogenation of thiolanes). In fact, several authorities have questioned the structure of the "alkylthiolanes" obtained from Canadian crude oil.[1] Challenger[2] states: "It was not proved, however, that the tetrahydrothiophene or thiophane ring was present in any of these compounds, which ranged in boiling point from 125 to 295°. The use of the term 'thiophane' was then hardly justified."

In summary, it can be stated that all types of thiophene homologs have been found in products obtained from natural sources. All of the possible methylthiophenes (mono-, di-, tri-, and tetra-) have been isolated from coal tar or shale oils. Other homologs such as ethyl-, propyl-, and butyl thiophenes have been isolated. Compounds closely related to thiophene, such as thianaphthene, dibenzothiophene, and dithienyl, are also found.

Specifically, thiophene has been isolated from coal tar,[3-5] lignite tar,[6,7] and shale oil[8-11]; the methylthiophenes from coal tar[1,5,12] lignite tar,[13]

[1] Mabery and Quayle, *Am. Chem. J.*, **35**, 404 (1906).
[2] Challenger, *J. Soc. Chem. Ind. (London)*, **48**, 622 (1929).
[3] V. Meyer, *Ber.*, **16**, 1465 (1883).
[4] V. Meyer, *Ber.*, **16**, 2970 (1883).
[5] Weissgerber, *Ber.*, **61**, 2116 (1928).
[6] Heusler, *Ber.*, **28**, 494 (1895).
[7] Saladini, *Ann. chim. applicata*, **18**, 337 (1928).
[8] Challenger, Jinks, and Haslam, *J. Chem. Soc.*, **127**, 162 (1925).
[9] Challenger, *J. Soc. Chem. Ind.*, **48**, 622 (1929).
[10] Challenger, *et al.*, *J. Inst. Petroleum Technol.*, **12**, 106 (1926).
[11] Dodonow and Soschestwenskaja, *Ber.*, **59**, 2202 (1926).
[12] V. Meyer and Kreis, *Ber.*, **17**, 787 (1884).
[13] Pfaff and Kreutzer, *Z. angew. Chem.*, **36**, 437 (1923).

shale oil,[8-11,14] crude oil,[15] and bituminous limestone[16]; the dimethyl-thiophenes from coal tar,[5,17-19] lignite tar,[13] shale oil,[8-10,20-23] and bituminous limestone[16]; the trimethylthiophenes from coal tar[5] and shale oil[8-10,14]; and tetramethylthiophene from coal tar.[5] Other alkyl-thiophenes found in similar sources are 2-ethylthiophene,[8-11,14,20] 3-ethyl-thiophene,[14] isomeric (iso- and normal) propylthiophenes,[8-10,14,22,24,25] and butylthiophenes.[24] Thiolane has been isolated in several instances.[8-10,15] Dithienyl has been isolated directly from coal tar.[26] Thianaphthene[27-30] and dibenzothiophene[27,28] have also been obtained from this source.

Austrian, Russian, and French shale oils are particularly high in thiophene content. Picon[31] recently summarized the data on these materials and described methods of separation of thiophene and its homologs from shale oils obtained in the Tyrol and Ain districts of France. Shale oils from the Ain contains about 16% sulfur, mostly in the form of thiophenes. Shale oil from Rifle, Colorado, contains less than 1% sulfur. Oils obtained from Indiana and midwestern shales contained 1–2% sulfur.

McKittrick[32] extracted a thermally cracked California naphtha with sulfur dioxide and subsequently treated the extract with aniline to produce a concentrate high in sulfur content. The concentrate was carefully fractionated and the fractions were treated with mercuric chloride and sodium acetate. In this manner, thiophene, 2-methyl-thiophene, 3-methylthiophene, 2,3-dimethylthiophene, 2-ethylthiophene, and 3-ethylthiophene were isolated as mercurichloride derivatives.

[14] Steinkopf and Nitschke, *Arch. Pharm.*, **278**, 360 (1940).
[15] Teutsch and Herzenberg, *Petroleum*, **30**, No. 20, 1 (1934).
[16] Chabrier, Tchoubar, and Le Tellier-Dupre, *Bull. soc. chim.*, 332 (1946).
[17] Schulze, *Ber.*, **17**, 2852 (1884).
[18] Messinger, *Ber.*, **18**, 563, 1636 (1885).
[19] Keiser, *Ber.*, **28**, 1804 (1895); **29**, 2560 (1896).
[20] Stadnikov and Weizmann, *Brennstoff-Chem.*, **8**, 343 (1927).
[21] Vozzhinskaya, *Chimika tverdogo Topliva*, **6**, 250 (1935).
[22] Leclere and Leclere, *Compt. rend.*, **194**, 286 (1932).
[23] Scheibler, *Ber.*, **48**, 1815 (1915).
[24] Scheibler and Rettig, *Ber.*, **59**, 1198 (1926).
[25] Haines, *et al.*, *U. S. Bur. Mines R. I.* **4060** (1946).
[26] Nahnsen, *Ber.*, **17**, 789 (1884).
[27] Weissgerber, *Brennstoff-Chem.*, **2**, 1 (1921).
[28] Boes, *Apoth.-Ztg.*, **17**, 565, 638 (1902).
[29] Weissgerber and Kruber, *Ber.*, **53**, 1552, 1566 (1920).
[30] Fricke and Spilker, *Ber.*, **58**, 24, 1589 (1925).
[31] Picon, *Compt. rend.*, **228**, 251 (1948); *Bull. soc. chim.*, **1949**, 289, 296; *Compt. rend.*, **227**, 1381 (1948).
[32] McKittrick, *Ind. Eng. Chem.*, **21**, 585 (1929).

IV. Color Reactions of Thiophene Compounds

Many color tests have been developed for thiophene compounds, but there is no single color test which is specific for members of the thiophene series.   Usually the same test can be used for the five-membered heterocyclics, in general, but with some gradation in color.

Only in rare instances is there any appearance of specific colors to distinguish isomers.   For example, the ceric nitrate test[1] listed below gives isomer color specificity in regard to 2- and 3-methylthiophene and these compounds are readily distinguishable by the test.   The dimethyl-thiophenes also give characteristic colors (see Table I-2).   Similarly, 2-acetyl-3-methylthiophene and 2-acetyl-4-methylthiophene give specific colors in this same test to the extent that the transient blue color of the

TABLE I-2. Color Reaction of Thiophene Compounds with Ceric Nitrate

Compound	Color in organic layer	Color change in inorganic layer
Thiophene	None to light brown	Brown ppt.
Alkylthiophene		
2-Methyl-	Brown	Bright purple ppt.
3-Methyl-	Brown	Deep blue ppt.
2-*n*-Propyl-	Red	None
2-*n*-Butyl-	Red	None
2-*tert*-Butyl-	Red	None
3-*tert*-Butyl-	Light orange	None
2,5-Di-(*tert*-butyl)-	None	None
2,3-Dimethyl-	Green	Green-brown ppt.
2,4-Dimethyl-	Red → purple	Red ppt.
3,4-Dimethyl-	Deep blue	Deep blue ppt.
2,5-Dimethyl-	Purple	Purple ppt.
2-Ethyl-	Red → red ppt.	None
2,3,4-Trimethyl-	Green → brown → purple ppt.	None
2,3,5-Trimethyl-	Purple → brown ppt.	None
2,3,4,5-Tetramethyl-	Blue → red → red-brown ppt.	None
Di-(5-methyl-2-thienyl)methane	Deep red	Red ppt.
Tri-(5-methyl-2-thienyl)methane	Bright-orange	Yellow
2-*tert*-Amyl-	Red	Colorless
1-(2-Thienyl)-(1,1,3,3-tetramethyl-butane)	Yellow	Yellow
2-Pinyl-	Yellow[b]	Colorless
2-Benzyl-	Brown	Blue ppt.

Table Continued

TABLE I-2 (*Continued*)

Compound	Color in organic layer	Color change in inorganic layer
Alkylenethiophene		
2-(α-Methylvinyl)thiophene	Blue → brown	Colorless
Acylthiophenes		
2-Acetyl-	Red	Colorless
2-Acetyl-3-methyl-	Red	Colorless
2-Acetyl-4-methyl-	Blue → red	Colorless
2-Acetyl-5-methyl-	Red	Colorless
2-Acetyl-3,4-dimethyl-	Red → brown → lt. red	Colorless
2-Acetyl-3,5-dimethyl-	Red → brown → pale yellow	Colorless
2-Acetyl-4,5-dimethyl-	Red → tan → lt. red	Colorless
2-Acetyl-5-ethyl-	Cherry red → tan → lt. red	Colorless
2-Acetyl-3,4,5-trimethyl-	Purple → brown → lt. red	Colorless
3-Acetyl-2,5-dimethyl-	Pink → tan → pink	Colorless
2-Acetyl-5-*tert*-butyl-	Deep red	Colorless
2-Acetyl-5-chloro-	Orange[a]	Light yellow
3-Acetyl-2,5-dichloro-	None	None
3-Acetyl-2,5-di-*tert*-butyl-	None	None
2-Propanoyl-	Red → deep brown	Colorless
2-Butanoyl-	Orange	Colorless
2-(2-Ethylbutanoyl)-	Light yellow	Yellow
2-Benzoyl-	Light yellow	Yellow
2-Thenoyl-	Yellow to tan	Colorless
2-(2-Thenoyl)-3-(4-)-methyl-	Green	Colorless
Halothiophenes		
2-Chloro-	Light red[a]	Yellow
2-Bromo-	Brown	Yellow
2,3-Dichloro-	Orange	Yellow
2,4-Dichloro-	Light yellow	Yellow
2,5-Dichloro-	None	None
2,5-Dibromo-	None	None
3,4-Dichloro-	Light yellow	Yellow
2,3,4-Trichloro-	Light yellow	Yellow
2,3,4,5-Tetrachloro-	None	—
2,2,3,4,5,5-Hexachlorothiolane	None	—
2,2,3,4,5,5-Hexachloro-3-thiolene	None	—
Thiophenecarbinols		
2-Thiophenecarbinol	Deep purple	—
2-(2-Thienyl)ethanol	Brown	—
2-(4-Methyl-2-thienyl)ethanol	Deep red → brown	—
2-(5-Chloro-2-thienyl)ethanol	Deep red	—

Table Continued

TABLE I-2 (*Continued*)

Compound	Color in organic layer	Color change in inorganic layer
Miscellaneous		
2-Thenylamine[c]	Brown ppt.[d]	Brown ppt.[d]
3-Methyl-2-thenylamine	Dissolves	Red
5-Methyl-2-thenylamine	Dissolves	Red
Di-(2-thenyl)amine	Brown ppt.[d]	Brown ppt.[d]
Di-(5-methyl-2-thenyl)amine	White ppt.[d]	—
2-Thiophenealdehyde	Red[d]	Colorless
5-Methyl-2-thiophenealdehyde	Deep red[d]	Colorless
2-Thiophenecarboxylic acid	None[a]	None
Ethyl 2-thiophenecarboxylate	Light green → blue[e]	[e]
2-Nitrothiophene	None	—
3-Thiophenethiol	Brown	Brown ppt.

[a] On warming. [b] Red on warming. [c] 2-Aminomethylthiophene. [d] Heat of reaction.
[e] Colors aqueous layer of reagent yellow. On warming, aqueous layer turns red, yellow, and colorless within a few seconds. Final color of organic layer is pink.

latter can be detected in mixtures with as little as 1 part of the 2-acetyl-4-methylthiophene to 10 parts of 2-acetyl-3-methylthiophene. Since these derivatives often are formed together in the acylation of 3-methyl-thiophene, this test has some merit.

The sodium nitroprusside test is convenient for the alkanoylthiophenes up to a 5-carbon alkane chain and is very sensitive with 2-acetyl-thiophene, 2-propanoylthiophene, and 2-butanoylthiophene. 1 part of 2-acetylthiophene can be detected in 10,000 parts of thiophene. For example, it has been used in our laboratory in studying new catalysts for the acylation of thiophene; if about 0.2 ml. of the reaction mixture is withdrawn periodically the formation of even very small amounts of the alkanoylthiophenes can be detected by the test.

The isatin test is sensitive to small amounts of thiophene compounds in crude mixtures but it seems to have no specificity for given series of compounds. It is reported to fail in testing for thiophenes in shale oils in the presence of large amounts of unsaturates.[2]

The more common color tests are described below in detail:

1. *Ceric Nitrate*.[1] Equal volumes, 0.1 to 1.0 ml., of ceric nitrate alcohol reagent[3] and the thiophene derivative to be tested are placed in a small test tube. Normally the color change takes place at the interface and spreads rapidly through

[1] Hartough, *Ind. Eng. Chem., Anal. Ed.*, **20**, 860 (1948), and unpublished data.
[2] Challenger, Jinks, and Haslam, *J. Chem. Soc.*, **127**, 162 (1925).
[3] Duke and Smith, *Ind. Eng. Chem., Anal. Ed.*, **12**, 201 (1940).

the organic layer.   Agitation is necessary to develop the final color.   These colors are listed in Table I-2.   If the samples to be tested are solids melting below 100°, the mixture is warmed in a steam bath or in boiling water.   Diluents change colors somewhat, but in some cases they can be used.   *Dioxane must not be used as a solvent*, since very often variations of color are obtained.

2. *Sodium Nitroprusside Test for Alkanoylthiophenes.*[4]   A modification of the method of Feigl and Zapport[5] was adopted for this test.   To 1.0 ml. of a saturated solution of sodium nitroprusside in alcohol is added one drop of 2-acetylthiophene. The mixture is diluted with 1.0 ml. of water and a few drops of 10% KOH in alcohol is added.   An intense red to purple color forms.   Change of the color to an intense blue upon addition of a few drops of glacial acetic acid is specific for the —COCH$_3$ grouping;   —COCH$_2$R groups give no color change upon addition of acetic acid.   Sensitivity of the test decreases rapidly with increase of the size of the R group;   2-butanoylthiophene gives a well-defined red color, but 2-de-canoylthiophene and 2-benzoylthiophene fail to give the test.

3. *The Isatin Test (Indophenine Reaction).*   About 1 ml. of a dilute solution of the compound in benzene, or an inert solvent, is mixed with a few milligrams of isatin and 1 ml. of concentrated sulfuric acid.   Development of a blue color indicates the presence of a thiophene compound.   There has been no systematic study of the limitations of this test and it has been used, for the most part, in detecting small amounts of thiophene and its homologs in benzene and coal tar distillates.

4. *The Laubenheimer Reaction.*[6–8]   The test is best run in the following manner.   A few milligrams of phenanthraquinone are dissolved in 1–2 ml. of glacial acetic acid.   One drop of the compound to be tested is added to this solution followed by the addition of about one ml. of concentrated H$_2$SO$_4$.   A blue to blue-green precipitate indicates the presence of a thiophene compound.   No systematic study of the test has been made.

5. *The Liebermann Test.*[9–12]   If 2–3 drops of the thiophene compound is dissolved in 1 ml. of thiophene-free benzene with 1 ml. of 8% KNO$_2$-concentrated sulfuric acid mixture, a blue to blue-green color develops on shaking.   No systematic study of the test has been carried out.

6. *Miscellaneous Color Tests.*   There are a variety of color reactions of thio-phene that have not received appreciable attention.   The thallin-nitric acid

[4] Hartough and Kosak, unpublished work.
[5] Feigl, *Spot Tests*, 3rd Ed., Elsevier, New York, 1946, p. 350.
[6] Laubenheimer, *Ber.*, **8**, 224 (1875).
[7] V. Meyer, *Ber.*, **16**, 2971 (1883).
[8] Odernheimer, *Ber.*, **17**, 1338 (1884).
[9] Liebermann, *Ber.*, **20**, 3231 (1887).
[10] Liebermann and Pleus, *Ber.*, **37**, 2461 (1904).
[11] Claisen and Manasse, *Ber.*, **20**, 2197 (1887).
[12] Schwalbe, *Ber.*, **37**, 324 (1904).
[13] Kreis, *Chem. Ztg.*, **26**, 523 (1902).
[14] Fletcher and Hopkins, *J. Physiol. (London)*, **35**, 247 (1907).
[15] Fearon, *Biochem. J.*, **12**, 179 (1918).
[16] Christomanos, *Biochem. Z.*, **229**, 248 (1930).
[17] Deniges, *Bull. soc. chim.*, [4] **5**, 649 (1909).
[18] Hilpert and Wolf, *Ber.*, **46**, 2215 (1913).

method of Kreis[13] gives an intense violet color and is said to be sensitive to one part in 100,000 in detecting thiophene in benzene. A deep red color develops when thiophene is treated with copper sulfate, lactic acid, and concentrated sulfuric acid.[14–16] Methylglyoxal and nascent bromine give a transient red color changing to violet, blue, and green.[17] Antimony pentachloride treatment of benzene containing small amounts of thiophene gives a transient reddish-yellow color slowly changing to green.[18] Sulfuric acid gives various colors with thiophene compounds and numerous unrelated color reactions are reported in the literature. However, there has been no attempt to correlate the diffuse and sometimes conflicting colors produced with various concentrations of this acid. The Liebermann test seems to produce more uniform results.

V. Estimation of Thiophene

The most recent compilation and comparison of methods for determining small amounts of thiophene in benzene by Claxton and Hoffert[1] shows that the method of Deniges[2] is very suitable if unsaturates are absent. The reproducibility was $\pm 0.005\%$ of thiophene. Unsaturates such as amylene, cyclohexene, or indene cause a considerable error by their reaction with Deniges' reagent, a mercuric sulfate solution. When an excess of the reagent is shaken with benzene containing a small amount of thiophene, a complex of thiophene and basic mercuric sulfate, $C_4H_4S \cdot HgS_3O_6$, is precipitated which can be filtered off, dried, and weighed. Results usually are high if unsaturates are present.

The American Society for Testing Materials tentatively recommended a method for the determination of thiophene in benzene which involves comparison of the color developed by an isatin – ferric chloride – sulfuric acid reagent with color standards made from known concentrations of thiophene in benzene.[3] Somewhat similar colorimetric methods for the estimation of thiophene in gasoline[4,5] and in gas samples[6] have been developed.

Other methods are as follows: (1) a gravimetric method[7] based on the precipitation of tetraacetoxymercurithiophene of which several modifications have been made [8–10] (a good description of the procedure is

[1] Claxton and Hoffert, *J. Soc. Chem. Ind.*, **65**, 333 (1946).
[2] Deniges, *Compt. rend.*, **120**, 628, 781 (1895); *Bull. Soc. Chim.* (3) **13**, 537 (1895).
[3] *A.S.T.M. Supplements*, **1947**, Part III-A, D931–47T, pp. 279–281.
[4] McKee, Herndon, and Withrow, *Anal. Chem.*, **20**, 301 (1948).
[5] Hakewill, Paper presented before Division of Fuel and Gas, A. C. S., Sept., 1948. See also Hakewill and Rueck, *Am. Gas Assoc. Proc.*, **28**, 529 (1946).
[6] Brady, *Anal. Chem.*, **20**, 512 (1948).
[7] Dimroth, *Ber.*, **32**, 759 (1899).
[8] Schwalbe, *Chem.-Ztg.*, **29**, 895 (1905).
[9] Paolini, *Gazz. chim. ital.*, **37**, 58 (1907).
[10] Paolini and Silbermann, *Atti accad. nazl. Lincei*, **24**, 209 (1915).

given by Spielmann and Schotz[11]);   (2) the Deniges method adapted to a
volumetric determination[12];   (3) the isatin test developed by Schwalbe[8]
into a semiquantitative method;   and colorimetric determinations based
on colors produced with (4) nitric acid and thallin,[13] (5) amyl nitrite and
sulfuric acid,[14] (6) with alloxan and sulfuric acid,[15] and (7) lactic acid,
sulfuric acid, and copper sulfate.[16,17]

Other recent methods are of the combustion type in which benzene
containing thiophene is burned in hydrogen over a hydrogenation
catalyst and the resulting hydrogen sulfide is determined by standard
techniques.[18]   Combustion with oxygen in which the sulfur is oxidized
to sulfur dioxide, which is determined by standard methods, appears to
be satisfactory if other sulfur compounds are absent.[19,20]   Methods such
as complex formation with aluminum chloride,[21] and conversion to 2-
benzoylthiophene by use of benzoyl chloride catalyzed with titanium or
tin tetrachlorides[22,23] have been used, but these methods are not specific
for thiophene.

Physical methods of analysis, now in the process of development in
many petroleum laboratories, involve the use of the mass spectrograph
and infrared spectrograph.   Ultraviolet absorption methods are also
under development.   Chapter IV summarizes some of the preliminary
work along this line undertaken in the Socony-Vacuum Laboratories.
Eventually, it is anticipated that these physical methods will outmode the
wet-chemical methods of analysis.

Methods of identification and determination of antihistaminic drugs
of the thenyl series have recently been described.[24]   The methods involve
identification of the products by their optical crystallographic properties
or by colorimetric methods with various alkaloidal reagents such as
Marquis' reagent, Buckingham's reagent, Frohde's reagent, and Man-
delin's reagent.

[11] Spielmann and Schotz, *J. Soc. Chem. Ind.*, **38**, 189T (1919).
[12] Meyer, *Compt. rend.*, **169**, 1402 (1919).
[13] Kreis, *Chem.-Ztg.*, **26**, 523 (1902).
[14] Leibermann, *Ber.*, **20**, 3231 (1887).
[15] Ekkert, *Pharm. Centralblatt*, **71**, 625 (1930).
[16] Christomanos, *Biochem. Z.*, **229**, 248 (1930).
[17] Fearon, *Biochem. J.*, **12**, 179 (1918).
[18] Gillo, *Ann. chim.*, **12**, 281 (1939).
[19] Thomas, Ivis, Abersold, and Hendricks, *Ind. Eng. Chem., Anal. Ed.*, **15**, 287 (1943).
[20] Reisz and Wohlberg, *Am. Gas Assoc. Proc.*, **25**, 259 (1943).
[21] Sabrou and Renaudie, International Benzene Conference, Rome, 1935.
[22] Stadnikov and Kashtanov, *J. Russ. Phys.-Chem. Soc.*, **60**, 1117 (1926).
[23] Stadnikov and Goldfarb, *J. Ber.*, **61**, 2341 (1928).
[24] Haley and Keenan, *J. Am. Pharm. Assoc. (Sci. Ed.)*, **38**, 85 (1949).

VI. Removal of Thiophene and Its Homologs from Coal Tar Aromatics and Petroleum Stocks

Table I-3 is a compilation of methods for the removal of thiophene and its homologs from coal tar or petroleum. Its abundance in these sources varies from approximately 0.1 to several weight percent, being most prevalent in cracked fractions of "high-sulfur" crude oils and in shale oils. It would be most difficult to assess the methods and state that any one of them is the best. Suffice it to say, that Victor Meyer's original method involving a "sulfuric acid wash" is probably the most convenient one and that it is still in wide use today. Other methods, such as high-temperature catalysis, are more applicable to refining techniques in the petroleum industry.

TABLE I-3. Removal of Thiophene and Its Homologs from Coal Tar Aromatics and Petroleum Stocks

Material containing thiophenic contamination	Method of removal	Ref.
Coal tar benzene	Sulfuric acid wash	1–4
Raw toluene and xylene	Sulfuric acid wash	5
Raw benzene	H_2SO_4, an unsat. alicyclic or heterocyclic hydrocarbon	6
Coal tar distillates	H_2SO_4, $NaNO_2$	7
Tar oils	90% H_2SO_4	8
Benzene	66° Bé. H_2SO_4, "starch yielding substances"	9
Benzene	95% H_2SO_4, an alkylating agent for benzene	10
Benzene	H_2SO_4, an aldehyde or phthalic anhydride	11
Petroleum stocks	H_2SO_4	12

Table continued

[1] V. Meyer, *Ber.*, **17**, 2641 (1884).
[2] Schulze, *Ber.*, **18**, 497 (1885).
[3] Gillies, *Gas World*, **104**, No. 2700, *Coking Sect.*, 52 (1936); *Chem. Abstr.*, **30**, 4657 (1936).
[4] Hoffert, Claxton, and Hancock, *Gas J.*, **214**, 103, 167 (1936).
[5] Schulze, *Ber.*, **17**, 2853 (1884).
[6] Kopelevich and Brodovich, Russ. Pat. 39,096 (1934); *Chem. Zentr.*, **1935**, II, 3619.
[7] Schwalbe, *Zeit. Farb. Tex. Ind.*, **3**, 461 (1904); *J. Chem. Soc. Abstr.*, **1905**, 124.
[8] Weissgerber, *Ber.*, **B61**, 2111 (1928).
[9] von Lauer and Ponchaud, U. S. Pat. 2,346,524 (1944).
[10] Bullard, Anderson, and McAllister, Brit. Pat. 579,781 (1946).
[11] Badische-Anilin und Soda Fabrik., Ger. Pat. 211,239 (1909).
[12] Wood, Lowy, and Faragher, *Ind. Eng. Chem.*, **16**, 1116 (1924).

TABLE I-3 *(Continued)*

Material containing thiophenic contamination	Method of removal	Ref.
Naphtha	Fuming H_2SO_4 and 66° Bé. H_2SO_4, 53° Bé. H_2SO_4 was ineffective	13
Shale oil distillates	96.5% H_2SO_4	14
Lignite oils	Concd. H_2SO_4	15
Bituminous primary distillates	Dil. H_2SO_4	16,16a
Shale oil	Concd. H_2SO_4	17
Schist and peat oils	H_2SO_4-H_3PO_4	18
Russian petroleum stocks	CH_2O and "naphthasulfonic acids"	19
Petroleum stocks	Sulfur dioxide	20
Naphtha	Sulfur dioxide extracted; the extract treated with aniline	21
Coal tar distillates	$HgCl_2$, $NaOOCCH_3$	22
Coal tar distillates	$HgSO_4$, HgO	23
Coal tar distillates	$Hg(OOCCH_3)_2$	24
Raw benzene	$Hg(OOCCH_3)_2$	25–27
Raw benzene	$HgSO_4$, HgO	28
Raw benzene	HgO, stearic acid	29
Sulfur rich oils	Mercury salts	30
Kimmeridge shale oils	$Hg(OOCCH_3)_2$	31
Gasoline	$Hg(NO_3)_2$	32,32a
Cracked rubber distillates	$Hg(OOCCH_3)_2$	33

Table continued

[13] Wood, Shelly, and Trusty, *Ind. Eng. Chem.*, **18**, 169 (1926).
[14] Leclere and Leclere, *Compt. rend.*, **194**, 286 (1932).
[15] Ruhemann and Baumbach, *Braunkohle*, **31**, 549, 565 (1932).
[16] French Pat. 721,698 (1930); *Chem. Abstr.*, **26**, 4069 (1932).
[16a] Picon, *Compt. rend.*, **228**, 251 (1948); *Bull. soc. chim.*, **1949**, 289, 296.
[17] Reichert, *Arch. Pharm.*, **276**, 316 (1938).
[18] Hahn and Nielsen, Danish Pat. 51,230 (1936); *Chem. Abstr.*, **30**, 6171 (1936).
[19] Stadnikov and Weizmann, *Brennstoff-Chem.*, **8**, 343 (1927).
[20] Challenger, *Ind. Chemist*, **2**, 445 (1926); *Chem. Abstr.*, **21**, 646 (1927).
[21] McKittrick, *Ind. Eng. Chem.*, **21**, 585 (1929).
[22] Heusler, *Ber.*, **28**, 488 (1895).
[23] Deniges, *Bull. soc. chim.*, [3] **13**, 537 (1885); *Compt. rend.*, **120**, 628, 781 (1895).
[24] Paolini and Silbermann, *Gazz. chim. ital.*, **45**, II, 385 (1915).
[25] Dimroth, *Ber.*, **32**, 760 (1899).
[26] Schwalbe, *Ber.*, **38**, 2208 (1905).
[27] Dimroth, *Ber.*, **35**, 2032 (1902).
[28] Jones, *J. Soc. Chem. Ind.*, **37**, 324T (1918).
[29] Ardagh and Furber, *J. Soc. Chem. Ind.*, **48**, 73T (1929).
[30] Scheibler, Brit. Pat. 155,259 (1920).
[31] Challenger, Haslam, Bramball, and Walden, *J. Inst. Petroleum Technol.*, **12**, 106 (1926).
[32] Ball, *U. S. Bur. Mines, Rept. Investigations*, **3591** (1942); *Chem. Abstr.*, **36**, 1763 (1942).
[32a] Mixer, *Chem. Eng. News*, **26**, 2434 (1948).
[33] Midgley, Henne, and Shepard, *J. Am. Chem. Soc.*, **54**, 2953 (1932).

TABLE I-3 (*Continued*)

Material containing thiophenic contamination	Method of removal	Ref.
Coal tar distillates..............AlCl₃		34,35
Raw benzene..................AlCl₃		36–39,39a
Petroleum stocks...............AlCl₃		12
Aromatic hydrocarbons.........AlCl₃·benzene complex		40
Benzene and toluene...........Chlorine and water		41,42
Benzene and toluene...........CaOCl₂		41
Naphtha.....................NaOCl (ineffective)		43
Kimmeridge shale oil...........Bromine and water		31
Petroleum stocks..............Chlorination with "hypochlorite"		20
Sulfur rich oils................Halogenation		30
Sulfur rich oils................Acetylation		30
Russian petroleum stocks.......CH₃COCl, SnCl₄		19
Schist tars..................CH₃COCl, AlCl₃		44
Benzene.....................(CH₃CO)₂O, activated clays		44a
Benzene and toluene...........Thermal cracking in absence of air at 1000–1400°F.		45
Raw benzene..................Heated in autoclave at 50 atm.		46
Petroleum distillates............Ammonia at high temperatures		47
Petroleum distillates............Hydrogenation		20
Petroleum distillates............Chromia or molybdena at 570–750°F., 20–50 atm. of hydrogen		48
Raw benzene..................ZnO or MoO₃ and hydrogen at high temperature and pressure		49
Raw benzene..................Hydrogen iodide vapors		50
Raw benzene..................Iodine and magnesium		51

Table continued

[34] French Pat. 240,111 (1895); Ger. Pat. 79,505 (1895).
[35] Haller and Michel, *Bull. soc. chim.*, [3] **15**, 390, 1065 (1896).
[36] Heusler, *Z. angew. Chem.*, **9**, 288, 318, 750 (1896).
[37] Boedtker, *Compt. rend.*, **123**, 310 (1896).
[38] Boedtker, *J. Chem. Soc.*, **72**, 25 (1895).
[39] Heusler, Ger. Pat. 83,494 (1895).
[39a] Holmes and Beeman, *Ind. Eng. Chem.*, **26**, 172 (1934).
[40] Scott, Brit. Pat. 571,256 (1945).
[41] Dutt and Hamer, Brit. Pat. 117,693 (1917).
[42] Willegerodt, *J. prakt. Chem.*, **33**, (3), 479 (1886).
[43] Wood, Green, and Provine, *Ind. Eng. Chem.*, **18**, 823 (1926).
[44] Scheibler and Rettig, *Ber.*, **B59**, 1198 (1926).
[44a] Hartough, Kosak, and Ried, U. S. Pat. 2,462,391 (1949).
[45] Evans, Brit. Pat. 112,878 (1917).
[46] Dunkel, *Brennstoff-Chem.*, **5**, 145 (1924).
[47] Perkin, *J. Inst. Petroleum Technol.*, **3**, 227 (1917).
[48] *Abstr. Petroleum* (London), **7**, No. 7, 125 (1944).
[49] I. G. Farbenind., Brit. Pat. 257,576 (1925).
[50] Nellenstein, *Chem. Weekblad*, **24**, 102 (1927).
[51] Thomas, *Compt. rend.*, **181**, 218 (1925).

TABLE I-3 (*Continued*)

Material containing thiophenic contamination	Method of removal	Ref.
Raw benzene	MoO_3 and hydrogen at 450°C.	52
Benzene and toluene	Raney nickel	53,54
Raw benzene	$CoS-MoS_3$ at 325°C.	55
Raw benzene	Cr_2O_3 or $CoS-Cr_2O_3$	56
Raw benzene	Chromium oxide gel at 470°C.	57
Raw benzene	"Alorco" Al_2O_3, $(NH_4)_2Cr_2O_7$ at 470°C.	57
Raw benzene	"Alorco" Al_2O_3, $(NH_4)_2MoO_6$ at 470°C.	57
Gasoline	Reduced NiO, CoO, Al_2O_3, MgO at 400°C.	58
Gasoline	Reduced CoO at 400°C.	58
Gasoline	Reduced MoO_3 at 400°C.	58
Petroleum fractions	Vanadium oxides and alumina	59
Petroleum fractions	20–25% cobalt molybdate on 80–75% alumina	60
Aromatic hydrocarbons	Vanadium oxides at 250–550°	61
Petroleum stocks	Bauxite	20
Petroleum stocks	Silica gel	20
Naphtha	Silica gel (ineffective)	13
Naphtha	Fuller's earth (ineffective)	13

Table continued

[52] Moldovskii and Prokopchuk, *J. Applied Chem. (U. S. S. R.)*, **5**, 619 (1932).
[53] Bougault, Cattelain, and Chabrier, *Bull. soc. chim.*, **7**, 781 (1940).
[54] Graul and Karabinos, *Science*, **104**, 557 (1946).
[55] Pease and Keighton, *Ind. Eng. Chem.*, **25**, 1012 (1933).
[56] Pease and Munroe, *Ind. Eng. Chem.*, **25**, 1013 (1933).
[57] Hummer and Taylor, *J. Am. Chem. Soc.*, **63**, 2801 (1943).
[58] Orlov and Broun, *Khim. tverdogo Topliva*, **3**, 867 (1932); *Chem. Abstr.*, **28**, 5822 (1934).
[59] Connolly, U. S. Pat. 2,324,067 (1943).
[60] Byrnes, U. S. Pat. 2,325,034 (1943).
[61] Downs, U. S. Pat. 1,590,965 (1926).
[62] Namefin and Sosnina, *J. Applied Chem. (U. S. S. R.)*, **7**, 123 (1934).
[63] Donath and Ditz, *J. prakt. Chem.*, [2] **60**, 566 (1899).
[64] Justes and Cronje, *Ber.*, **B71**, 2335 (1938).
[65] Steinkopf and Nitschke, *Arch. Pharm.*, **278**, 360 (1940).
[66] Lunge, *Coal Tar and Ammonia*, 1916 Ed., Vol. II, pp. 937, 934.
[67] Lake, U. S. Pat. 2,405,258 (1946).
[67a] Lake and Stribley, U. S. Pat. 2,439,777 (1948).
[68] Kruber, *Brennstoff-Chem.*, **13**, 187 (1932).
[69] Hutchison and Hopton, Brit. Pat. 443,094 (1936).
[70] Kemper and Guernsey, *Am. Gas Assoc. Proc.*, **24**, 364 (1942).
[71] Reeson and Moss, Brit. Pat. 249,312 (1925).
[72] Riesz and Wohlberg, *Am. Gas Assoc. Proc.*, **25**, 259 (1943).
[73] Thomas, Ivis, Abersold, and Hendricks, *Ind. Eng. Chem., Anal. Ed.*, **15**, 287 (1943).
[74] Claxton and Hoffert, *J. Soc. Chem. Ind.*, **65**, 333, 341 (1946).

TABLE I-3 (*Continued*)

Material containing thiophenic contamination	Method of removal	Ref.
Naphtha......................	Alumina (ineffective)	13
Kerosene.....................	HNO_3 (density 1.2)	62
Raw benzene..................	Alkaline $KMnO_4$	63
Raw benzene..................	Phosphorus pentoxide	64
Karwendol oil................	Sodium	65
Raw benzene..................	Cryoscopic methods	66
Coal tar fractions...........	Azeotropic distillation with acetone	67
Petroleum fractions..........	Azeotropic distillation	67a
Bituminous pitch.............	Fractionation	68
Light gases..................	Oil scrubbing	69
Manufactured gas.............	Oil scrubbing	70
Manufactured gas.............	Aq. $Fe(OH)_3$ in glycol or citrates	71
Gas streams..................	Systematic determination of all types of sulfur compounds	72,73
Benzene and toluene..........	Systematic determination of all types of sulfur compounds	74

The methods listed are all predicated on the fact that the thiophenes react much faster with such compounds as sulfuric acid, nitric acid, metal halides of the Friedel-Crafts type, oxidizing agents, the halogens, and metal oxides than do their aromatic isologs of the benzene series or the naphthenes and paraffins which they normally contaminate.

VII. Isomorphism and Physical Properties of Thiophene Compounds

Isomorphism, which results in the tendency to form solid solutions, has been noted frequently in the thiophene series. It occurs to the greatest extent with simple 2- and 3-substituted isomers. Melting points of mixtures of these substances are not always depressed and application of mixed melting point techniques to prove difference or identity in structure, while satisfactory in the majority of cases, should not be considered rigidly conclusive by themselves. Steinkopf,[1] however, emphasized this point too strongly and a good portion of his evidence has been shown to be incorrect. For example, a sizable portion of Steinkopf's data deals with the derivatives of 2,3,4- and 2,3,5-trichlorothio-

[1] Steinkopf, *Die Chemie des Thiophens*. Steinkopff, Leipzig, 1941, pp. 15–19.

phene which were later shown to be only the single isomer, 2,3,4-trichloro-thiophene.[2] (See Chapter VII for further discussion.) One can assume, therefore, that solid solutions occur about as frequently in the thiophene series as in other series of compounds.

Victor Meyer first noted that mixtures of 2- and 3-thiophenecarboxylic acids[3] and of 2,4- and 2,5-dinitrothiophenes, respectively, could not be separated by fractional crystallization. The melting points of both pairs of mixtures were lower than those of the respective individual

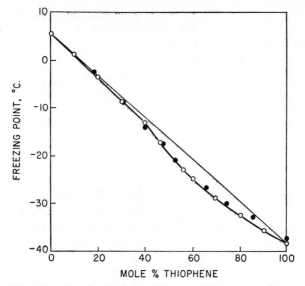

Fig. I-1. Freezing points of benzene-thiophene mixtures. (Open circles, results of Fawcett and Rasmussen; filled circles, results of Tsakalotos and Guye.)

compounds. Voerman[4] determined freezing point curves of mixtures of 2- and 3-thiophenecarboxylic acids and found ample evidence of mixed crystal formation. He observed two series of solid solutions with a gap of incomplete miscibility between 22.5 and 61–62% of the 3-acid. The 118° melting point observed by Meyer for a mixture of these compounds corresponds to a mixture of 82–83% 2-acid and 17–18% 3-acid.

Caesar and Branton[5] found that mixtures of 2- and 3-thienyl 2,4-dinitrophenyl sulfides failed to depress their respective melting points.

[2] Coonradt, Hartough, and Johnson, *J. Am. Chem. Soc.*, **70**, 2564 (1948).
[3] V. Meyer, *Ber.*, **19**, 628 (1886); *Ann.*, **236**, 200 (1886).
[4] Voerman, *Rec. trav. chim.*, **26**, 293 (1907).
[5] Caesar and Branton, Socony-Vacuum Laboratories, unpublished work.

The mixtures were made from samples of 2- and 3-thiophenethiols that were prepared in turn from authentic samples of 2-bromothiophene and 3-iodothiophene through a Grignard reaction. Fawcett[6] has shown that the freezing points of 2- and 3-methylthiophene are definitely lowered by addition of the other isomer. Mixtures of about 20 mole percent of toluene (f. p. $-95°$) in 2-methylthiophene (f. p. $-63.5°$) and in 3-methyl-thiophene (f. p. $-68.9°$) freeze at $-72.8°$ and $-76.5°$, respectively. These freezing points compare to the calculated figures of $-69.5°$ and $-74.1°$, assuming a straight line relationship between melting point and composition. A similar freezing point pattern is shown for mixtures of thiophene and benzene[7,8] (see Fig. I-1).

TABLE I-4. Comparison of Boiling Points and Melting Points of Thiophene and Benzene Derivatives

Single substituent	C_6H_5—		2-C_4H_3S—		3-C_4H_3S—	
	B.p.	M.p.	B.p.	M.p.	B.p.	M.p.
CH_3—	110.7	-95.1	112.5	-63.5	115.4	-68.9
Cl—	132.1	-45.2	128.3	-71.9	136–137	-62
Br—	156.2	-30.6	149–151	—	157–158	—
NO_2—	210.9	5.6–5.7	—	46.5	—	78–79
HO—	181.4	42–43	217–219	7–9	—	—
—CH≡NNHCONH$_2$	—	222	—	223–224	—	233–234
—COOH	249.2	121.7	—	129	—	138.4
—COCH$_3$	202.3	20.5	213.9	10.45	210	—
—SO$_2$Cl	251.5	14.5	—	32–33	—	47–48
2,4-$(NO_2)_2C_6H_3$—S—	—	121	—	119	—	133
—NHCOCH$_3$	—	113–114	—	160–161	—	145–148

Two substituents	—C_6H_4—		—C_4H_2S—	
	Position	M.p.	Position	M.p.
Cl	1,2	-17.6	2,3	-37.3
	1,3	-24.8	2,4	-37.2
	1,4	53	2,5	-50.9
	—	—	3,4	-0.5
Carboxyl and methyl	1,2	104–105	2,3	148
	1,3	110–111	2,4	120–121
	1,4	179–180	2,5	138–138.5
NO$_2$	1,2	117–118	—	—
	1,3	89.8	2,4	56
	1,4	173–174	2,5	78

[6] Fawcett, *J. Am. Chem. Soc.*, **68**, 1420 (1946).
[7] Fawcett and Rasmussen, *J. Am. Chem. Soc.*, **67**, 1705 (1945).
[8] Tsakalotos and Guye, *J. chim. phys.*, **8**, 340 (1910).

It has been stated in the literature that thiophene compounds boil and melt within a few degrees, generally higher, than their benzene isologs. To test this rule, ten simple derivatives of thiophene and benzene chosen from different classes of derivatives are listed in Table I-4. From this and from other tables appended to the chapters of the present book, a few definite conclusions can be drawn. The boiling points of mono-substituted thiophene derivatives are usually higher than those of the corresponding benzene derivatives, but not always so. The boiling points and melting points of the 3-substituted thiophenes are normally higher than those of the 2-substituted thiophenes. It would be most difficult, indeed, to predict the melting points of a 2- or 3-substituted thiophene from known data on the benzene isolog. The discrepancy becomes more apparent as one compares the melting points of some of the disubstituted derivatives of thiophene and benzene (see Table I-4). In one case (the methyl substituted acids), the melting points of the thio-phene series are generally higher, but, in the case of the isomeric dinitro- and dichlorothiophenes, the melting points of the thiophene compounds are uniformly lower.

VIII. Odor of Thiophene and Its Derivatives

The odor of thiophene, while distinguishable, is very much like that of benzene. The common derivatives such as those containing —COOH, —COCH₃, —CHO, —Cl, —Br, —I groups all have odors so similar to their benzene isologs that they would be indistinguishable to an un-practiced nose. The *tert*-butyl-, *tert*-amyl, and other *tert*-alkylthiophenes have a very pungent odor, somewhat similar to that of oak bark. Thiolane

TABLE I-5. Odors of Some Acylthiophenes

Compound	C-H odor No.[a]	Odor resemblance
2-Acetylthiophene...............	4447	Octyl aldehyde (slightly of mustard)
2-Benzoylthiophene.............	2114	Benzyl benzoate
2-Acetyl-3-methylthiophene......	4356	Methyl benzoate (but less fragrant)
2-Acetyl-4-methylthiophene......	5437	C₁₁ alcohol (but more fragrant)
2-Acetyl-5-methylthiophene......	4335	Phenylpropyl alcohol (but less fragrant)
2-Acetyl-5-chlorothiophene.......	3336	Diphenyl oxide (but less fragrant)
3-Acetyl-2,5-dichlorothiophene....	4346	Borneol (irritating to nose)
2-(2-Ethylbutanoyl)thiophene.....	4455	Carrot seed oil

[a] For description of C-H odor number see Crocker, *Flavor*, McGraw-Hill, New York, 1945.

(tetrahydrothiophene) has a typical sulfide odor which in no way resembles the odor of thiophene.   Thus it appears that the sulfur in the resonating thiophene nucleus is a pseudosulfur as far as odor is concerned and appears more like a typical cyclic —CH=CH— group.   No publications have appeared in the literature giving a thorough comparison of the odors of the five membered heterocyclics with that of benzene (see Chapter II, section XI, for miscellaneous references to this subject).

The author is greatly indebted to E. C. Crocker of Arthur D. Little, Inc., for the odor tests reported in Table I-5.   To quote Mr. Crocker, "None were of the perfume type, but the odors were not as bad as might be expected from the presence of sulfur atoms."

CHAPTER II

Biological and Pharmacological Activity of Thiophene and Its Derivatives

BY F. F. BLICKE

Introduction

The remarkable fact that certain physical and chemical properties of thiophene and benzene, and of corresponding derivatives of the two parent compounds are very similar aroused interest with respect to the biochemistry and pharmacology of these substances. Would the metabolism of a thiophene derivative resemble that of the corresponding benzene compound, and would both types of compounds produce similar effects on an animal organism?

Biochemical studies were begun almost as soon as thiophene derivatives became available and, to a limited extent, have been continued to the present time, but during late years the pharmacology of thiophene analogs of pharmacologically active benzene derivatives has been of special interest. At least one thiophene analog seems to have been prepared from every important therapeutic group in which active benzene derivatives are found.

Both biochemical and pharmacological studies have shown that the "equivalence" of a thiophene and a benzene nucleus—which is so easy to establish if only instances of similarities are mentioned and dissimilarities are disregarded—is by no means universal.

As the result of the extensive investigations of thiophene derivatives, only three of these compounds, Diatrin, Thenylene (Histadyl) and Chlorothen, have found clinical application, and all of these substances are antihistamine drugs.

I. General Biological Effects

Pure thiophene, administered to mice by inhalation, was found to be distinctly more toxic than benzene.[1] After dogs had been given

[1] Flury and Zernik, *Chem.-Ztg.*, **56**, 149 (1932).

thiophene, partly orally, partly subcutaneously, there was no increase in the amount of conjugated sulfate in the urine; hence it was thought that the fate of thiophene in this animal is different from that of benzene.[2] In a later study it was claimed that dogs given thiophene subcutaneously eliminated 5–12% of the substance as a conjugate. The effects of toxic doses of thiophene on a dog also were described.[3] During a recent investigation, it was observed that thiophene and 2-bromothiophene, unlike benzene and bromobenzene, were not excreted by rabbits in conjugation with N-acetylcysteine as mercapturic acids, nor did they lead to an increased urinary excretion of conjugated sulfates.[4] Thiophene affects the nervous system[5] and, to some extent, it is transformed into ethylmercaptan in the animal body.[3]

2-Nitrothiophene induces phenomena which resemble those associated with nitrobenzene, such as chocolate coloration of the blood.[6] Both the mono and dinitro compounds produce skin rashes.[7]

2-Thiophenealdehyde, administered orally or subcutaneously to rabbits or dogs, was eliminated in the urine as 2-thenoylglycine.[8] 2-Thiophenecarboxylic acid was stated to be "nontoxic," and when injected subcutaneously into rabbits as the sodium salt it was excreted as 2-thenoylglycine.[9] After oral administration to rabbits, 2-thiophenecarboxylic acid was metabolized similarly to benzoic acid; it was eliminated in the urine, partly unchanged, partly as 2-thenoylglycine.[10] The rate of excretion of 2-thenoylglycine is much slower than that of hippuric acid (benzoylglycine).[4] 2-Thiophenecarboxylic acid, after ingestion by human subjects, was found in the urine to the extent of 71% as 2-thenoylglycine; in dogs, 28% was eliminated in this form.[11] The sodium salt of 2-thiophenecarboxylic acid strongly retards the activity of tyrosinase and potato extract.[12]

A product which consisted of about 90% of 2-methylthienylcinchoninic acid, like phenylcinchoninic acid, increased the experimental urinary excretion of uric acid.[13] The administration of lithium thiophenesulfonate to rabbits also produced this effect.[14]

[2] Heffter, *Pflüger's Arch. ges. Physiol.*, **39**, 420 (1886).
[3] Christomanos, *Biochem. Z.*, **229**, 248 (1930).
[4] Private communication from Drs. H. B. Lewis and Max Chilcote.
[5] Christomanos, *Klin. Wochschr.*, **9**, 2354 (1930).
[6] Marmé and Meyer, *Ber.*, **18**, 1770 (1885).
[7] Steinkopf, *Die Chemie des Thiophens*. Lithoprinted by Edwards Brothers, Ann Arbor, Mich., 1941, p. 30.
[8] Cohn, *Z. physiol. Chem.*, **17**, 274 (1893).
[9] Jaffé and Levy, *Ber.*, **21**, 3458 (1888).
[10] Barger and Easson, *J. Chem. Soc.*, **1938**, 2100.
[11] Schempp, *Z. physiol. Chem.*, **117**, 41 (1921).
[12] Landsteiner and van der Scheer, *Proc. Soc. Exptl. Biol. Med.*, **24**, 692 (1927).
[13] Quevauviller, *Ann. pharm. franç.*, **4**, 237 (1946).
[14] Bertagni, *Biochem. e. terap., sper.*, **28**, 202 (1941).

The pharmacological action of phenylcinchoninic acid and its thiophene analog has been studied with respect to changes in calcemia.[15]

N-(2-Thenoyl)-p-phenylenediamine   (C_4H_3S—CO—NH—C_6H_4—NH_2) and N-benzoyl-p-phenylenediamine were diazotized, then coupled with pig serum.   Both products behaved alike in serologic experiments.[16]

Natural α-terthienyl exhibits no provitamin activity in the rat.[17]

Thienylalanine (β-2-thienyl-DL-alanine)[18] has been used in a number of microbiological investigations.   It caused marked inhibition of the growth of the yeast *Saccharomyces cerevisiae*, an action which could be prevented, to a large extent, by the addition of phenylalanine.   When it was added to the diet of young rats, it could not support growth in the absence of either phenylalanine or methionine.[19]   It inhibited the growth of *Escherichia coli*, and the inhibition was prevented by sufficient amounts of phenylalanine.[20]   The "antiphenylalanine" properties of thienylalanine have been investigated with *Saccharomyces cerevisiae*, *Escherichia coli*, *Streptococcus faecalis*, and *Lactobacillus arabinosus*.   It has been found[21] that only the L isomer, but not the D, inhibited the growth of *Saccharomyces cerevisiae*, *Escherichia coli*, and *Lactobacillus delbrueckii*, and that the inhibition of growth of rats produced by the DL, D, or L isomer is counteracted by phenylalanine.[22-23a]   Intravenous injection of thienylalanine into a rabbit brought about the appearance of a persistent ninhydrin reaction in the urine within two hours.[10]

Recently, β-3-thienylalanine has been synthesized,[24-25a] and its microbiological properties investigated.   For *Saccharomyces cerevisiae*, strain 139, its growth inhibitory properties were about twice those of β-2-thienylalanine, and it was about one-third more effective against *E. coli*.   The activity was reversed by phenylalanine.[25]   In the rat, β-3-thienylalanine proved to be a more potent antagonist to phenylalanine than the corresponding 2-thienyl derivative.[25a]

[15] Quevauviller and Girard, *Ann. pharm. franç.*, **5**, 98 (1947).
[16] Erlenmeyer, Berger, and Leo, *Helv. Chim. Acta*, **16**, 733 (1933).
[17] Zechmeister and Sease, *J. Am. Chem. Soc.*, **69**, 273 (1947).
[18] This substance has been synthesized by Yuan and Li, *J. Chinese Chem. Soc.*, **5**, 214 (1937); *Chem. Abstr.*, **32**, 496 (1938). Barger and Easson (footnote 10). du Vigneaud, McKennis, Jr., Simmonds, Dittmer, and Brown, *J. Biol. Chem.*, **159**, 385 (1945). Dittmer, Herz, and Chambers, *ibid.*, **166**, 541 (1946).
[19] du Vigneaud, McKennis, Jr., Simmonds, Dittmer, and Brown, *J. Biol. Chem.*, **159**, 385 (1945).
[20] Beerstecher, Jr., and Shive, *J. Biol. Chem.*, **164**, 53 (1946).
[21] Ferger and du Vigneaud, *J. Biol. Chem.*, **174**, 241 (1948).
[22] Dittmer, Ellis, McKennis, Jr., and du Vigneaud, *J. Biol. Chem.*, **164**, 76 (1946).
[23] Ferger and du Vigneaud, *J. Biol. Chem.*, **179**, 61 (1949).
[23a] See also Thompson and Wilkin, *Proc. Soc. Exptl. Biol. Med.*, **68**, 434 (1948).
[24] Campaigne, Bourgeois, Garst, McCarthy, Patrick, and Day, *J. Am. Chem. Soc.*, **70**, 2611 (1948).
[25] Dittmer, *J. Am. Chem. Soc.*, **71**, 1205 (1949).
[25a] Garst, Campaigne, and Day, *J. Biol. Chem.*, **180**, 1013 (1949).

It has been found that yeast can convert 2-thiophenealdehyde into 2-thenyl alcohol (2-thienylcarbinol).[26] In similar experiments with benzaldehyde, the products were benzyl alcohol (phenylcarbinol) and acetylphenylcarbinol.[27] Yeast transformed 2-thienylglyoxal (C_4H_3S—CO—CHO) into 2-thienylglyoxylic acid (C_4H_3S—CO—COOH).[28] From the action of brewer's yeast on phenylglyoxal there were obtained mandelic acid, benzoylcarbinol, and smaller amounts of benzyl alcohol, benzaldehyde, and phenylglyoxylic acid.[29]

It has been found that certain thiophene derivatives can act as precursors in the biosynthesis of penicillins when they are added to the culture medium. Thus, in the presence of N-(2'-hydroxyethyl)-2-thiopheneacetamide, *Penicillium notatum* produces 2-thiophenemethylpenicillin (2-thenylpenicillin), which is analogous to benzylpenicillin; by the addition of 3-thiophenemercaptoacetic acid, 3-thiophenemercaptomethylpenicillin is obtained.[30—34] Tested in the form of their sodium salt, 2-thiophenemethylpenicillin was found to be as active as, and 3-thiophenemercaptomethylpenicillin more active than, benzylpenicillin against *Staphylococcus aureus*.[30] The sodium salt of 2-thiophenemethylpenicillin proved to be the most effective of a number of biosynthetic penicillins against a benzylpenicillin-resistant strain of *Staphylococcus aureus*.[34]

II. Antihistamine Compounds

Known thiophene derivatives which are analogous in structure to Antergan and Pyribenzamine are listed in Table II-1. N-Phenyl-N-(2-thenyl)-N',N'-dimethylethylenediamine (I, Diatrin) was reported to be inactive,[35] but investigators in other laboratories found that it is about two-thirds as active as Antergan[36] or somewhat more active than indicated by this figure.[37] According to another report, it is qualitatively

[26] Dunn and Dittmer, *J. Am. Chem. Soc.*, **68**, 2561 (1946).
[27] Neuberg and Hirsch, *Biochem. Z.*, **115**, 282 (1921). Neuberg and Ohle, *ibid.*, **128**, 610 (1922).
[28] Fujise, *Biochem. Z.*, **236**, 241 (1931).
[29] Dakin, *J. Biol. Chem.*, **18**, 91 (1914).
[30] Behrens, Corse, Jones, Kleiderer, Soper, Van Abeele, Larson, Sylvester, Haines, and Carter, *J. Biol. Chem.*, **175**, 765 (1948).
[31] Corse, Jones, Soper, Whitehead, and Behrens, *J. Am. Chem. Soc.*, **70**, 2837 (1948).
[32] Jones, Soper, Behrens, and Corse, *J. Am. Chem. Soc.*, **70**, 2843 (1948).
[33] Soper, Whitehead, Behrens, Corse, and Jones, *J. Am. Chem. Soc.*, **70**, 2849 (1948).
[34] Behrens and Kingkade, *J. Biol. Chem.*, **176**, 1047 (1948).
[35] Viaud, *Produits pharm.*, **2**, 53 (1947).
[36] Kyrides, Meyer, and Zienty, *J. Am. Chem. Soc.*, **69**, 2239 (1947).
[37] Leonard and Solmssen, *J. Am. Chem. Soc.*, **70**, 2064 (1948).

similar to other ethylenediamine antihistamine drugs.[38]   Compound II, the N',N'-diethyl analog of I, is only about one-fifth as active as Antergan.[36]

TABLE II-1. Thiophene Analogs of Antergan and Pyribenzamine

No.	R	R′	X	Ref.
I	Phenyl	2-Thenyl	$CH_2CH_2N(CH_3)_2$	35–38
II	Phenyl	2-Thenyl	$CH_2CH_2N(C_2H_5)_2$	36
III	Phenyl	2-Thenyl	$CH_2CH_2NC_5H_{10}$	37
IV	Phenyl	2-Thenyl	$CH_2CH_2CH_2N(CH_3)_2$	37
V	Phenyl	2-Thenyl	$CH_2CH(CH_3)N(CH_3)_2$	37
VI	2-Pyridyl	2-Thenyl	$CH_2CH_2N(CH_3)_2$	36,37, 39–49
VII	2-Pyridyl	2-Thenyl	$CH_2CH_2NC_5H_{10}$	37
VIII	2-Pyridyl	2-Thenyl	$CH_2CH_2CH_2N(CH_3)_2$	37
IX	2-Pyridyl	2-Thenyl	$CH_2CH(CH_3)N(CH_3)_2$	37
X	2-Pyridyl	1-(2-Thienyl)-ethyl	$CH_2CH_2N(CH_3)_2$	49
XI	2-Pyridyl	1-(2-Thienyl)-butyl	$CH_2CH_2N(CH_3)_2$	49
XII	2-Pyridyl	5-tert-Butyl-2-thenyl	$CH_2CH_2N(CH_3)_2$	49
XIII	2-Pyridyl	3-Bromo-2-thenyl	$CH_2CH_2N(CH_3)_2$	49
XIV	2-Pyridyl	5-Chloro-2-thenyl	$CH_2CH_2N(CH_3)_2$	40,49
XV	2-Pyridyl	5-Bromo-2-thenyl	$CH_2CH_2N(CH_3)_2$	40,49
XVI	2-Pyridyl	3,5-Dibromo-2-thenyl	$CH_2CH_2N(CH_3)_2$	49
XVII	2-Pyridyl	5-Carboxy-2-thenyl	$CH_2CH_2N(CH_3)_2$	49
XVIII	5-Bromo-2-pyridyl	2-Thenyl	$CH_2CH_2N(CH_3)_2$	49
XIX	5-Bromo-2-pyridyl	5-tert-Butyl-2-thenyl	$CH_2CH_2N(CH_3)_2$	49
XX	5-Bromo-2-pyridyl	5-Chloro-2-thenyl	$CH_2CH_2N(CH_3)_2$	49
XXI	5-Bromo-2-pyridyl	5-Bromo-2-thenyl	$CH_2CH_2N(CH_3)_2$	49
XXII	2-Pyridyl	3-Thenyl	$CH_2CH_2N(CH_3)_2$	50,51
XXIII	2-Pyridyl	2-Chloro-3-thenyl	$CH_2CH_2N(CH_3)_2$	50,51
XXIV	2-Pyridyl	2-Bromo-3-thenyl	$CH_2CH_2N(CH_3)_2$	50,51
XXV	2-Pyridyl	2,5-Dichloro-3-thenyl	$CH_2CH_2N(CH_3)_2$	50,51
XXVI	2-Pyrimidyl	2-Thenyl	$CH_2CH_2N(CH_3)_2$	52

[38] Ercoli, Schachter, Hueper, and Lewis, J. Pharmacol. Exptl. Therap., **93,** 210 (1948).

[39] Weston, J. Am. Chem. Soc., **69,** 980 (1947).

[40] Clapp, Clark, Vaughan, English, and Anderson, J. Am. Chem. Soc., **69,** 1549 (1947).

N-(2-Pyridyl)-N-(2-thenyl)-N',N'-dimethylethylenediamine   (VI, Thenylene, Histadyl) was stated to be more active than I.[36]   Preliminary pharmacological data indicated that VI exhibits the same order of activity as Pyribenzamine and is about equally toxic,[39,40,43] but according to another report, it is not as active as Pyribenzamine.[44]   It has a potent antihistamine action when tested with the intact guinea pig placed in a histamine atmosphere.[41]   When the benzyl group in Pyribenzamine is replaced by the 5-chloro-2-thenyl or the 5-bromo-2-thenyl radical, the activity is increased and the toxicity decreased.[40,44]   It was reported that the general experimental and clinical efficacy of VI approaches but does not equal that of Pyribenzamine, but with certain patients it can be used more effectively and with fewer disturbances than the latter drug.[45]   Clinical comparison of I, VI, and Benadryl revealed a high degree of similarity.[48]

After a series of compounds, which included VI, X–XXI, and XXV, had been tested *in vitro* against histamine, it was claimed that none was as active as N-(2-pyridyl)-N-(5-chloro-2-thenyl)-N',N'-dimethylethylenediamine (XIV) or its bromo analog (XV).[49]   It was reported that compound XIV (Chlorothen) and the corresponding bromo compound were found to be more active than Pyribenzamine on the isolated guinea pig ileum.   Preliminary tests in animals indicated that, with respect to Pyribenzamine, they possess at least twice the antihistamine activity, twice the duration of action, and one-half the acute toxicity.[40]

Compound XXII was stated to be a highly active substance, and does not appear to be more toxic than other compounds of similar structure. It is more potent than the halo derivatives XXIII and XXIV.[51]

N - (2 - Pyrimidyl) - N - (2 - thenyl) - N,N' - dimethylethylenediamine (XXVI), the thiophene analog of Hetramine [N-(2-pyrimidyl)-N-benzyl-N,N'-dimethylethylenediamine], is a compound of very low activity.[52]

[41] Lee, Dinwiddie, and Chen, *J. Pharmacol. Exptl. Therap.*, **90**, 83 (1947).
[42] Ercoli, Schachter, Leonard, and Solmssen, *Arch. Biochem.*, **13**, 487 (1947).
[43] Roth, Richards, and Sheppard, *Federation Proc.*, **6**, I, 366 (1947).
[44] Litchfield, Jr., Adams, Goddard, Jaeger, and Alonso, *Bull. Johns Hopkins Hosp.*, **81**, 55 (1947).
[45] Feinberg and Bernstein, *J. Lab. Clin. Med.*, **32**, 1370 (1947).
[46] Leonard and Solmssen, *J. Am. Chem. Soc.*, **70**, 2064 (1948).
[47] Friedlaender and Friedlaender, *Am. J. Med. Sci.*, **215**, 531 (1948).
[48] *Proc. Staff Meetings Mayo Clinic*, **23**, 48 (1948).
[49] Clark, Clapp, Vaughan, Jr., Sutherland, Winterbottom, Anderson, Forsythe, Blodinger, Eberlin, and English, *J. Org. Chem.*, **14**, 216 (1949).
[50] Campaigne and LeSuer, *J. Am. Chem. Soc.*, **71**, 333 (1949).
[51] Lands, Hoppe, Siegmund, and Luduena, *J. Pharmacol. Exptl. Therap.*, **95**, 45 (1949).
[52] Biel, *J. Am. Chem. Soc.*, **71**, 1306 (1949).

TABLE II-2. Pyrrolidylethylamine Derivatives[53]

$$\begin{array}{c} R \\ \diagdown \\ R'CH_2 \end{array} NCH_2CH_2N \begin{array}{c} CH_2-CH_2 \\ | \\ CH_2-CH_2 \end{array}$$

No.	R	R'CH₂
I	Phenyl	2-Thenyl
II	Cyclohexyl	2-Thenyl
III	2-Thenyl	2-Thenyl
IV	2-Pyridyl	2-Thenyl
V	2-Pyridyl	5-Chloro-2-thenyl
VI	2-Pyrimidyl	5-Chloro-2-thenyl
VII	2-Quinolinyl	2-Thenyl

The effectiveness of N-(2-pyridyl)-N-(5-chloro-2-thenyl)-β-(1-pyrrolidyl)-ethylamine (V, Table II-2) is equal to about one-fourth that of Pyribenzamine.[53]

It has been found that certain substituted piperazines antagonize the effects of histamine.[54]

$$RR'CH-N \begin{array}{c} CH_2-CH_2 \\ \diagup \qquad \diagdown \\ CH_2-CH_2 \end{array} N-CH_3$$

(R = phenyl or p-chlorophenyl; R' = 2-thienyl)

TABLE II-3. Thiophene Analogs of Benadryl

RR'CH—O—R"

No.	R	R'	R"	Ref.
I	Phenyl	Phenyl	$CH_2CH_2N(CH_3)_2$	(Benadryl)
II	Phenyl	2-Thenyl	$CH_2CH_2N(CH_3)_2$	55
III	Phenyl	Phenyl	$CH_2CH_2N \begin{array}{c} CH_2-CH_2 \\ | \\ CH_2-CH_2 \end{array}$	55
IV	Phenyl	2-Thienyl	$CH_2CH_2N \begin{array}{c} CH_2-CH_2 \\ | \\ CH_2-CH_2 \end{array}$	55
V	2-Pyridyl	2-Thienyl	$CH_2CH_2N(CH_3)_2$	56

The activity of the thiophene compounds II and IV is less than that of the corresponding benzene derivatives I and III. Compound V is not as potent as the corresponding phenyl analog.

[53] Lincoln, Heinzelmann, and Hunter, *J. Am. Chem. Soc.*, **71**, 2902 (1949).
[54] Hamlin, Weston, Fischer, and Michaels, Jr., *J. Am. Chem. Soc.*, **71**, 2731 (1949)
[55] Wright, Kolloff, and Hunter, *J. Am. Chem. Soc.*, **70**, 3098 (1948).
[56] Sperber, Papa, Schwenk, and Sherlock, *J. Am. Chem. Soc.*, **71**, 887 (1949).

The antihistamine and antispasmodic properties of 2-[(2-thienyl)-phenylmethoxymethyl]imidazoline are rather weak.[57] 2-[N-(2-Thenyl)-anilinomethyl]imidazoline, a thiophene analog of Antistine [2-(N-benzylanilinomethyl)imidazoline], was found to be only 5% as active as Antergan, and N-(2-pyridyl)-2-thiophenecarboxamide, a thiophene analog of N-(2-pyridyl)benzamide,[58] proved to be inactive.[36]

III. Pressor Compounds

A number of thienylalkylamines and the corresponding phenyl-alkylamines have been tested for pressor activity (Table II-4). While

TABLE II-4. Pressor Activity of 2-Thienylalkyl- and Phenylalkylamines

No.	Compound	Activity[a]			
		Thiophene derivative	Ref.	Benzene derivative	Ref.
I	2-Thienyl—CH_2—NH_2	0	59	0	60
II	—CH_2—$NH(CH_3)$	0	59		
III	—$CH(NH_2)$—CH_3	0	59	0	60
IV	—$CH(NH$—$CH_3)$—CH_3	0	59		
V	—CH_2—CH_2—NH_2	++	10,59,61	++	60–62
VI	—CH_2—CH_2—$NH(CH_3)$	++	59	++	60
VII	—$CH(NH_2)$—CH_2—CH_3	0	59	0	62
VIII	—$CH(NH$—$CH_3)$—CH_2—CH_3	0	59		
IX	—CH_2—$CH(NH_2)$—CH_3	++	59,63,64	++	62,64,65
X	—CH_2—$CH(NH$—$CH_3)$—CH_3	++	59		
XI	—CH_2—CH_2—CH_2—NH_2	+	59	+	60,62
XII	—CH_2—CH_2—CH_2—$NH(CH_3)$	+	59		
XIII	—$CH(CH_3)$—CH_2—NH_2			++	62,64
XIV	—$CH(CH_3)$—CH_2—$NH(CH_3)$		66		
XV	—$CH(CH_3)$—$CH(NH_2)$—CH_3	Active	64	Active	64
XVI	—CO—CH_2—NH_2	Active	10,67		
XVII	—CO—$CH(CH_3)$—NH_2		66		68

XVIII	R(H or alkyl) R₂(H or alkyl)
	    | |
	—C————————CH—NR₃(R₄)
	    |
	R(H, OH or alkyl)
	R₃ and R₄ = H or alkyl
			69		

XIX	5-Phenyl-2-thienyl—CH_2—CH_2—NH_2	Active	70		
XX	5-p-Anisyl-2-thienyl—CH_2—CH_2—NH_2	Active	70		

[a] 0 = inactive or only slightly active; + = moderately active; ++ = activity about equals that of β-phenylethylamine.

[57] Dahlbom, *Acta Chem. Scand.*, **3**, 32 (1949); *Chem. Abstr.*, **43**, 6619 (1949).
[58] Mayer, *J. Allergy*, **17**, 153 (1946).

many of the data reported in the literature permit only semiquantitative comparisons to be made, it can be seen, nevertheless, that the pressor effects of the two types of amines are quite similar.

Although it has been stated that from the standpoint of pressor effect, (2-thienyl)isopropylamine [1-(2-thienyl)-2-aminopropane] and phenylisopropylamine, like β-(2-thienyl)ethylamine and β-phenylethylamine, are very comparable, or possibly identical,[63,64] the amines differ in other respects.   The thienyl compound is slightly less toxic than the benzene derivative.[63,64]   Administered orally to man, the thienylamine is considerably less active as a circulatory and as a central nervous system stimulant.[63] β-(2-Thienyl)ethylamine produces in rats about the same degree of central stimulation as β-phenylethylamine, but the former substance has a considerably lower threshold dose.[71]

IV. Local Anesthetics

The 2-thienyl analogs of cocaine,[72] α-Eucaine,[73] and Stovaine[73] have local anesthetic properties.   2-Thienyl β-piperidinoethyl ketone,[74,75] like phenyl β-piperidinoethyl ketone,[76] is a local anesthetic.[76]   The alkyl and basic alkyl esters of thiophenecarboxylic acids which have been tested for local anesthetic activity are reported in Table II-5.

Compound I was stated to be one-fourth as active as the corresponding benzoate, and one-sixth as active as procaine,[77] but according to a recent report it is inactive.[79]   Compound II exhibits only slight activity,

[59] Blicke and Burckhalter, *J. Am. Chem. Soc.*, **64**, 480 (1942).   Compounds tested by L. W. Rowe.
[60] Barger and Dale, *J. Physiol.* (*London*), **41**, 29 (1910).
[61] Tainter, *Quart. J. Pharm. Pharmacol.*, **3**, 584 (1930).
[62] Hartung and Munch, *J. Am. Chem. Soc.*, **53**, 1875 (1931).
[63] Alles and Feigen, *J. Pharmacol. Exptl. Therap.*, **72**, 267 (1941).
[64] Warren, Marsh, Thompson, Shelton, and Becker, *J. Pharmacol.*, **79**, 187 (1943).
[65] Alles, *J. Pharmacol.*, **47**, 339 (1933).   Alles and Feigen, *ibid.*, **72**, 267 (1941).
[66] J. H. Burckhalter, Dissertation, University of Michigan, 1942.
[67] Barger, *Some Applications of Organic Chemistry to Biology and Medicine.*   McGraw-Hill, New York, 1930, pp. 99–100.
[68] Hartung, *J. Am. Chem. Soc.*, **53**, 2248 (1931).
[69] Van Zoeren, U. S. Pat. 2,367,702 (1945).
[70] Graham, *Quart. J. Pharm. Pharmacol.*, **13**, 305 (1940).   Compounds prepared by Robinson and Todd, *J. Chem. Soc.*, **1939**, 1743.   In Graham's article the pharmacology of the amines has been presented in some detail.
[71] Schulte, Reif, Bacher, Jr., Lawrence, and Tainter, *J. Pharmacol. Exptl. Therap.*, **71**, 62 (1941).
[72] Steinkopf and Ohse, *Ann.*, **437**, 14 (1924).
[73] Steinkopf and Ohse, *Ann.*, **448**, 205 (1926).
[74] Levvy and Nisbet, *J. Chem. Soc.*, **1938**, 1053.
[75] Blicke and Burckhalter, *J. Am. Chem. Soc.*, **64**, 453 (1942).
[76] Mannich and Lammering, *Ber.*, **55**, 3515 (1922).
[77] Gilman and Pickens, *J. Am. Chem. Soc.*, **47**, 252 (1925).
[78] Carney, *Abstracts*, First National Medicinal Chemistry Symposium, Medicinal Chem. Div., A.C.S., Ann Arbor, Mich., 1948, p. 133.
[79] Campaigne and LeSuer, *J. Am. Chem. Soc.*, **70**, 3498 (1948).

TABLE II-5. Alkyl and Basic Esters of Thiophenecarboxylic Acids Tested as Local Anesthetics

(Y in the 2 or 3 position)

No.	X	Y	Position of Y	Ref.
I	H	$COOCH_2CH_2N(C_2H_5)_2$	2	77
II	H	$COOCH_2CH_2CH_2NH(CH_2)$	2	78
III	H	$COOCH_2CH_2CH_2N(C_4H_9)_2$	2	79
IV	H	$COOCH_2CH_2(CH_3)_2$	3	79
V	H	$COOCH_2CH_2N(C_2H_5)_2$	3	79
VI	H	$COOCH_2CH_2N(C_4H_9)_2$	3	79
VII	H	$COOCH_2CH_2NC_4H_8O*$	3	79
VIII	H	$COOCH_2CH_2CH_2N(C_4H_9)_2$	3	79
IX	H_2N	$COOCH_2CH_3$	2	80
X	CH_3CONH	$COOCH_2CH_3$	2	80
XI	H_2N	$COOCH_2CH_2N(C_2H_5)_2$	2	80

* NC_4H_8O = morpholino.

and is only one-half as potent as the corresponding derivative of benzoic acid.[78] Compounds III and VIII were shown to be weakly active substances which produce moderate irritation, and are about as toxic as Butyn.[79] Compounds IV, V, VI, and VII are inactive.[79]

The thiophene analog of Anesthesin (IX) produces anesthesia on the rabbit's cornea when applied as a powder, but its acetyl derivative (X) is inactive.[80] Especially interesting is compound XI, an analog of Procaine, which equals Procaine in potency.[80]

V. Hypnotics

Acetophenone exhibits hypnotic activity, but acetothienone is inactive.[81] 2-Acetylthiophene, 2-propanoylthiophene, and 2-butanoyl-thiophene were found to be quite toxic, and to be devoid of hypnotic properties.[82] 5-Ethyl-5-(2-thienyl)barbituric acid showed the same order of activity as phenobarbital when injected intraperitoneally into rats.[83] Chloralacetothienonoxime, analogous to chloralacetophenoxime $[C_6H_5(CH_3)C=NO \cdot CH(OH)CCl_3]$, has been prepared but its activity was not reported.[84] The latter compound was claimed to be free from

[80] Dann, *Ber.*, **76**, 419 (1943).
[81] Gilman, Rowe, and Dickey, *Rec. trav. chim.*, **52**, 395 (1933).
[82] Billman and Travis, *Proc. Indiana Acad. Sci.*, **54**, 101 (1945).
[83] Blicke and Zienty, *J. Am. Chem. Soc.*, **63**, 2945 (1941). Compound tested by J. W. Nelson.
[84] Steinkopf and Jaffé, *Ann.*, **413**, 333 (1917).

the side effects of chloral and acetophenone.[85]   Methyl methylthienyl ketone and methyl dimethylthienyl ketone are said to be devoid of hypnotic activity, and to be three to five times as toxic as acetophenone[86,87]; they exhibit little[87] or no[88] antiepileptic activity, although acetophenone definitely produced this effect.

VI. Antifebrides and Analgesics

Several thiophenic materials have been tested as antifebrides.   2-Acetamidothiophene (2-acetthiophenide), in contrast to acetanilide, is completely inactive, probably due to the fact that the hydrolytic product, 2-aminothiophene, is a very unstable substance.[89]   However, the action of 2-thenoyl-*p*-phenetidin is similar to that of phenacetin, and the activity of 2-thenoylquinine resembles that of 2-benzoylquinine.[73]   2-Acetothienone-*p*-phenetidide, which is analogous to the antifebride acetophenone-*p*-phenetidide,[90] has been synthesized, but its activity was not reported.[84]   2-(2-Thienyl)quinoline-4-carboxylic acid is said to be like cinchophen pharmacologically in experimental animals, but it colored the tissues and urine violet.[91]   The effect of 2-(5-methyl-2-thienyl)- and of   2-(2,5-dimethyl-3-thienyl)quinoline-4-carboxylic   acid   was   also

TABLE II-6. Thiophene Analogs of Amidone (Methadon)[95]

$$\begin{array}{ll} \text{Phenyl} \\ \qquad\searrow \!\! C\!-\!COC_2H_5 \\ \text{Phenyl}\nearrow \quad | \\ \qquad\quad CH_2CH(CH_3)N(CH_3)_2 \\ \qquad\qquad\qquad \text{Amidone} \end{array} \qquad \begin{array}{ll} \text{Phenyl} \\ \qquad\searrow \!\! C\!-\!X \\ \text{2-Thienyl}\nearrow \quad | \\ \qquad\qquad\quad Y \end{array}$$

No.	X	Y
I	COC_2H_5	$CH_2CH_2N(C_2H_5)_2$
II	COC_2H_5	$CH_2CH_2NC_4H_8O*$
III	COC_2H_5	$CH(CH_3)CH_2NC_4H_8O$
IV	$COOC_2H_5$	$CH_2CH_2N(C_2H_5)_2$
V	$COOC_2H_5$	$CH_2CH_2NC_4H_8O$
VI	$COOC_2H_5$	$CH(CH_3)CH_2NC_4H_8O$

* NC_4H_8O = morpholino.

[85] Jensen, *Pharm. Zentralhalle*, **37**, 816; *Chem. Zentr.*, **67**, II, 856 (1896); *ibid.*, **68**, I, 300 (1897).
[86] Quevauviller, *Compt. rend. soc. biol.*, **140**, 367 (1946).
[87] Quevauviller, *Ann. pharm. franç.*, **5**, 16 (1947).
[88] Quevauviller, *Compt. rend. soc. biol.*, **140**, 370 (1946).
[89] Steinkopf, *Ann.*, **403**, 23 (1914).
[90] Valentiner and Schwarz, *Chem. Zentr.*, **67**, II, 856 (1896); *ibid.*, **69**, II, 1189 (1898).
[91] Hartmann and Wybert, *Helv. Chim. Acta*, **2**, 60 (1919).

similar to that of cinchophen, but these compounds produced no coloration.

The 2-thienyl analog of Demerol (ethyl 1-methyl-4-phenylpiperidine-4-carboxylate) and a number of related thiophene compounds have been described.[92,93] Methyl 1-methyl-4-(2-thienyl)piperidine-4-carboxylate is less than one-half as active in experimental animals as Demerol.[94]

Compound I was found to be one-third as active, and compound V four times as active as Demerol.[95]

VII. Antispasmodics

Two series of basic alkyl esters of substituted 2-thienylacetic acids (I, II) and one series of substituted β-(2-thienyl)propionic acids (III) were prepared and tested for spasmolytic potency. (R$'$ = basic alkyl.)

    (I) 2-Thienyl—CH(R)—COOR$'$[96-99]

        (R = phenyl, benzyl, α-naphthyl, p-xenyl or 2-thienyl.)

   (II) 2-Thienyl—C(OH)(R)—COOR$'$[96-102]

        (R = methyl, cyclohexyl, phenyl, α-naphthyl or p-xenyl.)

  (III) 2-Thienyl—CH$_2$—CH(R)—COOR$'$[100]

        (R = propyl, cyclohexyl, cyclohexylmethyl, β-cyclohexylethyl, phenyl, benzyl, β-phenylethyl, 2-thienyl, 2-thenyl or β-(2-thienyl)ethyl.)

Several esters in series II exhibited unusually high activity. For example, when β-diethylaminoethyl or γ-diethylaminopropyl 2-thienylcyclohexylhydroxyacetate[101] was tested on the isolated intestine, which had been stimulated with acetylcholine, the average maximum effective dilution was 1:80,000,000.[96-98] β-Piperidinoethyl phenyl-2-thienylglycolate, because of its promising properties, was studied extensively in animals and also in human subjects.[102] Many of the highly active esters are also potent mydriatics.[98]

[92] Blicke, U. S. Pats. 2,425,721; 2,425,722; and 2,425,723 (1947).
[93] Martin Chanin, *Dissertation*, University of Michigan, 1945.
[94] Private communication.   Tests performed by Dr. C. V. Winder in the Parke, Davis and Co. laboratories.
[95] Brown, Cook, and Heilbron, *J. Chem. Soc.*, **1949**, S113.
[96] Blicke and Tsao, *J. Am. Chem. Soc.*, **66**, 1645 (1944).   Compounds tested by Dr. A. M. Lands and Miss V. L. Nash.
[97] Lands and Nash, *Proc. Soc. Exptl. Biol. Med.*, **57**, 55 (1944).
[98] Lands, Nash, and Hooper, *J. Pharmacol., Exptl. Therap.*, **86**, 129 (1946).
[99] Abreu and Troescher-Elam, *J. Pharmacol.*, **86**, 205 (1946).
[100] Blicke and Leonard, *J. Am. Chem. Soc.*, **68**, 1934 (1946).   Compounds tested by Dr. A. M. Lands and Miss Harriet McCarthy.
[101] Since hydroxyacetic acid is glycolic acid, these esters may also be called glycolates.
[102] Pickering, Abreu, Chen, Burnett, and Bostick, *J. Pharmacol. Exptl. Therap.*, **95**, 122 (1949).

Basic alkyl esters of 1-(2-thienyl)cyclopentanecarboxylic and 1-(2-thienyl)cyclohexanecarboxylic acid were found to be about equal in potency to the corresponding 1-phenyl derivatives which possess high spasmolytic activity.[103]   Other basic ethers (e.g., 18 amines of the general formula 2-thienyl—$(CH_2)_x$—NRR'; x = 1–4, R = hydrogen or ω-2-thienylalkyl, R' = alkyl or cycloalkyl) were prepared as potential antispasmodics, but their activity was not reported.[104]

Three compounds of the general type R—CO—C_4H_3S (C_4H_3S = 2-thienyl), in which R = β-dimethylaminoethyl (I), β-piperidinoethyl (II), or β-morpholinoethyl (III), have been prepared.[105]   Compounds I and III showed slight or no activity, but II was stated to be a potent antispasmodic. 1-(1-Piperidyl)-3-(2-thienyl)-3-pentanol was found to be less active than Trasentin.[106]

VIII. Anticonvulsants

5-(2-Thienyl)-5-R-hydantoins (R = alkyl, cycloalkyl, aryl, or aralkyl) have been described, in general, as anticonvulsants of very low toxicity which exhibit no sedative or hypnotic effect.[107]   5-(2-Thienyl)-5-phenylhydantoin, like Dilantin, has been found to be an effective anticonvulsant.[108,109]   Both 5,5-di-(2-thienyl)-[110] and 5-(2-thienyl)-5-(2-furyl)-hydantoin, as well as di-2-thienyl ketone, were tested, and the hydantoins were stated to be active compounds.[109]   A series of 1-R-5-(2-thienyl)-hydantoins (R = alkyl, alkenyl, cycloalkyl, or aralkyl) was prepared, but no compound tested was as active as Dilantin.[111]

A few other classes of thiophene compounds have also been tested. β-(2-Thenoyl)propionic acid is about 15% as active as diphenylhydantoin, but the following compounds proved to be inactive: 5-(2-thenoyl)-pentanoic, 7-(2-thenoyl)heptanoic, 8-(2-thenoyl)octanoic, and 9-(2-thenoyl)nonanoic acids and also 1,6-di-(2-thenoyl)hexane, 1,7-di-(2-thenoyl)heptane, and 1,8-di(2-thenoyl)octane.[82] 2-Phenyl-3-methyl-4-thiazolidone was found to be an anticonvulsant.   The corresponding 2-

[103] Tilford, Doerle, Van Campen, Jr., and Shelton, J. Am. Chem. Soc., 71, 1705 (1949).
[104] Frederick Leonard, Dissertation, University of Michigan, 1946.
[105] Denton, Turner, Neier, Lawson, and Schedl, J. Am. Chem. Soc., 71, 2048 (1949).
[106] Denton, Lawson, Neier, and Turner, J. Am. Chem. Soc., 71, 2050 (1949).
[107] Spurlock, U. S. Pat. 2,366,221 (1945).
[108] Goodman and Toman, Abstracts, First National Medicinal Chemistry Symposium, Medicinal Chem. Div., A.C.S., Ann Arbor, Mich., 1948, p. 93.
[109] Long, Abstracts, First National Medicinal Chemistry Symposium, 1948, p. 114.
[110] Bywater and Coleman, U. S. Pat. 2,468,168; Chem. Abstr., 43, 5805 (1949).
[111] Long, Miller, and Chen, J. Am. Chem. Soc., 71, 669 (1949).

thienyl derivative was synthesized, but its activity was not reported.[112] Although phenacetylurea has anticonvulsive properties, 2-thienylacetyl-urea is practically inactive.[113]

IX. Germicides

A number of diverse thiophene compounds are reported in the literature to have germicidal properties.

Shale oil, obtained from shale found in Tyrol, has been found to contain homologs of thiophene. The activity of Ichthyol, prepared by sulfonation of the oil, may be due, at least to some extent, to the presence of the thiophene derivatives in the oil.[114] It has been claimed that certain mercury derivatives of thiophene exhibit extraordinarily high potency as germicides, and that they are relatively low in toxicity, and possess other desirable properties.[115] Thiophene and tetrabromo-thiophene have been recommended or used as antiseptics, and sodium thiophenesulfonate and diiodothiophene have been employed in the treatment of skin diseases.[116] When a number of thiophene compounds, among them mercury derivatives such as 2-chloromercurithiophene, were tested, it was found that they were about as active as the corresponding benzene derivatives against *Staphylococcus aureus*, and in some instances they were more active.[116] Ethyl 3-hydroxy-5-methylthiophene-4-car-boxylate has been patented as a disinfectant.[117] 2-Sulfanilamidothio-phene (sulfathiophene)[118] has been synthesized, and it was stated[119] that, although it produced no toxic symptoms, it exhibited no curative effect on mice infected with pneumococcus Type I. The preparation of 2,5-dimethyl-3-(p-N-acetylsulfanilamido)thiophene has been described.[120] A number of tetramethylene sulfones (tetrahydrothiophene 1-dioxides), which contained a basic alkyl side chain, proved to be without any significant activity in amebiasis, filariasis, schistosomiasis, or leuschmaniasis.[121] 2-Tetrahydrothiophenecarboxylic acid and the corresponding 2,5-di-

[112] Troutman and Long, *J. Am. Chem. Soc.*, **70**, 3436 (1948).
[113] Spielman, Geiszler, and Close, *J. Am. Chem. Soc.*, **70**, 4189 (1948).
[114] *Ichthyol*, Merck and Co., New York, 1913. *Ichthyol*, U. S. Bureau of Mines, Circular No. 7042, 1938. Scheibler, *Ber.*, **48**, 1815 (1815); *ibid.*, **49**, 2595 (1916); *ibid.*, **52**, 1903 (1919); *Arch. Pharm.*, **258**, 70 (1920). Scheibler and Schmidt, *Ber.*, **54**, 139 (1921). Scheibler and Rettig, *Ber.*, **59**, 1194 (1926); *ibid.*, **59**, 1198 (1926). Scheibler, *Z. angew. Chem.*, **39**, 1397 (1926). Leclère, *Compt. rend.*, **194**, 286 (1932).
[115] Andersen, U. S. Pat. 2,085,065; *Chem. Abstr.*, **31**, 5951 (1937).
[116] Rhodehamel and Degering, *J. Am. Pharm. Assoc.*, **31**, 281 (1942).
[117] Benary, Germ. Pat. 282,914.
[118] Bost and Starnes, *J. Am. Chem. Soc.*, **63**, 1885 (1941).
[119] Seemann and Lucas, *Can. J. Research*, **19**, 291 (1941).
[120] Chabrier and Tchoubar, *Compt. rend.*, **220**, 780 (1945).
[121] Leffler and Krueger, *J. Am. Chem. Soc.*, **71**, 370 (1949).

carboxylic acid form complexes with silver salts which were claimed to be highly germicidal.[122] It was found that natural α-terthienyl is devoid of antibiotic potency against *Staphylococcus aureus, Bacillis subtilis, Escherichia coli,* and *Pseudomonas ovalis.*[17]

Although esters of *p*-aminobenzoic acid, such as ethyl *p*-aminobenzoate and β-diethylaminoethyl *p*-aminobenzoate, the latter in the form of its hydrochloride, exhibit an antagonistic action toward sulfonamides, it was found that neither ethyl 5-amino-2-thiophenecarboxylate nor β-diethylaminoethyl 5-amino-2-thiophenecarboxylate hydrochloride, which are comparable to the benzoic acid esters in local anesthetic activity, would counteract the inhibiting action of sulfanilamide on the growth of *Streptobacterium (Lactobacillus) plantarum.*[123]

Thiophene derivatives, analogous to such compounds as *p*-nitrobenzoic acid and *p*-aminobenzamide, were investigated for bacteriostatic properties. It was found that 5-amino-2-thiophenecarboxamide was inactive while the activity of 5-nitro-2-thiophenecarboxylic acid and of 5-nitro-2-thiophenecarboxamide compared favorably with that of the most potent sulfonamides, at least in their action on *Streptococcus hemolyticus.*[124]

The *in vitro* growth-inhibiting properties of *p*-nitrobenzoic acid, 5-nitro-2-thiophenecarboxylic acid, their ethyl esters and amides, the bis-(4-nitrophenyl), bis-(5-nitro-2-thienyl) sulfides and sulfones against *Staphylococcus aureus* and *albus* and *Streptobacterium plantarum* was determined. The activity of the ethyl ester and amide of 5-nitro-2-thiophenecarboxylic acid exceeded that of sulfathiazole. Bis-(5-nitro-2-thienyl) sulfide was stated to be one of the most active known synthetic compounds against *Staphylococcus.*[125]

The suppression of growth of a variety of bacteria and molds by a number of nitrothiophene derivatives, and the relative effectiveness of these substances in comparison with penicillin, dodecyldimethylbenzylammonium bromide, 8-hydroxyquinoline and sulfathiazole was studied.[126]

X. Analogs of DDT

Thiophene compounds, related to DDT, which have been examined for insecticidal properties are listed in Table II-7 on page 44.

Compound I, the thiophene analog of DDT,[127] has been found to be inactive as an insecticide against the housefly.[128] Although, qualita-

[122] Bayer and Co., Germ. Pat. 405,017 (1924).
[123] Dann and Möller, *Ber.*, **80**, 21 (1947).
[124] Johnson, Green, and Pauli, *J. Biol. Chem.*, **153**, 37 (1944).
[125] Dann and Möller, *Ber.*, **80**, 23 (1947).
[126] Dann and Möller, *Ber.*, **82**, 76 (1949).
[127] Peter, *Ber.*, **17**, 1341 (1884).
[128] Prill, Synerholm, and Hartzell, *Contrib. Boyce Thompson Inst.*, **14**, 341 (1946).

TABLE II-7. Analogs of DDT: R_2CHCCl_3

No.	R	Ref.
I	2-Thienyl	127–131
II	5-Chloro-2-thienyl	129–132
III	5-Bromo-2-thienyl	129–131
IV	5-Iodo-2-thienyl	130
V	4-Methyl-2-thienyl	129
VI	5-Methyl-2-thienyl	129,130
VII	5-tert-Butyl-2-thienyl	130
VIII	2,5-Dichloro-2-thienyl	131

tively, II resembles DDT in its mode of action, in general it is much less potent except when tested against insects highly resistant to DDT.[132]

Compounds I, II, III, V, and VI do not exhibit any appreciable insecticidal activity toward the two insects *Heliothrips haemorrhoidalis* or *Drosophila melanogaster* or any distinct fungicidal action against species of *Phytophthora*, *Dothiorella*, or *Macrosporium*.[129]   Compounds I, II, and III are also inactive against the German cockroach and the confused flour beetle.[129]   According to another report,[130] compound II seems to be as active as DDT against cockroaches while III and IV are less active; compound VI shows no insecticidal activity.

XI. Miscellaneous Compounds and Their Properties

A variety of thiophene derivatives having miscellaneous properties not listed in the above categories have been collected for the readers' convenience. 2-Thenoylcholine perchlorate possesses about one-tenth the activity of acetylcholine chloride on smooth muscle.[133]

2-(2-Thenyl)- and 2-(5-methyl-2-thenyl)-4,5-dihydroimidazole are said to act on the circulatory system of warm-blooded animals and also exhibit antimalarial activity.[134]

Like Dibenamine (N,N-dibenzyl-β-chloroethylamine), N-ethyl-N-(2-thenyl)-β-chloroethylamine was stated to be active as an adrenergic

[129] Metcalf and Gunther, *J. Am. Chem. Soc.*, **69**, 2579 (1947).   Fungicidal tests by Zentmeyer.
[130] Truitt, Mattison, and Richardson, *J. Am. Chem. Soc.*, **70**, 79 (1948).
[131] Feeman, Dove, and Amstutz, *J. Am. Chem. Soc.*, **70**, 3136 (1948).
[132] Metcalf, *Science*, **108**, 80 (1948).
[133] Carr and Bell, *J. Pharmacol. Exptl. Therap.*, **91**, 169 (1947).   Bell and Carr, *J. Am. Pharm. Assoc.*, **36**, 272 (1947).

blocking agent.[135]   The preparation of *N*-benzyl-*N*-(2-thenyl)-*β*-chloro-ethylamine has been reported.[136]   6-(2-Thenyl)-2-thiouracil has been reported to be three times,[137] and 6-benzyl-2-thiouracil ten times,[138] as active as 2-thiouracil as an antithyroid agent.   The 2-thienyl analog of atropine was prepared, but the amount obtained was not sufficient for pharmacological tests.[139]   The synthesis of 2-(5-aminothienyl)arsonic acid, a substance analogous to arsanilic acid, has been described.[140]

The odors of the following compounds resemble those of the corresponding benzene derivatives: 2-thenyl alcohol,[141] 2-thiophenealdehyde,[141] 3-thiophenealdehyde,[142] 2-thenoyl chloride,[143] 2-thiophenesulfonyl chloride,[144] and 2-[145] and 3-nitrothiophene.[7]   2-(2-Thienyl)benzotriazole and the corresponding 2-phenyl compound both possess an agreeable tea rose or geranium odor which is more pronounced in the case of the thienyl derivative[146]   (See Chapter I, Section VIII, for further details.)

Several nitrothiophenes have a sweet taste which, in some instances, rapidly changes to a bitter or burning sensation.[80,125]   The piperidide of 5-phenyl-2-thiophenecarboxylic acid, similar to piperine, has a pepper-like taste.[147]   If the carbon chain in the thiophene ring of the former compound is regarded as a conjugated system, then both compounds have structures which are quite similar.

2-Thenyl chloride,[141] 2-thenyl bromide,[148] 3-thenyl bromide,[149] *ω*-chloro-,[150] and *ω*-bromoacetothienone[151] are lachrymatory compounds. 2,5-Bis-(chloromethyl)thiophene[152] is both a lachrymator and a vesicant.

[134] Kyrides, U. S. Pat. 2,457,047 (1948).
[135] Nickerson, *Abstracts*, First National Medicinal Chemistry Symposium, Medicinal Chemistry Division, A.C.S., Ann Arbor, Mich., 1948, p. 70.
[136] Campbell, Ackerman, and Campbell, *J. Am. Chem. Soc.*, **71**, 2905 (1949).
[137] Miller, Dessert, and Anderson, *J. Am. Chem. Soc.*, **70**, 500 (1948).
[138] Anderson, Halverstadt, Miller, and Roblin, Jr., *J. Am. Chem. Soc.*, **69**, 273 (1947).
[139] Steinkopf and Wolfram, *Ann.*, **437**, 22 (1924).
[140] Finzi, *Gazz. chim. ital.*, **45**, II, 280 (1915); *Chem. Abstr.*, **10**, 1640 (1916).
[141] Biedermann, *Ber.*, **19**, 636 (1886).
[142] Steinkopf and Schmitt, *Ann.*, **533**, 264 (1938).
[143] Nahnsen, *Ber.*, **17**, 2192 (1884).
[144] Meyer and Kreis, *Ber.*, **16**, 2172 (1883).
[145] Meyer and Stadler, *Ber.*, **17**, 2648 (1884).
[146] Bogert and Stull, *J. Am. Chem. Soc.*, **48**, 248 (1926); *ibid.*, **49**, 2011 (1927).
[147] Steinkopf and Gording, *Biochem. Z.*, **292**, 368 (1937).
[148] von Braun, Fussgänger, and Kuhn, *Ann.*, **445**, 219 (1925).
[149] Campaigne and LeSuer, *J. Am. Chem. Soc.*, **70**, 1555 (1948).
[150] Peter, *Ber.*, **18**, 540 (1885).
[151] Brunswig, *Ber.*, **19**, 2890 (1886).
[152] Griffing and Salisbury, *J. Am. Chem. Soc.*, **70**, 3416 (1948).

CHAPTER III

Synthesis and Physical Properties
of Thiophene and Its Homologs

I. Synthesis of Thiophene and Its Homologs

The preparation of thiophene and its homologs has received serious consideration since their discovery in 1882. Prior to 1944 thiophene was available only in limited quantities at prohibitive prices and most investigators preferred to prepare their own thiophene by a great variety of methods. Although some of these methods gave workable yields, the final product was still expensive due to the cost of starting materials and processing difficulties.

At present two general methods are used for the preparation of thiophenes. The first involves a ring closure of butane, pentane, or isopentane (or their unsaturated analogs) with either elementary sulfur or a sulfur source such as hydrogen sulfide or sulfur dioxide. The second involves the ring closure of a γ-dicarbonyl compound with the phosphorus sulfides. The γ-dicarbonyl material may be in the form of a γ-diketone, a γ-dialdehyde, a succinic acid, or a γ-keto acid. The first method is more restricted than the second, since the conditions required to effect ring closure are so drastic that hydrocarbons of longer chain length than the hexanes are largely transformed to coke or tars.

As a matter of expediency, the preparation of thiophene and its homologs and the physical properties of these compounds are combined in the present chapter. This section is supplemented, in regard to preparation of thiophene homologs, by the methods of alkylation discussed in Chapter VI.

The physical properties of thiophene and its homologs are listed primarily in Tables III-3–III-6. A comparison of some physical properties with those of benzene isologs is given in Chapter I (Section VII). Physical properties related to structure are compiled in Chapter IV.

A. Synthesis of Thiophene and Its Homologs by Ring Closure of Hydrocarbons

Thiophene syntheses can be grouped into two general classes of ring closures wherein a C_4 unit is joined at the 1,4-carbons by a sulfur atom. The source of the C_4 unit is normally an alkane, an alkene, or an alkadiene, such as butane, the butenes, or butadiene or pentane, isopentane, the pentenes, and the pentadienes such as isoprene. The source of sulfur appears to be varied from hydrogen sulfide, elementary sulfur, the sulfur oxides, or even metal sulfides. Sulfur and hydrogen sulfide are normally used as the source of sulfur. The process described below is the best example of this type of synthesis.

Information on preparative methods has been summarized in Tables III-1 and III-2 and references to this discussion of preparative methods are listed in the footnotes to these tables.

[1] V. Meyer and Sandmeyer, *Ber.*, **16**, 2176 (1883).
[2] Steinkopf, *Chem. Ztg.*, **35**, 1098 (1911).
[3] Steinkopf and Kirchoff, Ger. Pat. 252,375 (1912); Brit. Pat. 16,810 (1912); U. S. Pat. 1,085,708 (1914).
[4] Steinkopf and Kirchoff, *Ann.*, **403**, 1 (1914).
[5] Steinkopf, *Ann.*, **403**, 11 (1914).
[6] Chichibabin, *J. Russ. Phys.-Chem. Soc.*, **47**, 703 (1915).
[7] R. Meyer and Wesche, *Ber.*, **50**, 422 (1917). R. Meyer and W. Meyer, *ibid.*, **51**, 1571 (1918).
[8] Stuer and Grub, U. S. Pat. 1,421,743 (1922).
[9] Steinkopf, *Ann.*, **428**, 123 (1922).
[10] Tomkinson, *J. Chem. Soc.*, **125**, 2264 (1924).
[11] Peel and Robinson, *J. Chem. Soc.*, **1928**, 2068.
[12] Briscoe, Peel, and Robinson, *J. Chem. Soc.*, **1928**, 2857.
[13] I. G. Farbenind., Brit. Pat. 326,795 (1930).
[14] Braun and Orlov, Russ. Pat. 32,494 (1933).
[15] Arnold, U. S. Pat. 2,336,916 (1943); Brit. Pat. 535,583 (1940).
[16] I. G. Farbenind., Brit. Pat. 305,603 (1927).
[17] Baker and Reid, *J. Am. Chem. Soc.*, **51**, 1566 (1929).
[18] Appleby and Sartor, *Abstracts*, 115th Meeting, A. C. S., San Francisco, March–April, 1949.
[19] Mailhe and Renaudie, *Compt. rend.*, **195**, 391 (1932).
[20] Mailsoff and Marks, *Ind. Eng. Chem.*, **25**, 780 (1933).
[21] Hessle, U. S. Pat. 1,877,478 (1932).
[22] Maihle, *Chimie et industrie*, **31**, 255 (1934).
[23] Shepard, Henne, and Midgley, *J. Am. Chem. Soc.*, **56**, 1355 (1934).
[24] Schneider, Bock, and Hauser, *Ber.*, **B70**, 425 (1937).
[25] Rasmussen, Hansford, and Sachanen, *Ind. Eng. Chem.*, **38**, 376 (1946).
[26] Coffmann, U. S. Pat. 2,410,401 (1946).
[27] Boyd and Wagner, U. S. Pat. 2,414,631 (1947).
[28] Rasmussen and Ray, *Chem. Inds.*, **60**, 593, 620 (1947).
[29] Braun, *J. Applied Chem. (U. S. S. R.)*, **6**, 262 (1933).
[30] Yur'ev, *Ber.*, **B69**, 440 (1936).
[31] Yur'ev, *Ber.*, **B69**, 1002 (1936).
[32] Yur'ev, *J. Gen. Chem. (U. S. S. R.)*, **8**, 1934 (1938).
[33] Yur'ev, *J. Gen. Chem. (U. S. S. R.)*, **9**, 628 (1939).
[34] Yur'ev, Minachev, and Samurskaya, *J. Gen. Chem. (U. S. S. R.)*, **9**, 1710 (1939).
[35] Yur'ev and Tronova, *J. Gen. Chem. (U. S. S. R.)*, **10**, 31 (1940).

TABLE III-1. Preparation of Thiophene and Thiophene Derivatives by Ring Closure

Hydrocarbon	Sulfur source	Conditions	Products	Ref.
Acetylene	S	Bubble through blg. S	Carbon, H_2S, CS_2, C_4H_4S	1,51
Acetylene	FeS_2	300–500°	H_2S, CS_2, C_4H_4S	2–5
Acetylene	H_2S	400°, cat. of Al_2O_3, Fe_2O_3, or Cr_2O_3	C_4H_4S	6
Acetylene	H_2S	Above 300° over Al_2O_3	Liq. condensate gave 40% thiophene and some ethylthiophenes	39
Acetylene	H_2, H_2S, FeS_2	640–670°	C_4H_4S	7
Acetylene	H_2S	320° over bauxite	C_4H_4S	8
Acetylene	H_2S	300° over $Ni(OH)_2$ cement	Mercaptans, C_4H_4S, and $CH_3C_4H_3S$	8
Acetylene	Pyrites	300–310°	C, H_2, H_2S, butadiene, CH_3CHO, CH_3COCH_3, CS_2, C_6H_6, C_4H_4S, 2- and 3-methylthiophenes, 2- and 3-ethylthiophenes, and 2,3-dimethylthiophene	9
Acetylene	H_2S with FeS, NiS, Co_2S_3, CuS, V_2O_5, or MnO_2 satisf.; H_2S with ZnO, ZnS, and CdS ineff.	300°	C_4H_4S	10
Acetylene	Molten sulfur	325°	77% CS_2, 9% C_4H_4S, 6% thiophthene	11
Acetylene		500°	77% CS_2, 12% C_4H_4S, 6% thiophthene	11
Acetylene		600°	83% CS_2, 5% C_4H_4S, 3% thiophthene	11
Acetylene	CS_2	200°	No reaction	12
		350°	Trace of C_4H_4S	12
		700°	10% C_4H_4S	12
Acetylene and methane	NH_3, H_2O, pyrites	300–500°	35% C_4H_4S	13
Acetylene	NH_3, H_2O, pyrites	300–500°	20% C_4H_4S	13

(Table continued)

TABLE III-1. Preparation of Thiophene and Thiophene Derivatives by Ring Closure (*Continued*)

Hydrocarbon	Sulfur source	Conditions	Products	Ref.
Acetylene	H_2S	Mixt. of Ni, Co, Mg carbonates and Al_2O_3 on pumice	C_4H_4S	14
Acetylene	H_2S	500–750° over PbS, MnS, CuS, SnS, MoS, CoS, or NiS on Al_2O_3	C_4H_4S	15
Acetylene	H_2S	$NiCO_3$ on Al_2O_3	40% of condensate was C_4H_4S. Other thiophenes such as Me-, Me₂, Et, and Pr present	29
Low mol. wt. hydrocarbons from destructive hydrogenation of coal	S or H_2S	500–800° over MnO_2, V, Mo or Cr oxides, MnS on Al_2O_3 or SiO_2	Thiophene and other S compds.	16
Heptane	S	300° in sealed tube for 24–28 hrs.	$C_7H_{10}S$ and small amount of C_4H_4S	17
Ethylene	H_2S	Activated alumina at 600°	12% C_4H_4S	18
Ethylenic hydrocarbons	H_2S	700° over SiO_2	Mercaptans and C_4H_4S	19,22
Benzene	H_2S	500° over BaS	C_4H_4S	20
Asphalt base oil containing sulfur	S	200–250° over iron oxides	Thiophene compounds	21
Butadiene	Molten S	Bubbled through at 320–420°	6% thiophene	23
Isoprene	Molten S	Bubbled through at 320–420°	47% 3-Methylthiophene	23
Dimethylbutadiene	Molten S	Bubbled through at 320–420°	31% 3,4-dimethylthiophene	23
Butadiene and butanes	H_2S	600°, Fe_2S_3—Al_2O_3	26% C_4H_4S	18
Butadiene	H_2S, pyrites	500°	8% C_4H_4S	24
		550°	22% C_4H_4S	24
		600°	32% C_4H_4S	24
Butane, butenes or butadiene	Sulfur vapors	700° no catalyst	20% C_4H_4S per pass, 70% ultimate yield. 3-Thiophenethiol	25,28,121–126
Pentane or isopentane	Sulfur vapors	700° no catalyst	2- or 3-Methylthiophene	25,28
Hexane	Sulfur vapors	700° no catalyst	Dimethyl- and ethylthiophene	125
Butadiene	Sulfur vapors	445°	C_4H_4S	26
Chloroprene	Sulfur vapors	445°	17% 3-Chlorothiophene	26
Alkyl mercaptans or sulfides	S	300–500°	C_4H_4S	27
Conjugated diolefins	H_2S	500–750°, dehydrogenating catalyst of Fe_2O_3 on Al_2O_3	Thiophene and alkylthiophenes	127
Furan	H_2S	Al_2O_3 at 400°	30% C_4H_4S	30,35
2-Methylfuran	H_2S	Al_2O_3 at 350°	11% 2-Methylthiophene	31

Hydrocarbon	Sulfur source	Conditions	Products	Ref.
Pyrrole	H_2S	Al_2O_3 at 350°	Small amount of C_4H_2S	31
2-Methyltetrahydrofuran	H_2S	Al_2O_3 at 400–440°	2-Methyltetrahydrothiophene	32,36
1,4-Butanediol	H_2S	Al_2O_3 at 400°	62.5% Tetrahydrothiophene	33
Tetramethylchlorohydrin	H_2S	Al_2O_3 at 250–400°	Tetrahydrothiophene	34
Dihydrofuran	H_2S	Al_2O_3 at 325°	Thiophene and tetrahydrothiophene	37
Mucic acid	BaS	Heated in sealed tube at 200°	12% $C_4H_3S-COOH \xrightarrow{-CO_2} C_4H_4S$	38
Toluene	S	Hot tube	Phenylthiophene, CS_2, H_2S	40
Benzene	S	Hot tube at bright red heat	CS_2, H_2S, trithienyl	41
Caprylene	S	Sealed tube	$C_8H_{12}S$ and a thiophene, $C_8H_8S_2$. Small amts. of $C_8H_{16}S$, $C_{16}H_{32}S$, and $C_{24}H_{42}S$	42
n-Octane	S	Sealed tube	$C_8H_{12}S$ and $C_8H_8S_2$ (a dimethyl-thiophthene)	43
n-Heptane	S	275–285° for 20 hrs. in steel autoclave	C, H_2S, dialkylthiophene and methylthiophthene	44
2,7-Dimethyloctane	S	275–285° for 20 hrs. in steel autoclave	$C_{10}H_{16}S$ and two isomers of $C_{10}H_8S_3$	44
Dibenzyl	S	180–200°	Tetraphenylthiophene	45
Dibenzyl ether or benzyl alcohol	S	180–200°	Tetraphenylthiophene	45
Tetraphenylcyclopentadienone	S	350°	Tetraphenylthiophene	46
1,3-Diphenyl-2-ketocyclopenta-phenanthrene (phenyl cyclone)	S	350°	3,4-Diphenylene-2,5-diphenyl-thiophene	47
Diphenylacetylene	S	250°	Tetraphenylthiophene	49
Acenaphthene	S	Fused	Tetraphenylthiophene	48
Stilbene	S	250°	60–70% of tetraphenylthio-phene	50
Diphenyl	S	$AlCl_3$	Dibenzothiophene	52
Ethylbenzene	S	340–350° in bomb	2,4-Diphenylthiophene	53
Acetophenone anil	S	Fused	28% 2,4-Diphenylthiophene	54
Butyrophenone anil	S	Fused	3,5-Diethyl-2,4-diphenylthio-phene	55
Cinnamic acid	S	240°	2,4- and 2,5-Diphenylthiophene	56
Styrene or ethylbenzene	H_2S	600° over Al_2O_3	Thianaphthene	57,58

TABLE III-2. Preparation of Thiophene and Its Homologs by Ring Closure of a —COCH$_2$CH$_2$CO— Unit with "Phosphorus Sulfides"

Starting material	Product	Yield, percent	Ref.
Disodium succinate or succinic anhydride	Thiophene	45–52	60,62,64, 65,72
Succinaldehyde	Thiophene	—	61,63
Levulinic acid	2-Methylthiophene	62	64,66,67, 69,70,71
C$_6$H$_5$COCH$_2$CH$_2$COOH	2-Phenylthiophene	—	64,68
p-CH$_3$C$_6$H$_4$COCH$_2$CH$_2$COOH	2-p-Tolylthiophene	—	64
C$_6$H$_5$—CH—COOH $\quad\quad$ | $\quad$ CH$_2$—COOH	3-Phenylthiophene	—	64
p-CH$_3$C$_6$H$_4$—CH—COOH $\quad\quad\quad$ | $\quad\quad$ CH$_2$—COOH	3-p-Tolylthiophene	—	64
p-CH$_3$O—C$_6$H$_4$—CH—COOH $\quad\quad\quad\quad$ | $\quad\quad\quad$ CH$_2$COOH	3-p-Anisylthiophene	—	64
Pyrotartaric acid	3-Methylthiophene	—	72

(Table continued)

[36] Yur'ev, Gusev, Tronova, and Yurilin, *J. Gen. Chem. (U. S. S. R.)*, **11**, 344 (1941).

[37] Yur'ev, Dubrovina, and Tregubov, *J. Gen. Chem. (U. S. S. R.)*, **16**, 843 (1946).

[38] Paal and Tafel, *Ber.*, **18**, 456 (1885).

[39] Chichibabin and Bagdassarjanz, *J. Russ. Phys.-Chem. Soc.*, **56**, 142 (1925); *J. prakt. Chem.*, (2) **108**, 201 (1924).

[40] Renard, *Compt. rend.*, **109**, 699 (1889).

[41] Renard, *Compt. rend.*, **112**, 49 (1891).

[42] Friedmann, *Ber.*, **49**, 1551 (1916).

[43] Friedmann, *Ber.*, **49**, 1344 (1916).

[44] Friedmann, *Refiner Natural Gasoline Mfr.*, **20**, 395 (1941).

[45] Sperl and Wierusz-Kowalski, *Chem. Polski*, **15**, 19 (1917).

[46] Dilthey, Schommer, Hoschen, and Dierichs, *Ber.*, **B68**, 1159 (1935). Dilthey, Ger. Pat. 628,954 (1936).

[47] Dilthey, Graef, Dierichs, and Josten, *J. prakt. Chem.*, (2) **151**, 185 (1938).

[48] Clapp, *J. Am. Chem. Soc.*, **61**, 2733 (1939).

[49] Smith and Hoehn, *J. Am. Chem. Soc.*, **63**, 1184 (1941).

[50] Baumann and Klett, *Ber.*, **24**, 3307 (1891).

[51] Bhatt, Nargund, and Kanga Shah, *J. Univ. Bombay*, **3**, 159 (1934).

[52] Gilman and Jacoby, *J. Org. Chem.*, **3**, 108 (1938).

[53] Glass and Reid, *J. Am. Chem. Soc.*, **51**, 3428 (1929).

[54] Bogert and Herrara, *J. Am. Chem. Soc.*, **45**, 238 (1923).

[55] Bogert and Andersen, *J. Am. Chem. Soc.*, **48**, 223 (1926).

[56] Baumann and Fromm, *Ber.*, **28**, 890 (1895).

[57] Moore and Greensfelder, *J. Am. Chem. Soc.*, **69**, 2008 (1947).

[58] Hansch and Blondon, *J. Am. Chem. Soc.*, **70**, 1561 (1948).

[59] V. Meyer, *Ber.*, **18**, 217 (1885).

[60] Schiff, *Ber.*, **18**, 1601 (1885).

[61] V. Meyer, *Die Thiophengruppe*, Braunschweig, 1888, p. 39.

[62] V. Meyer and Neure, *Ber.*, **20**, 1756 (1887).

[63] Harries, *Ber.*, **34**, 1488 (1901).

[64] Chrzaszczewska, *Roczniki Chem.*, **5**, 1, 33 (1925).

[65] Phillips, *Organic Syntheses*, Coll. Vol. II, p. 578.

[66] Paal, *Ber.*, **19**, 551 (1886).

[67] Kues and Paal, *Ber.*, **19**, 555 (1886).

[68] Kues and Paal, *Ber.*, **19**, 3141 (1886).

TABLE III-2. (*Continued*)

Starting material	Product	Yield, percent	Ref.
CH₃CH₂—CH—COONa 　　　| 　　CH₂—COONa	3-Ethylthiophene	—	73,75
$C_{18}H_{18}O_2$?	Di-(*p*-tolyl)thiophene	—	74
(CH₃)₂CH—CH—COOH 　　　　| 　　　CH₂COOH	3-Isopropylthiophene	—	75a,76
CH₃(CH₂)₃—CHCOOH 　　　　| 　　　CH₂COOH	3-*n*-Butylthiophene	—	77
C₆H₅COCH₂CH₂COCH₃	2-Methyl-5-phenylthiophene	60–70	78
CH₂OHCHOHCHOHCH₂OH	Thiophene	—	79
CH₃COCH₂CH₂COCH₃	2,5-Dimethylthiophene	—	80,89
CH₂COOH ↓　OH C ↑　COOH CH₂COOH	Thiophthene	—	—
	Thiophthene	—	81

Table continued

[69] Silberrad, *Gummi-Ztg.*, **25**, 1958 (1911).
[70] Vlastelitza, *J. Russ. Phys.-Chem. Soc.*, **46**, 790 (1914).
[71] Steinkopf and Thormann, *Ann.*, **540**, 1 (1939).
[72] Volhard and Erdmann, *Ber.*, **18**, 454 (1885).
[73] Damsky, *Ber.*, **19**, 3284 (1886).
[74] Hollemann, *Rec. trav. chim.*, **6**, 60 (1887).
[75] Gerlack, *Ann.*, **267**, 145 (1892).
[75a] Thiele, *Ann.*, **267**, 133 (1892).
[76] Scheibler and Schmidt, *Ber.*, **B54**, 139 (1921).
[77] Scheibler and Rettig, *Ber.*, **B59**, 1194 (1926).
[78] Paal, *Ber.*, **18**, 367 (1885).
[79] Paal and Tafel, *Ber.*, **18**, 688 (1885).
[80] Paal, *Ber.*, **18**, 2251 (1885).
[81] Biedermann and Jacobsen, *Ber.*, **19**, 2444 (1886).
[82] Zelinsky, *Ber.*, **20**, 2018 (1887).
[83] Paal and Puschel, *Ber.*, **20**, 2557 (1887).
[84] Grunewald, *Ber.*, **20**, 2585 (1887).
[85] Kapf and Paal, *Ber.*, **21**, 3053 (1888).
[86] Zelinsky, *Ber.*, **21**, 1835 (1888).
[87] Smith, *J. Chem. Soc.*, **57**, 643 (1890).
[88] Auwers and Bredt, *Ber.*, **27**, 1741 (1894).
[89] Kitt, *Ber.*, **28**, 1807 (1895).
[90] Youtz and Perkins, *J. Am. Chem. Soc.*, **51**, 3511 (1929).
[91] Shepard, *J. Am. Chem. Soc.*, **54**, 2951 (1932).
[92] Steinkopf, Merckoll, and Strauch, *Ann.*, **545**, 45 (1940).
[93] Justoni, *Gazz. chim. ital.*, **71**, 375 (1941).
[94] Baumann and Fromm, *Ber.*, **28**, 895 (1895).
[95] Dieckmann, *Ber.*, **35**, 3201 (1902).
[96] Fromm and Achert, *Ber.*, **36**, 534 (1903).
[97] Willgerodt and Merek, *J. prakt. Chem.*, [2] **80**, 192 (1909).
[98] Willgerodt and Hambrecht, *J. prakt. Chem.*, [2] **81**, 74 (1910).
[99] Willgerodt and Schultz, *J. prakt. Chem.*, [2] **81**, 382 (1910).
[100] Hinsberg, *Ber.*, **43**, 901 (1910).
[101] Benary, *Ber.*, **43**, 1943 (1910).

TABLE III-2 (*continued*)

Starting material	Product	Yield, percent	Ref.
$CH_3COCH_2\overset{\overset{\displaystyle CH_3}{\vert}}{CH}—COOH$	2,4-Dimethylthiophene	—	82
$CH_3CO—CH_2—\overset{\overset{\displaystyle C_6H_5}{\vert}}{\underset{\underset{\displaystyle CH_3}{\vert}}{C}}—COOH$	2-Methyl-4-phenylthiophene	—	83
$CH_3CO—\overset{\overset{\displaystyle CH_3}{\vert}}{CH}—CH_2COOH$	2,3-Dimethylthiophene	70	84,91
$C_6H_5COCH_2CH_2COC_6H_5$	2,5-Diphenylthiophene	60–70	85
$CH_4—\overset{\vert}{CH}—COOH$ $CH_3—\overset{\overset{\displaystyle C_6H_5}{\vert}}{CH}—COOH$	3,4-Dimethylthiophene	—	86
$C_6H_5CO\overset{\vert}{C}H—CH_2CO—C_6H_5$	2,3,5-Triphenylthiophene	—	87
$\underset{\underset{\displaystyle COOH}{\vert}}{CH_2}—\underset{\underset{\displaystyle COOH}{\vert}}{CH}—\underset{\underset{\displaystyle COOH}{\vert}}{CH}—\underset{\underset{\displaystyle COOH}{\vert}}{CH_2}$		—	88
$CH_3CO\overset{\overset{\displaystyle CH_3}{\vert}}{\underset{\underset{\displaystyle CH_2CH_3}{\vert}}{CH}}—CH_2COCH_3$	2,3,5-Trimethylthiophene	35–40	90
$CH_3COCH_2\overset{\overset{\displaystyle CH_2CH_3}{\vert}}{CH}—COOH$	2-Methyl-4-ethylthiophene	40	91
$CH_3CO\overset{\overset{\displaystyle CN}{\vert}}{\underset{\underset{\displaystyle CH}{}}{}}—CH_2COOH$	2-Methyl-3-ethylthiophene	—	92
$CH_3CO—\overset{\overset{\displaystyle CN}{\vert}}{CH}—CH_2COCH_3$		—	93

[102] Scholl and Seer, *Ann.*, **394,** 111 (1912).
[103] Fromm and Klinger, *Ann.*, **394,** 342 (1912).
[104] Hinsberg, *Ber.*, **45,** 2413 (1912).
[105] Friedlander and Kielbasinsky, *Ber.*, **45,** 3389 (1912).
[106] Benary and Bavarian, *Ber.*, **48,** 593 (1915).
[107] Benary, Ger. Pat. 282,914 (1913).
[108] Benary and Silberstrom, *Ber.*, **B52,** 1605 (1919).
[109] Brass and Kohler, *Ber.*, **B55,** 2543 (1922).
[110] Mann and Pope, *J. Chem. Soc.*, **123,** 1172 (1923).
[111] Seka, *Ber.*, **B58,** 1783 (1925).
[112] Benary and Kerckhoff, *Ber.*, **B59,** 2548 (1926).
[113] Fromm, Fantl, and Leibsohn, *Ann.*, **457,** 267 (1927).
[114] Mitra, *J. Indian Chem. Soc.*, **15,** 59 (1938).
[115] Guha and Iyer, *J. Indian Inst. Sci.*, **A21,** 115 (1938).
[116] Fredga, *J. prakt. Chem.*, **150,** 124 (1938).
[117] Mitra, Chakrabarty, and Mitra, *J. Chem. Soc.*, **1939,** 1116.
[118] Backer and Stevens, *Rec. trav. chim.*, **59,** 423 (1940).
[119] Chakrabarty and Mitra, *J. Chem. Soc.*, **1940,** 1385.
[120] Boyd, U. S. Pat. 2,440,671 (1948).

1. Socony-Vacuum Thiophene Process

The process[25] which involves ring closure of butane, butadiene, or butenes with sulfur, has been put in operation on a 1000-pound-per-day basis. Recent patents describe the process when applied to butane, the pentanes, and hexanes.[121-125] The following description of the operation by Rasmussen and Ray is reprinted from *Chemical Industries*.[126]

(a) The Process

The Socony-Vacuum thiophene process is essentially a dehydrogenation of normal butane using sulfur as the dehydrogenation agent, followed by cyclization with sulfur to form the thiophene ring. The reaction is believed to proceed stepwise with conversion of the butane to butene, butadiene, and finally thiophene. Hydrogen is removed by the sulfur, forming hydrogen sulfide. Side reactions include thermal cracking of butane to lighter hydrocarbons, complete dehydrogenation and sulfurization of cracked products to carbon disulfide, and polymerization, sulfurization, or both to a residuum. This residuum consists of thiophenethiols, thiophene homologs, and high-molecular weight, organic sulfur compounds. The product distribution is typical for single-pass operation:

Component	Weight percent
Thiophene	8
Butadiene	3
Butenes	6
Butane	26
Hydrogen sulfide	37
Carbon disulfide	2
Light hydrocarbons	3
Residuum	15
Total	*100*

The semicommercial plant is composed of a reaction system and a fractionation system (Fig. III-1). In the reaction system, C_4 hydrocarbons and sulfur are preheated, mixed, reacted, and quenched, to arrest further reaction. In the fractionation system, the quenched reactor effluent is separated by conventional continuous distillation into the desired product streams. These streams are quench tower bottoms, light hydrocarbons and hydrogen sulfide, C_4 hydrocarbons for recycle to the reaction system, and crude thiophene. The crude thiophene is fractionated in a batch still into thiophene, carbon disulfide, and still bottoms.

(b) Flow of Materials

Sulfur is melted (melting point approximately 240 °F.) in dual steam-heated pits and pumped through a coil in a gas-fired furnace where it is vaporized (normal

[121] Hansford, Rasmussen, Myers, and Sachanen, U. S. Pat. 2,450,658 (1948).
[122] Hansford, Rasmussen, and Sachanen, U. S. Pat. 2,450,659 (1948).
[123] Rasmussen and Hansford, U. S. Pat. 2,450,685 (1948).
[124] Rasmussen and Hansford, U. S. Pat. 2,450,686 (1948).
[125] Rasmussen and Hansford, U. S. Pat. 2,450,687 (1948).
[126] Rasmussen and Ray, *Chem. Inds.*, **60**, 593 (1947). Reprinted courtesy McGraw-Hill Publishing Co., Inc.
[127] Greensfelder and Moore, Brit. Pat. 603,103 (1948).

56

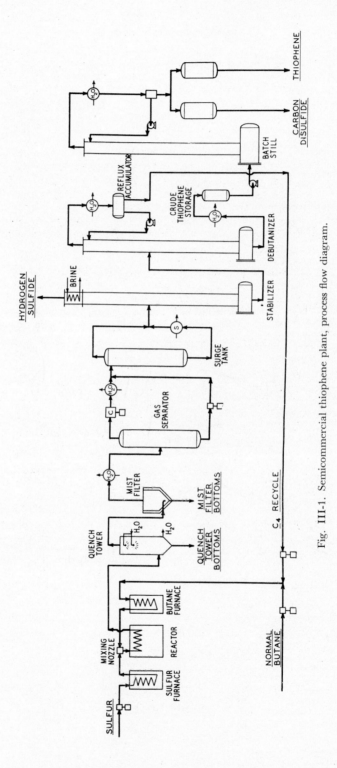

Fig. III-1. Semicommercial thiophene plant, process flow diagram.

boiling point, 832 °F.) and superheated to 1300 °F. Normal butane fresh feed and C_4 hydrocarbon recycle from the fractionation system are pumped through a coil in a second gas-fired furnace where the combined hydrocarbon stream is heated to 1050 °F. The hot sulfur and hydrocarbon vapors in about equal weight portions are then mixed and passed into a reaction coil placed inside a third gas-fired furnace. The reaction temperature is about 1050 °F. and the contact time is approximately two seconds.

Fig. III-2. Sulfur pit and pump right. Superheater and reactor furnaces left. Quench tower center background with batch still (thiophene distillation) to the right.

The reactor effluent passes into a quench tower where it is quenched to 150–175 °F. by water sprays. Quench tower bottoms and water settle in two layers at the bottom of the tower from which they are separately and continuously withdrawn. The quench tower overhead passes through a glass wool filter to remove entrained liquid. The filtered gas is then cooled to room temperature and fed to a gas separator where the condensed liquid is collected.

The gas from the gas separator is compressed to 180 psi or higher, cooled, and discharged into a surge tank where it is combined with liquid pumped from the gas separator and compressor intercooler. Liquid and noncondensed gas from the surge tank are fed to the stabilizer.

The purpose of the stabilizer is to remove overhead all components lighter than C_4 hydrocarbons. The overhead stream usually consists of 80 mole percent hydrogen sulfide and 20 mole percent light hydrocarbons. At typical operating conditions, the stabilizer reboiler is maintained at 200°F. and the pressure and temperature at the top of the tower are 165 psi and 75°F., respectively. The stabilizer net overhead is disposed of as waste at the present time and the bottoms are fed to the debutanizer.

The purpose of the debutanizer is to strip off the C_4 hydrocarbons for recycle to the reaction system leaving a crude thiophene product. The tower operates at about 65 psi with a top temperature of 135°F. and a reboiler temperature of 300°F. The overhead usually consists of 70 mole percent normal butane, 20 mole percent butenes, and 10 mole percent butadiene. The tower bottoms containing about 75 mole percent thiophene and 20 mole percent carbon disulfide are cooled and discharged into crude thiophene storage tanks.

Periodically, crude thiophene is charged to a 300-gallon batch still and fractionated into carbon disulfide, thiophene, and still bottoms. The distillation yields about 70 weight percent thiophene of over 99% purity. Intermediate cuts are returned to crude thiophene storage for refractionation.

The process can be made completely continuous by substitution of two continuous fractionation columns for the existing batch still. Carbon disulfide would then be taken overhead in the first column and thiophene in the second column.

(c) Equipment

The butane furnace consists of a helical pipe coil in a cylindrical refractory chamber. Heat is supplied by tangentially located, Venturi-type gas burners. A cylindrical refractory core confines the flue gas passage to provide high flue gas velocities, thus promoting heat transfer.

The sulfur and reactor furnaces consist of pipe coils placed in rectangular refractory chambers. Heat is supplied by multiple, Selas, radiant-type burners. The burners are spaced to give a uniform incidence of radiant heat on the entire coil. The stainless steel pipe coils are coated on the inside with a thin, bonded layer of aluminum to minimize corrosion by the sulfur-hydrogen sulfide vapors.

The stabilizer is a 12-inch diameter column containing 15 feet of $1/_2$-inch berl saddle packing. Heat is supplied to the reboiler by a steam-heated finned-tube exchanger. Refrigeration is supplied to the finned-tube partial condenser by a brine stream externally cooled by a conventional ammonia refrigeration system.

The debutanizer is a 10-inch diameter column containing 19 feet of $1/_2$-inch berl saddle packing. The reboiler is similar to the stabilizer reboiler. The overhead is totally condensed in a water-cooled, finned-tube exchanger and reflux is pumped back to the top of the column.

The batch still consists of a 12-inch diameter column and a gas-fired still pot. The column is packed to a height of 15 feet with $1/_2$-inch berl saddles. The overhead is condensed in a water-cooled finned-tube condenser and reflux is pumped back to the top of the column. The various fractions are collected in separate run-down tanks.

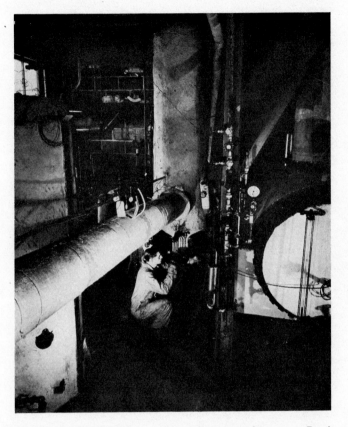

Fig. III-3. Reactor outlet running into quench tower. Batch thiophene still to the right.

The remaining equipment consists of conventional pumps, compressor, and tanks. Instruments are provided for recording and controlling flow rates, liquid levels, temperatures, and pressures at critical points throughout the plant.

The thiophene produced in the plant has the composition given in the following tabulation:

Component	Mole percent
Thiophene	99.0 Minimum
Carbon disulfide	1.0 Maximum
Benzene	0.1 Maximum

Hydrogen sulfide, carbon disulfide, and combined bottoms streams are not regularly processed further at present. In future operations these products may be marketed as produced, converted into marketable products, or processed by existing commercial methods to recover elemental sulfur.

Fig. III-4. Distillation flow indicator and control valve panel are to the right.   Stabilizer and debutanizer are to the left.

The bottoms from the quench tower, mist filter, and batch still constitute the process residuum. The residuum contains 50 or more weight percent of recoverable organic sulfur compounds. One of the most valuable components of the residuum is 3-thiophenethiol. Recovery of this material will result in an ultimate output of 3-thiophenethiol in excess of 300 pounds per operating day.

The semicommercial unit has a capacity of 1000 pounds of thiophene per stream day or 300,000 pounds per year with an 80% operating factor. The thiophene product from this process has a purity of 99%.

2. Miscellaneous Methods

Acetylene, over iron pyrites or passed through molten sulfur, was one of the earliest sources of synthetic thiophene. This reaction gave low yields and was complicated by many side reactions. For example, acetylene when passed over pyrites, or FeS₂, at 300° gave a condensate which contained about 40% of thiophene. The other 60% consisted of 1,3-butadiene, acetaldehyde, carbon disulfide, acetone, benzene, 2- and 3-methylthiophenes, 2,3-dimethylthiophene, and 2- and 3-ethylthiophenes.[9] Hydrogen, methane, and hydrogen sulfide were major constituents of the gaseous by-products. Steinkopf[9] accounts for the variety of thiophene products by equation (1). This latter reaction with methane

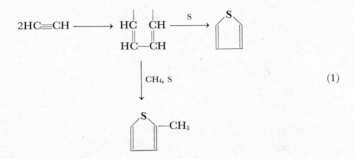

(1)

to form 2-methylthiophene has been confirmed by R. Meyer,[7] who noted increased yields of 2-methylthiophene when methane was introduced into the original reaction of acetylene and sulfur. To account for the ethylthiophenes and 2,3-dimethylthiophene from the reaction, Steinkopf proposed mechanisms (2) and (3). Thiophene and sulfur fail to react

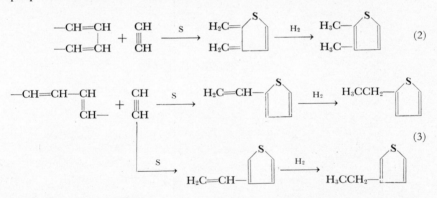

(2)

(3)

under the conditions of this process. The formation of 3-thiophenethiol from the Socony-Vacuum process would indicate a normal 1,2-addition of hydrogen sulfide to butadiene with subsequent dehydrogenation and ring closure. Thiophene and sulfur fail to react at 600° under the conditions of this process. The ring-closure step may involve the addition of two ·SH groups as free radicals to each end of the C_4 unit, which in turn splits out hydrogen sulfide (Eq. 4).

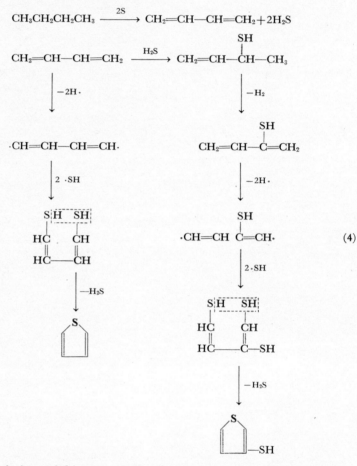

(4)

The variations of this type of ring closure involving acetylene, olefins, and other hydrocarbons are summarized in Table III-1.

Another recent synthesis of thiophene involves ring closure of butadiene with sulfur dioxide and subsequent reduction of the 3-thiolene-1-dioxide with hydrogen[120] (Eq. 4a). This synthesis, if applicable to all

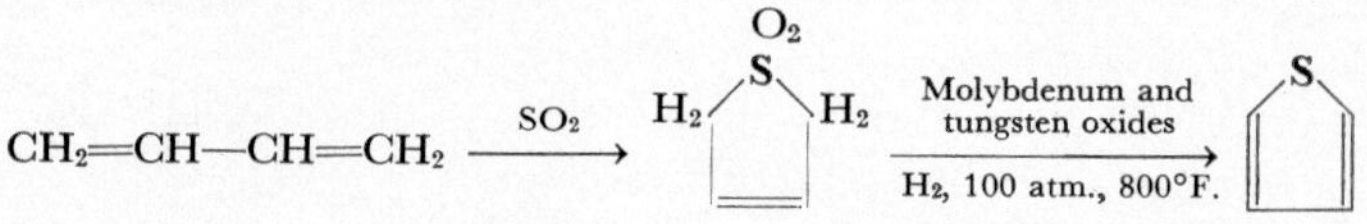

(4a)

dienes as implied in the patent literature,[120] may eventually rival the method of Paal (ring closure of the β-diketone system with phosphorus sulfides) as more conjugated dienes become available.

Preparation of alkylene thiophenes is ordinarily carried out by indirect methods (see Chapter VI).

B. Ring Closure of γ-Diketones, γ-Diacids, or γ-Keto Acids

Table III-2 summarizes the various reactions that have been carried out with the —CO—CH$_2$CH$_2$—CO— unit involving ring closure with a sulfide of phosphorus such as P$_2$S$_3$ or P$_4$S$_3$ (method of Paal[66]). Before the present commercial thiophene process was developed, the most convenient method of preparing thiophene consisted of heating the disodium succinate or succinic anhydride with phosphorus trisulfide, P$_2$S$_3$, or phosphorus heptasulfide, P$_4$S$_7$. On a laboratory scale, this method is still to be preferred. It is particularly adaptable to the preparation of various alkylthiophenes of known structure, as can be seen from Table III-2 (pages 52–54) and equations (5)–(8).

$$\text{Succinic anhydride or disodium succinate} \xrightarrow[\text{45–52\%}]{\text{P}_2\text{S}_3,\ \text{sand, heat}} \left[\begin{array}{c}\text{S}\\\end{array}\right] + \left[\begin{array}{c}\text{S}\\\end{array}\right]\text{—SH} \tag{5}$$

$$\text{CH}_3\text{COCH}_2\text{CH}_2\text{COOR} \xrightarrow{\text{P}_2\text{S}_3\ \text{or}\ \text{P}_2\text{S}_5} \left[\begin{array}{c}\text{S}\\\end{array}\right]\text{—CH}_3 \tag{6}$$

$$\underset{\overset{|}{\text{CH}_3}}{\text{ROOCCHCH}_2\text{COOR}} \xrightarrow{\text{P}_2\text{S}_3\ \text{or}\ \text{P}_2\text{S}_5} \left[\begin{array}{c}\text{S}\\\end{array}\right]\text{—CH}_3 \tag{7}$$

$$\underset{\overset{|}{\text{CH}_3}}{\text{CH}_3\text{COCH}_2\text{CHCOOR}} \xrightarrow{\text{P}_2\text{S}_3\ \text{or}\ \text{P}_2\text{S}_5} \text{H}_3\text{C—}\left[\begin{array}{c}\text{S}\\\end{array}\right]\text{—CH}_3 \tag{8}$$

The conditions of the reaction are variable. The reactants are normally heated to the point of initial reaction (usually 150°). The product distils directly from the vigorous reaction.

2-Thiophenethiol has been isolated from the alkaline washings of the raw thiophene[62] (see equation 5). This observation is interesting since only 3-thiophenethiol is formed in the butane and sulfur reaction. Since sulfur fails to react with thiophene at 600°, it can be assumed safely that the reactions forming both the 2- and 3-thiophenethiols involve the introduction of the —SH group into the system before ring closure is effected.   In general, substituted levulinic acids or, apparently, 1,4-diketones can be used in this synthesis.   The synthesis seems general to the structure of equation (9) (see Table III-2).

$$R—CO—\underset{\underset{R'}{|}}{CH}—\underset{\underset{R''}{|}}{CH}—CO—R''' \xrightarrow{P_2S_3} \underset{R''—\boxed{\qquad}—R'}{R'''—\boxed{\overset{S}{\diagup\diagdown}}—R} \qquad (9)$$

V. Meyer[59] studied the action of P_2S_x on such compounds as ethyl ether, ethyl sulfide, paraldehyde, crotonic acid, and butyric acid, producing, therefrom, small yields of thiophene.

Other miscellaneous ring closures, wherein a functional group such as an acid or hydroxyl is introduced simultaneously, are discussed in their respective chapters, but a bibliography of these methods[94-119] has been included in this chapter.

II. Physical Properties of Thiophene and Its Homologs

Tables III-3 to 7 represent an accumulation of data on the physical properties of thiophene, deuterothiophene, alkylthiophenes, alkylene-thiophenes, and thienylmethanes.   The syntheses of most of these materials are listed in Chapter VI.   Other physical properties of thiophene, such as dipole moment, activation energy, molecular refractions, etc., are listed in Chapter IV.   A comparison of the physical properties of thiophene, furan, and benzene has been made by Erlenmeyer and Leo (footnote 24, Table III-3).

TABLE III-3. Physical Properties of Thiophene

Property	Mm. of Hg	°C.	Ref.
Vapor pressure........................	63.2	20.2	11
	79.8	25.05	11
	96.6	29.2	11
	164.7	41.35	11
	243.4	50.6	11
	341.0	60.1	11
	490.0	70.5	11
	500	71	1
	600.0	76.6	1
	641.5	79.9	11
	700.0	81.45	1
	758.1	84.2	11
	760	84.12 (84.16)	1,2 (25)
	800	85.8	1
	900	89.7	1
	1074.6	110	25
	2026.0	130	25

Table continued

[1] Fawcett and Rasmussen, *J. Am. Chem. Soc.*, **67**, 1705 (1945).
[2] Footnote 1 supersedes data to be found in the following references: Beilstein's *Handbuch der organischen Chemie*, Vol. XVII, 4th ed., 1933, p. 30. Brühl, *Z. physik. Chem.*, **22**, 376 (1897). Cotton and Mouton, *Ann. chim. phys.*, [8] **28**, 220 (1913). Jacobs and Parks, *J. Am. Chem. Soc.*, **56**, 1513 (1934). Jaeger, *Z. anorg. Chem.*, **101**, 155 (1917). Jaeger and Kahn, *Proc. Acad. Sci. Amsterdam*, **18**, 269 (1915). Yur'ev, *Ber.*, **B69**, 440 (1936). Knops, *Ann.*, **248**, 204 (1888). Le Bas, *Chem. News*, **123**, 271 (1921). Maihle, *J. usines gaz.*, **45**, 209 (1921); *Chem. Abstr.*, **15**, 3201 (1921). Meyer, *Ber.*, **16**, 1471 (1883). Moore and Renquist, *J. Am. Chem. Soc.*, **62**, 1505 (1940). Nasini and Scala, *Gazz. chim. ital.*, **17**, 70 (1887). Nasini and Carrara, *ibid.*, **241**, 278 (1894). Peel and Robinson, *J. Chem. Soc.*, **1928**, 2068. Perkin, *ibid.*, **69**, 1204, 1251 (1896). Rechenberg, *J. prakt. Chem.*, **101**, 112 (1920). Schiff, *ibid.*, **18**, 1601 (1885). Steinkopf and Boetius, *Ann.*, **546**, 208 (1941). Tsakalotos and Guye, *J. chim. phys.*, **8**, 340 (1910).
[3] Lowry and Nesini, *Proc. Roy. Soc. (London)*, **A123**, 686 (1929).
[4] Schuster, *Z. anorg. allgem. Chem.*, **146**, 299 (1925).
[5] Walden, *Z. physik. Chem.*, **66**, 385 (1909).
[6] Schiff, *Ber.*, **18**, 1601 (1885).
[7] Powleski, *Ber.*, **21**, 2141 (1888).
[8] Grosse and Wackher, *Ind. Eng. Chem.*, *Anal. Ed.*, **11**, 614 (1939).
[9] Bonino and Manzoni-Ansidei, *Ricerca sci.*, **7**, I, No. 3–4 (1936); *Chem. Abstr.*, **31**, 3352 (1937); *Ber.*, **76**, 553 (1943).
[10] Knops, *Ann.*, **248**, 175 (1888).
[11] Nasini, *Proc. Roy. Soc. (London)*, **A123**, 711 (1929).
[12] Perkin, *J. Chem. Soc.*, **69**, 1244 (1896).
[13] Bonino and Manzoni-Ansidei, *Ber.*, **76**, 553 (1943).
[14] Hazato, *J. Chem. Soc. Japan*, **64**, 622 (1943); *Chem. Abstr.*, **41**, 3334 (1947). Pascal, *Ann. chim. phys.*, **19** [8], 56 (1910).
[15] Turner, *Z. physik. Chem.*, **35**, 428 (1901).
[16] Higashi, *Bull. Inst. Phys. Chem. Research (Tokyo)*, **11**, 729 (1932).

TABLE III-3 (*Continued*)

Property			Ref.
Freezing point, °C..............................		-38.30	1

	°C.	d_4^t	Ref.
Density...............................	20	1.0644	1
	25	1.0583	1
	30	1.0542	1

	°C.	Centipoises	Ref.
Absolute viscosity.........................	20	0.662	1
	25	0.621	1
	30	0.584	1

	°C.	n_D^t	Ref.
Index of refraction........................	20	1.5287	1,2
	25	1.5256	1,2
	30	1.5223	1,2

	°C.	n_α	Ref.
	20.2	1.5236	10

	°C.	n_γ	Ref.
	20	1.5519	10

			Ref.
Parachor...		187.4	1
Specific dispersion			
$[10^4(n_F - n_C)/d$ at $20°]$...........................		162.6	1
		162.4	8
Molar refraction at 20°.............................		24.365	1,24
Critical temperature................................		317°C.	3,7
		302–308°C.	6
Internal pressure at boiling point.....................		1618 atm.	4
		1820 atm.	5
Critical pressure....................................		44.7 atm.	7
Molecular susceptibility.............................		56.95×10^{-6}	9

Table continued

[17] Eggers, *J. Phys. Chem.*, **8**, 14 (1904).
[18] Kubo, *Sci. Papers Inst. Phys. Chem. Research (Tokyo)*, **29**, 122 (1936).
[19] Hassel and Naeshagen, *Tids. Kjemi Bergvesen*, **10**, 81 (1930); *Chem. Abstr.*, **25**, 2698 (1931).
[20] Thomsen, *Z. physik. Chem.*, **52**, 348 (1905).
[21] Bertholet and Matignon, *Bull. soc. chim.*, [3] **4**, 252 (1890).
[22] Moore, Renquist, and Parks, *J. Am. Chem. Soc.*, **62**, 1505 (1940).
[23] Jacobs and Parks, *J. Am. Chem. Soc.*, **56**, 1513 (1934).
[24] Erlenmeyer and Leo, *Helv. Chim. Acta*, **16**, 1381 (1933).

TABLE III-3 (*Continued*)

Property			Ref.
Magnetic rotation			
(spec. rotation, 17.7°)..........................		2.1867	12
(mol. rotation, 15°)............................		9.578	12
Diamagnetic susceptibility			
(spec. susceptibility, 10^{-6} c.g.s.).....................		0.726	13,14
(mol. susceptibility, 10^{-6} c.g.s.).....................		48.70	13

Property	°C.	k	Ref.
Dielectric constant.......................	16	$2.76 \pm 2\%$	15,16, 18
	130	2.85	17
Electric moment.................................		0.53×10^{-18}	27
		0.54	26
		0.63	19,24
Heat of combustion			
constant pressure, kcal./mole.......................		-610.64	20
		-670.9	21
		-667.39	22
		-667.19	25
constant volume, kcal./mole.......................		-669.5	21
Heat of formation (298.16°K.)			
liquid thiophene, kcal./mole.......................		19.62 (19.52)	22 (25)
gaseous thiophene, kcal./mole.....................		27.82	25
Heat of fusion, cal./g.............................		14.11	23
Heat of transition, cal./g...........................		3.44	23
Heat of vaporization, $\Delta H_{vap.}$ at boiling point, cal./mole..		7,760	1
		7,522	25
Entropy, S_{298}, E.U. per mole ± 1.....................		42.2	23
		43.30	25
Free energy, ΔF_{298}.................................		26,300	23

[25] Waddington, Knowlton, Scott, Oliver, Todd, Hubbard, Smith, and Huffman. *J. Am. Chem. Soc.*, **71**, 797 (1949). This article was received too late for detailed study and discussion. Other thermodynamic data are included in the article. Further discussions on it will be found in Chapter IV.
[26] Robles, *Rec. trav. chim.*, **58**, 111 (1939).
[27] Keswani and Freiser, *J. Am. Chem. Soc.*, **71**, 218 (1949).

TABLE III-4. Physical Properties of Deuterothiophene, C_4D_4S[1]

Boiling point (760 mm.), °C................	82.8–83.3
Freezing point, °C.........................	-38.83—38.54
$n_D^{20.8}$	1.52660
d_4^{20}	1.11382

[1] Steinkopf and Boetius, *Ann.*, **546**, 208 (1941).

TABLE III-5. Physical Properties of Thiophene Homologs[a]

Substituent	M.p., °C.	B.p. °C.	B.p. Mm.	n_D^{20}	Density	Density t/t	Ref.
2-Ethyl-	—	132–134	760	1.5127	0.990	24/?	1–4,44,48
3-Ethyl-	—	135–136	760	—	1.0012	16/?	5–7
2,5-Dimethyl-	(−62.57)	135.5–136(1364)	760	1.5126	0.98587	19/4	8–11,44,48,(52)
2,4-Dimethyl-	—	137–138(140.7)	760	1.5130	0.9956	20/?	12,44,(52)
2,3-Dimethyl-	−49.1 to −48.9	140.2–141.2 (142.5)	760	1.5188	1.0021	20/4	13–16,31,44,48,(52)
3,4-Dimethyl-	—	144–146(147.7)	760	1.5212	1.0078	23/21.5	5,17,44,(52)
2-Propyl-	—	157.5–159.5	760	1.5048	0.9683	20/4	1,3,10,18,19
3-Propyl-	—	160–162	760	1.5057	0.9716	20/4	19
2-Isopropyl-	—	152.0	760	1.5037	0.9673	20/4	19,20–23
3-Isopropyl-	—	155.5 (157)	760	1.5060	0.9722	20/4	19,20,21,24
2-Ethyl-5-methyl-	−68.6 to −68.4	159.8–160.4	760	1.5073	0.9663	20/4	3,16,48
2-Ethyl-3-methyl-	−60 to −59	53–55 / 160–161.5	22 / 760	1.5092 (22.5)	0.9792	22.5/4	25
3-Ethyl-5-methyl-	—	162–164	760	1.5098	0.9742	20/4	16
3-Ethyl-2-methyl-	—	156–157	760	—	—	—	25
2,3,4-Trimethyl-	—	160–163(172.7)	760	(1.5208)	—	—	12,47,(52)
2,3,5-Trimethyl-	—	163–165(164.5)	746	1.5131(1.5112)	0.9753	20/4	26,48,(52)
2,3,4,5-Tetramethyl-	—	182–184 (187–189)	760	1.5196	0.9442	21/21	17,48
2,5-Dimethyl-3-ethyl-	—	182–184	760	1.5026	—	—	43
2-Methyl-5-propyl-	—	179.5–180.5	760	1.49788	0.9514	20/4	48
2-tert-Butyl-	−59.2	163.9	760	1.50149	0.9574	20/4	20,23
3-tert-Butyl-	−54.8	168.9	760	1.50896	0.9537	20/4	20,23
2-n-Butyl-	—	181–182	740	1.5014	—	—	1,8,27
3-n-Butyl-	—	181–181.5 / 181	770 / 760	1.51005	0.9570	20/4	46 / 27
2,5-Diethyl-	—	181–183 / 63–66	760 / 14	1.5036	0.962	14/?	4,28 / —

[a] See p. 71 for references to this table.

Substituent	M.p., °C	B.p. °C	B.p. Mm.	n_D^{20}	Density	Density t/t	Ref.
3,4-Diethyl-	—	185–187	760	1.5156 (17)	—	—	4
2-Isoamyl-	—	74–75	11	—	—	—	3
2-Ethyl-5-propyl-	—	196–197	760	—	—	—	29
2,3,5-Trimethyl-4-ethyl-	—	204–206	748	—	0.9609	20/4	26
2-n-Hexyl-	—	79–82	1	1.5132	0.946	20/4	30
2,5-Dipropyl-	—	213–214	760	1.4970	—	—	29
2,3,5-Triethyl-	—	104–107	15	1.5101	—	—	4
2,5-Dimethyl-3,4-diethyl-	—	214–217	—	—	—	—	31
2-Ethyl-5-isoamyl-	—	103.5–106.5	12	—	0.9573	15/?	29
2,5-Dimethyl-3-n-hexyl-	—	255–260	760	—	—	—	43
2-n-Octyl-	—	257–259	760	1.4824	0.920	20/4	30,32
2-n-Nonyl-	—	106–108	1	—	—	—	—
2-n-Cetyl-	10	128–131	1	1.4763	0.906	20/4	30
2-Methyl-5-n-octyl-	—	199–204	3	—	—	—	51
2-Benzyl-	—	270	760	—	—	—	32
2-(2-Methylbenzyl)-	—	257–262	760	—	—	—	3,33
2,5-Dibenzyl-	—	140–145	13	—	—	—	3
2-Vinyl-	—	220–222	12	—	—	—	33
4-Methyl-2-vinyl-	—	65.5–66.5	48	1.5720	1.0429	—	34–38,49
5(4)-tert-Butyl-2-vinyl-	—	86.5–87.5	45	1.5590 (25°)	—	—	34
1-Phenyl-1-(2-thienyl)-ethylene-	68	104–105	24	1.5357	—	—	34
$\begin{smallmatrix}C_6H_5\\2\text{-}C_4H_3S\end{smallmatrix}\!\!\Big>\!\!C{=}CH{-}\alpha{-}C_{10}H_7$	162	265	11	—	—	—	39
$\begin{smallmatrix}C_2H_5\\2\text{-}C_4H_3S\end{smallmatrix}\!\!\Big>\!\!C{=}C\!\!\Big<\!\!\begin{smallmatrix}C_2H_5\end{smallmatrix}$	—	210–212	18	1.5780 (24.5)	—	—	39
$\begin{smallmatrix}C_6H_5\\2\text{-}C_4H_3S\end{smallmatrix}\!\!\Big>\!\!C{=}C\!\!\Big<\!\!\begin{smallmatrix}CH_2C_6H_5\end{smallmatrix}$	—	210	9	—	—	—	39

(Table continued)

TABLE III-5 (Continued)

Substituent	M.p., °C.	B.p. °C.	B.p. Mm.	n_D^{20}	Density	Density t/t	Ref.
$(CH_3)_3C$ C=C with H and C_6H_5	—	169–170	14	1.5856 (24°)	—	—	39
$2\text{-}C_4H_3S$ \ $2\text{-}C_4H_3S$ / C=CHC$_6$H$_5$	—	225	13	—	—	—	50
$2\text{-}C_4H_3S$ \ C=CHC$_6$H$_5$	85	230–236	15	—	—	—	50
$2,5\text{-}(CH_3)_2\text{-}3\text{-}C_4H_2S$ \ $2\text{-}C_4H_3S$ / C=CHC$_6$H$_5$	113	290–295	15	—	—	—	50
$p\text{-}C_6H_5\text{-}C_6H_4$ \ $5\text{-}CH_3\text{-}2\text{-}C_4H_2S$ / C=CHC$_6$H$_5$	90	Above 300	13	—	—	—	50
$p\text{-}C_6H_5\text{-}C_6H_4$ \ C=CHC$_6$H$_4$, 2-Allyl-	—	158.5–159	760	1.5281 (20.5°)	1.0175	20.5/4	40
2-Isopropenyl-	—	166–167	727	1.5586 (25°)	1.0075	25/25	41,45
C_2H_5	—	66–67	20	—	1.022	—	—
$2\text{-}C_4H_3S$—C=CHCH$_3$	—	90–91.5	16	—	—	—	42
$2\text{-}C_4H_3S$—C(C$_5$H$_{11}$)=CH$_2$	—	165–168	62	—	0.9697 (13°)	—	41
5-Bromo-2-vinyl-	—	64–65	5	1.6160 (25°)	1.668	25/25	45,49
5-Chloro-2-vinyl-	—	56–57	7	1.5780 (25°)	1.199	25/25	45,49
2,5-Dichloro-3-vinyl-	—	55–56	1	1.5908 (25°)	1.361	25/25	45
3,4,5-Trichloro-3-vinyl-	—	83–84	1	1.6106 (25°)	1.502	25/25	45
5-Bromo-2-isopropenyl-	—	84–85	3	1.6038 (25°)	1.631	25/25	45
5-Chloro-2-isopropenyl-	—	78–79	10	1.5720 (25°)	1.182	25/25	45
2,5-Dichloro-3-isopropenyl-	—	77–78	1	1.5831 (25°)	1.306	25/25	45
3,4,5-Trichloro-2-isopropenyl-	—	93–94	2	1.5920 (25°)	1.446	25/25	45
5-Chloro-2-allyl-	—	80–82	7	1.5787 (25°)	1.157	25/25	45

1 V. Meyer and Kreis, Ber., 17, 1559 (1884).
2 Schleicher, Ber., 18, 3016 (1885).
3 Steinkopf and Schubart, Ann., 424, 1 (1920).
4 Steinkopf, Frömmel, and Leo, Ann., 546, 199 (1941).
5 Steinkopf, Ann., 403, 11 (1914).
6 Damsky, Ber., 19, 3283 (1886).
7 Gerlach, Ann., 267, 146 (1892).
8 Opolski, Anz. Akad. Wiss. Krakau, 1905, 553; Chem. Zentr., 1905, II, 1796.
9 Paal, Ber., 18, 2251 (1885).
10 Ruffi, Ber., 20, 1746 (1887).
11 R. Meyer and Wesche, Ber., 50, 429 (1917).
12 Zelinsky, Ber., 20, 2017, 2025 (1887).
13 Demuth, Ber., 19, 1857 (1886).
14 Paal and Püschel, Ber., 20, 2559 (1887).
15 Grünwald, Ber., 20, 2585 (1887).
16 Shepard, J. Am. Chem. Soc., 54, 2951 (1932).
17 Zelinsky, Ber., 21, 1835 (1888).
18 Töhl and Eberhard, Ber., 26, 2947 (1893).
19 Scheibler and M. Schmidt, Ber., 54, 139 (1921).
20 Appleby, Sartor, Lee, and Kapranos, J. Am. Chem. Soc., 70, 1552 (1948).
21 Haines, Wanger, Helm, and Ball, U. S. Bur. Mines, R. I., 4060, 1946.
22 Schleicher, Ber., 19, 672 (1886).
23 Kutz and Corson, J. Am. Chem. Soc., 68, 1477 (1946).
24 Thiele, Ann., 267, 133 (1892).
25 Steinkopf, Merckoll, and Strauch, Ann., 545, 45 (1940).
26 Youtz and Perkins, J. Am. Chem. Soc., 51, 3511 (1929).
27 Scheibler and Rettig, Ber., 59, 1194 (1926).
28 Muhlert, Ber., 19, 633 (1886).
29 Steinkopf, Augestad-Jensen, and Donat, Ann., 430, 78 (1922).
30 Campaigne and Diedrich, J. Am. Chem. Soc., 70, 391 (1948).

31 Weissgerber, Ber., 61, 2117 (1928).
32 von Schweinitz, Ber., 19, 644 (1886).
33 Steinkopf and Hanske, Ann., 541, 257 (1939).
34 Schick and Hartough, J. Am. Chem. Soc., 70, 1646 (1948).
35 Nazzaro and Bullock, J. Am. Chem. Soc., 68, 2121 (1946).
36 Mowry, Renoll, and Huber, J. Am. Chem. Soc., 68, 1105 (1946).
37 Strassburg, Gregg, and Walling, J. Am. Chem. Soc., 69, 2141 (1947).
38 Kuhn and Dann, Ann., 547, 293 (1941).
39 Buu-Hoi and Hiong-Ki-Wei, Compt. rend., 220, 175 (1945).
40 Grischkewitsch-Trokhimowskii, J. Russ. Phys.-Chem. Soc., 43, 201 (1911); Chem. Abstr., 6, 223 (1912).
41 Thomas, Bull. soc. chim., 5 [4], 732 (1909).
42 Domracheva, J. Russ. Phys.-Chem. Soc., 46, 866 (1914); Chem. Abstr., 9, 1754 (1915).
43 Buu-Hoi and Nguyen-Hoan, Rec. trav. chim., 67, 309 (1948).
44 Unpublished work of Hartough and Dickert. Refractive indices of 2,3-dimethyl-, 2,4-dimethyl, 2,5-dimethyl-, and 3,4-dimethylthiophenes determined on high purity samples. J. W. Schick determined the refractive index of 2-ethylthiophene.
45 Backman and Heisey, J. Am. Chem. Soc., 70, 2378 (1948).
46 Hartough, unpublished work. Data listed were obtained from sample prepared from the semicarbazone of 2-butanoylthiophene by the Wolf-Kishner reaction.
47 The boiling point of this compound is not listed in footnote 12. Steinkopf, Die Chemie des Thiophens. Steinkopff, Dresden, 1941, p. 36, lists the boiling point given.
48 King and Nord, J. Org. Chem., 14, 638 (1949).
49 Emerson and Patrick, J. Org. Chem., 13, 729 (1948).
50 Buu-Hoi and Nguyen-Hoan, Rec. trav. chim., 68, 5 (1949).
51 Impure product reported by Denison and Condit, Ind. Eng. Chem., 37, 1102 (1945).
52 Hartough, J. Am. Chem. Soc., 73, in press.

TABLE III-6. Physical Properties of the Methylthiophenes[a,b]

	2-Methylthiophene	3-Methylthiophene
Boiling point, °C., at 500 mm..................	98.5	101.3
600......................	104.4	107.2
650......................	107.2	109.9
700......................	109.7	112.5
760......................	112.5	115.4
800......................	114.3	117.2
850......................	116.4	119.3
900......................	118.4	121.3
dt/dp at 760 mm., °/mm......................	0.046	0.046
Freezing point, °C............................	−63.5	−68.9 I
		−74.1 II
Density d_4^t, at 20°C...........................	1.0194	1.0216
25..............................	1.0140	1.0162
30..............................	1.0086	1.0110
Refractive indices, n_D^t, at 20°C.................	1.5203	1.5204
25....................	1.5174	1.5175
30....................	1.5144	1.5146
$10^4(M_f - N_c)/d$ at 20°.......................	162	159
Absolute viscosity, centipoise, at 0°C...........	0.944	0.902
20.............	0.716	0.687
25.............	0.669	0.642
30.............	0.629	0.607
Molecular refractivity at 20°C..................	29.29	29.23

[a] Fawcett, *J. Am. Chem. Soc.*, **68**, 1420 (1946).
[b] Data in the above table supersede data to be found in the following references: Opolski, *Forts. von Anz. Akad. Wiss. Kraukau*, 548 (1905). Auwers and Kohlhass, *J. prakt. Chem.*, (2) **108**, 321 (1924). Lowry and Nasini, *Proc. Roy. Soc. (London)*, **A123**, 688 (1929). Midgley, Henne, and Shepard, *J. Am. Chem. Soc.*, **54**, 2957 (1932). Shepard, Henne, and Midgley, *ibid.*, **56**, 1355 (1934). Jurjew, *Ber.*, **B69**, 1002 (1936).

TABLE III-7. Physical Properties of the Thienylmethanes

$$\begin{array}{c} R \\ R' \end{array}\!\!\Big\rangle\!C\!-\!R''' \\ R'' \end{array}$$

Substituents	B.p., °C. (mm.)	M.p., °C.	Ref.
R = R′ = 2-C_4H_3S	267 (760)	45–47	1,2
	125–126 (9)	—	—
R = R′ = 5-CH_3-2-C_4H_2S	135–136 (4)	38–39	3,4
R = R′ = 2,5-$(CH_3)_2$-3-C_4HS	160–165 (13)	72	11
R = 2-C_4H_3S; R′ = C_6H_5	257–262 (760)	—	5
R = R′ = 2-C_4H_3S; R″ = CH_3	270–280 (760)	—	6
R = R′ = 2-C_4H_3S; R″ = C_2H_5	About 290	—	6

Table continued

TABLE III-7.   Physical Properties of Thienylmethanes (*Continued*)

Substituents	B.p., °C. (mm.)	M.p. °C.	Ref.
R = R' = 2-C_4H_3S; R'' = C_6H_{13}	200–203 (20?)	—	6
R = R' = R'' = 2-C_4H_3S	—	49–50	6
R = R' = R'' = 5-CH_3-2-C_4H_2S	174–175 (0.7)	70–71	7
R = R' = 2-C_4H_3S; R'' = C_6H_5	—	74–75	6,8
R = R' = 2-C_4H_3S; R'' = m-$CH_3C_6H_4$	210–220 (20)	—	8
R = R' = 5-NH_2-2-C_4H_2S; R'' = C_6H_5	212 (6)	42.5–43	7
R = R' = 5-I-2-C_4H_2S; R'' = C_6H_5	—	89	6
R = R' = 2-C_4H_3S; R'' = o-$NO_2C_6H_4$	—	84	8
R = R' = 2-C_4H_3S; R'' = m-$NO_2C_6H_4$	—	105	8
R = R' = 2-C_4H_3S; R'' = p-$NO_2C_6H_4$	—	89–90	8
R = C_4H_3S; R' = R'' = R''' = C_6H_5	433–438 (760)	239	9,10
R = 5-CH_3-2-C_4H_2S; R' = R'' = R''' = C_6H_5	—	181–182	10
R = 5-C_2H_5-2-C_4H_2S; R' = R'' = R''' = C_6H_5	—	111	10
R = 5-Cl-2-C_4H_2S; R' = R'' = R''' = C_6H_5	—	204–205	10
R = 5-I-2-C_4H_2S; R' = R'' = R''' = C_6H_5	—	184–185	10

III. Synthesis and Properties of the Hydrothiophenes

Presented below is a brief outline of the basic methods of preparation of the five-membered heterocyclic ring system, C_4S.   Neither reactions nor preparation of the functional derivatives of this class of compounds are discussed, except for the preparation of acids by direct reduction of thiophenecarboxylic acids.

Numerous references to these compounds in the past decade and the relationship of this class of compounds to certain antibiotics will be accumulated in another volume of this series.   Therefore, no attempt has been made to set forth a comprehensive literature survey of the hydro-thiophenes.   It is suggested, if additional information is desired, that the work of Karrer (1940–1949), du Vigneaud (1938–1942), and R. R. Baker (1947–1949) be consulted.

[1] Peter, *Ber.*, **17**, 1345 (1884).
[2] Blicke and Burckhalter, *J. Am. Chem. Soc.*, **64**, 478 (1942).
[3] Hartough, Lukasiewicz, and Murray, *J. Am. Chem. Soc.*, **70**, 1149 (1948).
[4] Meisel and Hartough, unpublished work, found product obtained by condensing 2-methylthiophene and formaldehyde with sulfurous acid to be crystalline.
[5] Steinkopf and Hanske, *Ann.*, **541**, 257 (1939).
[6] Nahke, *Ber.*, **30**, 2037 (1897).
[7] Hartough, unpublished work. Products prepared by condensation of 2-methylthiophene with respective aldehydes in presence of activated clays at the reflux temperature of toluene.
[8] Tohl and Nahke, *Ber.*, **29**, 2205 (1896).
[9] Weisse, *Ber.*, **28**, 1537 (1895).
[10] Weisse, *Ber.*, **29**, 1402 (1896).
[11] Buu-Hoi and Nguyen-Hoan, *Rec. trav. chim.*, **68**, 5 (1949).

A. Thiolenes (Dihydrothiophenes)

Recently, Birch, and McAllen[1] described the preparation of both 2- and 3-thiolene from the hydrogenation of thiophene with sodium in liquid ammonia (eq. 1).   In addition, 2-butene-1-thiol, butenes, and hydrogen sulfide were obtained in the reduction.

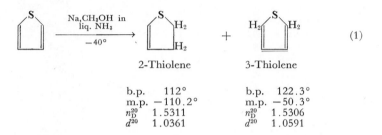

2-Thiolene   3-Thiolene

b.p.   112°   b.p.   122.3°
m.p. −110.2°   m.p. −50.3°
n_D^{20} 1.5311 n_D^{20} 1.5306
d^{20} 1.0361 d^{20} 1.0591

These investigators indicated that the product obtained from the reaction of sodium sulfide and 1,4-dibromo-2-butene[1a] that was previously designated as "3-thiolene" (b.p.   103–105°, n_D^{20} 1.4813, d_4^{21} 0.978) was in reality a sulfur compound of unestablished structure.

Steinkopf and Kohler[2] have reported from the chlorination of thiophene a compound that they believed to be pentachloro-2- or 3-thiolene, but recent investigators[3] have not been able to duplicate these results.

A hexachloro-3-thiolene, however, can be prepared from the chlorination of thiophene or tetrachlorothiophene in the presence of catalytic amounts of iodine.[4]   (See equation 2.)   This compound can be con-

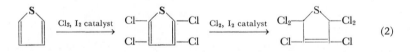

verted with sodium methoxide to a 2,2,5,5-tetramethoxy-3,4-dichloro-3-thiolene (eq. 3).   Hexachloro-3-thiolene forms resinous products with ammonium thiocyanate.

[1] Birch and McAllen, *Nature*, **165**, 899 (1950).
[1a] Slobodin, *J. Gen. Chem. (U. S. S. R.)*, **8**, 714 (1938).
[2] Steinkopf and Kohler, *Ann.*, **532**, 250 (1937).
[3] Coonradt and Hartough, *J. Am. Chem. Soc.*, **70**, 1158 (1948).
[4] Coonradt, Hartough, and Norris, unpublished work.

With ethyl diazoacetate, thiophene is reported to form ethyl bicyclo-Δ^2-α-penthiophene-5-carboxylate (*Ring Index* calls this ring system 2-thia-bicyclo[3.1.0]-3-hexene), a condensed thiolene ring system.[5] (See equation 4.)

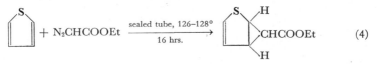

$$\text{(4)}$$

Dihydrofuran cannot be converted to the thiolenes by the action of hydrogen sulfide over alumina.[6] If a product is formed it undergoes an internal hydrogenation-dehydrogenation like that of terpenes and only thiophene and tetrahydrothiophene are obtained.

B. Dihydrothianaphthenes

Both isomeric forms of the dihydrothianaphthenes are known. Their nomenclature and physical properties are tabulated below.

2,3-Dihydrothianaphthene   1,3-Dihydroisothianaphthene

B.p.	104° at 13 mm.	B.p.	108° at 14 mm.
d_4^{21}	1.129	d_4^{26}	1.1430
Sulfone, m.p.	98°	Sulfone, m.p.	150–152°

The synthesis of (a) is accomplished from thianaphthene by reduction with sodium in ethanol.[7] (See equation 5.) It does not form a picrate and is separated as a liquid from unchanged thianaphthene, which forms a crystalline picrate, by repeated treatment with picric acid. It is also

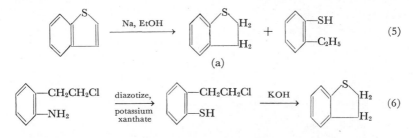

$$\text{(5)}$$

$$\text{(6)}$$

[5] Steinkopf and Augestad-Jensen, *Ann.*, **428**, 154 (1922).
[6] Yur'ev, Dubrovina, and Tregubov, *J. Gen. Chem. (U. S. S. R.)*, **16**, 843 (1946).
[7] Fricke and Spilker, *Ber.*, **58**, 24, 1589 (1925).

obtained in low yield from the catalytic hydrogenation of thianaphthene.[7]

Formation may also be effected by ring closure (Eq. 6).[8]   The synthesis of (b) is accomplished by simple ring closures of o-xylylene dimercaptan or o-xylylene dibromide[9-11] (Eqs. 7 and 8).

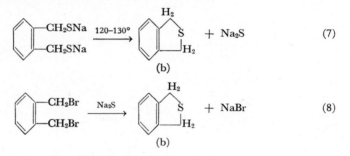

$$\text{(b)} \qquad\qquad (7)$$

$$\text{(b)} \qquad\qquad (8)$$

C. Thiolanes

There are two general methods of preparing thiolanes.   The first involves the simple ring closure of the 1,4-dihalobutanes[12-19] (Eq. 9).

$$\text{X—CH}_2\text{CH}_2\text{CH}_2\text{—X} \xrightarrow{\text{Na}_2\text{S, alcohol}} \qquad\qquad (9)$$

Yields by this method appear to decrease with the different halides in the order I > Br > Cl.   With 1,4-diiodobutane the yield is 50% of theory.[18]   The process can be modified for the preparation of various alkyl thiolanes (see Table III-8).   The yield of thiolane can be greatly improved if 50% alcohol is used instead of 95% or absolute alcohol as suggested in prior references.[12-19]   Thus, an 85% yield of the product is obtained when 1,4-dichlorobutane is refluxed for 20 hours at 80° with sodium sulfide nonahydrate in 50% alcohol.[19a]   This work also indicated that an excess of the sodium sulfide was essential to completely decompose the 1,4-dichlorobutane.   Unreacted 1,4-dichlorobutane forms a constant

[8] Braun, *Ber.*, **58**, 2165 (1925).
[9] Leser, *Ber.*, **17**, 1824 (1884).
[10] Hafner, *Ber.*, **22**, 2902 (1889).
[11] Autenrieth and Bruning, *Ber.*, **36**, 183 (1903).
[12] Braun and Trumpler, *Ber.*, **43**, 545 (1910).
[13] Bost and Conn, *Ind. Eng. Chem.*, **23**, 93 (1931).
[14] Bost and Conn, *Oil Gas J.*, **32**, No. 3, 17 (1933).
[15] Grischkevich-Trokhimowskii, *J. Russ. Phys.-Chem. Soc.*, **48**, 901 (1916).
[16] Marvel and Williams, *J. Am. Chem. Soc.*, **61**, 2714 (1939).
[17] Bennett and Hock, *J. Chem. Soc.*, **1927**, 477.
[18] Roblès, *Rec. trav. chim.*, **58**, 111 (1939).
[19] Menon and Guha, *Ber.*, **B64**, 544 (1931).
[19a] Bishop, Socony-Vacuum Laboratories, unpublished work.

boiling mixture with thiolane. The constant boiling mixture contains approximately 4% 1,4-dichlorobutane and boils at 122.5–123.5°.[19a]

The second general method involves replacement of oxygen in the tetrahydrofurans with sulfur. The replacement is conveniently carried out by passing hydrogen sulfide and tetrahydrofuran over alumina at about 400°C[6,20-23] (Eq. 10). While yields are low in this procedure,

$$H_2S, Al_2O_3, 400° \qquad (10)$$

they can be improved if the process is conducted with 1,4-butanediol (Eq. 11).

$$HOCH_2CH_2CH_2CH_2OH \xrightarrow{H_2S,\ Al_2O_3,\ 400°} \qquad (11)$$

Alkylthiolanes are prepared similarly. 1,6-Hexanediol rearranges during dehydration to 2-ethyltetrahydrofuran and is converted to 2-ethylthiolane with hydrogen sulfide.[24] 2,5-Dimethylthiolane is prepared from 2,5-dimethyltetrahydrofuran in 68% yield.[25]

Thiolane has been prepared by direct hydrogenation of thiophene. Reduced palladium gives a 71% yield, but two parts of catalyst are required for one part of thiophene.[26] Cawley and Hall[27] have found that molybdenum disulfide is a convenient catalyst for the hydrogenation of thiophene. The yield of thiolane is 52% but the conversion per pass is very low (Eq. 12).

$$\xrightarrow{H_2,\ MoS_2,\ 200\ atm.,\ 200°} \qquad (12)$$

Mabery and Quayle[28] have isolated various alkylthiolanes from petroleum sources. It is to be noted that the original nomenclature used by these authors is not in use today, e.g., their heptylthiophane, $C_7H_{14}S$, is a propylthiophane or a propylthiolane, their octylthiolane is

[20] Yur'ev and Prokina, *J. Gen. Chem.* (*U. S. S. R.*), **7**, 1868 (1937).
[21] Yur'ev, *J. Gen. Chem.* (*U. S. S. R.*), **8**, 1934 (1938).
[22] Yur'ev, *J. Gen. Chem.* (*U. S. S. R.*), **9**, 628 (1939).
[23] Yur'ev and Medowschtschikov, *Chem. Zentr.*, II, **1940**, 1578.
[24] Yur'ev, Gusev, Tronova, and Yurilin, *J. Gen. Chem.* (*U. S. S. R.*), **11**, 344 (1941).
[25] Yur'ev, Tronova, L'vova, and Ya Bukshpan, *J. Gen. Chem.* (*U. S. S. R.*), **11**, 1128 (1941).
[26] Mozingo, *et al.*, *J. Am. Chem. Soc.*, **67**, 2092 (1945).
[27] Cawley and Hall, *J. Soc. Chem. Ind.*, **62**, 116T (1943).

probably an iso- or *tert*-butylthiolane, and their isooctylthiolane, from the boiling points and densities, can be predicted to be an iso- or normal butylthiolane.   The physical constants of these compounds are listed in Table III-8; the names are assigned with some misgivings, since Mabery and Quayle did not furnish adequate proof that a thiolane ring existed. It will be noted that refractive indices and densities increase with increasing boiling points.   If the compounds were actually as named one would expect indices and densities to be inversely related to boiling points.

TABLE III-8. Physical Constants of Thiolane and Its Homologs

Compound	B.p., °C.	d_4^{20}	n_D^{20}	Ref.
Thiolane..................	121.2	0.9998	1.5047	1
	120.2–120.5	0.9967	1.5047	12,18
		0.9607 (18°)	1.4871 (18°)	15
	m.p. −96.2	—	—	1
2-Methylthiolane..........	132.5 (750)	0.9564 (18°)	1.4886	15
	131.2–131.5 (756)	0.9541	1.4922	21
	130 (685)	—	—	19
3-Methylthiolane..........	137.5–138.5	0.9596 (18.5°)	—	20
2,5-Dimethylthiolane.......	141	0.9220	1.4822	25
2-Ethylthiolane............	155.5–156.5 (742)	0.9451	1.4896	24
2,5-Dipropylthiolane.......	74–75 (1)	0.8958	1.4795	16
3,4-Dipropylthiolane.......	65–66 (1)	0.9129	1.4830	16
Propylthiolane, $C_7H_{14}S$.....	158–160	0.8870	1.4680	28
Butylthiolane, $C_8H_{16}S$.......	167–169	0.8929	1.4860	28
Isobutylthiolane, $C_8H_{16}S$....	183–185	0.8937	—	28
Pentylthiolane, $C_9H_{18}S$......	193–195	0.8997	1.4746	28
Hexylthiolane, $C_{10}H_{20}S$.....	207–209	0.9074	1.4766	28
Heptylthiolane, $C_{11}H_{22}S$....	128–130 (50)	0.9147	1.4800	28
Decylthiolane, $C_{14}H_{28}S$......	266–268	0.9208	1.4892	28
Dodecylthiolane, $C_{16}H_{32}S$...	283–285	0.9222	1.4903	28
Tetradecylthiolane, $C_{18}H_{36}S$.	290–295	0.9235	—	28

D. Preparation of 3-Thiolene- and Thiolanecarboxylic Acids

Only one thiolenecarboxylic acid, the 4-methyl-3-thiolene-2-carboxylic acid, has been prepared[29,30] (Eq. 13).   In general, sodium amalgam reduces a thiophenecarboxylic acid to the tetrahydrothiophene or

[28] Mabery and Quayle, *Am. Chem. J.*, **35**, 404 (1906).
[29] Rinkes, *Rec. trav. chim.*, **54**, 940 (1935).
[30] Steinkopf and Jacob, *Ann.*, **515**, 273 (1935).

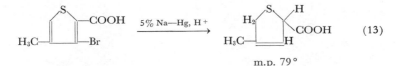

$$m.p.\ 79°$$

thiolanecarboxylic acid.   2-Thiolanecarboxylic acid,[31] m.p. 51°, 3,5-dimethyl-2-thiolanecarboxylic acid,[15] m.p. 98.5–99.5°, and 2,5-thiolane-dicarboxylic acid,[32] m.p. 162° (dimethyl ester, m.p. 150°) have been prepared by this method.   The last acid, 2,5-thiolanedicarboxylic acid, is also prepared by ring closure of α,α'-dibromoadipic acid with sodium sulfide.[33]

[31] Ernst, *Ber.*, **20**, 518 (1887).
[32] Ernst, *Ber.*, **19**, 3275 (1886).
[33] Bayer and Co., Ger. Pat. 405,017 (1925).

CHAPTER IV

Molecular Structure and Spectroscopy of Thiophene and Its Derivatives

By Frank P. Hochgesang

Introduction

The structure of thiophene has been studied in some detail, usually in relation to the other five-membered ring compounds, furan, pyrrole, etc., but very little information is available concerning thiophene derivatives. The geometrical configuration of the thiophene nucleus, first approximated from electron diffraction studies, has been considered from many viewpoints. Spectroscopic information combined with thermodynamic data leaves little doubt that the thiophene ring is planar and that the nuclei of the four carbon and one sulfur atoms are spaced about an axis of symmetry which passes through the sulfur nucleus. The electronic structure contains mobile electrons from the conjugated double bonds which, along with some electrons from the decet possible about the sulfur atom, doubtless exert great influence upon the chemical properties of this molecule. Dipole moment measurements have been made on numerous thiophene derivatives and their relation to resonance within the thiophene nucleus studied. The dipole studies have led to a better qualitative understanding of the chemical reactivity of the thiophene nucleus. Attempts to interpret the spectroscopic studies to supply quantitative information about molecular structure in terms useful to the organic chemist have met with slight success.

Detailed structure information accumulates slowly. Empirical information derived from a survey of spectral data of pure compounds not only allows quantitative analyses to be made but also may be used to elucidate structure by comparison with known compounds. (See Section III.) Every effort has been made to include all literature references. Certain odd properties somewhat related to molecular structure but not of great importance have been briefly summarized in Section I.C for the sake of completeness.

I. Molecular Structure and Related Properties

A. Bond Distances and Angles of Thiophene

The planar structure of the thiophene ring appears to be generally accepted. Geometrical data established by Schomaker and Pauling[1] from electron diffraction studies lead to the structure shown in Figure IV-1. The bond distances and angles are similar to those of cyclopentadiene, furan, and pyrrole (as ascertained in the same study) with the exception that the C—S—C angle is roughly 10° smaller than the C—O—C and C—N—C angles, respectively. The values proposed by Schomaker and Pauling are in Table IV-1 along with their comparative data for the three similar 5-membered ring compounds. It should be noted that appropriate values were assumed for C=C and C—C,

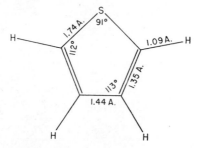

Fig. IV-1. Schematic diagram of bond distances and angles of thiophene from Schomaker and Pauling's[1] electron diffraction data.

since relative values of bond distances in heterocyclic molecules containing only light atoms could not be determined by electron diffraction. The ring bond distances deemed reasonable led to qualitative agreement only when the bond angles were adjusted to make the cross-ring distances equal.

In a most recent investigation, Longuet-Higgins[2] has considered the electronic structure of thiophene and related molecules on the basis of molecular orbitals involving hybridization of p and d atomic orbitals. He established, by taking into account the participation of sulfur $3d$ orbitals in the π conjugation of a thiophene derivative, that it is possible to elucidate the electronic structure of any thiophene derivative from that of the benzene analog. Applying this procedure the bond order and bond lengths in thiophene were determined to be:

[1] Schomaker and Pauling, *J. Am. Chem. Soc.*, **61**, 1769 (1939).
[2] Longuet-Higgins, *Trans. Faraday Soc.*, **45**, 173 (1949).

	"C—S"	"C=C"	"C—C"
Mobile order..........	0.59	0.73	0.61
Length in A...........	1.68 ± 0.02	1.38	1.40

These bond lengths differ by a few percent from those of Schomaker and Pauling. The uncertainty in the C—S bond length arises from the uncertainty of the normal lengths of single and double bonds between carbon and sulfur.[2]

TABLE IV-1. Geometrical Data Established by Schomaker and Pauling[1] from Electron Diffraction Study

	Thiophene	Furan	Pyrrole	Cyclopentadiene
Bond Distances, A.				
C—H (assumed)	1.09	1.09	1.09	1.09
C—C (assumed).........	1.44	1.46	1.44	1.46 ± 0.04*
C—X (calcd.)	1.74 ± 0.03	1.41 ± 0.02	1.42 ± 0.02	1.53*
C=C (assumed)	1.35	1.35	1.35	1.35
Bond Angles, Degrees				
C—X—C (calcd.)........	91 ± 4	107 ± 4	105 ± 4	101 ± 4
X—C=C (calcd.)........	112 ± 3	109 ± 3	110 ± 3	109 ± 3
C=C—C (calcd.)........	113 ± 3	107 ± 2	108 ± 2	110 ± 2

* For cyclopentadiene the unconjugated C—C distance (*i.e.*, C—X in above table) was assumed to be 1.53 A. as found for cycloparaffins and the conjugated single bond distance calculated.

B. Dipole Moments and Resonance in Thiophene Nucleus

Resonance and associated properties have been studied from several viewpoints. Taking into consideration bond lengths, resonance energies, and dipole moments Schomaker and Pauling[1] suggested that the reason-

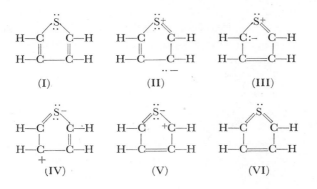

ably stable structures I–VI are important.   Their conclusions[1,3] as to the contributions of the various structures were:

Type I....................................70%
Types II and III.........................20%
Types IV, V, and VI......................10%

and it was pointed out that Types IV through VI require a sulfur atom with a decet of electrons.   While the valence-bond method is qualitatively convincing it cannot be extended to thiophene analogs when bond lengths and dipole moments are not available.   Some additional weaknesses are discussed in the following paragraphs.

Longuet-Higgins[2] pointed out that the chemical mimicry discovered by Victor Meyer, *i.e.*, the close similarity in physical and chemical properties between aromatic hydrocarbons containing the group —CH=CH— and the corresponding sulfur compounds in which this group is replaced by formally bivalent sulfur —S— involves properties which are usually related to mobile electrons; *e.g.*, near ultraviolet absorption spectrum,[4] first ionization potential,[5] resonance energy,[6] and behavior in substitution reactions, conveniently summarized as "aromatic character."   However, Longuet-Higgins' statement, summarized below, of the relative "aromaticity" of the 5-membered heterocyclics is not in agreement with the conclusions of other workers as derived from chemical considerations.   A more detailed discussion of the "aromaticity order" within the 5-membered heterocyclics as arrived at from chemical reasoning is presented later in Chapter V.   Furan and pyrrole, although somewhat aromatic in character, are said by Longuet-Higgins[2] to be less so than thiophene, and similar relations reportedly hold between the higher analogs of these compounds.   Yet a consideration of the dipole moments on the basis of the valence-bond theory indicates that thiophene should be as reactive chemically as furan.   On the other hand, the molecular orbital theory postulates a "hybridization moment" due to the π electrons in thiophene which is not present in tetrahydrothiophene, thereby explaining the difference in dipole moment between these compounds (see Table IV-3).   Also, such a hybridization moment cannot be present in furan because the only atomic orbital on the oxygen atom which can take part in the conjugation is a $2p$ orbital which is centered on the oxygen nucleus. Thus it is shown that the differences in dipole moment between furan and

[3] Pauling, *Nature of the Chemical Bond.*   Cornell Univ. Press, Ithaca, 1939, p. 208.
[4] Milazzo, quoted by Walsh, *Quart. Revs.*, **2**, 85 (1948).
[5] Price, *Chem. Revs.*, **41**, 257 (1947).
[6] Wheland, *The Theory of Resonance.*   Wiley, New York, 1944.

thiophene and their tetrahydro derivatives arise from different causes; *i.e.*, in furan a resonance moment is responsible for the observed lowering of the dipole moment whereas hybridization of the π orbitals on the sulfur atom is responsible for the lowering in thiophene. Summarizing comments concerning chemical reactions, Longuet-Higgins states as follows:

"First, since two of the resonance integrals in thiophene are slightly less than the corresponding ones in benzene, the electronic structure of thiophene will be intermediate between that of benzene and that of butadiene, being closer to that of benzene. Therefore, one can understand why thiophene is rather more susceptible to attack than benzene, and why such attack normally takes place at the 2- rather than the 3-position. The second point concerns the effect of substitution on the thiophene nucleus, which will be determined by the 'mutual polarisabilities' of the various pairs of atoms.[7] Now in butadiene the mutual polarisability of positions 1 and 2 is much greater (-0.402) than that of positions 2 and 3 (-0.045), so the same will be true to a lesser extent in the carbon skeleton of thiophene. This idea is borne out by the properties of 2,4-dimethylthiazole in which the 2-methyl group is readily oxidized and condenses with ketonic reagents, whereas the 4-methyl group is unreactive."

Daudel *et al.*[8a] in a recent paper briefly discussed thiophene as a mesomeric molecule; *i.e.*, in a state intermediate between the various valence-bond structures proposed. Such a picture of the structure is undoubtedly correct. However, many quantitative details yet remain to be worked out for thiophene. As is well known,[8b] the valence bond approach considers resonance to occur among various canonical structures possible for the molecule. The mobile bond order, from which bond lengths are calculated, is equal to the weighted average of all structures in which the bond appears double. This method frequently refers to bond order (*indice de liaison*) as "double bond character" of a bond. The molecular orbital theory arrives at bond order after considering the resonance energy to arise from a delocalization of electrons into orbits covering the whole molecule. The mobile bond order is then the sum of all partial bond orders contributed by each π electron. Attempts to provide absolute data for reactivity of certain positions in compounds of a homologous series involve the calculation of free valence (*indice de valence libre*) which in the valence bond approach is the sum of the weights of all structures in which the chosen atom is not joined by a double bond to one or other of its nearest neighbors. In the molecular orbital method the free valence is the difference between the maximum total bond order observed for the

[7] Coulson and Longuet-Higgins, *Proc. Roy. Soc.* (*London*), **A192,** 16 (1947).
[8a] Daudel, P. and R., Buu-Hoï·, and Martin, *Bull. soc. chim.* (5), **15,** 1202 (1948). See also Klages, *Ber.*, **82,** 358 (1949).
[8b] For a general discussion the reader is referred to "The Labile Molecule," *Discussions of the Faraday Society*, No. 2, 1947.

TABLE IV-2. Calculated Resonance Energies

Compound	Resonance energy, kcal./mole	Reference	Compound	Resonance energy, kcal./mole	Reference
Thiophene..........29		6	Furan...........24		6
31		1	23		1
Benzene 41		6	Pyrrole..........24		6
39		1	31		1

TABLE IV-3. Dipole Moments

Compound	$\mu \times 10^{18}$	Reference
Thiophene	0.53	9a (See footnote 13)
	0.54	10
	0.63	11a
Tetrahydrothiophene	1.87	10
Selenophene	0.41	10
Tetrahydroselenophene....................	1.79	10
Furan.................................	0.67	10
Tetrahydrofuran.........................	1.68	10
Pyrrole	1.80	10
Pyrrolidine	1.57	10
2-Nitrothiophene.........................	4.23	9a
	4.12	12
2-Chlorothiophene	1.60	9a
2-Bromothiophene........................	1.37	9a
2-Iodothiophene.........................	1.14	9a
2,5-Dichlorothiophene....................	1.12	9a
Tetrabromothiophene......................	0.73	9a
2-Methylthiophene........................	0.67	9b
3-Methylthiophene	0.82	9b
2-Thenyl chloride........................	1.58	9b
2-Thiophene aldehyde	3.55	9b
2-Acetylthiophene	3.37	9b
2-Carbethoxythiophene	1.91	9b

atom involved and the total bond order calculated for that atom in a given structure.   Of course, the greater the free valence, the greater the homolytic activity will be.[8b]   Heterolytic activity, on the other hand and by either method, will be determined by the total charge on an atom.[8b] Heterolytic activity will be considerably affected by the polarizability of the atom.[8b]

Daudel et al.[8a] present diagrams of free valence for thiophene, pyrrole, furan, and benzene and also diagrams of charge and bond order for thiophene, pyrrole, and furan, but they do not mention how these were derived (see Fig. IV-2). They remark only that these results are in agreement with chemical behavior in nitration, sulfonation, etc., wherein attack takes place in the α position. Further, the mesomeric diagrams are said to show that hydrogenation of furan takes place more readily than of pyrrole and thiophene, all of which are more readily hydrogenated than benzene.[8a]

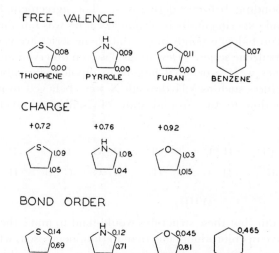

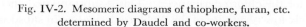

Fig. IV-2. Mesomeric diagrams of thiophene, furan, etc. determined by Daudel and co-workers.

Resonance energies have been calculated, with results as recorded in Table IV-2.

[9a] Keswani and Freiser, *J. Am. Chem. Soc.*, **71**, 218 (1949).
[9b] Keswani and Freiser, *J. Am. Chem. Soc.*, **71**, 1789 (1949).
[10] Robles, *Rec. trav. chim.*, **58**, 111 (1939).
[11a] Erlenmeyer and Leo, *Helv. Chim. Acta*, **16**, 1381 (1933), reporting data obtained by Hassel and Naeshagan and others.
[11b] Lipscomb, "Techniques in the Determination of Crystal Structures at Low Temperatures," paper presented before Seventh Conference on X-ray and Electron Diffraction, Univ. of Pittsburgh, November 7 and 8, 1949. Earlier data are summarized by Wyckoff, *The Structure of Crystals*, 2nd ed., 1931, p. 385, and Supplement, 1935, p. 159, Reinhold, New York.
[12] Oesper, Lewis, and Smyth, *J. Am. Chem. Soc.*, **64**, 1130 (1942).
[13] Taking into account Onsager's considerations, *J. Am. Chem. Soc.*, **58**, 1486 (1936), for obtaining electric moments of molecules in the liquid state, Lumbroso, *Compt. rend.*, **228**, 77 (1949), reports results for thiophene comparable to those obtained by other methods. Freiser, in a private communication of April 15, 1949, reports two additional references: (a) $\mu = 0.53$–0.54 in benzene or hexane by Higashi, *Bull. Inst. Phys. Chem. Res.* (*Tokyo*), **11**, 729 (1932); and (b) $\mu = 0.58$ at 329–474°K. in gas phase by Kubo, *Sci. Papers Inst. Phys. Chem. Res.* (*Tokyo*), **29**, 122 (1936). Freiser comments that a gas phase value presumably is closest to the true value and, further, that the value of 0.63 for thiophene (footnote 11a) is in disagreement with many later determinations.

Dipole moments have recently been reported for a number of halogenated derivatives[9a] and methylthiophene derivatives.[9b]   Robles' data,[10]
which were used by Schomaker and Pauling, and other data are collected
in Table IV-3.   Keswani and Freiser compared the observed moment
values for the 2-halothiophenes with those calculated on the basis of
vector addition of component groups, largely using group values obtained
from corresponding benzene derivatives.   The agreement between the
calculated and experimentally determined values was fair and confirmed
that the carbon-halogen bonds in the thiophene series are very similar to
those in the benzene series.   Deviations between observed and calculated
moment values were attributed largely to dipole-polarizability interac-
tions.   Structures such as VII through X were believed to make significant contribution to the ground state of 2-chlorothiophene:

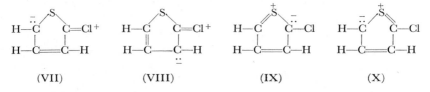

| (VII) | (VIII) | (IX) | (X) |

It is pointed out that these structures would tend to make the sulfur more
electronegative in chlorothiophene than in thiophene itself, which suggests
decreased participation of the sulfur electrons in the thiophene ring
resonance for the chloro derivatives.   This is substantiated chemically by
the relatively low reactivity of the 2-chloro derivative in substitution reactions which involve the thiophene nucleus.   Mutual inductance of the
sulfur and 2-substituent (similar to *ortho* disubstitution) causes an observed
decrease in moments from the calculated values.   The fact that this
deviation is less for chlorine substitution than for bromine or iodine is
suggested as a possible indication of the greater influence of structures
involving a double bond between carbon and chlorine over that of
bromine or iodine.

The excellent agreement between calculated and observed values
encountered for 3-methylthiophene was considered indicative of similarity
between the 3-position in thiophene and the *meta* position of disubstituted
benzenes.   2-Thenyl chloride was found to resemble benzyl chloride.
Oesper, Lewis, and Smyth[12] concluded that for 2-nitrothiophene the
contribution of polar structures was approximately the same as the
roughly analogous polar structures in nitrobenzene and that the amount
of double bond character in the carbon-nitrogen bond is about the same in
the two molecules.   Keswani and Freiser report that 2-thiophenealdehyde
and 2-acetylthiophene yielded large positive deviations between calcu-

lated and observed values, indicating that the thiophene nucleus can participate in certain resonance structures with substituents in the 2-position, *i.e.*, resonance structures of some 2-substituted thiophenes involving the nucleus were found to be more polar than corresponding monosubstituted benzene derivatives. That resonance can occur between the thiophene nucleus and certain substituents in the 2-position is confirmed by the ultraviolet absorption spectra for 2-vinyl- and 2-acetyl-thiophene, Section III.A.

Freiser[14] has commented that the dipole moment obtained in the case of dichlorothiophene confirms the experimentally observed change in the character of halogenation of thiophene beyond the dichloro stage *i.e.*, the tendency to add chlorine to the nucleus rather than to substitute the 3,4-positions. If the resonance structures of dichlorothiophene involving double bond formation between the chlorine and nuclear carbon are important enough to minimize the participation of the sulfur electrons in the resonance of the thiophene nucleus, then the compound should act more as an olefin as is found.[15]

C. Miscellaneous Related Properties

Miscellaneous properties somewhat related to molecular structure are collected in this section. Where the original reference was not available, the *Chemical Abstracts* summary was consulted as noted in the footnote. Many of these papers are summarized very briefly and are included primarily to make the literature search complete.

Ochiai[16] reports a theoretical consideration of the polarization of heterocyclic rings with aromatic character, including thiophene. Collision areas of thiophene and benzene have been determined from calculations on vapor viscosities. Lowry and Nesini[17] report that collision areas are lowered about 10% when sulfur is replaced by —CH=CH—, *i.e.*, comparing thiophene with benzene. Various physical properties of thiophene, furan, and benzene were compared by Erlenmeyer and Leo[11a] as shown in Table IV-4. A direct comparison of the boiling points of 19 benzene and thiophene derivatives is given.

Lippmann[19] has determined the electrooptical constant for thiophene among a large number of organic compounds in an article concerning electric birefringence in liquids and its relation to chemical composition and constitution. Cabannes and Granier[20] measured the depolarization of diffuse light by thiophene and other compounds for the liquid and vapor states at various temperatures and pressures. Preiswerk[21] followed the magnetorotatory power of thiophene, pyrrole,

---

[14] Private communication from H. Freiser, Jan. 5, 1949.
[15] See pages 173 and 223.
[16] Ochiai, *Chem. Abstr.*, **33**, 3791 (1939); *J. Pharm. Soc. Japan*, **58**, 1025–39 (1938), in German, **59**, 20–28 (1939).
[17] Lowry and Nesini, *Proc. Roy. Soc. (London)*, **A123**, 686 (1929).
[18] Bruni and Natta, *Atti accad. nazl. Lincei*, **11**, 929, 1058 (1930).
[19] Lippmann, *Z. Elektrochem.*, **17**, 15 (1911); *Chem. Abstr.*, **5**, 1012 (1911).
[20] Cabannes and Granier, *Compt. rend.*, **182**, 885 (1926).
[21] Preiswerk, *Helv. Phys. Acta*, **7**, 203 (1933); *Chem. Abstr.*, **28**, 2999 (1934).

furan, and benzene to the beginning of absorption. Cotton and Mouton[22] in a review paper concerning magnetic birefringence and chemical constitution report magnetic double refraction properties of thiophene.

Auwers and Kohlhaas[23] in an article entitled "Spectrochemistry of Thiophene Derivatives" report b.p.; d_4^{20} and d_4^t; n^t for He, α, β, and γ; M_α, M_D, $E\Sigma$, etc., for thiophene and 25 derivatives.

TABLE IV-4. Miscellaneous Data[a] Collected by Erlenmeyer and Leo[11a]

Property	Thiophene	Furan	Benzene
Activation data			
$k_{70}° \times 10^4$	102.3	41.3	57
E	11,670	11,550	11,400
α..................................	292,700	98,700	110,000
Coefficient of friction			
$\eta \times 10^4$	66.3	39.7	64.4
Crystallographic data at $-170°$ [18]			
Crystal system.......................Tetragonal[b]			Orthorhombic
a	7.22[b]		7.34
b................................	—[b]		9.52
c................................	9.54[b]		6.74
Volume of unit cell $\times 10^{24}$.............	498		471
Density	1.11		1.099
Parachor...........................	187.4		192.1
Molecular refraction			
M_D................................	24.3	18.28	26.1

[a] These authors do not state the units for many of the properties recorded. The original article (footnote 11a) should be consulted in case of question.
[b] Lipscomb[11b] in a later study verbally reports thiophene to be orthorhombic with cell dimensions $a = 9.76$ A., $b = 7.20$ A., $c = 6.67$ A.

Steinkopf[24] summarizes and discusses structural formulae proposed by numerous early investigators. In his 1941 publication he remarks: "Thus, despite its defects, the simple formula of Meyer[25] (XI) is still the best expression of the physical and chemical behavior of thiophene."

(XI)

[22] Cotton and Mouton, *Ann. chim. phys.*, **28**, 209 (1913).
[23] Auwers and Kohlhaas, *J. prakt. Chem.*, **108**, 321 (1924); *Chem. Zentr.*, **1925**, I, 1194.
[24] Steinkopf, *Die Chemie des Thiophens*. 1941, page 2. Lithoprinted by Edwards Bros., Ann Arbor, Mich., 1944.
[25] Meyer, *Ber.*, **16**, 1465 (1883).

II. Theoretical Considerations from the Viewpoint of Spectroscopy and Summary of Published Spectral Data

The interpretations of molecular structure as deduced essentially from spectroscopic information, unfortunately, cannot be stated in terms of the conventional structural formulae of the organic chemist. As a result of the qualitative and semiquantitative application of approximation methods of quantum mechanics, much is now understood about absorption peaks in terms of energy levels within molecules. In even the simplest molecules, however, the rich collection of energy levels associated with the electronic, vibrational, and rotational degrees of freedom leads to a highly complicated spectrum and recourse is usually taken to considering various atomic groupings within the larger molecules. Certain empirical relationships between spectra and structure are frequently found which serve as a powerful tool to elucidate structure and characterize new compounds. Much of the information of this latter type for thiophene and its derivatives has direct application and will be reserved for separate discussion in Section III on applied spectroscopy.

A. Electronic Absorption Spectra

The ultraviolet absorption spectrum of thiophene has been investigated by many workers, but, except for ionization potentials, only semiquantitative or comparative information has been obtained concerning molecular structure.

The earliest spectroscopic investigation of thiophene is believed to be that of Pauer,[26] who in 1897 reported that thiophene vapor and liquid exhibit ultraviolet absorption bands. Hartley and Dobbie[27] one year later, reported that thiophene in ethyl alcohol exhibited complete absorption in the ultraviolet at wavelengths shorter than 2573 A. Bass[28] in 1948 reports that thiophene when used for short wavelength cut-off filters for the ultraviolet is effective up to 2480 A. at a concentration of 1.0 g./liter in isooctane and up to 2590 A. at 100 g./liter. (Bass notes that thiophene is unstable in the ultraviolet radiation from a mercury arc.) Purvis[29] reported that thiophene in the liquid state and in solution in ethyl alcohol shows no sharp absorption bands in the ultraviolet region, only general

[26] Pauer, *J. Chem. Soc., Abstracts*, **72**, 393 (1897); *Ann. d. Physik* [N. F.], **61**, 376 (1897).
[27] Hartley and Dobbie, *J. Chem. Soc.*, **73**, 604 (1898).
[28] Bass, *J. Optical Soc. Am.*, **38**, 977 (1948).
[29] Purvis, *J. Chem. Soc.*, **97**, 1648 (1910).

absorption beginning about 2500 A.   Thiophene in the vapor state yielded bands at 2590, 2530, 2415, 2406, and 2395 A.

Mohler[30] reports curves showing the absorption in the region 3000–2000 A. in hexane solution for various sulfides (including thiophene), a sulfoxide, sulfone, and disulfide (Dithian) and discusses the effect of the C—S—C group.   Godart[31] measured the ultraviolet spectra of thiophene XII, thiophthene XIII, and thianaphthene XIV in solution in hexane for

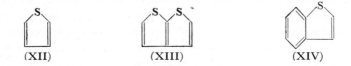

(XII)   (XIII)   (XIV)

comparison with benzene and naphthalene.   A similarity was found between benzene and XII and naphthalene and XIII.   The ultraviolet spectrum of thiophene vapor was also determined and the relation between this spectrum and its infrared and Raman spectra is discussed. Milazzo[32] finds agreement between transitions as indicated by ultraviolet and Raman spectra and concludes, after photographing the quartz ultraviolet spectrum with great dispersion, that the bands observed between 2600 and 2000 A. are to be attributed to at least two electronic transitions, perhaps three.

Price and Walsh[33] in a detailed experimental and theoretical study have determined the absorption spectra of cyclic dienes, thiophene, and pyrrole in the vacuum ultraviolet.   For thiophene, the 2400–2100 A. region exhibits bands having a frequency separation of *ca.* 965 cm.$^{-1}$, which reportedly corresponds to a valence frequency of conjugated double bonds in an excited state.   This differs from an earlier tentative vibration analysis proposed by Menczel.[34]   Price and Walsh found the 2400–2100 A. region to be followed by a region of transparency terminated fairly abruptly by the start of a strong system of bands about 1880 A.   The first two strong bands of this system have a separation of 540 cm.$^{-1}$ which corresponds to 470 cm.$^{-1}$ for similar bands in cyclopentadiene.   The main ethylenic frequency is reported to be near 1250 cm.$^{-1}$ The region between 1600 and 1400 A. is occupied by a large number of fairly sharp bands which gradually diminish in intensity toward shorter wavelengths.

[30] Mohler, *Helv. Chim. Acta*, **20**, 1188 (1937); *Chem. Abstr.*, **32**, 426 (1938).
[31] Godart, *J. Chim. Phys.*, **34**, 70 (1937); *Chem. Abstr.*, **31**, 4595 (1937).
[32] Milazzo, *Experientia*, **3**, 370 (1947).   Also see footnote 4.
[33] Price and Walsh, *Proc. Roy. Soc. (London)*, **A179**, 201 (1941).
[34] Menczel, *Z. physik. Chem.*, **125**, 161 (1927).

These are apparently electronic bands accompanied by little, if any, vibration, converging to an ionization limit at approximately 1400 A. The following formula represents the most prominent Rydberg series found:

$$\nu_0^n = 72{,}170 - R/(n + 0.90)^2$$

Price and Walsh[33] conclude that the spectra obtained are due to the excitation of a π electron from the conjugated double-bond electrons. The spectra of these "cyclic dienes" exhibit considerable similarity among themselves. Certain systematic differences found indicate the magnitude of the effect of adjacent atoms or groups on these electrons. The electronic structures of these heterocyclics have been treated theoretically by Huckel[35] and by Mulliken.[36] Reference should be made to the detailed discussion by Price and Walsh which in the light of considerable additional data critically reviews, and differs somewhat with, the earlier interpretations. A few specific points[33] which may be of interest are as follows. (1) Only in furan is there marked tendency to homocyclic conjugation. (Homocyclic conjugation occurs when all the unsaturation or π electrons are equivalent.) In this respect pyrrole is more similar to thiophene than furan, a fact which is in agreement with the resonance energy of 31 kcal./mole for thiophene and pyrrole but of 23 kcal./mole for furan, and other arguments. (2) Hyperconjugation is not so important in cyclic hexa- and pentadienes as previously supposed. (3) To account for differences in ionization potential between open chain dienes and cyclic dienes, Price and Walsh state that resonance to Dewar type structures such as XV and XVI is quite probable for the cyclic dienes.

(XV)   (XVI)

They state that these structures contribute about 20% to the resonance in benzene and most probably an equal portion in the cyclic dienes. The higher ionization values (see Table IV-5) for thiophene, pyrrole, and furan over cyclic hexa- and pentadienes probably arise from the higher electron affinity of the attached groups in these molecules. This has the effect of withdrawing negative charge from the double bonds and so increasing the ionization potential of the associated electrons.

[35] Huckel, *Z. Elektrochem.*, **43**, 779 (1937).
[36] Mulliken, *J. Chem. Phys.*, **7**, 339 (1939).

TABLE IV-5. Ionization Potentials of Some Cyclic Dienes[33]

Compound	Ionization potential in volts		
	From Rydberg series	From electron impact	
Cyclohexadiene...........	8.4	—	—
Cyclopentadiene..........	8.58	8.4 ± 0.1	—
Pyrrole..................	8.9	9.0	—
Thiophene...............	8.91 ± 0.02	9.0 ± 0.05	9.20 ± 0.10[b]
Furan...................	9.01 ± 0.01 (10.8)[a]	9.0 (10.6)[a]	—
2-Methylthiophene........	—	—	8.82 ± 0.10[b]
3-Methylthiophene........	—	—	8.82 ± 0.10[b]

[a] These values are reported to be the second ionization potential; all others represent the first ionization potentials.
[b] Electron impact values determined at Socony-Vacuum Laboratories, reported by private communication from R. E. Honig, April 5, 1949, who notes that the values from Rydberg series as given above should be recomputed using the new conversion factor of 8067.49 cm.$^{-1}$ = 1 electron volt. For example, for thiophene the correction is 8.91 × 8103.74/8067.49 = 8.95 eV.

Little information is to be found in the literature concerning ultraviolet and visible spectra of thiophene derivatives. Abe[37a] reports the absorption maxima for 2-acetylthiophene and 2-acetylfuran to be found at 2260 and 2670 A., respectively, and comments that this absorption is due to the presence of the CO group. He concludes that the effect of the CO group on pentacyclic ring compounds is the same as that of a methyl group, a result in disagreement with spectra presented in Section III.A and also in disagreement with the chemical behavior. Koch,[37b] in an extensive discussion of absorption spectra and structure of organic sulfur compounds, mentions the visible-light absorption of 3,4-diphenylthiophene sulfone and 4-hydroxy-3-methylthiophene sulfone and the resonance forms presumably associated therewith.

Thiophene might be considered as a chromophore having its wavelength of maximum absorption near 235 mμ, at which wavelength the log molar extinction (log ϵ) is about 3.9 (see Table IV-8).

B. Electronic Emission Spectra

The only reference found to an investigation of fluorescence spectra of thiophene was that by Fialkovskaya,[38] who reports that fluorescence under ultraviolet excitation was not observed with thiophene but only when the benzene ring was in the structure being examined. The vapor state ultra-

[37a] Abe, *Chem. Abstr.*, **33**, 2033 (1939); *J. Chem. Soc. Japan*, **59**, 1117 (1938).
[37b] Koch, *J. Chem. Soc.*, **1949**, 410.
[38] Fialkovskaya, *Chem. Abstr.*, **33**, 4127 (1939); *J. Phys. Chem. (U. S. S. R.)*, **11**, 533 (1938).

violet absorption of thiophene and other heterocyclics was also determined.

Harkins and Jackson[39] report a spectroscopic study of the decomposition and synthesis of organic compounds, including thiophene, by elec-
trical discharges.   In the electrodeless discharge thiophene was found to
decompose into sulfur atoms (S), and molecules (S_2), and carbon mono-
sulfide molecules (CS) in addition to molecules of carbon (C_2) and of
monohydrocarbon (CH), atoms of hydrogen (H) and of carbon (C), and
ions of carbon (C^*), these latter as were found for hydrocarbons also.
The product produced, most of which clung tenaciously to the discharge
flask, consisted of powder and heavy scales of a very dark color with a sort
of metallic luster.   The spectrum, beautifully colored with purple and red,
showed the line spectrum of S very prominently, the band spectrum of S_2,
and a very striking set of bands due to CS which extended from 2850 to
2460 A.

C. Vibration Spectra

The earliest infrared study of thiophene is believed to be that of
Coblentz.[40]   In 1905, he determined its spectrum from 0.8 to 2.8 μ using
a quartz prism spectrometer and also the continuation to 15 μ as observed
with a rock salt prism spectrometer.   Coblentz remarks that Julius[41] in
1892 reported an infrared spectrum for benzene which appeared to have
thiophene present as an impurity due to the presence of bands at 5.6 and
7.3 μ which correspond to strong bands of thiophene.   The infrared spectra of thiophene, thiophthene, and thianaphthene were measured by
Godart,[31] who discussed the infrared, Raman, and ultraviolet data with
reference to benzene and naphthalene for comparison.   Further infrared
data in the region from 1 to 15 μ, or portions thereof, will be found in footnote 42.   Absorption spectra in the region 0.6 to 1.0 μ are reported[43] for
thiophene, methyl and dimethyl derivatives and differences discussed.

[39] Harkins and Jackson, *J. Chem. Phys.*, **1**, 37 (1933).
[40] Coblentz, *Investigations of Infrared Spectra*, Part I.   Carnegie Institution of
Washington, 1905, pp. 35, 98.
[41] Julius, *Verhandl. Koninkl. Akad. Wetenschap. Amsterdam*, Deel I, No. 1 (1892).
[42] (a) Barnes and Brattain, *J. Chem. Phys.*, **3**, 446 (1935).   (b) Abe and Kobayashi,
Chem. Abstr., **31**, 3386 (1937); *J. Chem. Soc. Japan*, **58**, 242 (1937).   (c) Manzoni-
Ansidei and Rolla, *Chem. Abstr.*, **32**, 8933 (1938); *Atti. accad. nazl. Lincei. Classe
sci. fis., mat. e nat.*, **27**, 410 (1938).   (d) Barnes, Liddel, and Williams, *Ind. Eng.
Chem., Anal. Ed.*, **15**, 659 (1943); see also Barnes, Gore, Liddel, and Williams,
Infrared Spectroscopy, Industrial Applications. Reinhold, New York, 1944.   (e)
Thompson, *J. Chem. Soc.*, **1944**, 183.   (f) American Petroleum Institute Research
Project 44 at the National Bureau of Standards.   Catalog of Infrared Spectro-
grams.   Serial #364 and #740 for thiophene (liquid, 2 to 15 μ) contributed by
Socony-Vacuum Laboratories and U. S. Bureau of Mines, respectively.   (g)
Randall, Fowler, Fuson, and Dangl, *Infrared Determination of Organic Structures*.
Van Nostrand, New York, 1949, pp. 7, 17, 92, 226.
[43] Barchewitz and Garach, *Compt. rend.*, **208**, 2071 (1939).

TABLE IV-6. Vibration Spectra of Thiophene[48]

Raman			Infrared			
			Vapor	Liquid		
Δv, cm.$^{-1}$	I	ρ	cm.$^{-1}$	cm.$^{-1}$	μ	Assignment[a]
375	0	(dp)			$(26.6)^b$	$832 - 453 = 379$
453	3	dp			$(22.1)^{bc}$	23, out-of-plane ring bending
565	1	dp		Not active		18, out-of-plane ring bending
604	6	0.34	605	605	16.5	1, symmetric ring bending
686	2	1.01		Not active		19, C—H bending out-of-plane
			710	710	14.1	22, C—H bending out-of-plane
748	4	1.00		Not active		20, C—H bending out-of-plane
832	7	0.08	836	836	12.0	3, ring "breathing"
						24, weak C—H bending
866	1	1.00	872	870	11.5	10, ring bending
898	$^1/_2$	dp	909	904	11.1	11, C—H bending
1032	10	0.11	1035	1035	9.66	2, C—H bending
1079	9	0.43	1077	1080	9.26	4, C—H bending
			1252	1255	7.96	14, ring bending
				1290	7.75	12, C—H bending
1358	9	0.13			$(7.31)^b$	5, symmetric ring bending
1404	12	0.35	1405	1405	7.11	6, symmetric ring bending
				1479	6.76	Combination
				1565	6.39	Combination
				1590	6.30	15, ring mode controlled by C=C

(Weak infrared bands at 1715, 1770, 1805, 1905, 1960, 2090, 2168, 2230, 2280 cm.$^{-1}$.)

2996	1	p				7 and 16, C—H stretching
3078	8b	p (Hg)		3110	3.22	8 and 17, C—H stretching
3108	10	0.33 (Hg)				C—H stretching, also 3(1032) = 3096

[a] Numbering of the modes of vibration follows that used by Lord and Miller for the analogous molecule pyrrole (*J. Chem. Phys.*, **10**, 328, 1942).
[b] Wavelengths correspond to Raman frequencies and represent bands possible but not reported in infrared.
[c] A strong band at 22.08μ was found in the spectrum recorded in Figure IV-10.

Spectra in the region from 5 to 20 μ for thiophene, other heterocyclics, and many thiophene derivatives are reported and discussed by Lecomte and co-workers.[44]   Randall *et al.*[42g] point out that compounds having a high degree of conjugation like benzene, pyridene, thiophene, etc., exhibit double-bond bands, but no mode of vibration of the ring can be recognized upon substitution.   Substitution produces pronounced shifts in the vibrations of the parent ring.   They predict that subclassifications in regard to the location of substitutions on the ring will be possible.   Raman

[44] (a) Lecomte, *Bull. soc. chim.*, **1946**, 415.   (b) Garach and Lecomte, *ibid.*, **1946**, 423.   (c) Garach and Lecomte, *Compt. rend.*, **222**, 74 (1936).

spectroscopic data concerning thiophene, related compounds, and derivatives have been reported and discussed by many workers.[45]

The most recent and complete investigations of the vibration spectrum of thiophene are the Raman study by Reitz[46] and the infrared study by Thompson and Temple.[47] Using these spectral data plus vapor-heat-capacity data and taking advantage of previous partial assignments, Waddington and co-workers[48] have made a complete, although not entirely certain vibrational assignment for thiophene. This assignment along with the Raman and infrared data is recorded in Table IV-6. Calculations based upon the structure (as indicated by electron diffraction) and measured dipole moment of thiophene indicate the possibility of a number of pure rotational transitions in the far infrared or microwave regions, but none have been found.[49] The microwave spectrum from 18,000 to 26,000 kilo-megacycles has been searched with a sensitivity of 10^{-8} cm.$^{-1}$ but no lines appeared. The failure to find lines probably is due to their low intensity, since thiophene is a rather heavy molecule for present microwave technique.[49]

D. Thermodynamic Functions from Spectroscopic and Molecular Structure Data

Relatively complete thermodynamic information about thiophene in the low pressure region has been established by Waddington and co-

[45] (a) Venkateswaran, *Indian J. Phys.*, **5**, 145 (1930); *Phil. Mag.*, **15**, 263 (1933). (b) Venkateswaran and Bhagavantam, *Indian J. Phys.*, **7**, 585 (1933). (c) Bhagavantam, *ibid.*, **7**, 79(1932). (d) Bonino, *Chem. Abstr.*, **30**, 2849 (1936); *IX Congr. intern. quim. pura aplicada*, 4, 3 (1934). *Chem. Abstr.*, **29**, 3603 (1935); *Gazz. chim. ital.*, **65**, 5 (1935). *Chem. Abstr.*, **30**, 88 (1936); *Gazz. chim. ital.*, **65**, 371 (1935). *Chem. Abstr.*, **31**, 3388 (1937); *Ricerca sci.*, **7**, II, No. 3–4, 3 pp. (1936). *Chem. Abstr.*, **31**, 4206 (1937); *Atti accad. nazl. Lincei. Classe sci. fis., mat. e nat.*, **24**, 288 (1936); *Ibid.*, 374. *Chem. Abstr.*, **33**, 7195 (1939); *Atti X congr. intern. chem.*, **2**, 141 (1938). (e) Bonino and Manzoni-Ansidei, *Z. physik. Chem.*, **B25**, 327 (1934). *Chem. Abstr.*, **31**, 4207 (1937); *Atti accad. nazl. Lincei. Classe sci. fis., mat. e nat.*, **24**, 207 (1936). *Chem. Abstr.*, **31**, 3388 (1937); *Ricerca sci.*, **7** (I), No. 7–8, 2 pp. (1936). (f) Bonino and Dinelli, *Ricerca sci.*, **66** (I), 505 (1935). (g) Dupont and Dulow, *Bull. soc. chim.*, (5), **3**, 1639 (1936); and with Desreux, *ibid.*, 1659. (h) Redlich and Stricks, *Sitzber. Akad. Wiss. Wien*, Abt. IIb, **145**, 77 (1936). (i) Manzoni-Ansidei, *Chem. Abstr.*, **32**, 4879 (1938); *Ricerca sci.*, 8 (II), No. 3–4, 2 pp. (1937). (j) Kohlrausch and Seka, *Ber.*, **B71**, 985 (1938). (k) Simon and Kirret, *Chem. Abstr.*, **34**, 3592 (1940); *Naturwissenschaften*, **28**, 47 (1940). (l) Hibben, *The Raman Effect and Its Chemical Applications.* Reinhold, New York, 1939, pp. 260, 287. (m) Kohlrausch, *Ramanspektren.* Lithoprinted by Edwards Bros., Ann Arbor, Mich., 1945, p. 343. (n) Truchet and Chapron, *Chem. Zentr.*, **106**, 217 (1935), p. 343.
[46] Reitz, *Z. physik. Chem.*, **B33**, 179 (1936); *ibid.*, **B38**, 275 (1937).
[47] Thompson and Temple, *Trans. Faraday Soc.*, **41**, 27 (1945).
[48] Waddington, Knowlton, Scott, Oliver, Todd, Hubbard, Smith and Huffman, *J. Am. Chem. Soc.*, **71**, 797 (1949).
[49] Private communications from C. H. Townes and E. Bright Wilson, Jr., October, 1949.

workers.[48] The several types of investigation carried out by them include: (*1*) low-temperature heat capacity; (*2*) vapor pressure; (*3*) heat of vaporization, vapor heat capacity, gas imperfection,[50] and entropy of the ideal gas; (*4*) heat of combustion and heat of formation; and (*5*) thermodynamic functions from spectroscopic and molecular structure data. Since data concerning items (*1*) through (*4*) above have been listed in moderate extent in Chapter III, only item (*5*) will be presented here.

Using their vibrational assignment, Waddington *et al.*[48] calculated the vapor heat capacity and entropy by means of the harmonic oscillator-rigid rotator approximation. The difference between the observed and calculated values of vapor heat capacity, see Table IV-7(*a*), probably represents the contribution to the heat capacity of anharmonicity and other factors neglected in the harmonic oscillator-rigid rotator treatment. That this is the case, rather than that the vibrational assignment is incorrect, is substantiated by the fact that benzene (where little doubt of the assignment exists) yields values similar both in magnitude and temperature dependence. Using the geometrical data of Schomaker and Pauling,[1] moments of inertia were calculated for thiophene as follows: $I_x = 156.6 \times 10^{-40}$ g. sq. cm.; $I_y = 262.1 \times 10^{-40}$; and $I_z = 105.6 \times 10^{-40}$. Using these moments of inertia, the symmetry number of 2, and the values of the fundamental constants given by Wagman *et al.*[51] the entropy was calculated with results as shown in Table IV-7(*b*). The authors comment that the close agreement of the two sets of entropy values shows that crystalline thiophene approaches zero entropy at the absolute zero. It is also a confirmation of the planar structure (C_{2v} symmetry) for the thiophene molecule. Values of various thermodynamic functions calculated by the methods of statistical mechanics for temperatures up to 1500°K. are reported in Table IV-7(*c*). Included are:

Free energy function...................$(H_0^0 - F_T^0)/T$
Heat content function ....$H_T^0 - H_0^0$
Entropy...................................S_T^0
Heat capacity.............................C_{pT}^0

It is pointed out[48] that these functions were calculated on the basis of the harmonic oscillator-rigid rotator approximation and may be somewhat in error, especially at the higher temperatures, because of the neglect of the contributions of anharmonicity and other factors.

[50] Bigassi, *Atti. accad. nazl. Lincei*, **16**, 48 (1932), has reported concerning the equation of state for thiophene and related compounds.
[51] Wagman, Kilpatrick, Taylor, Pitzer, and Rossini, *J. Research Natl. Bur. Standards*, **34**, 143 (1945).

TABLE IV-7.[48]

(a) Vapor Heat Capacity (in cal./°/mole) of Thiophene

Temp., °K.	C_p^0 (obs.)	C_p^0 (calcd.)	C_p^0 (obs.) — C_p^0 (calcd.)
343.95	20.05	19.91	0.14
371.20	21.55	21.36	0.19
402.30	23.17	22.92	0.25
436.20	24.76	24.48	0.28
471.15	26.27	25.96	0.31

(b) Entropy (in cal./°/mole) of Thiophene

Temp., °K.	Calorimetric (obs.)	Molecular structure (calcd.)
318.52	67.83	67.81
336.24	68.88	68.84
357.32	70.04	70.05

(c) Thermodynamic Functions of Thiophene

Temp., °K.	$(H_0^0 - F_T^0)/T$, cal./°/mole	$H_T^0 - H_0^0$, kcal./mole	S_T^0, cal./°/mole	C_{pT}^0, cal./°/mole
298.16	55.98	3.172	66.62	17.32
300	56.05	3.204	66.72	17.43
400	59.45	5.224	72.51	22.81
500	62.62	7.728	78.08	27.10
600	65.64	10.59	83.32	30.46
800	71.27	17.22	92.80	35.27
1000	76.42	24.61	101.03	38.56
1500	87.52	45.24	117.68	43.33

III. Applied Spectroscopy

Introduction

Theoretical considerations relating molecular spectra to molecular structure usually require that the spectra be obtained from samples in the vapor state using spectrographs of high resolution and that spectra be studied over wide temperature ranges and extended to spectral regions not readily accessible. Emission and fluorescence spectra should be available in addition to absorption spectra, etc. However, largely by empirical correlations, various accessible spectral regions have been found to yield data which permit quantitative analysis for specific compounds and qualitative information to aid in an elucidation of compound structure. Frequently this information is obtained on samples in the liquid state (or in solution in a relatively transparent solvent) wherein many fine features of the spectra are "smeared out" by intermolecular attraction and rather broad generalizations made. For such reasons, data of direct analytical interest have been collected in this separate section. Some earlier data have been repeated in addition to collecting spectra for many additional derivatives. A moderate collection of data, all taken under specified experimental conditions which are more or less generally available, is presented herein in sufficient detail so that analytical use may be made thereof.

A. Ultraviolet Absorption Spectra[52]

Ultraviolet absorption data obtained in the author's laboratory are presented in Figures IV-3 through IV-9 for the compounds summarized in Table IV-8. All samples were examined in solution in iso-octane at suitable concentrations for precise transmission measurements in a cell of 1 cm. thickness. Spectra were obtained using a Cary[53] Recording Spectrophotometer which recorded absorbancy (i.e., optical density) from which the molecular extinction coefficient in liters/mole-cm. was calculated in the usual manner.[54]

Resonance within the thiophene ring gives rise to an ultraviolet spectrum with a broad maximum (in liquid solution) near 231 mμ, log ϵ = 3.85. The saturated ring compound, thiolane, exhibits only very weak near ultraviolet absorption as would be expected. Methyl substitution on the thiophene nucleus in the 2- or 3-position, ethyl substitution in the 2-position, and 2,3-dimethyl substitution shift the thiophene maximum only 3 mμ to longer wavelengths. 2,5-Dimethyl substitution and 2-halogen substitution shift the maximum +5 mμ and 3,4-dimethyl +7 mμ to 238 mμ. 2,3-Dibromo is quite similar to 2-bromo but 2,5-dibromo shifts the maximum +21 mμ to 252 mμ. This pronounced effect of substitution in the positions adjacent to the sulfur atom also is indicated for the 2,5-

---

[52] In addition to the literature references discussed in Section II.A, ultraviolet absorption spectrograms have been published by American Petroleum Institute Research Project 44 at the National Bureau of Standards, Washington, D. C., as follows: for thiophene, serial numbers 38, 136, and 208 contributed by Union Oil Co. of Calif., Socony-Vacuum Laboratories, and Bureau of Mines, respectively; for 2- and 3-methylthiophenes, serial numbers 137 and 138, respectively, these and the following all contributed by Socony-Vacuum Laboratories; 2-ethylthiophene, #309; 2,3-, 2,4-, 2,5-, and 3,4-dimethylthiophenes, #310 through #313, respectively; 2-ethenylthiophene, #314; 2-acetylthiophene, #315; 2-chlorothiophene, #316; 2-bromothiophene, #317; and 2,3- and 2,5-dibromothiophene, #318 and 319, respectively.

[53] Cary, Ind. Eng. Chem., **39,** 75A (1947).

[54] For a general introduction to both the theory and practice of spectroscopy the reader is referred to Harrison, Lord, and Loofbourow, *Practical Spectroscopy.* Prentice-Hall, New York, 1948.

TABLE IV-8. Summary of Ultraviolet Absorption Data (All Samples in Solution in Iso-octane)

Compound	Absorption maximum		Wavelength of cut-off, mμ	
	$\lambda_{max.}$, mμ[a]	log $\epsilon_{max.}$[b]	λ (log ϵ = 2.5)[c]	λ (log ϵ = 1.0)[d]
Thiolane....................	220	2.9	227	258
Thiophene..................	231	3.85	248	254
2-Methylthiophene...........	234	3.88	253	261
3-Methylthiophene...........	234	3.72	255	262
2,3-Dimethylthiophene........	234	3.78	260	267
2,5-Dimethylthiophene........	236	3.88	262	271
3,4-Dimethylthiophene........	238	3.76	257	264
2-Ethylthiophene............	234	3.92	254	262
2-Vinylthiophene............	273	4.04	304	313
2-Acetylthiophene...........	256	4.00 ⎫	304	365
	273	3.87 ⎭		
2-Chlorothiophene...........	236	3.89	261	270
2-Bromothiophene...........	236	3.92	267	285
2,3-Dibromothiophene........	239	3.89	280	303
2,5-Dibromothiophene........	252	3.96	291	312
Thianaphthene..............	227	4.40 ⎫		
	249–258	3.83 ⎪		
	281	3.21 ⎬	302.5	313
	289	3.32 ⎪		
	296.9	3.50 ⎭		
3,4-Thiolanedithione.........	227	3.85 ⎫		
	251	3.87 ⎪	465	?
	332	3.61 ⎢		
	412	3.66 ⎭		

[a] Wavelength of major absorption maxima in millimicrons.
[b] Log molar extinction coefficient, liters/mole cm., at $\lambda_{max.}$.
[c] Wavelength at which log ϵ = 2.5.
[d] Wavelength at which log ϵ = 1.0.

dimethyl derivative where the band broadens considerably.   3,4-Dimethylthiophene has a cut-off near 264 mμ, whereas 2,5-dimethyl absorbs with similar intensity to 271 mμ.   C=C or C=O substituted in the 2-position, as in the 2-vinyl and 2-acetyl derivatives, produces a pronounced bathochromic effect wherein $\lambda_{max.}$ is shifted +40 mμ to 273 mμ and the long wavelength cut-off is shifted even more.[55]   This is comparable to the effect observed when C=C is added to a conjugated chain, in which case

[55] The weak, but definite, absorption of 2-acetylthiophene from 310 to 365 mμ (see Figure IV-6) is believed to be real and not due to impurity.   The purity of this sample was established by freezing point methods to be 99.8%.

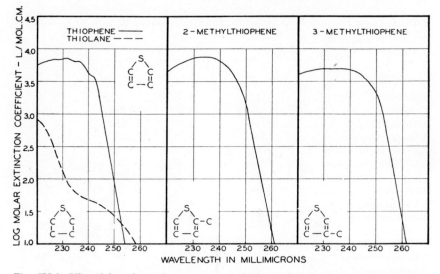

Fig. IV-3. Ultraviolet absorption spectra of thiolane, thiophene, 2- and 3-methyl-thiophenes in isooctane solution.

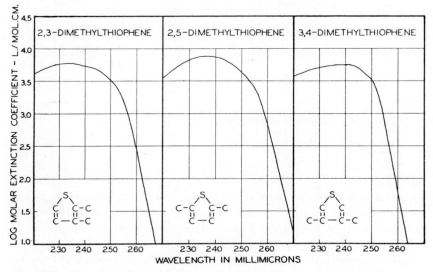

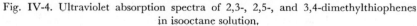

Fig. IV-4. Ultraviolet absorption spectra of 2,3-, 2,5-, and 3,4-dimethylthiophenes in isooctane solution.

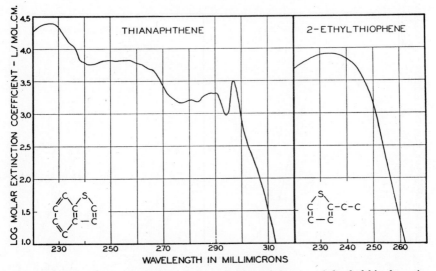

Fig. IV-5. Ultraviolet absorption spectra of thianaphthene and 2-ethylthiophene in isooctane solution.

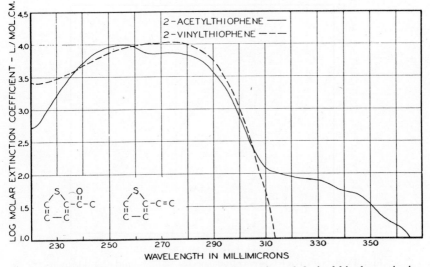

Fig. IV-6. Ultraviolet absorption spectra of 2-acetyl- and 2-vinylthiophenes in iso-octane solution.

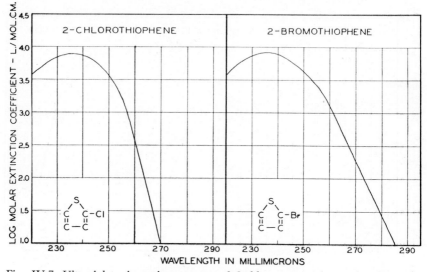

Fig. IV-7. Ultraviolet absorption spectra of 2-chloro- and 2-bromothiophenes in isooctane solution.

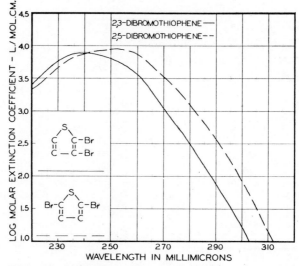

Fig. IV-8. Ultraviolet absorption spectra of 2,3- and 2,5-dibromo-thiophenes in isooctane solution.

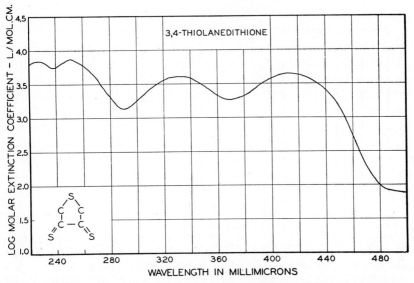

Fig. IV-9. Ultraviolet absorption spectrum of 3,4-thiolanedithione in isooctane solution.   Note change in wavelength scale from preceding figures.

$\lambda_{max.}$ increases by roughly 30 mμ.   However, log ϵ usually increases by about 0.3 per C=C link when added to an open chain, whereas log ϵ increased only about 0.1 in the 2-position thiophene substitution.   For all alkyl and/or halogen substitutions investigated to date, log ϵ remained near 3.9, *i.e.*, the intensity of absorption remained nearly constant.   Thus the thiophene nucleus acts as a chromophoric group with $\lambda_{max.}$ near 235 mμ and log ϵ about 3.9.   Groups which can conjugate with the thiophene nucleus produce a pronounced bathochromic effect.

Condensed multiple ring thiophene compounds probably will exhibit absorption at progressively longer wavelengths in the ultraviolet, as has been found for the aromatic series benzene, naphthalene, anthracene, etc. This is indicated by thianaphthene, Figure IV-5, wherein the longest $\lambda_{max.}$ occurs at 297 mμ.   A compound believed to be 3,4-thiolanedithione, Figure IV-9, exhibits an extended region of absorption, the longest $\lambda_{max.}$ occurring at 412 mμ, nearly in the blue, which indicates the C=S group to show an enormous bathochromic effect when attached to the thiophene nucleus.

B. Infrared Absorption Spectra

Although moderately numerous infrared investigations of thiophene, its derivatives, and related compounds have been reported in the literature (as was noted in Section II.C of this chapter), only the spectrum of thiophene has been interpreted in any detail.   Very few of the published spectra are available in useful form.   Spectra of thiophene, thiolane, and many of their derivatives have been determined in the author's laboratory.[56]   These cover the region from 2 to 15μ and, in many cases, extend to 25μ.   Spectrograms plotted as percent transmission *vs.* wavelength are presented in Figures IV-10 through IV-18.   The wavelengths and frequencies which correspond to the absorption bands are recorded in Tables IV-9 to IV-17.

Since the infrared equipment used to obtain these data is not so well known as the ultraviolet and mass spectrometry instruments, it will be described in slightly more detail.   These data were obtained on a spectrometer equipped with NaCl and KBr prisms of 15-cm. base length mounted in a Littrow arrangement in which the collimating mirror is a 10° off-axis paraboloid of 1-meter focal length.[57]   The prisms are mounted on a drum which can be rotated to bring the desired prism into position and locked therein to reproduce the calibrated wavelength setting.   The NaCl region has been examined in most cases using a Nernst Glower as the source of radiation and the KBr region using a Globar. The radiation from the source is interrupted roughly 6 times per second.   After passing through the sample and spectrometer, the intensity of this alternating exit radiation is measured by a nickel-ribbon bolometer arranged in an electronic bridge circuit.   The *ca.* 6 cycle/sec. output is amplified, rectified, and recorded on a pen and ink, stripchart recorder.   The spectrum is scanned stepwise from long to short wavelength decreasing the slit-width appropriately.   Stray light in the instrument is negligible except for the long wavelength extreme of each prism.   Where necessary, especially for KBr from 20 to 25μ, stray light corrections were made.   A single piece of NaCl or KBr of thickness comparable to that of the two windows of each cell was used to obtain 100% transmittance deflections except that when solutions were used a solvent cell of suitable thickness was sometimes used.

Cell thicknesses (and solvent concentration when used) were varied in an effort to obtain measurable values of transmittance at all spectral regions although this ideal was not completely realized.   Cell and solvent data are recorded on the tables and figures.   The cell length noted on the figures near each compound name is the thickness used over the major spectral range.   Other thicknesses used for selected spectral regions are shown on the spectrograms.

[56] All infrared spectrograms presented in Figures IV-10 through IV-17 have been, or are to be, published in the Catalog of Infrared Spectrograms, American Petroleum Institute Research Project 44 at the National Bureau of Standards, Washington, D. C., from spectrograms contributed by Socony-Vacuum Laboratories, Paulsboro, N. J.

[57] The spectrometer minus the detector and source was supplied by Gaertner Scientific Corporation.   The optical arrangement is essentially the same as described by McAlister, Matheson, and Sweeney, *Rev. Sci. Inst.*, **12**, 314 (1941).

The spectrum of thiophene thus obtained, Table IV-9A and Figure IV-10A, agrees well with earlier data used for the structure determination which is recorded in Table IV-6. A strong band was found at 22.08 μ, in agreement with the vibrational assignment,[48] but in a region not investigated previously except by Raman technique. The spectrum of thiolane, Figure IV-10B, is completely different from that of thiophene. Although the short wavelength region is much more complex than is indicated by these spectrograms which were obtained using a rock salt prism in this region, certain generalizations may be observed. The C—H stretching vibrations about the thiophene nucleus are found near 3.25 μ, similar to their location in a terminal olefinic group and at slightly shorter wavelengths than in phenyl groups. Fox and Martin[58] have investigated this region in detail, and it appears possible to correlate strong bands near 3.38 and 3.42 μ with the C—H valency vibrations in paraffinic hydrocarbons of methyl and methylene groups, respectively. A band near 3.49 μ is apparently due to unresolved vibrations of both methyl and methylene groups. For thiolane, bands are found near 3.37 and 3.48 μ and the band near 3.25 μ is absent, thus suggesting a "paraffinic" nature for the CH_2 groups of thiolane. Of course, the alkyl groups attached in the methyl-, dimethyl-, and ethylthiophenes exhibit strong absorption in the 3.4 to 3.5 μ region. The intensity of the 3.25 μ band decreases with increasing substitution on the thiophene nucleus.

Neglecting some relatively weak bands between 3.5 and 6.0 μ, which are probably combination bands, the next prominent band occurs at 6.30 μ in thiophene. Waddington et al.[48] assign this band to ν_{15} (in the nomenclature of Lord and Miller[59] to which the reader should refer for a complete diagram of the modes of vibration), a ring frequency apparently

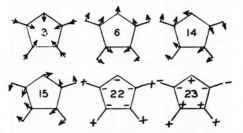

Schematic diagram of a few vibration modes of thiophene[59] (similar to those proposed by Lord and Miller for the analogous molecule, pyrrole). Arrows indicate direction of motion in plane; plus and minus, above and below plane.

[58] Fox and Martin, *Proc. Roy. Soc.* (*London*), **A175**, 208 (1940).
[59] Lord and Miller, *J. Chem. Phys.*, **10**, 328 (1942).

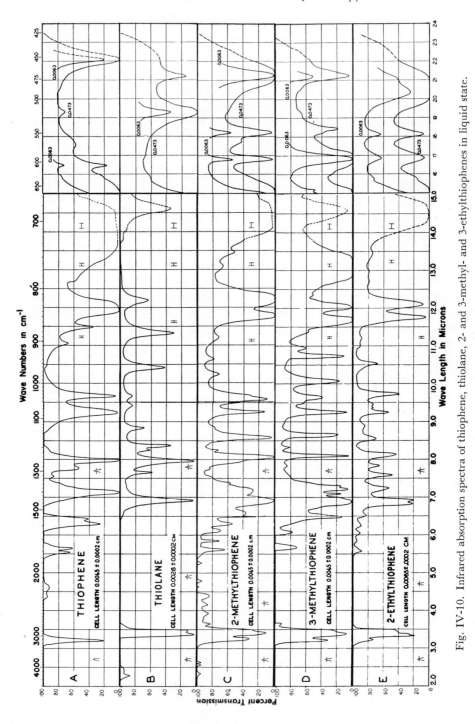

Fig. IV-10. Infrared absorption spectra of thiophene, thiolane, 2- and 3-methyl- and 3-ethylthiophenes in liquid state.

TABLE IV-9. Tabulated Data for Spectra of Figure IV-10

Thiophene		Thiolane		2-Methyl-thiophene		3-Methyl-thiophene		2-Ethyl-thiophene	
Spectrum									
A		B		C		D		E	
Cell lengths, cm.									
0.0063		0.0028		0.0063		0.0063		0.0063	
0.0065		0.0063		0.0065		0.0065		0.0065	
0.0473		0.0473		0.0473		0.0473		0.0473	
λ in μ	ν in cm.⁻¹	λ in μ	ν in cm.⁻¹	λ in μ	ν in cm.⁻¹	λ in μ	ν in cm.⁻¹	λ in μ	ν in cm.⁻¹
3.20	3125	2.28	4390	2.33	4290	3.22	3110	3.22s	3105
4.35	2300	3.37	2970	2.56	3905	3.39	2950	3.34	2995
4.62	2165	3.48	2870	2.63	3800	3.46s	2890	3.37s	2970
5.54	1805	6.92	1445	3.27	3060	3.66	2730	5.57	1795
5.65	1770	7.66	1306	3.42	2925	5.66	1768	5.84	1712
6.29	1590	7.95	1258	3.48s	2875	6.08	1645	6.04	1656
6.43	1555	8.24s*	1213	3.65	2740	6.48	1542	6.23	1605
7.15	1399	8.37	1195	3.92	2550	6.88	1454	6.52	1534
7.55	1325	8.83	1132	4.15	2410	7.08	1412	6.83	1464
7.78	1285	9.42	1061	4.41	2270	7.22	1386	6.92	1445
8.00	1250	9.67	1034	4.62	2165	7.30s	1370	7.24	1381
9.26	1080	10.42	960	4.78	2090	7.82	1280	7.59	1318
9.66	1035	11.32	883	5.26	1901	8.09	1236	7.83	1277
11.06	904	12.20	820	5.62	1779	8.33	1200	8.13	1230
11.49	871	14.62	684	5.85	1709	8.66	1154	8.55	1170
11.93 (ca.)	838	19.30	518	6.12	1633	9.25	1081	8.90	1124
14.03 (ca.)	713	21.18	472	6.29	1589	9.50s	1052	9.25	1081
16.47	607	22.0?s	455	6.50	1538	9.64	1038	9.36	1068
17.52 (ca.)	571			6.58	1519	10.08	992	9.46	1057
19.30	518			6.92	1445	10.74	932	9.72	1029
22.08	453			7.18	1392	10.95	914	10.53	950
				7.38s	1355	11.40s	878	11.75	851
				7.75s	1290	11.68	857	12.12	825
				8.06	1240	12.03	832	14.50 (ca.)	690
				8.25s	1212	12.35	810	15.75s	635
				8.59	1164	13.10 (ca.)	764	16.85	593
				8.86s	1128	14.59	687	18.12	552
				9.26	1078	15.12	661	20.35	491
				9.56	1046	16.82	595	21.0s	475
				9.65s	1036	18.42	543	22.5?s	445
				10.24	977	21.26	470		
				10.63	941				
				11.21	892				
				11.78	849				
				12.20 (ca.)	820				
				13.10	763				
				13.47	742				
				14.4 (ca.)	694				
				16.79	596				
				17.72s	564				
* s denotes band occurs as a				18.21	549				
shoulder on a strong band.				21.24	471				

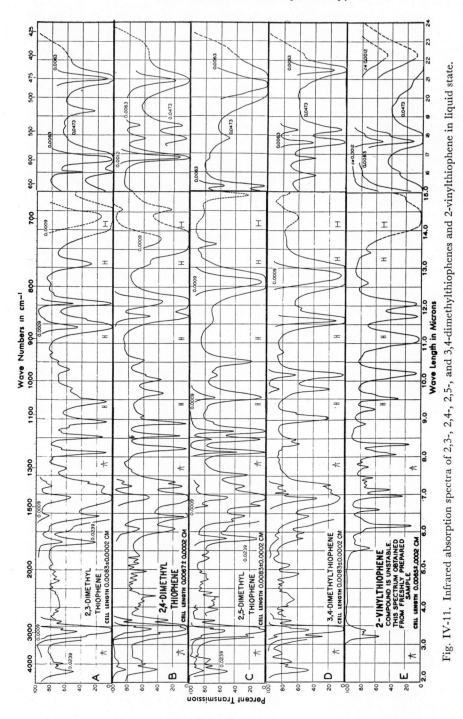

Fig. IV-11. Infrared absorption spectra of 2,3-, 2,4-, 2,5-, and 3,4-dimethylthiophenes and 2-vinylthiophene in liquid state.

TABLE IV-10. Tabulated Data for Spectra of Figure IV-11

2,3-Dimethylthiophene	2,4-Dimethylthiophene	2,5-Dimethylthiophene	3,4-Dimethylthiophene	2-Vinylthiophene
Spectrum A	B	C	D	E

Cell lengths, cm.

A	B	C	D	E
0.0009	0.0009	0.0009	0.0009	0.0012
0.0063	ca. 0.0012	0.0063	0.0063	0.0063
0.0083	0.0063	0.0083	0.0239	0.0065
0.0239	0.0067	0.0239	0.0473	0.0473
0.0473	0.0239	0.0473		
	0.0473			

λ in μ	ν in cm.$^{-1}$	λ in μ	ν in cm.$^{-1}$	λ in μ	ν in cm.$^{-1}$	λ in μ	ν in cm.$^{-1}$	λ in μ	ν in cm.$^{-1}$
2.30	4350	2.33	4290	2.30	4350	2.30	4350	3.21	3115
2.51	3985	2.48	4030	2.46	4065	2.46s	4065	3.32s	3010
3.21s*	3115	2.56s	3905	2.63	3800	2.53	3950	3.38s	2960
3.37	2970	3.29	3040	3.21s	3115	2.76	3620	5.57	1795
3.45s	2900	3.42	2925	3.38	2960	3.22s	3105	6.17	1620
3.64	2750	3.49s	2865	3.45s	2900	3.38	2960	6.59	1517
5.73	1745	3.66	2730	3.66	2730	3.45s	2900	6.95	1438
6.43	1555	3.95	2530	5.82	1718	3.64	2750	7.12	1404
6.92	1445	4.01	2495	6.28s	1592	4.89	2045	7.24	1381
7.22	1385	4.07	2455	6.43	1555	5.14	1945	7.35	1361
7.33s	1364	4.16	2405	6.69	1494	5.84	1712	7.44	1344
7.70	1298	4.30	2325	6.92	1445	5.99	1669	7.73	1293
8.11	1233	4.37s	2290	7.22	1385	6.43	1555	7.85	1273
8.52	1173	4.49	2225	7.51	1331	6.92	1445	8.06	1240
8.93	1119	4.64	2155	8.12	1231	7.02s	1424	8.32	1201
9.46	1057	4.73	2115	8.46	1182	7.09	1410	8.87	1127
9.80	1020	4.84	2065	8.67	1153	7.26	1377	9.24	1082
10.30	971	4.96	2015	9.55	1047	8.37	1194	9.53	1049
11.42	875	5.07	1972	10.16	984	8.47	1180	10.20	980
12.05	830	5.17	1934	10.51	951	9.02	1108	11.11	900
13.10	763	5.27	1898	12.62 (ca.)	792	9.77	1023	11.72	853
14.34 (ca.)	697	5.36	1866	13.63	734	10.14	986	12.05	829
16.03	624	6.08	1645	14.91	670	10.75	930	12.60	793
16.68	600	6.41	1560	15.27	655	11.59	862	13.41	745
19.30	518	6.92	1445	17.82	561	12.80 (ca.)	781	14.39 (ca.)	695
21.01	476	7.22	1385	20.66 (ca.)	484	14.34 (ca.)	697	16.03s	624
		7.34	1362			15.86	631	17.67	566
		7.66s	1305			16.79	596	18.07s	553
		8.23	1215			17.62	568	22.27	449
		8.57	1167			18.31	546		
		8.90	1124			21.49	465		
		9.10	1099						
		9.67	1034						
		10.04	996						
		10.16s	984						
		10.55	948						
		11.72	853						
		12.12	825						
		13.12s	762						

* s as in Table IV-9.

B (contd.)			
λ	ν	λ	ν
13.80	725	17.82	561
14.56	687	18.52	540
16.85	593	20.93	478

112

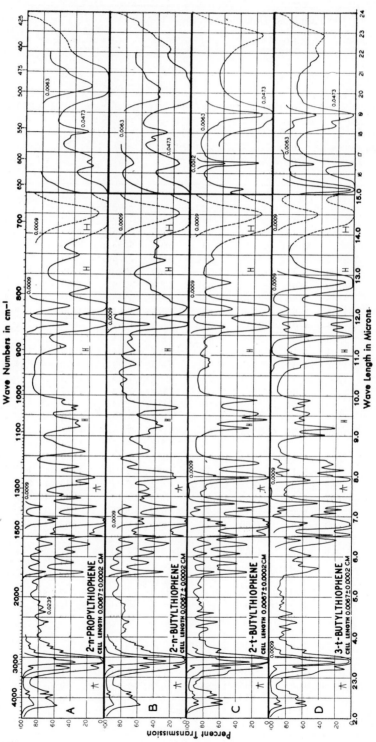

Fig. IV-12. Infrared absorption spectra of 2-*n*-propyl-, 2-*n*-butyl-, 2-*tert*-butyl-, and 3-*tert*-butylthiophenes.

TABLE IV-11. Tabulated Data for Spectra of Figure IV-12

2-*n*-Propylthiophene		2-*n*-Butylthiophene		2-*tert*-Butylthiophene		3-*tert*-Butylthiophene	

Spectrum

A		B		C		D	

Cell lengths, cm.

0.0009		0.0009		0.0009		0.0009	
0.0063		0.0063		*ca.* 0.0012		*ca.* 0.0012	
0.0067		0.0067		0.0063		0.0063	
0.0239		0.0239		0.0067		0.0067	
0.0473		0.0473		0.0239		0.0239	
				0.0473		0.0473	

λ in μ	ν in cm.$^{-1}$	λ in μ	ν in cm.$^{-1}$	λ in μ	ν in cm.$^{-1}$	λ in μ	ν in cm.$^{-1}$
2.32	4310	2.32	4310	2.33	4290	2.32	4310
2.56	3905	2.55	3920	2.43	4115	2.42	4130
2.66	3760	2.63	3800	2.56	3905	2.53s	3955
3.24	3085	3.25s	3075	2.66s	3760	2.66s	3760
3.38	2960	3.41	2935	2.87	3485	2.95s	3390
3.48s*	2875	3.48s	2875	2.99s	3345	3.22	3105
3.66	2730	3.65s	2740	3.13s	3195	3.38	2960
3.77	2655	3.75s	2665	3.24	3085	3.65s	2740
3.84	2605	3.84s	2605	3.38	2960	3.69s	2710
3.99	2505	4.15	2410	3.48s	2875	3.77	2655
4.15	2410	4.20	2380	3.66	2730	3.92	2550
4.33s	2310	4.38	2285	3.69	2710	4.07	2455
4.38	2285	4.65	2150	3.92	2550	4.20	2380
4.62	2165	4.81	2080	3.99	2505	4.37	2290
4.75	2105	4.90	2040	4.20	2380	4.60	2175
4.89	2045	5.31	1883	4.38	2285	4.77	2095
5.31	1883	5.63	1776	4.61	2170	4.87	2055
5.62	1779	5.86	1706	4.77	2095	4.96	2015
5.85	1709	6.11	1637	4.87	2055	5.02	1992
6.12	1634	6.34	1577	4.96	2015	5.14	1946
6.32	1582	6.52	1534	5.25	1905	5.71	1751
6.52	1534	6.61s	1513	5.63	1776	5.84	1712
6.61	1513	6.83	1464	5.73	1745	6.04	1656
6.87	1456	6.94	1441	5.84	1712	6.41	1560
6.95	1439	7.24	1381	6.09	1642	6.55	1527
7.24	1381	7.46	1340	6.32	1582	6.78	1475
7.46	1340	7.54	1326	6.55	1527	6.85	1460
7.55	1325	7.69	1300	6.78	1475	7.09	1410
7.82	1279	7.97	1255	6.86	1458	7.17	1395
7.97	1255	8.08	1238	6.94s	1441	7.32	1366
8.24	1214	8.30	1205	7.17	1395	7.62	1312
8.62	1160	8.62	1160	7.32	1366	7.90	1266
9.24	1082	8.75s	1143	7.70	1299	7.95	1258
9.33	1072	9.07s	1103	7.97	1255	8.03s	1245
9.64	1037	9.22	1085	8.03s	1245	8.15	1227
9.74	1027	9.33s	1072	8.33	1200	8.30	1205
9.88s	1012	9.69	1032	9.20	1087	8.39s	1192
11.21	892	10.01	999	9.40	1064	9.03	1107
11.76	850	10.13	987	9.56	1046	9.20	1087
12.21	819	10.39	962	9.89	1011	9.40	1064

Table continued

TABLE IV-11 (*continued*)

2-*n*-Propylthiophene		2-*n*-Butylthiophene		2-*tert*-Butylthiophene		3-*tert*-Butylthiophene	
λ in μ	ν in cm. $^{-1}$	λ in μ	ν in cm. $^{-1}$	λ in μ	ν in cm. $^{-1}$	λ in μ	ν in cm. $^{-1}$
12.67	789	10.75	930	10.73	932	9.56	1046
13.48	742	11.11	900	10.81	925	9.77	1024
14.52	689	11.39	878	10.91	917	9.89	1011
16.36	611	11.77	850	11.23	890	10.71s	934
16.74	597	12.17	822	11.52s	868	10.92	916
17.71 (*ca.*)	565	12.37s	808	11.71	854	11.51	869
18.02	555	12.51s	799	12.16	822	11.70	855
20.26	494	12.71s	787	12.80	781	11.89	841
21.05 (*ca.*)	475	13.36	749	13.39	747	12.15	823
		13.70	730	14.52	689	12.83	779
		14.54	688	15.24	656	14.50	690
		16.47	607	16.51	606	15.24	656
		17.67	566	18.41 *ca.*	543	16.49	606
		18.02	555	18.93	528	18.41	543
		19.83	504	22.91	436	18.93	528
		20.22	495			21.37 *ca.*	468
		21.05 *ca.*	475			21.85	458
		22.16	451			22.83	438

*s denotes band occurs as a shoulder on a stronger band.

largely controlled by the carbon-carbon double bonds.   Vibration mode ν_{15} and a few others of special interest are illustrated schematically on page 107. This band is absent in thiolane, appears weakly in 2-methylthiophene, but is so diminished in intensity as to be uninterpretable in the other alkyl derivatives.   The well-known C=C stretching fundamental which occurs in olefins near 6.10 μ (1640 cm.$^{-1}$), of course, does not appear as such in thiophene.   The strong band at 6.17 μ in 2-vinyl-thiophene, Figure IV-11E, doubtless is this C=C stretching band, but in this case is shifted to slightly longer wavelength (lower frequency) by interaction with the thiophene nucleus.   The absence of the C=C stretching fundamental does not signify a lack of "double bond character" of the thiophene nucleus.   The frequency would be expected to be altered due to the restrictions placed upon it by enclosure in the ring and also, being essentially symmetrical, would probably be inactive or weak in the infrared spectrum.

The next strong band in thiophene, 7.15 μ, again according to its schematic mode of vibration (ν_6) should be strongly influenced by the carbon double bonds.   This band is not useful for a qualitative indication of the thiophene nucleus because the region is overlapped by the strong deformation absorptions of methylene and methyl groups near 6.9 and

7.2 μ, respectively.   It should be noted, however, that a strong band does occur near 7.1 μ for all derivatives in which alkyl substitution is absent.

A band at 7.96 μ in thiophene is ascribed to ν_{14}, a schematic mode of vibration in which, briefly summarized, the S atom attempts to vibrate between adjacent C atoms.   A similar strong band is found in thiolane at 7.95 μ, in 2-methylthiophene at 8.06 μ, in 3-methyl- at 8.09 μ, in 2-ethyl- at 8.13 μ, in 2,3- and 2,5-dimethyl- at 8.11 and 8.12 μ, in 2-vinyl- at 8.06 μ, but was not found in 3,4-dimethylthiophene.   This mode of vibration appeared to be ideal for qualitative identification of S in a five-membered ring, since it should be little affected by substitution.   Indeed, a strong band near 8.1 μ is found in the thiol-, acetyl-, and many of the halogen derivatives.   Its notable absence at this location in both the 3,4-dimethyl-, and 2,3-, 2,4-, and 3,4-dichlorothiophenes suggests that the frequency is susceptible to interaction with other vibrations, thereby causing a considerable shift in frequency and/or loss of intensity.   Hence, a band from 7.95 to 8.15 μ, if present, apparently identifies S in a five-membered ring, but its absence does not exclude the possible presence of the group.   It may be of interest to comment that this spectral region is relatively transparent in hydrocarbons except for highly branched isomers (e.g., the quaternary carbon, neopentyl, group especially in terminal position).

A strong band near 8.5 μ is present in all alkyl thiophenes studied with the exception that it is only of medium intensity in 2-ethyl- and 3,4-dimethylthiophenes.   3,4-Dimethylthiophene exhibits a strong band at 9.02 μ at which place the other alkyl derivatives are reasonably transparent.

The thiophene bands at 9.26 and 9.66 μ, which are reportedly due to C—H deformation modes, carry through the mono-alkyl derivatives with little change but are considerably altered in the dimethyl derivatives and in thiolane.

3-Alkyl substitution may be indicated by a strong band at 10.0 to 10.2 μ, but only two such compounds were available for study.   Of course, this band is strongly overlapped when olefins with the C=C in terminal position are present, the latter having very strong bands at 10.0–10.1 and 10.9–11.0 μ.[60b]   In 2-vinylthiophene these bands appear at 10.20 and 11.11 μ.

The strong band of thiophene at 12.0 μ is ascribed to a "ring breathing" mode (ν_3) with some contribution from an out-of-plane hydrogen bending mode.   This band is not present in thiolane.   In all of the mono-alkyl derivatives a doublet appears centered near 11.9 μ.   This doublet is also present in 2-vinylthiophene, 2-thiophenethiol, 2-chloro-, and 2-

[60a] Thompson and Torkington, Proc. Roy. Soc. (London), A184, 3 (1945).
[60b] Rasmussen et al., J. Chem. Phys., 15, 120 (1947).

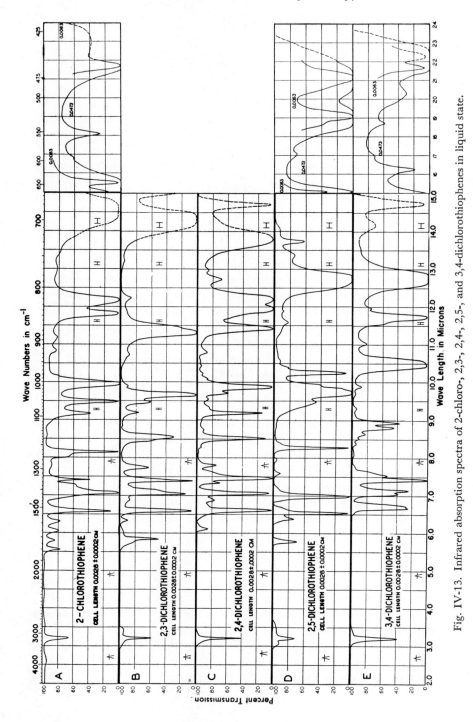

Fig. IV-13. Infrared absorption spectra of 2-chloro-, 2,3-, 2,4-, 2,5-, and 3,4-dichlorothiophenes in liquid state.

TABLE IV-12. Tabulated Data for Spectra of Figure IV-13

2-Chloro-thiophene		2,3-Dichloro-thiophene		2,4-Dichloro-thiophene		2,5-Dichloro-thiophene		3,4-Dichloro-thiophene	
Spectrum A		B		C		D		E	
Cell lengths, cm.									
0.0028		0.0028		0.0028		0.0028		0.0028	
0.0063						0.0063		0.0063	
0.0473						0.0473		0.0473	
λ in μ	ν in cm.$^{-1}$	λ in μ	ν in cm.$^{-1}$	λ in μ	ν in cm.$^{-1}$	λ in μ	ν in cm.$^{-1}$	λ in μ	ν in cm.$^{-1}$
3.21	3120	3.21	3115	3.20	3125	3.21	3120	3.20	3125
5.56	1798	5.84	1712	6.11	1636	5.78	1730	6.66	1502
5.80	1724	6.34	1577	6.60	1515	6.38	1570	6.71	1490
6.06	1650	6.59	1517	6.87	1455	6.54	1530	7.05s	1418
6.31	1585	6.87s*	1456	7.06	1416	6.99	1430	7.13	1403
6.58	1520	7.05	1418	7.34s	1362	7.59	1317	7.42	1348
7.06	1416	7.39	1353	7.46	1340	8.28	1208	7.54s	1326
7.41	1349	7.74	1292	7.81	1280	9.47s	1056	8.39	1192
8.14	1228	8.55	1170	8.52	1173	9.72	1029	8.51	1175
9.17	1091	9.18	1089	8.75	1142	10.24	976	8.63	1159
9.49	1054	9.47	1056	9.18	1089	10.39s	962	8.81	1135
9.95	1005	9.64	1037	9.54	1048	11.57	864	8.93	1120
11.83	845	9.89s	1011	9.72s	1028	12.76 (ca.)	784	9.29	1076
12.20	810	10.73	932	10.78	927	13.37	748	9.87	1013
14.00	714	11.31	884	11.41	876	13.74	728	10.45	957
14.58 (ca.)	686	12.25	816	11.95	836	15.06	664	11.03	907
15.47	646	14.34 (ca.)	697	12.20	819	17.06	586	11.72	853
18.11	552			12.74	784	19.07	524	11.96s	836
21.71	461			12.98	770	21.13 (ca.)	473	12.76 (ca.)	784
				13.78	725			14.15	707
				14.72	679			14.73	679
								16.25	615
								16.95s	590
								18.69	535
								20.30 (ca.)	493
								21.69	461
								22.27	449

* s denotes band occurs as a shoulder on a stronger band.

bromothiophene. In 2,3-dimethylthiophene the doublet is more complex, and the doublet is not apparent for 2,5- and 3,4-dimethylthiophenes. Since this "ring breathing" vibration mode is another which would be expected to be little affected by substitution on the nucleus, the doubling and disappearance of this band again (as mentioned for the 7.96 μ band) is suggestive of interaction or coupling of ν_3 with some frequency occurring upon substitution.

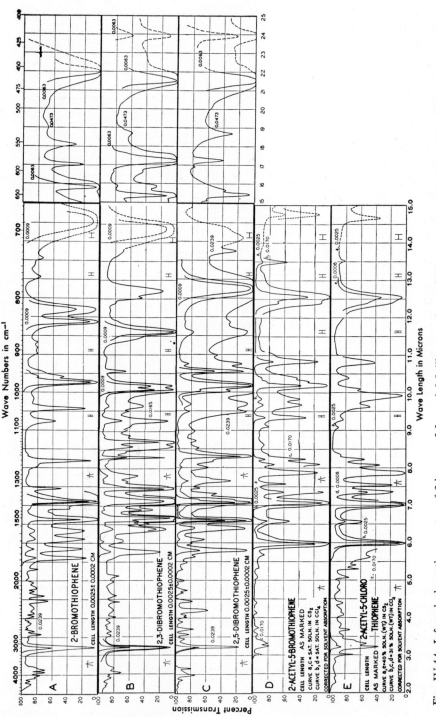
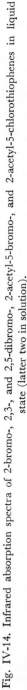

Fig. IV-14. Infrared absorption spectra of 2-bromo-, 2,3-, and 2,5-dibromo-, 2-acetyl-5-bromo-, and 2-acetyl-5-chlorothiophenes in liquid state (latter two in solution).

TABLE IV-13. Tabulated Data for Spectra of Figure IV-14

2-Bromo-thiophene		2,3-Dibromo-thiophene		2,5-Dibromo-thiophene		2-Acetyl-5-bromothiophene		2-Acetyl-5-chlorothiophene	
Spectrum									
A		B		C		D		E	
Cell lengths, cm.									
0.0009		0.0009		0.0009		0.0025		0.0008	
0.0025		0.0025		0.0025		0.0170		0.0025	
0.0063		0.0063		0.0063		Liquid solution		0.0170	
0.0239		0.0165		0.0239		corrected		Liquid solution	
0.0473		0.0239		0.0473				corrected	
		0.0473							
λ in μ	ν in cm.$^{-1}$	λ in μ	ν in cm.$^{-1}$	λ in μ	ν in cm.$^{-1}$	λ in μ	ν in cm.$^{-1}$	λ in μ	ν in cm.$^{-1}$
2.56	3905	2.54	3940	2.48	4030	3.02	3310	3.02	3310
2.63	3800	3.21	3115	2.66	3760	3.24	3085	3.23	3095
3.22	3105	5.76	1736	3.23	3095	3.32	3010	3.32s	3010
5.61	1782	6.04	1655	3.43	2915	5.68	1761	3.53s	2835
5.85	1709	6.36	1572	3.57	2800	5.98	1672	3.69	2710
6.11	1636	6.52s	1533	3.70	2700	6.58	1520	4.39	2280
6.34	1577	6.59s	1517	4.20	2380	7.07	1414	5.08	1969
6.63	1508	6.67	1499	4.45	2250	7.35	1361	5.30	1887
7.11	1406	6.89	1451	4.74	2110	7.58	1319	5.42	1845
7.45	1342	7.13	1402	4.99	2005	7.87	1271	5.63s	1776
8.19	1221	7.46	1340	5.80	1724	8.09	1236	5.99	1669
9.24	1082	7.82	1278	6.09	1643	8.24	1214	6.57	1522
9.57	1044	8.30	1204	6.38	1567	8.60	1163	7.02	1425
10.27	973	8.59	1164	6.59	1517	9.10	1099	7.35	1361
10.42s*	959	8.71	1148	7.08	1412	9.34	1071	7.55	1325
11.88	841	9.23	1083	7.15s	1398	9.68	1033	7.86	1272
12.20	819	9.49	1053	7.65	1307	9.83	1017	8.07	1239
13.07	765	9.62	1039	8.01	1248	10.19	981	8.23	1215
13.55	738	10.07	993	8.30	1205	10.30s	971	8.33s	1200
14.54 (ca.)	688	10.16	984	8.52	1173	10.40s	962	9.06	1104
15.81	633	10.56	946	8.71	1148	10.84	923	9.27	1079
17.03	587	11.62	860	8.98	1113	12.41s	806	9.61	1041
18.12	552	12.53s	798	9.49	1053	12.57	796	9.92	1008
22.02	454	12.72	786	9.67	1034	13.50	741	10.09s	991
		14.39 (ca.)	694	10.03s	997	14.77	677	10.38	963
		15.12	661	10.17	983			10.79	927
		15.35	652	10.55	948			12.54	797
		15.86	631	10.75	930			13.52	740
		16.63	601	10.98	910			14.66	682
		17.23	580	11.62 (ca.)	860				
		18.69	535	11.85	843	C (contd.)			
		21.53	464	12.76 (ca.)	783	λ	ν		
		23.90	418	13.75	727	16.90s	592		
				14.10 (ca.)	709	17.26	579		
				15.12s	661	18.69	535		
				15.43	648	21.55 (ca.)	464		
				15.64s	639	23.90	418		

* s denotes band occurs as a shoulder on a stronger band.

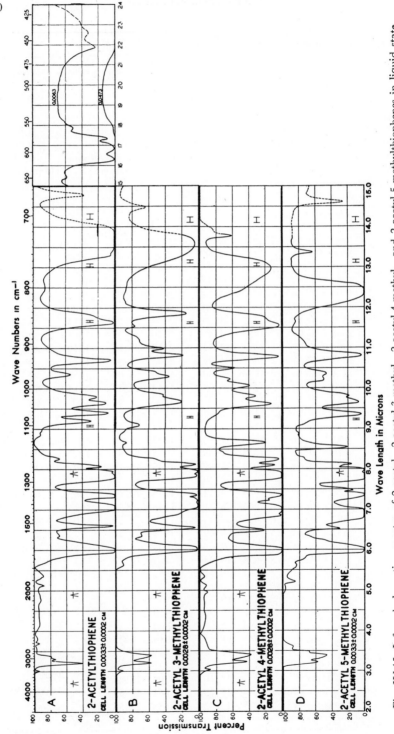

Fig. IV-15. Infrared absorption spectra of 2-acetyl-, 2-acetyl-3-methyl-, 2-acetyl-4-methyl-, and 2-acetyl-5-methylthiophenes in liquid state.

TABLE IV-14. Tabulated Data for Spectra of Figure IV-15

2-Acetyl-thiophene		2-Acetyl-3-methylthiophene		2-Acetyl-4-methylthiophene		2-Acetyl-5-methylthiophene	
Spectrum							
A		B		C		D	
Cell lengths, cm.							
0.0033		0.0028		0.0028		0.0033	
0.0063							
0.0473							
λ in μ	ν in cm.$^{-1}$	λ in μ	ν in cm.$^{-1}$	λ in μ	ν in cm.$^{-1}$	λ in μ	ν in cm.$^{-1}$
3.21	3120	3.21	3120	3.23	3095	3.23s	3095
3.30s*	3030	3.40	2940	3.40	2940	3.40	2940
6.00	1667	6.01	1664	6.01	1664	5.21	1919
6.61	1513	6.55	1527	6.48	1543	6.04	1655
7.05	1418	7.09	1410	6.87s	1456	6.52	1534
7.34	1362	7.22	1385	7.00	1428	6.90	1449
7.81	1280	7.35	1360	7.23	1383	7.36	1359
7.95s	1258	7.84	1275	7.38	1355	7.47s	1339
8.07s	1239	7.93	1261	7.85	1274	7.82	1279
8.27s	1209	8.12	1231	8.10	1234	7.97	1255
9.20	1087	8.66	1155	8.25	1212	8.12s	1231
9.40	1064	9.08	1101	8.66	1155	8.55	1169
9.64	1037	9.66	1035	9.61	1040	9.35	1069
9.80	1020	9.83s	1017	9.80	1020	9.64	1037
10.36	965	10.29	972	10.06	994	9.80s	1020
10.71	934	10.82	924	10.23s	977	10.22	978
11.64	859	10.98	911	10.50	952	10.36	965
13.70 (ca.)	730	11.54s	866	10.78	928	10.81	925
14.78	676	11.85	844	11.54	866	12.38 (ca.)	808
15.41	649	13.60 (ca.)	735	12.98 (ca.)	770	13.37	748
16.30	614	14.48	691	13.78	725	14.61	684
16.85	594						
17.33	577						
17.82	561						
21.89	457						
22.57	443						

* s denotes band occurs as a shoulder on a stronger band.

The largest difference observed between the 2-alkyl and the 3-methyl derivatives is an extremely strong band present in the latter at 13.1 μ, the difference occurring also in the 2- and 3-thiophenethiols. This band may be indicative of monosubstitution in the 3-position on the thiophene nucleus. Unfortunately, the 3-halo or 3-acetyl derivatives were not available for study, and the situation becomes complex upon polysubstitution.

The extremely intense band of thiophene centered near 14.1 μ is ascribed to a symmetrical hydrogen bending mode (ν_{22}), wherein the

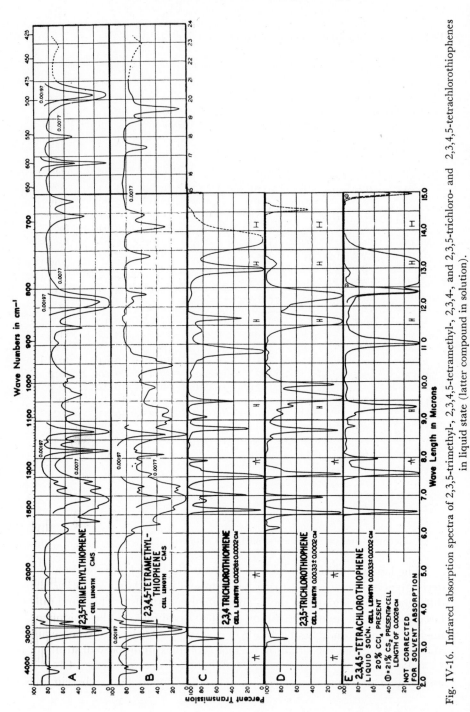

Fig. IV-16. Infrared absorption spectra of 2,3,5-trimethyl-, 2,3,4-, and 2,3,5-trichloro- and   2,3,4,5-tetrachlorothiophenes in liquid state (latter compound in solution).

TABLE IV-15. Tabulated Data for Spectra of Figure IV-16

2,3,5-Trimethyl-thiophene		2,3,4,5-Tetramethyl-thiophene		2,3,4-Trichloro-thiophene		2,3,5-Trichloro-thiophene		2,3,4,5-Tetrachloro-thiophene	
Spectrum									
A		B		C		D		E	
Cell lengths, cm.									
0.00197		0.00197		0.0028		0.0033		0.0028	
0.0077		0.0077						0.0033	
								Liquid solution not corrected	
λ in μ	ν in cm.⁻¹	λ in μ	ν in cm.⁻¹	λ in μ	ν in cm.⁻¹	λ in μ	ν in cm.⁻¹	λ in μ	ν in cm.⁻¹
2.34	4275	2.34	4275	3.21	3120	3.20	3130	6.58	1520
2.44s*	4100	2.45s	4080	6.62	1510	6.15	1630	7.58	1320
3.43	2915	2.94	3400	6.87s*	1456	6.55	1530	7.97	1250
3.52	2840	3.45	2900	7.01	1426	6.96	1437	8.83	1132
3.67	2725	3.50s	2855	7.49	1335	7.58	1319	9.13s	1095
4.04 (ca.)	2475	3.67	2725	7.93	1261	8.52s	1167	9.33	1072
4.44	2250	3.84	2605	8.78	1139	8.73	1145	11.00	909
4.85	2060	3.96	2525	9.08	1101	9.16	1091	12.37	808
6.10 (ca.)	1639	4.05	2470	9.49	1054	9.36s	1068	14.96	668
6.34	1577	4.88 (ca.)	2050	10.81	925	9.58	1044		
6.69s	1495	6.03	1658	11.33	883	9.92	1008		
6.91	1447	6.24	1603	11.69	855	11.59	863		
7.22	1385	6.64	1506	12.98	770	12.29	814		
7.39	1353	6.93	1443	13.78 (ca.)	726	13.14	762		
8.22	1217	7.16	1397			14.56	687		
8.45	1183	7.25	1379						
8.71	1148	7.58	1319						
9.19	1088	7.91	1264						
9.68	1033	8.10	1235						
9.81s (ca.)	1019	8.22	1217						
10.04s (ca.)	996	8.64	1157						
10.17	983	8.92	1121						
11.06	904	9.04	1106						
11.46	873	9.25 (ca.)	1081						
12.15	823	9.86	1014						
14.44	693	10.07	993						
14.82	675	10.45	957						
16.63	601	10.61s (ca.)	943						
18.07	553	11.53	867						
20.26	494	11.83 (ca.)	845						
22.83 (ca.)	438	12.15	823						
		12.34	810						
		13.35	749						
		14.14	707						
		14.46	692						
		17.42	574						
		18.88	530						
		19.47	514						
		22.98 (ca.)	435						

* s denotes band occurs as a shoulder on a stronger band.

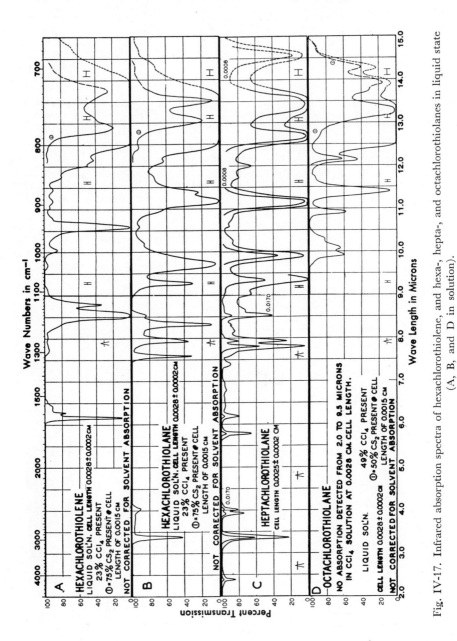

Fig. IV-17. Infrared absorption spectra of hexachlorothiolene, and hexa-, hepta-, and octachlorothiolanes in liquid state (A, B, and D in solution).

TABLE IV-16. Tabulated Data for Spectra of Figure IV-17

Hexachlorothiolene		Hexachlorothiolane		Heptachlorothiolane		Octachlorothiolane	
Spectrum							
A		B		C		D	
Cell lengths, cm.							
0.0015		0.0015		0.0008		0.0015	
0.0028		0.0028		0.0025		0.0028	
Liquid solution		Liquid solution		0.0170		Liquid solution	
not corrected		not corrected				not corrected	
λ in μ	ν in cm.$^{-1}$	λ in μ	ν in cm.$^{-1}$	λ in μ	ν in cm.$^{-1}$	λ in μ	ν in cm.$^{-1}$
6.16	1620	3.37	2970	2.38	4200	9.92	1008
6.28s*	1590	4.04	2480	3.37	2970	10.07	993
8.55	1169	7.59	1320	3.93	2545	10.92	916
8.80	1136	7.93	1261	4.02	2490	11.41	876
10.04	996	8.32	1202	5.78	1730	12.14	824
10.58	945	8.55s	1169	6.18	1618	13.28	754
11.18	894	9.27	1079	7.38	1355	13.90	719
11.44	874	9.73	1028	7.81	1280	14.27	700
12.15	823	10.19s	981	7.93	1261		
12.90	776	10.59	944	8.53	1172		
13.76	737	11.18	894	9.03s	1107		
		11.39s	878	9.34	1071		
		12.12	826	9.90	1010		
		12.44	815	11.15	897		
		13.06	766	11.72	853		
		13.52	740	12.00	833		
				12.68	789		
				13.43	745		
				14.58	686		

* s denotes band occurs as a shoulder on a stronger band.

hydrogen atoms vibrate in unison out of the plane of the nucleus. A band of moderate intensity in thiolane at 14.6 μ may be of similar origin. A very strong band, probably due to this mode, is found near 14.5 μ in all monoalkylthiophenes, 2,3-dimethyl-, 2-vinyl-, both thiols, and many of the halogen derivatives. This band is weak or absent in the 2,5- and 3,4-dimethylthiophenes, these compounds again being the exceptions.

In the spectral region from 15 to 25 μ available to a KBr prism spectrometer, previous workers report a Raman line at 453 cm.$^{-1}$ ($=22.1$ μ) ascribed to an out-of-plane ring bending mode (ν_{23}) which should be present in the infrared but which had not been reported apparently only because this spectral region had not been searched. A strong band is found

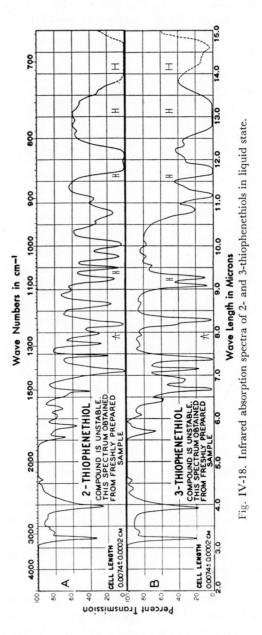

Fig. IV-18. Infrared absorption spectra of 2- and 3-thiophenethiols in liquid state.

TABLE IV-17. Tabulated Data for Spectra of Figure IV-18

	2-Thiophenethiol		3-Thiophenethiol	
Spectrum	A		B	
Cell lengths, cm.				
	0.0074		0.0074	
λ in μ	ν in cm.$^{-1}$	λ in μ	ν in cm.$^{-1}$	
3.22	3110	3.21	3120	
3.96	2525	3.92	2550	
5.57	1795	5.71	1750	
5.84	1712	6.08s	1645	
6.23	1605	6.46s	1548	
6.64	1506	6.68	1497	
7.09	1410	6.91	1447	
7.46	1340	7.15	1399	
7.74	1291	7.36	1359	
7.97	1255	8.28	1208	
8.19	1221	9.07	1102	
8.66	1155	9.26	1080	
9.23	1083	10.84	922	
9.49	1054	11.16	896	
9.75	1026	11.76	850	
10.03	997	12.34s	810	
10.54s*	949	13.27 (ca.)	753	
10.78	928	14.61	684	
11.11s	900			
11.85 (ca.)	844			
12.12 (ca.)	825			
14.35 (ca.)	695			

*s denotes band occurs as a shoulder on a stronger band.

in the spectrum reported herein at 22.08 μ in thiophene. Also, in all thiophene derivatives studied in this region a strong band is found between 20.7 and 22.2 μ, a frequency difference of only about 35 cm.$^{-1}$. This band, then, appears to be one which always occurs strongly when the thiophene nucleus is present. However, the band must be used with caution for qualitative identification because a few other compounds are known to absorb in this region. Some of the outstanding conflicts may include (1) the weak absorption of thiolane which peaks at 21.18 μ; (2) a few aromatic compounds, e.g., 1-methyl-4-ethylbenzene at 21.6 μ, p-xylene at 20.6 μ, and toluene at 21.5 μ. Most paraffins and olefins are reasonably transparent in this region, although an occasional (usually highly branched) isomer of either class is known to absorb somewhat near this region.

Thiolane has a fairly strong band at 19.30 μ, a region transparent for all other compounds studied except 2,3-dimethylthiophene. Monoalkyl substitution on the thiophene nucleus always (again within the compounds studied) is associated with a pair of bands near 16.9 and 18.2 μ. Monoalkyl substitution in the 3-position may cause an increase in the intensity of the 16.9 μ band and an intensity decrease of the band near 18.2 μ. Monoalkyl substitution in the 2-position apparently yields these bands with quite similar intensities. A search of the spectra of the dimethylthiophenes reveals that the 16.9 μ band probably is indicative of alkyl substitution in the 3-position regardless of substitution in other positions. The 18.2 μ band, on the other hand, apparently is sensitive to other substituent groups and cannot be relied upon except for monoalkyl substitution in the 2-position.

The above comments concerning alkyl substitution on the thiophene nucleus are summarized in Table IV-18 (page 130). Again, note that these conclusions are based upon the spectra of the relatively few compounds available, as yet, for study. Doubtless the conclusions will have to be altered somewhat and extended as other compounds are studied. Within the limitations of the available spectra, the thiophene nucleus can be identified in the presence of alkyl substitution principally by the presence of strong bands at (a) 3.25 μ (absent in thiolane), (b) 7.95 to 8.15 μ (missing in 3,4-dimethylthiophene and present in thiolane), (c) 14.0 to 14.5 μ (weak in 2,5- and 3,4-dimethylthiophenes and present at medium intensity in thiolane), and (d) 20.7 to 22.2 μ (weak absorption by thiolane at 21.1 μ) combined with the absence of the strong band of thiolane at 19.3 μ.

Alkyl substitution on the thiophene nucleus is indicated by the presence of the above plus bands at (a) 3.4 to 3.5 μ (present in thiolane, paraffins, etc.), (b) 6.9 μ (present in thiolane, paraffins, etc.), (c) 7.2 μ (absent in thiolane but present in paraffins), (d) 8.5 μ (medium intensity).

Monoalkyl substitution on the thiophene nucleus is indicated by the presence of both groups above plus bands at (a) doublet near 9.25 and 9.65 μ (9.65 μ strong for 2-alkyls- and weak for 3-alkyls-), (b) doublet near 11.8 and 12.2 μ, (c) doublet near 16.9 and 18.2 μ (of similar intensity for 2-alkyl- but 18.2 μ weak for 3-alkyl-), (d) 10.1 μ strong for 3-alkyl- but absent for 2-alkyl- (present in 3,4-dimethylthiophene but not in 2,3-), and (e) 13.1 μ strong for 3-alkyl- but absent for 2-alkyl- (present in 2,3-dimethylthiophene but not in 3,4-).

Thus monoalkyl substitution in the 3-position appears to have definite spectral characteristics. Monoalkyl substitution in the 2-position also should be identified with fair certainty in the absence of 3-substitution, but would be difficult to specify uniquely in a mixture of 2- and 3-monoalkyls. Polyalkyl substitution is indicated by intensification of the alkyl C—H stretching bands near 3.45 μ, but use of this band would depend upon establishing the absence of paraffins, monoolefins, etc.

Concerning thiophene derivatives other than the alkyls, the derivatives of any given type are too few to even attempt a detailed correlation of structure and spectra. Gross qualitative details are summarized in Table IV-19 on page 131 and include the following:

The S—H stretching mode doubtless corresponds to the strong bands in the thiophenethiols (Fig. IV-18) near 3.95 μ. Sheppard[61] has found the S—H deformation frequency to occur at 11.9 μ in the Raman spectrum of ethyl mercaptan, but that the band was absent in the infrared spectrum. Thus the fact that a strong band appears at 11.8 μ in both thiophenethiols appears to be merely a coincidence. The C—S stretching mode is well known[61] to occur in the region of 700 to 600 cm.$^{-1}$ (14.3 to 16.7 μ), the lower frequencies being observed for compounds of molecular weight similar to thiophene. Unfortunately, the KBr prism was not in operation at the time the thiophenethiols were available so this region was not investigated. A strong infrared band of this origin would be expected in the spectrum. As noted above, the thiophenethiols apparently follow the general correlations proposed for the monoalkylthiophenes.

In the acetyl derivatives, Figure IV-15, the C=O stretching mode doubtless corresponds to the very intense band at 6.0 μ as has been reported for many compounds which contain carbonyl groups of ketone type.[62] Thompson[62] reports acetyl groups to exhibit characteristic absorption in the region 16.2 to 17.1 μ and strong bands at 16.30 and 16.85 μ are found in 2-acetylthiophene, one or both of which may be of this nature. Isomeric acetylmethylthiophenes exhibit sufficient spectral difference in the 2–15 μ region so that quantitative analyses may be performed readily.

Infrared spectra for various halogen substituted thiophenes, thiolene, and thiolanes are presented in Figures IV-13, IV-14, IV-16, and IV-17. Halothiophenes do not conform to all the correlations observed for the alkylthiophenes, although certain coincidences may be observed as was noted previously. The C—Cl stretching mode is reported[62] to exhibit infrared absorption in the region 12.6 to 14.0 μ. In the chlorothiophenes a strong band is observed which decreases in wavelength from 14.5 to 12.8 μ in the series 2-chloro, 2,3-, 2,4-, 2,5-, and 3,4-dichloro. A strong band is observed near 13.5 μ for hexachlorothiolene; hexa-, hepta-, and octachlorothiolanes; and 2,3,4-trichlorothiophene (Figures IV-16 and IV-17),

[61] Sheppard, *J. Chem. Phys.*, **17**, 79 (1949).
[62] Thompson, *J. Chem. Soc.*, **1948**, 328.

TABLE IV-18. Characteristic* Infrared Absorption Bands of Alkylthiophenes and Thiolane

λ in μ	ν in cm.$^{-1}$	Possible assignment and remarks
3.25	3075	C—H stretching fundamental about thiophene nucleus and in olefins. Decreasing intensity with increasing substitution.
3.38 3.42 3.49	2960 2925 2865	Related to CH_3 and CH_2 fundamentals in paraffins. This 3 μ region for alkylthiophenes must be investigated with higher resolution before extended use can be made thereof. Intensification of these bands upon dimethyl substitution on the thiophene nucleus is the best present indication of "polyalkylthiophenes."
6.30	1585	Ring frequency "controlled" by C=C, prominent in thiophene but very weak or absent in most all derivatives.
6.9	1450	Deformation frequency of methylene groups.
7.2	1390	Deformation frequency of methyl groups.
7.95 to 8.15	1260 to 1225	Present in all alkylthiophenes except 3,4-dimethylthiophene. Present in thiolane. A band between 7.95 and 8.15 μ apparently identifies S in a five-membered ring, but its absence does not exclude the possible presence of the group.
9.02	1110	3,4-Dimethylthiophene absorbs here and all other alkyl derivatives are reasonably transparent.
9.25	1080	Present in thiophene and monoalkyl derivatives. Considerably altered in thiolane and dimethylthiophenes.
10.1	990	Best indication found for presence of 3-alkyl substituion. Badly overlapped in presence of olefins with C=C in terminal position.
11.8 12.2	847 820	Singlet in thiophene, absent in thiolane, doublet in all monoalkylthiophenes, "confused" in dimethyl derivatives.
13.1	763	Strong in the 3-methyl and 3-thiol derivatives. Absent in 2-alkyl and 2-thio derivatives. Apparently indicative of 3-thiol- or monoalkyl substitution on thiophene nucleus.
14.0 to 14.5	714 to 690	Strongest band of thiophene, strong in most all alkyls both thiols, and many halothiophenes. Weak in 2,5- and 3,4-dimethylthiophenes.
16.9	592	Indicative of alkyl substitution on thiophene nucleus. Strong when substituent is in 3-position regardless of adjacent alkyl substituents.
18.2	549	Of similar intensity to 16.9 μ band for 2-monoalkyl substitution, of lesser intensity for 3-monoalkyl substitution, and "confused" for polyalkyl substitution.
19.30	518	Strong band for thiolane, transparent for all other compounds studied herein except 2,3-dimethylthiophene.
20.7 to 22.2	483 to 450	Out-of-plane ring bending mode in thiophene. Strong band *always* found when thiophene ring was present, slight absorption by thiolane and occasional strong absorption by a few aromatics, paraffins, and olefins.

* These conclusions are based upon the relatively few compounds studied to date and doubtless will be altered somewhat and extended as other compounds are studied.

TABLE IV-19. Characteristic* Infrared Absorption Bands of Derivatives (Other Than Alkyl) of Thiophene, Thiolene, and Thiolane

λ in μ	ν in cm.⁻¹	Possible assignment and remarks
3.95	2530	S—H stretching fundamental. Strong in mercaptans.
6.0	1670	Ketonic C=O.
6.10	1640	C=C stretching fundamental of olefins. Strong when C=C is a terminal group but weak or absent when group is nonterminal or at a center of symmetry of molecule. Found at 6.17 μ in 2-vinylthiophene.
7.1	1410	Overlapped by alkyl C—H but useful as qualitative indication of presence of thiophene nucleus in absence of alkyl substitution.
10.1	990	Indicative of olefins with C=C in terminal position.
10.9	915	
11.9	840	A doublet centered (see spectra) about this position was found for the following substituents in the 2-position on thiophene, vinyl, thiol, chloro, and bromo. Also see Table IV-18.
12.8 to 14.5	780 to 690	Strong band in chlorothiophenes which decreases in wavelength with increasing substitution. May be C—Cl fundamental but similar band is also present in bromothiophenes.
14.3 to 16.7	700 to 600	C—S stretching fundamental not investigated in thiophenethiols but expected to occur near the longer wavelength specified
16.30 16.85	613 593	One, or both, may be qualitative evidence for presence of acetyl group.
17.0	588	May be C—Br fundamental. Absent in 2-chlorothiophene, present in 2-bromo- and dibromothiophenes.
23.9	418	Present in dibromothiophenes, absent in 2-bromo and all other derivatives.

* See footnote to Table IV-18 on facing page.

but is not found in 2,3,5-trichloro- or 2,3,4,5-tetrachlorothiophenes. But similar bands are observed for the bromothiophenes wherein the C—Br mode would be expected to occur at longer wavelength. Thus the origin of these bands is uncertain. The 2-chloro- and 2-bromothiophenes yield similar spectra which, with one exception, vary only slightly in band location. The single exception is a band at 17.03 μ, present in 2-bromo- but absent in 2-chloro-, which thus may be the C—Br stretching mode. This band does not, however, make an obvious, orderly wavelength shift in going to the dibromo derivatives as was the case with the band suspected to be due to the C—Cl mode. Dibromothiophenes yielded the longest wavelength band observed for the thiophene derivatives studied in the KBr region. Both 2,3- and 2,5-dibromothiophenes have a fairly strong and sharp band at 23.9 μ. This band is absent in 2-bromothiophene.

The possible use of infrared and mass spectra for the detection of thiophene and its homologs among the sulfur compounds in petroleum has been mentioned.[63] It is estimated that for qualitative distinction the minimum concentration of thiophene in admixture with hydrocarbons required is 1% by infrared spectroscopy and 5% by mass spectroscopy.[63]

C. Mass Spectral Data

Thiophene, when bombarded with electrons of 50 volts acceleration, readily loses an electron to form the parent ion $C_4H_4S^+$, $m/e = 84$ ($m/e =$ mass to charge ratio).   Dissociation also occurs; the major fragments are:

Fragment	m/e	Intensity
$C_2H_2S^+$	58	63% as abundant as parent ion
C_2HS^+	57	14
CHS^+	45	54
$C_3H_3^+$	39	28

Thiolane, on the other hand, dissociates more readily than it forms a parent ion and yields fragments as follows:

Parent ion	m/e	Intensity
$C_4H_8S^+$	88	54% compared to m/e 60
$C_4H_7S^+$	87	16
$C_2H_4S^+$	60	100 (*i.e.*, most prominent ion)
$C_2H_3S^+$	59	17
$C_4H_7^+$	55	12
$C_4H_6^+$	54	13
CH_2S^+	46	32
CHS^+	45	37
$C_3H_5^+$	41	10
$C_3H_3^+$	39	14
$C_3H_3^+$	27	24

A strong fragment with $m/e = 47$ (26% as abundant as $m/e = 60$) appears. This would correspond to CH_3S^+. However, this ion could be formed only by a rearrangement of fragments, not by direct fragmentation, from thiolane.   It could not be due to a doubly charged ion, since such an ion would require a weight greater than the parent molecule.

2- and 3-Methylthiophenes lose one hydrogen and an electron to form the most intense ion fragment in their mass spectra.   The dissociation patterns are quite similar.   Only slight differences occur in relative ion abundance as follows:

Parent ion	m/e	Intensity	
		2-Methyl-	3-Methyl-
$C_5H_6S^+$	98	57%	55%
$C_5H_5S^+$	97	100	100
CHS^+	45	22	26
$C_3H_3^+$	39	14	11

[63] Seyfried, *Chem. Eng. News*, **27**, 2482–6, and 2516 (1949).

2,3-Dimethylthiophene loses a methyl group plus an electron to yield $m/e = 97$ as the most prominent ion, the same major ion as was the case with the monomethylthiophenes.   2,4-Dimethylthiophene was not available for mass spectrometry study.   2,5- and 3,4-Dimethylthiophenes have major ions at $m/e = 111$ at the loss of one hydrogen atom plus one electron.   Major ions in the dissociation patterns are as follows:

| Parent ion | m/e | Intensity | | |
| | | Dimethylthiophenes | | |
		2,3-	3,4-	2,5-
C_6H_8S	112	88%	72%	82%
C_6H_7S	111	84	100	100
C_5H_6S	98	11	3	4
C_5H_5S	97	100	45	58
C_6H_5	77	12	9	12
C_2H_3S	59	15	r(3)	24
C_2H_2S	58	11	3	8
C_4H_5	53	11	5	9
C_4H_3	51	13	6	12
CHS	45	32	33	20
C_3H_3	39	19	20	15
C_2H_3	27	19	9	14

All three dimethylthiophenes exhibit considerable ion abundance at $m/e = 28$ (29, 18, and 25% for 2,3-, 3,4-, and 2,5-, respectively) which would correspond to $C_2H_4^+$ as one possibility, but this ion cannot be formed by simple fragmentation, only by rearrangement.   These large peaks could be due to the doubly charged ion, $C—S—C^{++}$, mass 56.

2-Thiophenethiol most readily forms the parent ion $C_4H_3S—SH^+$, $m/e = 116$.   The most abundant fragments are:

Parent ion	m/e	Intensity
C_3H_3S	71	90%
C_3HS	69	16
C_2H_2S	58	14
CHS	45	48
C_3H_3	39	16

These mass spectrometric data[64] are summarized in Table IV-20 and are recorded in detail in Table IV-21.   The most important conditions of operation are recorded in Table IV-21 so that operating variables may be duplicated, thereby allowing these data to be used for semiquantitative

[64] Mass spectrograms similar to those recorded in Table IV-21 have been published in a Catalog of Mass Spectral Data by American Petroleum Institute Research Project 44 at the National Bureau of Standards, Washington, D. C., under serial nos. 158 through 162 for thiophene, 2- and 3-methylthiophenes, thiolane, and 2-thiophenethiol, all contributed by Socony-Vacuum Laboratories, Paulsboro, N. J.   The dimethylthiophenes are in the process of publication.

TABLE IV-20. Summary of Dissociation Patterns

Mass-to-charge ratio	Atoms in ion CHS	Thiophene $\begin{smallmatrix}S\\C=C\\C=C\end{smallmatrix}$ (84)	Thiolane (88)	2-Methyl-thiophene (98)	3-Methyl-thiophene (98)	2,3-Dimethyl-thiophene (112)	3,4-Dimethyl-thiophene (112)	2,5-Dimethyl-thiophene (112)	2-Thiophene thiol C—SH (116)	Remarks
12	100	—	o	o	o	o	o	o	0	
14	120	+	o	o	o	—	—	—	—	
15	130	i,r	r	o	o	—	—	—	i,r	
26	220	—	+	—	—	+	+	+	—	
27	230	+	+	+	+	+	+	+	+	
32	001	+	o	o	o	—	—	—	+	
37	310	++	—	—	—	—	—	—	+	
38	320	+	+	+	+	+	+	+	i,r	
39	330	+/i,r	+	+	+	+	+	+	+	
40	340	i,r	—	—	—	—	—	—	—	
44	101	—	o	o	o	o	o	o	—	
45	111	+	++/++	+	+	+/+	+/+	+/+	+/+	
46	121	+/i,r	i	i,r	i,r	i,r	i,r	i,r	i,r	
49	410	—	—	—	—	+	—	+	—	
50	420	+	—	—	—	+	o	o	—	
51	430	—	o	—	—	+	+	+	—	
52	440	o	—	+	+	+	+	+	+	
53	450		+	—	—	+	o	o	+	
54	460		+	—	—				—	
55	470		o	+	+	r	r	+	r	
56	201	—	+	o	o	r	r	r	—	
57	211	+	+	—	—	o	o	o	o	
58	221	++	+	+	+				+	
59	231	r	+/+	+	—	+	+	++	+	
60	241	r	+/+	i,r	—	i,r	r	i,r	r	
63	530		++	—	—	—	—	—	—	
64	002		++	o	o					
65	550		++	—	—	—	—	—	—	
66	560		++					r		
67	570		++	o	o	+	+	r*	—	

*r > 5%

Mass-to-charge ratio	Atoms in ion CHS	Thiophene (84)	Thiolane (88)	2-Methyl-thiophene (98)	3-Methyl-thiophene (98)	2,3-Dimethyl-thiophene (112)	3,4-Dimethyl-thiophene (112)	2,5-Dimethyl-thiophene (112)	2-Thiophene thiol (116)	Remarks
68	301	+	o	+	+	+	+	+	−	
69	311	o	o	−	−	−	−	−	+	
70	321	o	o	−	−	+	+	+	++	
71	331		o	o	o	o	o	−	+++	
72	341		−						i,r	
73	351								i	
76	102	−							0*	
77	650	−				o	o	o		*CHS₂
78	660	+				o	o	o		
79	670	++				o	o	o		
81	411	−	o			+	+	++	−	
82	421	−	o			−	−	+	−	
83	431	+	o			o	o	−	−	
84	441	+++++	o			−	o	o		
85	451	i	−			−	−	−		
87	471		++						−*	*C₂S₂
88	481		+++			+	+	++	−	
89	212		i			−	−	−	−	
90	222		i			−	−	−		
95	531		+	0	0	−	0	−		
97	551			+++	+++	++	++	++		
98	561			+++	+++	++	++	+++		
99	571			i	i	−	−	−		
109	651					+	+	−		
110	661					+	+	++		
111	671					++	++++	+++		
112	681					+++++	+++++	+++++		
116	442								+++++	

Blank: No peak found or peak not possible and isotopic and/or rearranged ions less than 1% of major ion.

i: Isotopic ion greater than 1% of major ion.

r: Rearranged ion greater than 1% of major ion.

0: Ion possible but less than 1% of major ion.

−: Ion present at 1 to 5% of intensity of major ion.

+: Ion present at 5 to 25% of intensity of major ion.

++: Ion present at 25 to 50% of intensity of major ion.

+++: Ion present at 50 to 75% of intensity of major ion.

++++: Ion present at 75 to 100% of intensity of major ion.

+++++: Ion present at 100%, i.e., most intense ion.

TABLE IV-21. Mass Spectra of Thiophene and Some Derivatives.   Consolidated Engineering Corp. Mass Spectrometer Model 21-102

50-Volt Electron Bombardment.

(See notes at end of table for explanation of symbols and abbreviations)

Mass charge ratio	Thiophene		Thiolane		2-Methyl-thiophene		3-Methyl-thiophene		2,3-Dimethyl-thiophene		3,4-Dimethyl-thiophene		2,5-Dimethyl-thiophene		2-Thiophene-thiol	
	P.O.	R.I.	P.O.	R.I.	P.O.	R.I.	P.O.	R.I.	P.O.	R.I.	P.O.	R.I.	P.O.	R.I.	P.O.	R.I.
12	C	1.15	C	0.18	C	0.17	C	0.21	C	0.16	C	0.10	C	0.10	C	0.79
13	i,r	0.94		0.20	i,r	0.19	i,r	0.23		0.16		0.12		0.09		0.46
14		0.41	CH_2	0.84		0.32		0.35	CH_2	2.42	CH_2	1.51	CH_2	2.00	i,r	0.17
14.1															m	0.04
15	r	0.20	r	3.00	CH_3	0.92	CH_3	0.92	CH_3	3.59	CH_3	2.84	CH_3	3.29	r	0.17
16				0.02					i	0.68	i	0.39	i	0.57		
19.5							d	0.04								
24	C_2H	0.33	C_2H	0.30	C_2H	0.04	C_2H	0.03		0.02		0.08				0.19
25	d	1.67	d	0.04		0.33	d	0.33	C_2H	0.21	C_2H		C_2H	0.14	C_2H	0.79
25.5		0.03														
26	C_2H_2	5.50	C_2H_2	6.14	C_2H_2	2.38	C_2H_2	2.55	C_2H_2	3.53	C_2H_2	1.29	C_2H_2	2.47	C_2H_2	2.42
27	i,r	1.70	C_2H_3	24.0	C_2H_3	7.84	C_2H_3	8.83	C_2H_3	19.4	C_2H_3	9.10	C_2H_3	14.4	i,r	1.81
27.2					i,r	0.52	m	0.06								
28	r	0.41	C_2H_4	4.54	d	0.08	i,r	0.55	r	28.9	r	18.0	r	24.8		0.18
29	d	0.09	r	3.16			d	0.03	r	0.85	r	0.50	r	0.52	d	0.19
30			i	0.02	d	0.18	d	0.07				0.01				
31					d	0.03	d	0.02	d	0.05	d	0.02	d	0.02		
31.5							m	0.04								0.02
32	S	2.99	S	0.98	S	0.83	S	0.64	S	7.51	S	3.96	S	6.37	S	4.22
33	i,r	0.78	i,r	1.04	i,r	0.35	i,r	0.27	i,r	0.39	i,r	0.15	i,r	0.44	SH	3.09
34	i,r	0.32	i,r	1.46	i,r	0.13	i,r	0.11	i,r	0.24	i,r	0.12	i,r	0.31	i,r	2.81
34.9	m	0.06			m	0.05	m	0.04	d	0.12	d	0.06	d	0.14		
35				0.94												
36		1.03	r	0.10		0.25		0.21		0.12		0.12		0.08		0.21
37	C_3H	6.53	C_3H	1.00	C_3H	2.84	C_3H	2.33	C_3H	1.79	C_3H	1.86	C_3H	1.60	C_3H	0.86
37.0	m	0.08	m	0.04												4.84
38	C_3H_2	8.17	C_3H_2	2.22	C_3H_2	4.96	C_3H_2	3.83	C_3H_2	3.80	C_3H_2	4.46	C_3H_2	3.67	C_2H_2	6.33
39	C_3H_3	28.1	C_3H_3	14.0	C_3H_3	13.5	C_3H_3	10.9	C_3H_3	19.0	C_3H_3	20.1	C_3H_3	14.6	C_3H_3	16.4

Mass charge ratio	Thiophene		Thiolane		2-Methyl-thiophene		3-Metoyl-thiophene		2,3-Dimethyl-thiophene		3,4-Dimethyl-thiophene		2,5-Dimethyl-thiophene		2-Thiophene-thiol	
	P.O.	R.I.	P.O.	R.I.	P.O.	R.I.	P.O.	R.I.	P.O.	R.I.	P.O.	R.I.	P.O.	R.I.	P.O.	R.I.
39.0			m	0.12												
39.2	i,r	1.79			i,r	0.69									m	0.22
40.0	m	0.87	C_3H_4	2.00			C_3H_4	0.52	C_3H_4	2.27	C_3H_4	2.40	C_3H_4	1.55	i,r	3.35
40.5	d	0.65	C_3H_5	10.1	d	0.02									d	0.12
41	d	1.68	d	0.08	i,r	0.48	i,r	0.30	i,r	6.97	i,r	6.82	i,r	3.21	d	0.60
41.5	d	0.16	C_3H_6	3.82											d	0.04
42	d	3.95	d	0.14	r	0.07			r	0.43	r	0.36	r	0.24	d	0.09
42.5	d	0.20	d,r	1.90											d	0.01
43	d	0.22	d	0.14					r	0.21	r	0.09	r	0.08		
43.5																
44	CS	1.73	CS	0.34	CS	0.43	CS	0.49	CS	0.45	CS	0.33	CS	0.32	CS	3.42
44.2															m	0.31
44.5			d	0.02												
45.0	CHS	54.2	CHS	36.8	CHS	21.7	CHS	26.2	CHS	31.6	CHS	33.0	CHS	20.0	CHS	47.5
45.5			m	0.18	m	0.18										
46.0	i,r	1.32	CH_2S	31.9	i,r	1.45	i,r	1.73	i,r	1.43	i,r	1.71	i,r	1.12	r	2.91
46.1																
46.5			m	0.48	d	0.27	d	0.15	d	0.09	d	0.02	d	0.08		
47.0	i	2.38	i,r	26.0	i,r	2.31	i,r	2.18	i,r	2.49	i,r	2.27	i,r	1.90	i,r	2.41
47.1																
47.5			m	0.26	d	0.11	d	0.08	d	0.05			d	0.12		
48		0.60	i	2.00	d	0.84	d	0.74	d	0.24	d	0.13	d	0.16		0.46
48.5					d	0.18	d	0.33	d	0.05	d	0.02	d	0.09		
49	C_4H	3.01	i	1.40	C_4H	3.24	C_4H	3.14	C_4H	1.34		0.46	C_4H	0.88	C_4H	1.66
49.5					d	0.14	d	0.13								
50	C_4H_2	6.45	C_4H_2	1.40	C_4H_2	3.49	C_4H_2	4.22	C_4H_2	7.73	C_4H_2	2.96	C_4H_2	6.91	C_4H_2	2.95
50.0					m	0.03	m	0.07								
51	C_4H_3	3.81	C_4H_3	1.54	C_4H_3	3.85	C_4H_3	4.19	C_4H_3	13.3	C_4H_3	5.62	C_4H_3	12.0	C_4H_3	2.14
51.5															r	0.03
52	C_4H_4	0.20	C_4H_4	0.40	C_4H_5	1.31		1.58	C_4H_5	3.76	C_4H_5	1.63	C_4H_5	3.67		2.24
53			C_4H_5	4.62	C_4H_5	8.54	C_4H_5	8.23	C_4H_6	11.0		5.34		9.18		0.26
53.1					m	0.05	m	0.85	d	1.19						
54			C_4H_6	13.0	i,r	0.90	i,r				d	0.79	r	0.96		
54.5										0.11		0.08	d	0.08		

Table continued

TABLE IV-21 (*Continued*)

Mass charge ratio	Thiophene		Thiolane		2-Methyl-thiophene		3-Methyl-thiophene		2,3-Dimethyl-thiophene		3,4-Dimethyl-thiophene		2,5-Dimethyl-thiophene		2-Thiophene-thiol	
	P.O.	R.I.	P.O.	R.I.	P.O.	R.I.	P.O.	R.I.	P.O.	R.I.	P.O.	R.I.	P.O.	R.I.	P.O.	R.I.
55	—	—	C_4H_7	12.0	—	—	—	—	r	3.22	r	2.78	r	2.10	—	—
55.5	—	—	—	—	—	—	—	—	d	0.24	d	0.25	d	0.17	—	—
56	C_2S	1.53	C_2S	0.64	C_2S	0.28	—	0.20	C_2S	0.38	C_2S	0.43	C_2S	0.25	C_2S	1.89
56.5	—	—	—	—	—	—	—	—	—	—	—	0.02	—	—	—	0.13
57	C_2HS	13.7	C_2HS	2.44	C_2HS	3.67	C_2HS	3.12	C_2HS	3.64	C_2HS	1.04	C_2HS	2.47	C_2HS	9.11
57.5	—	—	—	—	—	—	—	—	—	—	—	—	—	—	—	0.33
58.1	C_2H_2S	62.9	C_2H_2S	8.22	C_2H_2S	6.30	C_2H_2S	4.65	C_2H_2S	10.9	C_2H_2S	2.89	C_2H_2S	7.81	C_2H_2S	14.0
58.5	m	0.38	—	—	—	—	—	—	—	—	—	—	—	—	—	0.49
59	r	2.39	C_2H_3S	17.6	C_2H_3S	4.87	r	1.37	C_2H_3S	15.3	r	3.25	C_2H_3S	24.1	r	2.54
59.5	r	2.75	—	—	i,r	0.62	—	—	—	—	—	—	—	—	d	0.08
60.0	—	—	C_2H_4S	100	—	—	—	0.40	—	1.21	—	0.46	—	1.21	—	0.50
61	—	0.10	r	4.12	C_5H_3	1.41	—	0.74	—	1.63	—	0.85	—	1.67	m	0.04
62	—	—	i	4.40	—	1.71	—	0.92	—	1.66	—	1.29	—	1.08	—	0.14
63.0	—	—	i.r.	0.16	m	2.62	C_5H_3	1.53	—	2.88	—	2.36	C_5H_3	2.04	—	0.06
64	—	—	—	—	—	0.05	—	0.26	C_5H_4	0.42	C_5H_3	0.39	—	0.28	S_2	2.61
65	—	—	—	—	C_5H_5	0.38	C_5H_5	2.05	C_5H_5	3.82	C_5H_5	3.27	C_3H_5	2.17	—	0.46
66	—	—	—	—	—	2.29	—	0.13	C_5H_6	1.85	C_5H_6	1.86	r	1.49	—	0.59
67	—	—	—	—	i	0.14	—	0.66	C_5H_7	7.48	C_5H_7	5.76	r	5.44	—	0.21
68	C_3HS	0.56	C_3H_2S	0.58	—	0.02	C_3HS	6.00	C_3HS	0.83	C_3HS	0.87	—	0.64	C_2S	2.30
69	C_3H_2S	6.85	—	—	—	0.55	C_3H_2S	1.78	C_3H_2S	6.79	C_3H_2S	8.32	C_3HS	6.37	C_3HS	16.1
70	—	0.32	—	0.10	C_3H_2S	5.69	—	—	—	2.09	—	2.64	—	2.10	C_3H_2S	5.33
71	C_3H_3S	0.31	C_3H_3S	0.66	C_3H_3S	1.71	C_3H_3S	4.26	C_3H_3S	5.01	C_3H_3S	8.34	C_3H_3S	6.51	C_3H_3S	90.1
72	—	—	C_3H_4S	0.22	C_3H_4S	3.60	C_3H_4S	0.62	C_3H_4S	0.74	C_3H_4S	2.06	C_3H_3S	1.41	i,r	13.6
73	—	—	C_3H_5S	3.90	i	0.51	i	0.20	i	0.46	i	0.63	i	0.64	i	4.29
74	—	—	—	—	—	0.16	—	0.02	—	0.59	—	0.41	—	1.16	—	0.59
75	—	—	i	0.18	—	—	—	—	—	0.33	—	0.21	—	0.60	—	0.06
76	—	—	—	0.18	—	—	—	—	—	0.16	—	0.09	—	0.24	CS_2	1.51
77	—	—	—	—	—	—	—	—	C_6H_5	11.5	C_6H_5	8.57	C_6H_5	11.9	CHS_2	0.99

Mass charge ratio	Thiophene P.O.	Thiophene R.I.	Thiolane P.O.	Thiolane R.I.	2-Methyl-thiophene P.O.	2-Methyl-thiophene R.I.	3-Methyl-thiophene P.O.	3-Methyl-thiophene R.I.	2,3-Dimethyl-thiophene P.O.	2,3-Dimethyl-thiophene R.I.	3,4-Dimethyl-thiophene P.O.	3,4-Dimethyl-thiophene R.I.	2,5-Dimethyl-thiophene P.O.	2,5-Dimethyl-thiophene R.I.	2-Thiophene-thiol P.O.	2-Thiophene-thiol R.I.
78	—	—	—	—	—	—	—	—	C_6H_6	4.87	C_6H_6	3.99	C_6H_6	5.82	—	0.24
79	—	—	—	—	—	—	—	—	C_6H_7	2.37	C_6H_7	3.70	C_6H_7	2.25	—	0.14
80	—	0.64	—	—	—	0.09	—	0.09	—	0.22	—	0.28	—	0.17	—	0.62
81	C_4HS	4.18	C_4HS	0.18	C_4HS	0.77	C_4HS	0.92	C_4HS	0.96	C_4HS	0.58	C_4HS	0.55	C_4HS	3.86
82	C_4H_2S	2.93	C_4H_2S	0.16	C_4H_2S	0.94	C_4H_2S	0.94	C_4H_2S	1.19	—	0.71	—	0.79	C_4H_2S	3.91
83	C_4H_3S	5.82	C_4H_3S	0.08	—	0.38	—	0.39	—	0.87	—	0.65	—	0.45	C_4H_3S	2.66
84	P	100	C_4H_4S	0.20	—	0.16	—	0.08	C_4H_4S	1.82	C_4H_4S	1.27	C_4H_4S	0.85	C_4H_4S	3.10
85	i	4.99	C_4H_5S	2.82	—	0.05	—	0.02	C_4H_5S	4.79	C_4H_5S	2.71	C_4H_5S	2.24	—	0.48
86	i	4.44	—	0.38	—	—	—	—	—	0.35	—	0.21	—	0.16	—	0.17
87	i	0.19	C_4H_7S	15.9	—	—	—	—	i	0.20	i	0.12	i	0.10	i	—
88	i	0.01	C_4H_8S	53.5	—	—	—	—	—	—	—	—	—	—	C_2S_2	2.59
89	—	—	i	3.40	—	—	—	—	—	—	—	—	—	—	C_2HS_2	3.84
90	—	—	i	2.34	—	—	—	—	—	—	—	—	—	—	$C_2H_2S_2$	1.74
91	—	—	i	0.08	—	—	—	0.21	—	—	—	—	—	—	i+	0.63
92	—	—	—	—	—	0.98	—	0.74	—	0.12	—	0.04	—	0.13	i+	0.15
93	—	—	—	—	—	0.12	—	0.08	—	0.92	—	0.64	—	0.87	—	—
94	—	—	—	—	—	0.91	—	0.70	—	0.15	—	0.09	—	0.14	—	—
95	—	—	—	—	C_5H_3S	0.43	C_5H_3S	0.40	C_5H_3S	1.18	C_5H_3S	0.80	C_5H_3S	1.69	—	—
96	—	—	—	—	—	0.36	—	0.40	—	0.28	—	0.21	—	0.27	—	—
96.0	—	—	—	—	—	—	—	—	—	—	—	—	—	—	—	—
97	—	—	—	—	C_5H_5S	100	C_5H_5S	100	C_5H_5S	100	C_5H_5S	44.5	C_5H_5S	57.9	—	—
98	—	—	—	—	P	57.1	P	55.2	C_5H_6S	10.5	C_5H_6S	3.28	C_5H_6S	4.14	—	—
99	—	—	—	—	i	7.54	i	7.37	C_5H_7S	4.76	C_5H_7S	2.00	C_5H_7S	2.65	—	—
100	—	—	—	—	i	2.49	i	2.42	i	0.46	—	0.11	—	0.16	C_3S_2	0.30
101	—	—	—	—	i	0.16	i	0.14	i	0.02	—	—	—	—	—	0.49
102	—	—	—	—	—	—	—	—	—	—	—	—	—	—	—	0.06
103	—	—	—	—	—	—	—	—	—	—	—	—	—	—	—	0.09
105	—	—	—	—	—	—	—	—	—	0.05	—	0.06	—	0.05	—	—
106	—	—	—	—	—	—	—	—	—	0.05	—	0.06	—	0.04	—	—
107	—	—	—	—	—	—	—	—	—	0.03	—	0.02	—	0.02	—	—
108	—	—	—	—	—	—	—	—	—	0.19	—	0.11	—	0.10	—	—
109	—	—	—	—	—	—	—	—	C_6H_5S	2.26	C_6H_5S	1.35	C_6H_5S	1.08	—	—
110	—	—	—	—	—	—	—	—	C_6H_6S	2.23	C_6H_6S	1.64	C_6H_6S	1.40	—	—

Table continued

TABLE IV-21 (Continued)

Mass charge ratio	Thiophene		Thiolane		2-Methyl-thiophene		3-Methyl-thiophene		2,3-Dimethyl-thiophene		3,4-Dimethyl-thiophene		2,5-Dimethyl-thiophene		2-Thiophene-thiol	
	P.O.	R.I.	P.O.	R.I.	P.O.	R.I.	P.O.	R.I.	P.O.	R.I.	P.O.	R.I.	P.O.	R.I.	P.O.	R.I.
111	—	—	—	—	—	—	—	—	C_6H_7S	84.0	C_6H_7S	100	C_6H_7S	100	—	—
112	—	—	—	—	—	—	—	—	C_6H_8S	87.5	C_6H_8S	72.3	C_6H_8S	81.7	—	—
113	—	—	—	—	—	—	—	—	i	9.71	i	9.28	i	9.98		0.04
114	—	—	—	—	—	—	—	—	i	4.06	i	3.34	i	3.78		0.30
115	—	—	—	—	—	—	—	—		0.24		0.21		0.23		9.01
116	—	—	—	—	—	—	—	—	—	—	—	—	—	—	$C_4H_4S_2$	100
117	—	—	—	—	—	—	—	—	—	—	—	—	—	—	i	6.98
118	—	—	—	—	—	—	—	—	—	—	—	—	—	—	i	8.84
119	—	—	—	—	—	—	—	—	—	—	—	—	—	—	i	0.53
120	—	—	—	—	—	—	—	—	—	—	—	—	—	—		0.21

Sensitivity for Indicated Peak in Divisions per Micron

Peak 84	25.7	Peak 60	18.0	Peak 97	34.6	Peak 97	42.5	Peak 97	19.4	Peak 111	23.5	Peak 111	26.1	Peak 116	23.9

Notes

1. Purity of compounds > 99.5%
2. Relative intensities at 50 ion volts. 9 micro amps. Catcher current.

Symbols

P.O., peak origin
R.I., relative intensities
p, parent molecular ion
m, metastable ion
i, isotopic ion
r, rearranged ion
d, doubly-charged ion

Relative sensitivity for n-butane at peak 43—36.4

Relative intensities for n-butane

15	5.56
27	39.2
29	44.3
43	100
58	12.2

Metastable ion transitions

14.1	(82+) → (34+)	+48		45.4	(69+) → (56+)	+13
27.2	(53+) → (38+)	+15		46.1	(50+) → (48+)	+2
34.9	(58+) → (45+)	+13		47.1	(51+) → (49+)	+2
37.0	(39+) → (38+)	+1		50.0	(52+) → (51+)	+1
39.0	(41+) → (40+)	+1		53.1	(95+) → (71+)	+24
39.2	(80+) → (56+)	+24		58.1	(82+) → (69+)	+13
40.0	(84+) → (58+)	+26		60.0	(84+) → (71+)	+13
44.2	(71+) → (56+)	+15		63.0	(65+) → (64+)	+1
45.0	(47+) → (46+)	+1		96.0	(98+) → (97+)	+1

analysis without the necessity of rerunning the pure compounds for calibration.   The instrument and method used are essentially the same as described by Washburn *et al.*[65]

[65] Washburn, Wiley, and Rock, *Ind. Eng. Chem., Anal. Ed.*, **15**, 541 (1943).

CHAPTER V

Factors Affecting Substitution Reactions in the Thiophene Nucleus

Introduction

Prior to 1933 it was believed that electronegative substituents, which direct entering groups toward the *meta*-position in the benzene series, also direct always to this position in the thiophene series. Until this belief was disproved by Rinkes[1] it led to the assignment of incorrect structures to many thiophene compounds. Again, it was not until the work of Appleby, Sartor, Lee, and Kapranos[2] that invariability of mono substitution in the 2-position was seriously questioned. These authors showed that almost equal amounts of 2- and 3-alkylthiophenes are formed by the alkylation of thiophene with olefins, and their observation has been checked in our laboratories over wide ranges of conditions and catalysts.

It must be recognized that, whereas all positions in the unsubstituted benzene nucleus are equivalent, the replacement of the —CH=CH— unit by the hetero atom, sulfur, introduces a factor into the thiophene nucleus that goes far toward controlling subsequent substitution. Thus nuclear substituents on the thiophene nucleus produce orientations only in competition with or in conjunction with the strong directive influence already present.

I. Resonance in the Thiophene Nucleus

The possible resonating forms of thiophene are given by structures I–VI[3] (1). II–V may have two resonating forms, each at the —C—S—C— linkage. Schomaker and Pauling calculated from their studies that

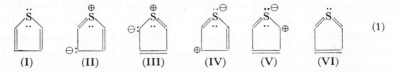

$$(1)$$

(I)   (II)   (III)   (IV)   (V)   (VI)

---

[1] Rinkes, *Rec. trav. chim.*, **51–54**, four articles listed in footnotes 14, 16, 25, and 32.
[2] Appleby, Sartor, Lee, and Kapranos, *J. Am. Chem. Soc.*, **70**, 1552 (1948).
[3] Schomaker and Pauling, *J. Am. Chem. Soc.*, **61**, 1769 (1939).

structures II and III contribute approximately 20% of the resonance hybrid.   Structures IV to VI, where more than eight electrons are present in the outer shell of the sulfur atom, contribute another 10%.

Considering typical nucleophilic substitution of the thiophene nucleus, the resonating form II would give predominantly 3-substituted thiophenes; thus its contribution to the resonance hydrid should be less than that of III. It appears that the most important resonating charged form is III, which would form the normal 2-substituted thiophenes.   Resonating forms IV to VI, if they occur to any great extent, would add entering substituents at the sulfur atom, leading to either rearrangement or rupture of the ring and accounting for the usual ring rupture of thiophene with strong acids and oxidizing agents.   In the metalation of thiophene, sodium causes only a small amount of ring scission, but potassium causes complete scission, indicating an attachment of the potassium to the sulfur atom of one of the resonating forms IV, V, or VI.

II. Directive Influence of the Sulfur Atom in Monosubstitution Reactions

There has been little organized research on the ratio of isomers formed in monosubstitutions of the thiophene nucleus, but a survey of the literature (Table V-1) shows that primary substitution occurs chiefly—sometimes apparently exclusively—at the 2-position.   Alkylation and nitration are the only two reactions studied that have given significant amounts of 3-substituted products, while with the other monosubstitutions of thiophene the maximum ratio of 3- to 2-substituted product is 1:32.   In alkylation reactions the ratio approaches 1:1, and it seems likely that the 3-alkylthiophene is formed by a mechanism not involving substitution as the first step. It is well known that thiophene polymerizes with concentrated sulfuric acid to "black resinous masses."   In that respect it behaves almost like butadiene.   (For further discussion on polymerization of thiophene see Chapter VI.)   Ethylene, in the presence of the usual alkylation catalysts employed in the thiophene series, fails to alkylate thiophene.   Propylene gives only low yields.   Isobutylene reacts rapidly, while 1- and 2-butene are in the same order of reactivity as propylene.   Thus it might be that the alkylation of thiophene with olefins involves a copolymerization mechanism with a subsequent rearrangement to the mixed alkylation products.

Table V-1 lists several types of reactions and the ratio of isomers formed in the respective reactions.

TABLE V-1. Isomer Formation in Monosubstitution Reactions

Type reaction	Ref.	Entering group		Ratio of 2 to 3 substitution
		2-Position	3-Position	
Acylation	6	100%	None detected[a]	—
Alkylation...............	2	50–60%	50–40%	1:1
Chlorination.............	4,5	99.7%	0.3%	330:1
Nitration[b]...............	7	97%	3%	32:1
Aminoalkylation..........	8	100%	None detected[a]	—
Sulfonation.............	7	Major	Trace	—

[a] Amounts of less than 1% would not have been detected by the methods used.
[b] By V. Meyer's method.[9]

III. Directive Influences of Typical *Ortho-Para*-Directing Groups on the Thiophene Nucleus

Only for the chlorination of 2-chlorothiophene has the ratio of isomeric products been determined[4,5] At 50° this reaction gives 99% of 2,5-dichloro- and 1% of 2,3-dichlorothiophene. The combined tendencies of the chlorine atom and the nuclear sulfur atom to direct the second chlorine atom to the 5-position naturally predominate, but the residual tendency of the chlorine atom to orient to the *ortho* (in this case to the 3-) position has not entirely disappeared. Hartough and Kosak[10] did not note isomer formation in the acylation of 2-methylthiophene. Schick and Hartough[11] similarly did not observe the formation of isomers in the metalation of 2-methylthiophene. However, the presence of about 1% of a 3-isomer would not have been detected by the methods used. It appears, therefore, that a typical *ortho-para*-directing group in the 2-position, which would orient to the 3- and 5-positions, coupled with the tendency of the sulfur atom to orient to the 5-position, gives a directing factor of at least 100 to 1 in favor of the 5-position over the 3-position.

When the directing group is in the 3-position a different behavior is encountered. Let us consider the polarized structure III for thiophene as applied to 3-methylthiophene (2):

[4] Coonradt and Hartough, *J. Am. Chem. Soc.*, **70**, 1158 (1948).
[5] Coonradt, Hartough, and Johnson, *J. Am. Chem. Soc.*, **70**, 2564 (1948).
[6] Hartough *et al.*, *J. Am. Chem. Soc.*, **68**, 2639 (1946); **69**, 1012, 1014, 3093, 3096, 3098 (1947); **70**, 867 (1948).
[7] Steinkopf and Hopner, *Ann.*, **501**, 174 (1933).
[8] Hartough, unpublished work.
[9] V. Meyer, *Die Thiophengruppe*. Braunschweig, 1888, p. 125.
[10] Hartough and Kosak, *J. Am. Chem. Soc.*, **69**, 3093 (1947).
[11] Schick and Hartough, *J. Am. Chem. Soc.*, **70**, 1645 (1948).

(2)

In this case the electron pair of the sulfur may shift toward the 5-carbon forming the ionic structure similar to the resonating form III in thiophene.   Reactivity of the 2-position is accentuated by the *o*-directing methyl group, which has the tendency of forcing an electron pair toward the ring.   Thus any entering electrophilic group would find electrons more available at the 2-carbon than at any other place on the ring.   This kind of reasoning accounts for the greater reactivity of 2- and 3-methylthiophenes compared to thiophene itself.   In 3-methylthiophene, there is apparently also a small tendency to increase the electron density in the 5-position, so as to activate the latter; this effect is noted in certain reactions (see Table V-2).

TABLE V-2. Isomer Formation during Monosubstitution Reactions
      in the 3-Methylthiophene Nucleus

| | Entering group | | |
Type reaction	2-Position	5-Position	Ref.
Acylation	80%	20%	10
Aminomethylation	100%	0	12
Halogenation	100%	0	13
Metalation	0	100%	11
Nitration	Major	Trace	14

According to Table V-2, substitution in the 2-position is heavily favored in a number of reactions over substitution in the 5-position.   In the acylation of 3-methylthiophene[10] four acyl groups enter the 2-position for every one such group entering the 5-position irrespective of the amount of catalyst, the molar ratio of the reactants, and the reaction conditions.[8] However, in the metalation of 3-methylthiophene, sodium enters the molecule exclusively in the 5-position.[11]   This is rather hard to explain but fortunate from the synthetic viewpoint.   Since the product undergoes typical Grignard reactions, compounds are easily obtained which would otherwise be very difficult to prepare.

[12] Hartough and Meisel, *J. Am. Chem. Soc.*, **70**, 4018 (1948).
[13] Steinkopf and Kohler, *Ann.*, **532**, 250 (1937).
[14] Rinkes, *Rec. trav. chim.*, **52**, 1052 (1933).

IV. Directive Influences of Typical
Meta-Directing Groups

When thiophene is substituted by an electronegative substituent in the 2-position such as a —NO₂, —COOH, —COR, —SO₃H, or —SO₂Cl, *i.e.*, a normal *meta*-directing group, there is tendency to overcome the directive influence of the sulfur atom of the nucleus and a mixture of products results. The product obtained in the major proportion is still the 5-substituted thiophene, but 4-substitution (*meta*) occurs to a minor extent. Only in a few cases have the actual percentages been determined but the ratio of 5-substitution to 4-substitution probably is of the order of about 10 to 1.

There are two exceptions to these conclusions. 2-Thiophenesulfonyl chloride appears to give a 3:8 ratio of 5- to 4-substituted products and 2-acylthiophenes give only 2,5-diacylthiophenes (though in low yields).

Table V-3 summarizes the data on this subject.

TABLE V-3. Directive Influence of Typical *Meta*-Directing Groups on the Thiophene Nucleus

Meta-directing group in 2-position	Entering group	Position entered		Ref.
		5-Position	4-Position (*meta*)	
—NO₂	—NO₂	90–95%	10–5%	7
—NO₂	—SO₃H	Major	Not deter.	7
—COOH	—NO₂	Major	Trace	16
—COOH	—Halogen	Major	Not deter.	8
—COCH₃	—NO₂	Major	Minor	16
—COCH₃	—COCH₃	100%	0	17
—COCH₃	—SO₃H	Removes acyl group		15
—SO₃H	—NO₂	97.5%	2.5%	7
—SO₃H	—SO₃H	Major	Minor	7
—SO₂Cl	—NO₂	27%	73%	7
—SO₂Cl	—Cl	Minor	Major	7
—SO₂Cl	—SO₂Cl	Minor	Major	7

Thiophene compounds, having a typical *meta*-directing group in the 3-position, become substituted in the 5-position exclusively. There appears to be no exception in the literature to this statement. This is, of

---

[15] Krekeler, *Ber.*, **19**, 676, 2627 (1886). Schleicher, *ibid.*, **19**, 660 (1886). Muhlert, *ibid.*, **19**, 1620 (1886).
[16] Rinkes, *Rec. trav. chim.*, **51**, 1134 (1932).
[17] Hartough and Kosak, *J. Am. Chem. Soc.*, **69**, 1012 (1947).

course, to be anticipated since the 5-position, being *meta* to the 3-position, is also activated by the sulfur and the two effects are additive.

Thiophene derivatives containing two *meta*-directing groups are not known to undergo further ring substitution.   The two substituents on the thiophene nucleus will always be in such a position that a third entering group must enter in an *ortho* position.   Preparation of thiophene derivatives containing three *meta*-directing groups can be accomplished by replacement reactions such as the following.[18]   The order of replacement (Eq. 3) is given numerically.

$$
\text{I}\underset{\text{I}}{\overset{\text{S}}{\bigcirc}}\text{--NHCOCH}_3 \quad \xrightarrow{\text{N}_2\text{O}_3,\ \textit{stepwise replacement}} \quad \begin{array}{l} 1 \to \text{NO}_2 \\ 3 \to \text{NO}_2 \end{array}\underset{\text{--NO}_2 \gets 2}{\overset{\text{S}}{\bigcirc}}\text{--NHCOCH}_3 \tag{3}
$$

It is interesting to note that the order of fission, *i.e.*, the order of replacement of the carbon-iodine bonds for the three positions is 5, 3, and finally 4, a fact also deducible from observations on a different method[19] (Eq. 4).   In terms of ease of hydrogen replacement in an electropositively

$$
\text{I}\underset{\text{I}}{\overset{\text{S}}{\bigcirc}}\text{--CH}_3 \xrightarrow[\text{Mg, CH}_3\text{I}]{} \xrightarrow[\text{H}_2\text{O}]{} \text{I}\underset{\text{I}}{\overset{\text{S}}{\bigcirc}}\text{--CH}_3 \xrightarrow[\text{Mg, CH}_3\text{I}]{} \xrightarrow[\text{H}_2\text{O}]{} \text{I}\overset{\text{S}}{\bigcirc}\text{--CH}_3 \tag{4}
$$

substituted (substituted, *i.e.*, with an electron-repelling group of the *ortho-para*-directing series) thiophene nucleus, it can be stated that the order of replacement is 5, 3, and 4.   This order has been substantiated by halogenation of 2-chlorothiophene[5] and by the bromination of 2-acetamidothiophene (*N*-(2-thienyl)acetamide).[20]

V. Methods of Synthesis in the Thiophene Series Based on Directive Influences in the Thiophene Nucleus

Synthesis of the typical 2-substituted thiophenes is dealt with in the following chapters in connection with the discussion of the respective thiophene derivatives.   The syntheses of 3-substituted thiophenes are summarized below because of their more complex nature.   For detailed procedures supplementing this summary, see Appendix I.

[18] Priestley and Hurd, *J. Am. Chem. Soc.*, **69**, 1173 (1947).
[19] Steinkopf and Hanske, *Ann.*, **527**, 264 (1937).
[20] Hurd and Priestley, *J. Am. Chem. Soc.*, **69**, 859 (1947).

A. Preparation of 3-Substituted Thiophenes

3-Alkylthiophenes

Since alkylation of the nucleus of thiophene gives almost equal amounts of 2- and 3-alkylthiophenes, this method can be applied to the preparation of members of this class of compounds wherein the carbon chain length is greater than two. 2-Ethylthiophene has not yet been prepared by direct alkylation. Unfortunately, the typical Friedel-Crafts reaction with alkyl halides and thiophene gives only very low yields and has never been used with ethyl or methyl halides. If one is to obtain either 3-methyl- or 3-ethylthiophene or any 3-n-alkylthiophene, they may be prepared by a Wurtz-Fittig reaction on 3-iodothiophene. Otherwise, a ring closure must be effected. The present commercial thiophene process produces 3-methylthiophene from isopentane and sulfur but no data were presented to indicate that the reaction can be extended to other 3-alkylthiophenes.[21] 3-Methylthiophene and 3-chlorothiophene are prepared by the action of sulfur on isoprene and chloroprene, respectively, but this reaction has not been extended to the 3-alkylthiophenes generally (see Chapter III for further details) (Eq. 5).

$$CH_3CH_2\overset{\overset{\displaystyle CH_3}{|}}{C}HCH_3 \xrightarrow{\text{sulfur, 1100°F.}} \text{(thiophene)}—CH_3 \tag{5}$$

Ring closure of substituted succinic acids is also a convenient method.[22] (Eq.6). However, the synthesis of the succinic acid is sometimes more diffi-

$$\overset{\overset{\displaystyle CH_2COONa}{|}}{R}—CHCOONa \xrightarrow{P_2S_3 \text{ or } P_4S_7} \text{(thiophene)}—R \tag{6}$$

cult than the synthesis of 3-iodothiophene. The method above has been carried out only when R— is an alkyl group. Citric acid, when treated in the same manner, gives thiophthene:[23]

$$\overset{\overset{\displaystyle CH_2COOH}{|}}{HO—\overset{\overset{\displaystyle }{|}}{C}—COOH} \xrightarrow{P_2S_3} \text{(thiophthene)} \tag{7}$$
$$\underset{\displaystyle CH_2COOH}{|}$$

[21] Hansford, Rasmussen, and Sachanen, *Ind. Eng. Chem.*, **38**, 376 (1946).
[22] Paal and Tafel, *Ber.*, **18**, 456 (1885). Volhard and Erdmann, *Ber.*, **18**, 454 (1885).
[23] Biedermann and Jacobsen, *Ber.*, **19**, 2447 (1886). Oster, *ibid.*, **37**, 3350 (1904).

3-Nitrothiophene

3-Nitrothiophene occurs among the products of nitration of thiophene only to a minor extent (less than 5%).   The best method for its preparation[7,23a] consists of the nitration of 2-thiophenesulfonyl chloride followed by removal of the —SO₂Cl group (Eq. 8).

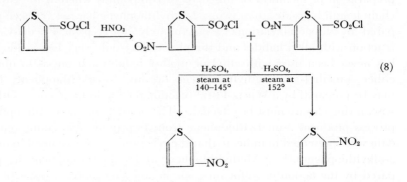

$$\tag{8}$$

The effect of temperature in the selective removal of the —SO₂Cl group provides a convenient method of separation of the isomers.

3-Chlorothiophene

The same method as above was used with some modifications[13] (Eq. 9).   It was difficult to stop the chlorination at the first stage, i.e., at the 4-

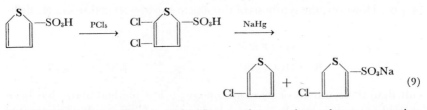

$$\tag{9}$$

chloro-2-thiophenesulfonyl chloride, and carrying the preparation through to the 4,5-dichloro derivative gave the best yields.

3-Bromothiophene

While the bromination of 2-thiophenesulfonyl chloride probably could be carried out, a simpler method is available for the preparation of 3-bromothiophene[24] (Eq. 10).

[23a] Burton and Davy, *J. Chem. Soc.*, **1948**, 528.
[24] Steinkopf, *Ann.*, **543**, 128 (1940).

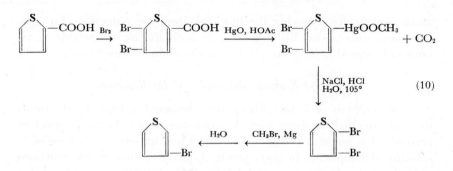

$$(10)$$

3-Iodothiophene

The preparation of 3-iodothiophene as an intermediate in thiophene chemistry is of extreme importance. However, the method is expensive and would involve recovery of considerable amounts of iodine if it were used on a large scale, for it consists of periodination of thiophene and removal of three of the iodine atoms by reduction[25] (Eq. 11).

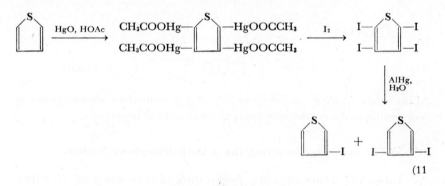

$$(11$$

3,4-Diaminothiophene

The synthesis developed by Mozingo and co-workers[26] for the preparation of 3,4-diaminothiophene is illustrative of the type of synthesis that can be carried out by blocking the reactive 2,5-positions with bromine

$$(12)$$

[25] Rinkes, *Rec. trav. chim.*, **53**, 463 (1934).
[26] Mozingo *et al.*, *J. Am. Chem. Soc.*, **67**, 2092 (1945).

atoms and finally removing the blocking atoms by reduction (Eq. 12).
3,4-Diaminothiophene, like 2- and 3-aminothiophene, is unstable in air
but can be stored in aqueous solutions under an inert atmosphere.

3-Thenyl Bromide and Some of Its Reactions

The synthesis of 3-thenyl bromide[27] (reported in 1948) by the treatment of 3-methylthiophene with *N*-bromosuccinimide in the presence of
peroxides has made available a convenient and important synthesis of 3-substituted thiophenes in good yields (Eq. 13).   Some of the reactions
carried out by Campaigne and Le Suer are listed in equation (14).[27]

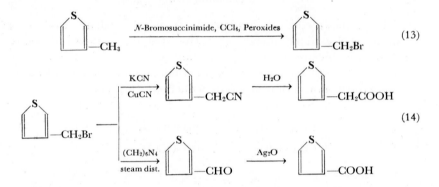

$$(13)$$

$$(14)$$

Many other syntheses are obvious and this intermediate should prove of
more value to the synthetic organic chemist as time progresses.

B. Syntheses Involving the 3-Methylthiophene Nucleus

Table V-4 summarizes the preparation of derivatives of 3-methyl-thiophene.   In most cases it can be presumed that if the methyl group
were replaced by any other simple electron-donating (*ortho-para*-directing)
group, the same series of syntheses could be carried out.

C. Synthesis of the Six Isomeric Methylthiophenecarboxylic Acids

While it is not possible to discuss here the synthesis of all classes of
isomeric derivatives of thiophene the synthesis of the six isomeric methyl-thiophenecarboxylic acids can be considered as representative.   The

[27] Campaigne and Le Suer, *J. Am. Chem. Soc.*, **70**, 1555 (1948).

TABLE V-4. Typical Syntheses with 3-Methylthiophene

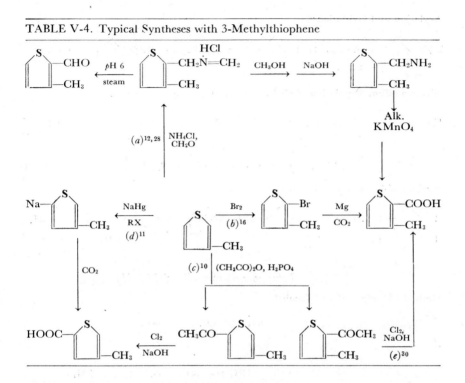

syntheses used in the preparations below are of such a nature that if one wanted a group such as —CH₂CH₂OH, —COCH₃, —(CH₂)ₙCH₃, —CH=CH₂, or —OH one might treat the intermediate Grignard reagent with the proper chemical. These, then, serve as model equations for the syntheses of the six isomeric disubstituted derivatives of any given thiophene series wherein at least one of the substituents is an electropositive group.

5-Methyl-2-thiophenecarboxylic Acid (I)

Grignard Method[29]

$$(15)$$

---

[28] Hartough and Dickert, *J. Am. Chem. Soc.*, **71**, 3922 (1949).
[29] This reaction has not actually been carried out but will presumably proceed with considerable ease under the conditions listed in footnote 31.

Acylation and Oxidation[30]

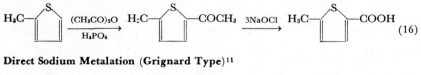

$$(16)$$

Direct Sodium Metalation (Grignard Type)[11]

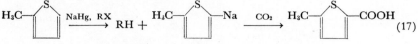

$$(17)$$

2-Methyl-4-thiophenecarboxylic Acid (II)

Method of Steinkopf and Hanske[19]

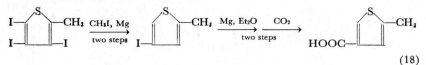

$$(18)$$

2-Methyl-3-thiophenecarboxylic Acid (III)

Method of Steinkopf and Jacob[31]

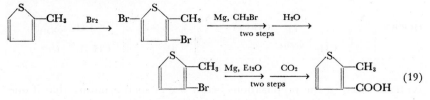

$$(19)$$

3-Methyl-2-thiophenecarboxylic Acid (IV)

Grignard Method[31]

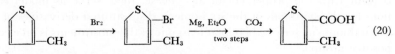

$$(20)$$

Also see other methods in Table V-4.

4-Methyl-2-thiophenecarboxylic Acid (V)

Sodium Metalation Method[11]

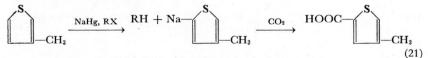

$$(21)$$

[30] Hartough and Conley, *J. Am. Chem. Soc.*, **69**, 3096 (1947).
[31] Steinkopf and Jacob, *Ann.*, **515**, 273 (1935).

Acylation Method[10, 30]

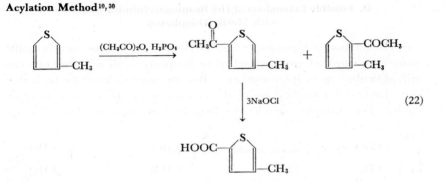

(22)

Method of Steinkopf and Jacob[31]

It should be noted that this method gave 4-methyl-2,5-dihydrothio-phene-2-carboxylic acid as pointed out by Rinkes[32] instead of 4-methyl-2-thiophenecarboxylic acid. But the method is of general interest as a possible general synthetic method (23):

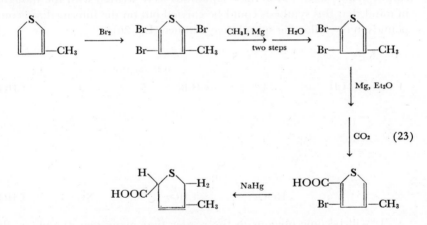

(23)

4-Methyl-3-thiophenecarboxylic Acid (*VI*)

Method of Steinkopf and Hanske[33]

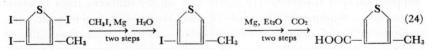

(24)

[32] Rinkes, *Rec. trav. chim.*, **54**, 940 (1935).
[33] Steinkopf and Hanske, *Ann.*, **532**, 236 (1937).

D. Possible Extensions of the Bromosuccinimide Reaction with Methylthiophenes

The method of Campaigne and Le Suer[27] for introducing a bromine atom into a methyl group attached to thiophene is so new that one can only speculate as to its extensions.   But the potentialities are such that new classes of compounds are easily within reach if the synthesis is applicable.   For example, consider the hypothetical equation (25).   The di-

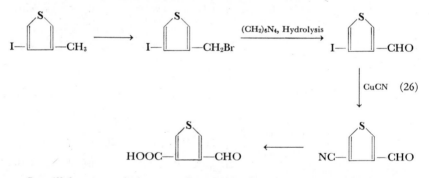

aldehydes of thiophene other than 3,4-dibromo-2,5-thiophenedialdehyde have never been synthesized, but they should be very interesting chemicals.

The equations under "Preparation of the Six Isomeric Methylthiophenecarboxylic Acids" were specifically chosen so that, if this synthesis can be adapted to the isomeric acids, many new thiophene compounds can be synthesized.   Also these equations were written with the thought in mind that this synthesis could be carried out on the intermediate compounds in the following speculative manner (Eq. 26):

It will become obvious to the reader that many new thiophene derivatives are within reach by some of the synthetic methods developed in the past decade.   In a number of cases these discoveries were made on the supposition that thiophene chemistry was totally different from benzene chemistry.   Statements appearing in short chapters on heterocyclic compounds in many organic chemistry textbooks that read essentially as follows—"Thiophene chemistry is quite similar to benzene chemistry. Thiophene is perhaps more reactive and it, therefore, can be classed as a 'superaromatic' "—have definitely hindered thiophene research.   Unfortunately this concept stems directly from the discoverer of thiophene, Victor Meyer.

Organic chemists who in the future will be the greatest contributors to thiophene chemistry will not rely on this concept so implicitly and will proceed on the theory that the chemistry of thiophene and benzene is to be compared about as closely as a zoologist would compare the tortoise and the boa constrictor; they are in the same class but of widely separated species.

CHAPTER VI

.

Alkylation, Polymerization, Hydrogenation and Miscellaneous Reactions of Thiophene

Introduction

This chapter summarizes some of the less common reactions of thiophene chemistry—less common in the sense that the research in an individual field is not extensive enough to be treated as a single entity in an individual chapter. The introduction of alkyl groups is not to be construed as a reaction of lesser importance than in the benzene series, but the methods used are similar to those for benzene chemistry, *i.e.*, the Wurtz-Fittig, the Clemmensen, and the Wolff-Kishner reactions are widely employed.

Direct alkylation of thiophene, which produces both 2- and 3-alkyl-thiophenes in nearly equal proportions, is in an embryonic stage and the fundamentals of this reaction are not well understood. The alkylation of thiophene is still one of the most fruitful fields of thiophene chemistry for future research. A better understanding of the thiophene nucleus and of the forces controlling substitution will follow a proof of a mechanism for the alkylation of thiophene. Polymerization of thiophene, in a strict sense, has been shown to be an alkylation reaction wherein two moles of thiophene add to the double bonds of one thiophene nucleus, thus producing 2,4-di-(2-thienyl)thiolane.

Hydrogenation of thiophene is still an unsolved problem. Two methods have been developed, but large amounts of catalysts are required to prevent poisoning, or the conversions are very low. The methods are no more than curiosities at the moment.

I. Introduction of Alkyl Groups

Alkylthiophenes are easily prepared by ring closures involving substituted succinic or levulinic acids. These reactions are discussed in more detail in Chapter III. The preparation of alkylthiophenes by direct alkylation is a more recent innovation.

159

Originally, in Victor Meyer's laboratory, it was found expedient to produce alkylthiophenes, especially 2-alkylthiophenes, by the Wurtz-Fittig reaction (1). Variations of this reaction, first developed by Meyer

$$\text{(thiophene)} \xrightarrow{\text{I}_2,\ \text{HgO}} \text{(2-iodothiophene)} + 2\text{Na} + \text{RI} \longrightarrow \text{(2-R-thiophene)} + 2\text{NaI} \qquad (1)$$

and Kreis,[1] are to be found in the references below.[2–10] Although the iodo derivatives are generally preferred, the bromo derivatives undergo this reaction in somewhat lower yields.

The Clemmensen reduction of acylthiophenes has been widely used as a method for preparing alkylthiophenes (Eq. 2) (R is an alkyl group).

$$\text{(thiophene)}-\text{CO}-\text{R} \xrightarrow{\text{ZnHg, HCl}} \text{(thiophene)}-\text{CH}_2-\text{R} \qquad (2)$$

This method appears to be applicable throughout the series and has been extended to the normal C_9 hydrocarbon. References to this general method are listed below.[11–16]

Shepard[17] prepared 2-ethyl-5-methylthiophene in 40% yields by the action of moist caustic (5 g. H_2O, 50 g. KOH) on the semicarbazone of 2-acetyl-5-methylthiophene (Eq. 3). In a similar manner, 2,5-diethyl-

$$\underset{\substack{\| \\ \text{NNHCONH}_2}}{\text{H}_3\text{C}-\text{(thiophene)}-\text{C}-\text{CH}_3} \xrightarrow{\text{KOH, fuse}} \text{H}_3\text{C}-\text{(thiophene)}-\text{CH}_2\text{CH}_3 \qquad (3)$$

thiophene can be prepared from the phenylhydrazone of 2-acetyl-5-ethyl-thiophene.[18] This method is adaptable to the preparation of the di-

[1] V. Meyer and Kreis, *Ber.*, **17**, 1558 (1884).
[2] Bonz, *Ber.*, **18**, 549 (1885).
[3] Schleicher, *Ber.*, **18**, 3015 (1885).
[4] Schweinitz, *Ber.*, **19**, 644 (1886).
[5] Muhlert, *Ber.*, **19**, 633 (1886).
[6] Demuth, *Ber.*, **19**, 1857 (1886).
[7] Ruffi, *Ber.*, **20**, 1746 (1887).
[8] Zelinsky, *Ber.*, **21**, 1835 (1888).
[9] Eberhard, *Ber.*, **27**, 2919 (1894).
[10] Opolski, *Anz. Akad. Wiss. Krakau*, **1905**, 550; *Chem. Zentr.* **1905**, II, 1796.
[11] Steinkopf and Schubart, *Ann.*, **424**, 1 (1920).
[12] Scheibler and Schmidt, *Ber.*, **54**, 139 (1921).
[13] Scheibler and Rettig, *Ber.*, **59**, 1194 (1926).
[14] Weissgerber, *Ber.*, **61**, 2117 (1928).
[15] Youtz and Perkins, *J. Am. Chem. Soc.*, **51**, 3511 (1929).
[16] Campaigne and Diedrich, *J. Am. Chem. Soc.*, **70**, 391 (1948).
[17] Shepard, *J. Am. Chem. Soc.*, **54**, 2951 (1932).
[18] Steinkopf, Frommel, and Leo, *Ann.*, **546**, 199 (1941).

methylthiophenes. 2,3-Dimethylthiophene has been prepared in 60% yield from 3-methyl-2-thiophenealdehyde semicarbazone and 2,5-dimethylthiophene results from the semicarbazone of 5-methyl-2-thiophenealdehyde in a 78% yield when the materials are heated in a stream of nitrogen at 100–250°[18a] (Eq. 4). Another modification of this method

$$H_3C-\!\!\!\overset{S}{\underset{\big|\big|}{\diagdown}}\!\!\!-CH\!=\!NNHCONH_2 \;+\; KOH \;\;\xrightarrow[78\%]{\substack{5g.\ of\ H_2O,\ heat \\ at\ 100\ to\ 250°}}\;\; H_3C-\!\!\!\overset{S}{\underset{\big|\big|}{\diagdown}}\!\!\!-CH_3 \qquad (4)$$

30 g.   50 g.

involving decomposition of the azine derivatives in ethylene glycol has recently been extended to several mixed alkylthiophenes, the isomeric methylthiophenes, and to halothiophenes.[18b]

Direct alkylation of thiophene with metal halides of the Friedel and Crafts type was first investigated by Schleicher,[19] who found that thiophene, dissolved in a 12-fold excess of petroleum ether and the calculated amount of isopropyl bromide, was converted in low yields to isopropylthiophene when aluminum chloride was added slowly to the mixture. This same reaction can be carried out with thiophene, benzal chloride, and aluminum chloride to produce a dithienylphenylmethane.[20] In a similar manner, the same product is prepared from benzotrichloride.[21] Benzenediazonium chloride and thiophene, in the presence of aluminum chloride, are reported to give a phenylthiophene.[22] Aluminum chloride can be used to effect macro-ring closures with phenylated thiophene compounds.[23] It can also be used to alkylate thiophene with unsaturated esters of aliphatic carboxylic acids, e.g., ethyl undecylenate.[23a]

Zinc chloride is considered to be an effective catalyst for the alkylation of phenol when alcohols are employed as the alkylating agents. This procedure was adapted to the alkylation of thiophene by Steinkopf,[24] who prepared 2-benzylthiophene and 2,5-dibenzylthiophene from the reaction of benzyl alcohol and thiophene in the presence of molecular amounts of zinc chloride as a catalyst. Tohl and Nahke[20] had previously found it satisfactory for the condensation of benzaldehyde and thiophene, thus producing a dithienylphenylmethane.

[18a] Hartough, unpublished work.
[18b] King and Nord, J. Org. Chem., 14, 638 (1949).
[19] Schleicher, Ber., 19, 672 (1886).
[20] Tohl and Nahke, Ber., 29, 2205 (1896).
[21] Nahke, Ber., 30, 2041 (1897).
[22] Mohlau and Berger, Ber., 26, 1994 (1883).
[23] Steinkopf, Ann., 519, 297 (1935).
[23a] Buu-Hoï and Dat Xuong, Bull. soc. chim., 1949, 751.
[24] Steinkopf, Ann., 541, 238 (1939).

Another general method for the alkylation of thiophene involves the use of aldehydes with an acidic catalyst,[20,25—28,33,33a] zinc chloride,[20] or phosphorus pentoxide.[20,21,29,30,31] Montmorillonite clays cause condensation of benzaldehyde with 2-methylthiophene. A quantitative yield of di-(5-methyl-2-thienyl)phenylmethane is obtained.[32]

Resins are produced with formaldehyde and sulfuric acid that can be thermally cured to form a Bakelite-type resin[26] (Eq. 5). A Bakelite-type

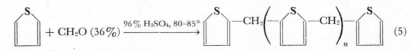

resin is produced from co-condensation of phenol and thiophene with aqueous formaldehyde and 96% sulfuric acid in an autoclave at 105°. To insure incorporation of both thiophene and phenol into the same polymer chain, the product is best produced by introducing phenol into the partially polymerized thiophene-formaldehyde mixture.[26] This technique produces a more brittle resin than thiophene alone. The phenol-thiophene-formaldehyde resin is very similar to phenol-formaldehyde resins. It can be cured with hexamethylenetetramine at 150° in fifty-five seconds, and is suitable, when ground to a powder, as a molding powder.

More recently, thiophene has been found to react with olefins to produce a mixture of 2- and 3-alkylthiophenes and a mixture of isomeric dialkylthiophenes. Naturally occurring clays of the montmorillonite type are effective alkylation agents for thiophene when propylene, isobutylene, or *tert*-butyl alcohol is employed.[34,34a] The use of orthophosphoric acid with isobutylene and thiophene to produce alkylation was noted by these workers and by Appleby and co-workers.[35] The latter also found[35] that a mixture of 2- and 3-alkylthiophenes was formed in their work and suggested that the physical constants given by Kutz and Corson[34] indicated a

[25] Peter, *Ber.*, **17**, 1346 (1884).
[26] Caesar and Sachanen, *Ind. Eng. Chem.*, **40**, 922 (1948). Caesar, U. S. Pat. 2,453,086 (1949). Caesar and Sachanen, U. S. Pat. 2,448,211 and 2,453,085 (1948).
[27] Cristol and Haller, *J. Am. Chem. Soc.*, **68**, 140 (1946).
[28] Truitt, Mattison, and Richardson, *J. Am. Chem. Soc.*, **70**, 79 (1948).
[29] Weisse, *Ber.*, **28**, 1537 (1895); *ibid.*, **29**, 1402 (1896).
[30] Nahke, *Ber.*, **30**, 2037 (1897).
[31] Levi, *Ber.*, **19**, 1623 (1886).
[32] Hartough, unpublished work.
[33] Ancizar-Sordo and Bistrzychi, *Helv. Chim. Acta*, **14**, 141 (1931).
[33a] Feeman, Dove, and Amschutz, *J. Am. Chem. Soc.*, **70**, 3136 (1948).
[34] Kutz and Corson, *J. Am. Chem. Soc.*, **68**, 1477 (1946); *ibid.*, **71**, 1503 (1949).
[34a] Caesar and Sachanen, U. S. Pat. 2,448,211 (1948).
[35] Appleby, Sartor, Lee, and Kapranos, *J. Am. Chem. Soc.*, **70**, 1552 (1948).

mixture. A short discussion of a possible mechanism for this reaction and of the distribution of the isomers formed is given in Chapter V.

Other catalysts that bring about alkylation of thiophene with olefins are boron trifluoride complexes,[25a,36,36a] 80% sulfuric acid,[36] a mixture of sulfur acid and 85% orthophosphoric acid,[36a] ethanesulfonic acid,[36a] stannic chloride,[36a] and aluminum chloride.[36] Stannic chloride causes alkylation of thiophene with olefinic hydrocarbons in which the double bond is attached to a completely substituted carbon atom, e.g., R_2C=CH_2. Olefinic materials such as propene, 2-butene, and isopropylethylene fail to react under similar conditions. Addition of nitromethane or nitroethene to such mixtures promotes the condensation of thiophene with these unreactive materials in the presence of stannic chloride.[36a] Isopropylethylene, on reaction with thiophene with the above indicated catalysts, gave 2-*tert*-amylthiophene, the product received by alkylation of thiophene with trimethylethylene. This indicated a rearrangement of the double bond prior to alkylation.

2-Bromothiophene is reported to undergo alkylation with catalysts effecting substitution of thiophene.[36a] This compound appears to be more difficult to alkylate than thiophene. Substitution occurred in the 5-position with methallyl chloride and with trimethylethylene.

Aluminum chloride has only been employed as a catalyst for the alkylation of thiophene with olefins in the case of diisobutylene.[36] The deactivating influence of thiophene on aluminum chloride is overcome by complexing it with diisobutylene before addition of thiophene to the mixture. The product is a mixture of mono-*tert*-octyl-(1,1,3,3-tetramethyl-butane) and di-*tert*-octylthiophene.

Weinmayr has found that hydrofluoric acid can be employed as a catalyst for the alkylation of thiophene.[36b] Resinification of the thiophene is avoided by adding a mixture of olefin and thiophene to hydrofluoric acid at ambient temperatures. No attempt was made to determine the percentage of 2- and 3-isomers obtained in the alkylations with propylene, propylene tetramer, 2-ethyl-1-butene, diisobutylene, 1-hexene, and 1-octene. An attempt to alkylate thiophene in benzene diluent using 1-

[25a] Hansford and Caesar, U. S. Pat. 2,469,823 (1949).

[36] Caesar, *J. Am. Chem. Soc.*, **70**, 3623 (1948).

[36a] Pines, Kvetinskas, and Vesely, Preprints of Symposium on Organic Sulfur Compounds as Related to Petroleum, sponsored by Division of Petroleum Chemistry of the American Chemical Society, San Francisco meeting, March, 1949, pp. 67–71.

[36b] Weinmayr, Paper presented before the South Jersey Section of the American Chemical Society meeting in miniature, May 17, 1949.

hexene and hydrofluoric acid gave a product consisting mainly of hexyl-benzene (85%) and a small amount of hexylthiophene (15%).   This is extremely interesting in view of the fact that benzene can be used as a diluent in normal substitution reactions such as acylations, halogen-ations, sulfonations, etc.

Attempts to alkylate 2-chlorothiophene and 2-bromothiophene with hydrofluoric acid and an olefin gave partial replacement of the halogen moiety by an alkyl group.[36b]   2-Thiophenecarboxylic can be alkylated with isopropyl ether in hydrofluoric acid.   The structure of the resultant isopropylthiophenecarboxylic acid was not determined.[36b]

II. Preparation of Alkenylthiophenes

A number of alkenylthiophenes have been prepared.   There have been no methods developed for the alkylation of thiophene with ethylene or ethyl halides, which is unfortunate from the standpoint of the production of vinylthiophene by dehydrogenation of ethylthiophene.   2-Vinylthio-phene has been prepared by the reduction of 2-acetylthiophene to the alco-hol which is then dehydrated[37–39] (Eq. 6):

$$\text{S}\text{—COCH}_3 \xrightarrow[\text{60–70\%}]{\text{Al isopropoxide}} \text{S}\text{—CHOHCH}_3 \xrightarrow{-\text{H}_2\text{O}} \text{S}\text{—CH}{=}\text{CH}_2 \qquad (6)$$

Bachman and Heisey have also applied this synthesis to the production of the halogenated vinylthiophenes.[39a]   In a typical cobalt chloride-cata-lyzed Grignard reaction 2-vinylthiophene can be produced in about 30% yields from the 2-thienylmagnesium bromide and vinyl chloride[40] (Eq. 7).

$$\text{S}\text{—MgBr} \xrightarrow[\text{about 30\%}]{\text{ClCH}{=}\text{CH}_2,\ \text{CoCl}_2} \text{S}\text{—CH}{=}\text{CH}_2 \ + \ \text{MgBrCl} \qquad (7)$$

The most convenient method for the preparation of 2-vinylthiophenes is the method of Schick and Hartough[41] through transmetalation with sodium (Eq. 8).   This method has also been used to prepare 5-methyl-2-

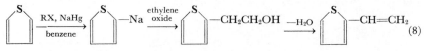

$$\text{S} \xrightarrow[\text{benzene}]{\text{RX, NaHg}} \text{S}\text{—Na} \xrightarrow{\text{ethylene oxide}} \text{S}\text{—CH}_2\text{CH}_2\text{OH} \xrightarrow{-\text{H}_2\text{O}} \text{S}\text{—CH}{=}\text{CH}_2 \qquad (8)$$

[37] Kuhn and Dann, *Ann.*, **547**, 293 (1941).
[38] Mowry, Renoll, and Huber, *J. Am. Chem. Soc.*, **68**, 1105 (1946).
[39] Nazzaro and Bullock, *J. Am. Chem. Soc.*, **68**, 2121 (1946).
[39a] Bachman and Heisey, *J. Am. Chem. Soc.*, **70**, 2378 (1948).
[40] Strassburg, Gregg, and Walling, *J. Am. Chem. Soc.*, **69**, 2141 (1947).
[41] Schick and Hartough, *J. Am. Chem. Soc.*, **70**, 1646 (1948).

vinylthiophene, 4-methyl-2-vinylthiophene, and 5-*tert*-butyl-2-vinylthiophene.   2-Allylthiophene can be prepared from allyl bromide and 2-thienylsodium.[42]   This compound has also been prepared from allyl bromide and 2-thienylmagnesium iodide.[43]   With acetone this Grignard reagent gives isopropenylthiophene.[44]   With methyl *n*-amyl ketone, it gives the corresponding isoheptenylthiophene.[44]   Other olefins of this type are made by similar methods.[45,45a,46]   Bachman and Heisey added aldehydes and ketones to the chloro- and bromo-2-thienylmagnesium halides to produce the corresponding alcohols which were subsequently dehydrated to the halogenated vinylthiophenes.[39a]   Emerson and Patrick prepared 2-vinylthiophene by chloroethylation of thiophene.[46a]   Subsequent dehydrohalogenation of the 1-(2-thienyl)ethyl chloride was carried out with pyridine to give a 50% yield of 2-vinylthiophene (Eq. 9).

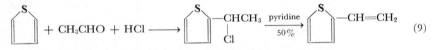

$$(9)$$

III. Polymerization of Thiophene and Its Homologs

Victor Meyer noted in 1883 that sulfuric acid polymerized thiophene to an amorphous solid.[47]   While the ease with which thiophene polymerized was a generally accepted fact, few references occurred in the ensuing years to actual substances causing the resinification.   Two references[48,49] report that hydriodic acid at about 140° with thiophene gives coke, hydrogen sulfide, and sulfur.   Klatt[50] and Fredenhagen[50a] noted that thiophene with hydrogen fluoride reacted rapidly to give an amorphous red solid.   This was substantiated in our Laboratories in acylation studies and by Kutz and Corson[34] in alkylation studies.   Recently, the polymerization of thiophene to amorphous solids has been carried out with ferric and stannic chlorides.[51]   Aluminum chloride dropped into thiophene is al-

[42] Schick and Hartough, unpublished work.
[43] Grischkewitsch-Trochimovski, *J. Russ. Phys.-Chem. Soc.*, **43**, 201 (1911).
[44] Thomas, *Bull. soc. chim.*, [4] **5**, 732 (1909).
[45] Buu-Hoï and Hiong-Ki-Wei, *Compt. rend.*, **220**, 175 (1945).
[45a] Buu-Hoï and Nguyen-Hoan, *Rec. trav. chim.*, **67**, 309 (1948).
[46] Domracheva, *J. Russ. Phys.-Chem. Soc.*, **46**, 864 (1914).
[46a] Emerson and Patrick, *J. Org. Chem.*, **13**, 729 (1948).
[47] V. Meyer, *Ber.*, **16**, 1468 (1883).
[48] Klages and Liecke, *J. prakt. Chem.*, [2] **61**, 328 (1900).
[49] Nellensteyn, *Chem. Weekblad*, **24**, 102 (1927).
[50] Klatt, *Z. anorg. allg. Chem.*, **232**, 393 (1937).
[50a] Fredenhagen, *Z. physik. Chem.*, **A164**, 176 (1933).
[51] Bruce, Challenger, Gibson, and Allenby, *J. Inst. Petroleum Technol.*, **34**, 226 (1948).

most instantly coated with an amorphous resin of thiophene.   It is thus deactivated and can be separated easily from the excess thiophene by decantation.[52]   Apparently this is one of the reasons that aluminum chloride is ineffective as a Friedel-Crafts catalyst with thiophene and alkyl halides.   This appears to be the cause of deactivation of aluminum chloride in benzene alkylation when thiophene is present.   The use of thiophene-free benzene in alkylation reactions is accepted practice.

Studies in these Laboratories[53] have indicated that thiophene polymerizes to "trimeric" and "pentameric" substances with mild polymerizing agents such as montmorillonite clays, synthetic silica-alumina gels, and with 100% orthophosphoric acid.   The structure of the trimer, which was established by destructive hydrogenation of the heterocyclic rings to the C_{12} hydrocarbon, 5-methylhendecane, indicates that the reaction takes place as demonstrated in equation 10.   The presence of the central

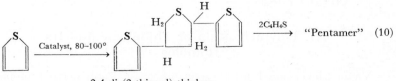

2,4-di-(2-thienyl)-thiolane

thiolane ring structure was established by infrared spectrograms.   A small amount of a dimeric material, b.p. 140–145° at 5 mm., n_D^{20} 1.626, is obtained as a foreshot in the distillation of the 2,4-di(2-thienyl)thiolane, b.p. 169–171° at 1.1 mm., n_D^{20} 1.6455.   The pentameric material has not been purified sufficiently for characterization.

The alkylthiophenes react at room temperature in the presence of clays to produce the trimers and pentamers.   The structures of these products have not been established but, on the basis of results with thiophene, the following structures for the products from the 2- and 3-methylthiophenes may be postulated (Eq. 11).

The vinylthiophenes polymerize at room temperature, and more rapidly at elevated temperatures in the presence of benzoyl peroxide, into very pale yellow to orange-colored, clear polymers.[53a]   2-Vinylthiophene has been shown to copolymerize with styrene at slower rates than o-chlorostyrene or α-vinylpyridine but faster than styrene with itself.[53b]

[52] Hartough, unpublished work.
[53] Meisel, Hartough, and Johnson, J. Am. Chem. Soc., **72**, 1910 (1950).
[53a] Schick and Hartough, J. Am. Chem. Soc., **70**, 1646 (1948).
[53b] Walling, Briggs, and Wolfstirn, J. Am. Chem. Soc., **70**, 1543 (1948).

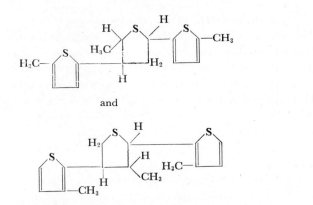

and   (11)

IV. Hydrogenation of Thiophene

Thiophene has been successfully hydrogenated to thiolane(tetra-hydrothiophene) by several methods.   These methods depend on large amounts of catalysts or on careful control of reaction conditions.   For example, molybdenum disulfide at 200° and 200 atm. of hydrogen pressure caused hydrogenation of thiophene to thiolane but the conversions were of very low order.   Of the thiophene converted, approximately 52% appeared as thiolane.   Other products were butyl sulfide (11%) and butyl mercaptan (6%).[54]   Mozingo and co-workers[55] obtained a 70% yield of thiolane by the use of palladium deposited on charcoal.   The method is not practical from any standpoint other than laboratory convenience, since two parts of reduced palladium on charcoal were required to reduce one part of thiophene.   Other references to the hydrogenation of thiophene are listed below.[56−61]

Hydrogenation of thiophene normally removes the sulfur atom as hydrogen sulfide and reduces the carbon chain to butane.   This is a convenient method for the determination of structures, and has been used successfully in two instances.[35,53]

Current desulfurization problems in the petroleum industry can be

[54] Cawley and Hall, *J. Soc. Chem. Ind.*, **62**, 116 (1943).
[55] Mozingo, *et al.*, *J. Am. Chem. Soc.*, **67**, 2092 (1945).
[56] Roberti, *Atti IV congr. nazl. chim. pura applicata* (1932), **1933**, 785; *Chem. Abstr.*, **29**, 4151 (1935).
[57] Orlov and Broun, *Khim. Tverdogo Topliva*, **3**, 817 (1932).
[58] Moldavskii and Kumari, *J. Gen. Chem.* (*U. S. S. R.*), **4**, 298–309 (1934).
[59] Maxted and Evans, *J. Chem. Soc.*, **1937**, 603.
[60] Maxted and Morrish, *J. Chem. Soc.*, **1941**, 132,
[61] Maxted, *J. Chem. Soc.*, **1945**, 204,

solved by hydrogenation of the crude oil which effectively removes all types of sulfur.   One of the most effective catalysts is cobalt molybdate.[61a]

Thiophene poisoning of hydrogenation catalysts for benzene was first pointed out by Willstätter and Hatt in 1912.[62]   These investigators found that benzene containing 0.01 mg. of thiophene per gram of benzene could not be hydrogenated over platinum.

Nickel catalysts are rapidly poisoned by thiophene.[63-67,67a]   Raney nickel has been used to remove the last traces of thiophene from benzene.[68,69]

Many of the catalysts which are used for hydrogenation will, under other conditions, effect partial hydrogenation or dehydrogenation.   2-Methylthiophene passed over copper in a hydrogen atmosphere is reported to give isoprene.[70]   Thiolane, when passed over platinum deposited on charcoal at 400°, dehydrogenates to give 32% thiophene and undergoes ring rupture to give butylenes and hydrogen sulfide.[71]   Nickel on alumina completely destroys thiolane, but nickel sulfide on alumina at 350° gives an 18% yield of thiophene.[71]

Hydrogenation of benzene and pyridine containing thiophene can be carried out by a "detoxication" process involving a short hydrogenation period to selectively absorb the thiophene on the surface of the catalyst.[72a]   It is thereby converted to thiolane and is oxidized to the nontoxic sulfone of thiolane with hydrogen peroxide.

While thiophene does not exchange hydrogen for deuterium with deuterium oxide like pyrrole, it does exchange slowly in the presence of platinum black at 100–150° with all hydrogens taking part.[72]

1,1-Dioxo-3-thiolene, the reaction product of sulfur dioxide and butadiene, is hydrogenated to thiophene in the following manner (Eq. 12).[73]   The reaction is said to be applicable to the production of alkylated thio-

[61a] *Petroleum Refiner*, Sect. 2, **27**, 250 (1948).
[62] Willstätter and Hatt, *Ber.*, **45**, 1471 (1912).
[63] Kubota and Yoshikawa, *Japan. J. Chem.*, **2**, 45 (1925).
[64] Kubota and Yoshikawa, *Sci. Papers Inst. Phys. Chem. Research (Tokyo)*, **3**, 33 (1925).
[65] Roberti, *Gazz. chim. ital.*, **63**, 46 (1933).
[66] Yoshikawa, *Bull. Inst. Phys. Chem. Research (Tokyo)*, **14**, 308 (1935).
[67] Elgin, *Ind. Eng. Chem.*, **22**, 1290 (1930).
[67a] Rubinshtein and Pribytkova, *Doklady Akad. Nauk. (U. S. S. R)*, **61**, 285 (1948).
Fuel Abstracts, **5**, No. 3, p. 59 (1949).
[68] Bougault, Cattelain, and Chabrier, *Bull. soc. chim.*, **7**, 781 (1940).
[69] Graul and Karabinos, *Science*, **104**, 557 (1946).
[70] Silberrad, *Gummi-Ztg.*, **25**, 1959 (1911).
[71] Yur'ev and Borisov, *Ber.*, **B69**, 1395 (1936).
[72] Koizumi and Titani, *Bull. Chem. Soc. Japan*, **13**, 95 (1938).
[72a] Maxted, *J. Chem. Soc.*, **1947**, 624; **1948**, 1091; *J. Soc. Chem. Ind.*, **67**, 93 (1948).
Maxted and Walker, *J. Chem. Soc.*, **1948**, 1093.
[73] Boyd, U. S. Pat. 2,440,671 (1948).

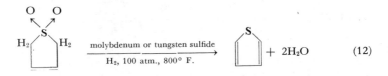

$$\text{(12)}$$

phenes, the position of the alkyl groups on the thiophene nucleus depending upon the orientation in the original butadiene.

V. Miscellaneous Chemical Reactions of Thiophene

Chemically, thiophene is much less stable than benzene.   Ring rupture with evolution of hydrogen sulfide begins to take place at about 200° in the presence of montmorillonite clays, alumina, silica gel, and synthetic alumina-silica gel cracking catalysts.[52]   In the presence of acids such as 100% orthophosphoric acid some ring rupture is noted at the boiling point.[53]   Sulfur dioxide is evolved during polymerization processes with sulfuric acid.[52]   Thallous hydroxide caused degradation of the nucleus and is reported to give thallous succinate and thallous sulfide.[74]   Thallous acetate does not react.[74a]   Potassium causes ring rupture and forms potassium sulfide while sodium is inactive.[75]   Thiophene is reported to form an ozonide when ozone in oxygen is bubbled through a suspension of thiophene in water.[76]   Thiophene undergoes autoxidation in light and is decomposed to sulfuric and oxalic acids.[77]

Hydrogen peroxide reacts with thiophene, but the products formed are of undetermined structure.[78,79]   The proposed structures should be considered in the light of the results of later investigators who failed to prepare sulfones of thiophene.[80]   The only thiophene derivatives reported to form sulfones are 3,4-dimethylthiophene,[80a] 3,4-diphenylthiophene,[80a,80b] and tetraphenylthiophene.[80b]

Thiophene undergoes typical aromatic substitution reactions that are listed in later chapters.   In general, these are much faster in the thiophene series than in the benzene series.   Many reactions that fail with benzene or at most proceed very slowly, such as aminomethylation, chloromethyl-

[74] Morgan and Ledbury, *J. Chem. Soc.*, **121**, 2882 (1922).
[74a] Gilman and Abbotts, *J. Am. Chem. Soc.*, **65**, 122 (1943).
[75] Schleiber, *Ber.*, **49**, 2596 (1916).
[76] Weyl, *Chem.-Ztg.*, **25**, 292 (1901).
[77] Sernagiotto, *Gazz. chim. ital.*, **50**, I, 226 (1920).
[78] Lanfry, *Comp. rend. Acad. Sci.*, **153**, 73, 821 (1911).
[79] Lanfry, *Comp. rend. Acad. Sci.*, **154**, 1090 (1912).
[80] Steinkopf, *Ann.*, **430**, 96 (1923).
[80a] Backer and Stevens, *Rec. trav. chim.*, **59**, 1141 (1940).
[80b] Hinsberg, *Ber.*, **48**, 1611 (1915).

TABLE VI-1. Effect of Thiophene Compounds on Octane Number of Gasoline Containing Tetraethyl Lead

0.1% sulfur in gasoline as	Octane No.	Decrease in octane No.
None	83	—
Thiophene	79	4
2-Methylthiophene	79	4
3-Methylthiophene	79	4
tert-Butylthiophene	78	5
3,4-Dimethoxythiophene	77	6
2-Thenyl alcohol	78	5
2-Thiophenealdehyde	77	6
2-Chlorothiophene	76	7
2-Thenyl chloride	74	9
Di-(2-thenyl)amine	79	4
3-Thiophenethiol	69	14
Unleaded fuel	60	—
3-Methylthiophene in unleaded fuel	60	0

ation, and mercuration, proceed with ease in the thiophene series.   It is unnecessary to draw a chemical distinction between thiophene and benzene other than to say that they are distinct chemical compounds to be compared only because both happen to be aromatic compounds.   Further, thiophene cannot easily be compared to pyrrole and furan, since there are many reactions of these materials that fail with the thiophenes. In this category is the reaction with maleic anhydride which proceeds smoothly with furan and anomalously with pyrrole but fails to proceed with thiophene.[81]   Otto found that thiophene could be copolymerized with maleic anhydride in the presence of peroxides to compounds having molecular weights of 5,000–10,000.[82]   2-Nitrothiophene has been shown to copolymerize with styrene in the presence of benzoyl peroxide to give a compound of the type $C_6H_5CO_2(C_8H_8)_{10}C_4H_2SNO_2 \cdot O_4$.[82a]

Thiophene appears to react more slowly in alkylation reactions than benzene and no alkylation with ethylene has yet been reported.   In a similar manner, ethyl diazoacetate reacts much more slowly with thiophene than with benzene to give the ethyl ester of bicyclo-Δ-2-penthiophene-5-carboxylic acid[83] (Eq. 13).

[81] Diels, Ber., A69, 198 (1936).
[82] Otto, Socony-Vacuum Laboratories, unpublished work.
[82a] Price, J. Am. Chem. Soc., 65, 2380 (1943).
[83] Steinkopf and Augestad-Jensen, Ann., 428, 154 (1922).

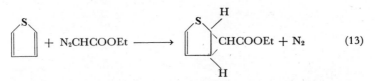

$$+ \; N_2CHCOOEt \; \longrightarrow \; \text{CHCOOEt} + N_2 \qquad (13)$$

Thiophene forms a complex with o-toluidine hydrobromide[84]: o-$CH_3C_6H_4NH_2 \cdot HBr \cdot 2C_4H_4S$. A more complex molecule, $3Ni(CN)_2 \cdot 3NH_3 \cdot C_4H_4S$, is formed with nickel cyanide-ammonia.[85]

Sulfur compounds in gasoline exert a deleterious effect on the induced octane number when tetraethyl lead is added. In this respect thiophene and its derivatives appear to have the least effect.[86] Table VI-1 gives the data obtained on a reference fuel (60 octane number) containing 3 ml. of tetraethyl lead per gallon. Addition of thiophene and its homologs to Diesel fuel gives no improvement in cetane number.[87]

Thiophene, 2-methylthiophene, and 3-methylthiophene act as inhibitors for the polymerization of trichloroethylene in a solvent used for the degreasing of iron and aluminum, said polymerization being catalyzed by contact of the solvent with the metals.[88]

[84] Prokofjeff, *J. Russ. Phys.-Chem. Soc.*, **29**, 87 (1897).
[85] Hoffmann and Arnoldi, *Ber.*, **39**, 339 (1906).
[86] Livingston, *Oil Gas J.*, **46**, 80 (1948); *Ind. Eng. Chem.*, **41**, 888 (1949).
[87] Smolak and Nelson, *Petroleum Refiner*, **27**, 405 (1948).
[88] Klabunde, U. S. Pat. 2,440,100 (1948).

CHAPTER VII

Halothiophenes and Haloalkylthiophenes

I. 2-Fluorothiophene

2-Fluorothiophene is the only member of the fluoro derivatives of thiophene known. It is prepared in low yield (10%) by the action of arsenic trifluoride on 2-iodothiophene at 90–100° in nitromethane solvent.[1] Unsuccessful attempts were made to prepare this compound from 2-chlorothiophene and 2-bromothiophene with both aluminum and arsenic trifluorides. The action of fluoboric acid on thiophenediazonium chloride failed to yield 2-fluorothiophene. It boils at 82° (760 mm.) and has a refractive index, n_D^{20}, of 1.4971.

II. Chlorothiophenes and Haloalkylthiophenes

The reactions of thiophene with chlorine have been more completely studied than those with bromine or iodine. Thiophene is halogenated very rapidly at temperatures ranging from −30° to its boiling point, 84°, in the absence or presence of light with or without the aid of a catalyst. Within the range of −30 to 80° both substitution of the thiophene nucleus and addition of chlorine to the thiophene nucleus take place. When either of the reactive 2,5-positions is unsubstituted the main reaction is substitution. After 2,5-dichlorothiophene is formed by substitution, addition to the nucleus is the predominant reaction. All of the possible chlorine substitution products can be isolated from the direct chlorination of thiophene after the metastable addition products are dehydrochlorinated. Products arising from direct substitution of the thiophene nucleus are 2- and 3-chlorothiophene, 2,3- and 2,5-dichlorothiophene, and, possibly, some 2,3,5-trichlorothiophene. Other substitution products including 2,3,4,5-tetrachlorothiophene, are formed by dehydrochlorination of the addition products.

Addition products are formed at temperatures ranging from −30 to 80° by direct addition of chlorine to the double bonds. One might anticipate that the chlorine addition products of thiophene would have

[1] Van Vleck, *J. Am. Chem. Soc.*, **71**, 3256 (1949).

173

insecticidal properties similar to those of the chlorine addition products of benzene. While these thiophene derivatives are mild vesicants and lachrymators they have practically no insecticidal activity against the common house fly.

A. Chlorine Addition Products of Thiophene

Unstable chlorine addition products were observed as early as 1884 when Weitz[1a] first chlorinated thiophene and dibromothiophene. None were isolated, however, until 1937 when Steinkopf and Kohler[2] reported the isolation of a "hydrogen chloride-addition product of tetrachlorothiophene," C_4HCl_5S. It was obtained by direct chlorination of thiophene or by perchlorination of 2-thiophenecarboxylic acid. A later attempt to isolate this compound from addition of hydrogen chloride to tetrachlorothiophene or from the perchlorination of thiophene was unsuccessful.[3]

2,3,4,5-Tetrachlorothiolane[3] (I) has been isolated from the direct chlorination of thiophene by cooling the freshly chlorinated reaction mixture below $-10°$ (Eq. 1). The temperature of the chlorination reaction

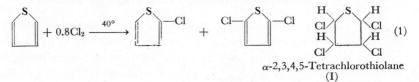

$$\alpha\text{-2,3,4,5-Tetrachlorothiolane}$$
(I)

in the range of -30 to $+80°$ does not affect appreciably the formation of addition products. With variation of the molar ratio of chlorine to thiophene, the yield of I varies from 10% at 0.5 to 1.9% at 3.0, reaching a maximum of 13% at 0.8. Compound I is not further chlorinated at $40°$ in carbon tetrachloride solution. Above $115°$, I can be chlorinated but the products have not been adequately studied.

2,3,4,5-Tetrachlorothiolane can exist in six geometric forms but only two have been isolated and characterized. Two other isomers are believed to exist but have not been obtained in the pure form. The α-isomer, m.p. $111.5–113.5°$, is isolated by direct cooling of the reaction mixture. The β-isomer, m.p. $44.5–46°$, is obtained by first removing the α-isomer by crystallization. The liquid filtrate is fractionated *in vacuo* to obtain the β-isomer.[3]

[1a] Weitz, *Ber.*, **17**, 794 (1884).
[2] Steinkopf and Kohler, *Ann.*, **532**, 250 (1937).
[3] Coonradt and Hartough, *J. Am. Chem. Soc.*, **70**, 1158 (1948).

2,2,3,4,5-Pentachlorothiolane is formed from the addition of chlorine to 2-chlorothiophene at $-30°$.[3] The yield is low, since substitution of chlorine in the nucleus is still the major reaction even at this low temperature.   Only one of the four geometric isomers of this series was isolated.[3]

2,2,3,4,5,5-Hexachlorothiolane is formed in high yields from perchlorination of thiophene and from the addition of chlorine to 2,5-dichlorothiophene[3] (Eq. 2).

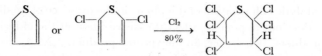

$$(2)$$

A heptachlorothiolane can be obtained in very low yields by precise fractionation *in vacuo* of perchlorination mixtures.[4] Its structure has not been determined.   An attempt to prepare a compound of this type by the addition of chlorine to 2,3,5-trichlorothiophene was fruitless.[3] Only 2,3,4,5-tetrachlorothiophene and a product containing a thiolene ring, possibly the C_4HCl_5S of Steinkopf, could be detected by infrared spectrograms. Heptachloro-3-methylthiolane was isolated from the perchlorination of 2,4,5-triiodo-3-methylthiophene[2] (Eq. 3).

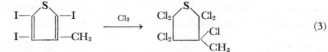

$$(3)$$

Backer and Strating have prepared dichlorothiolane homologs from isoprene and dimethylbutadiene with sulfur chloride[5] (Eqs. 4 and 5).

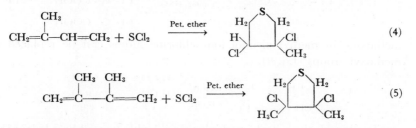

$$(4)$$

$$(5)$$

Octachlorothiolane was first prepared by Willgerodt in 1886 by passing chlorine through 2-iodothiophene[6] (Eq. 6). Recently the same product has been obtained in yields of about 70% by chlorination of

[4] Coonradt, Hartough, and Norris, to be published.
[5] Backer and Strating, *Rec. trav. chim.*, **54** [4], 52 (1935).
[6] Willgerodt, *J. prakt. Chem.*, [2] **33**, 150 (1886).

thiophene in the presence of molar amounts of iodine.[4]   The iodine tri-chloride formed in the reaction can be used to catalyze the original reaction of thiophene and chlorine to obtain similar yields.   The catalyst in the reaction is presumed to be iodine monochloride or iodine trichloride.

$$\text{(image)} \xrightarrow{\text{Cl}_2} \text{(image)} + \text{ICl}_3 \tag{6}$$

Catalytic chlorination of thiophene in the presence of small amounts of iodine does not appear to affect the distribution of the chlorine-substitution products.   However, an unexpected product, 2,2,3,4,5,5-hexachloro-3-thiolene, is formed in near quantitative yields on perchlorination[4] (without the catalytic amount of iodine, 2,2,3,4,5,5-hexachlorothiolane is formed).   (See Eq. 7.)   Continued chlorination gives no octachloro-

$$\text{(image)} \xrightarrow[80\%]{\text{excess Cl}_2,\ 0.1\ \text{g. atom I}_2} \text{(image)} \tag{7}$$

thiolane and at least 0.5 gram atom of iodine is required before this latter product can be detected in the reaction mixture.[4]   Evolution of chlorine from hexachloro-3-thoilene takes place above 160° and tetrachloro-thiophene is formed.   Oxidation of hexachloro-3-thiolene with fuming nitric acid gives dichloromaleic acid (Eq. 8).   With an excess of sodium

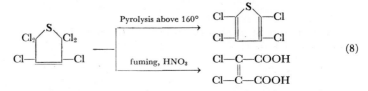

$$\tag{8}$$

methoxide in methyl alcohol four chlorine atoms can be replaced by methoxyl groups (Eq. 9).

$$\text{(image)} \xrightarrow[\text{CH}_3\text{OH}]{\text{NaOCH}_3} \text{(image)} \tag{9}$$

In general, the polychlorothiolanes are stable toward heat below 150° and can usually be distilled *in vacuo* without decomposition.   They can be decomposed to the respective chlorothiophenes by pyrolysis, alcoholic caustic, solid sodium or potassium hydroxide, hot aqueous sodium carbonate, or zinc dust or iron filings in water or alcohol.[3,7]   Since pyrolysis

[7] Coonradt, Hartough, and Johnson, *J. Am. Chem. Soc.*, **70**, 2564 (1948).

decomposes these materials, chlorination at pyrolysis temperatures yields essentially the substitution products expected from the pyrolytic dehydrochlorination of the respective addition products.[7]

Table VII-1 indicates the distribution of polychlorothiophenes obtained from the dehydrochlorination of the chlorothiolanes by the various methods investigated. Evidently, alcoholic caustic causes an initial attack on the thiophene nucleus at a β-carbon which, in turn, forces removal of an α-chlorine atom. Thus 2,4- and 3,4-dichlorothiophene are formed in about equimolar quantities from α-tetrachlorothiolane (Eq. 10). II may lose the second hydrogen atom from the other β-position and

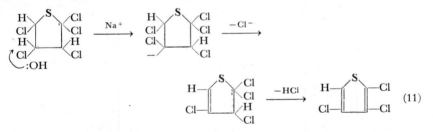

(10)

(II)

thus produce 3,4-dichlorothiophene or, since there is now an allylic chlorine at the 4-position, the α-hydrogen may be attacked by the hydroxyl group followed by removal of β-chlorine atom at the 4-position. This process then would produce 2,4-dichlorothiophene.

In a similar manner, 2,2,3,4,5-pentachlorothiolane loses the chlorine from the 5-position in the first step of the alkaline dehydrochlorination and 2,3,4-trichlorothiophene is formed in preference to 2,3,5-trichlorothiophene (Eq. 11).

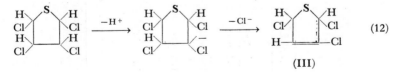

(11)

Pyrolysis, which produces a mixture of 2,4-dichlorothiophene and 2,3-dichlorothiophene from the α-tetrachlorothiolane, appears to remove the β-proton in a manner similar to the loss involved in the dehydro-

(12)

(III)

TABLE VII-1. Isomeric Chlorothiophenes Formed by Dehydrochlorination of Chlorothiolanes

Removal of HCl from	Method	Chlorothiophenes formed						
		2,5-	2,3-	2,4-	3,4-	2,3,4-	2,3,5-	2,3,4,5-
α-Tetrachlorothiolane[3]	Pyrolysis	Trace	50%	50%	—	—	—	—
	Alc. KOH	2%	0	44%	54%	—	—	—
Pentachlorothiolane[3]	Pyrolysis	—	—	—	—	8%	92%	—
	Alc. KOH	—	—	—	—	65%	35%	—
Hexachlorothiolane[3]	Pyrolysis	—	—	—	—	—	—	100%
	Alc. KOH	—	—	—	—	—	—	100%
	Aq. Zn dust[a]	70%	—	—	—	—	—	—
Hexachloro-3-thiolene[4]	Pyrolysis	—	—	—	—	—	—	100%
	Alc. KOH	—	—	—	—	—	—	100%
	Aq. Zn dust[a]	Minor component	—	—	—	Trace	Trace	Major component

[a] Thiophene and monochlorothiophene also detected, probably formed by the reductive action of zinc or from impurities of tetra- and pentachlorothiolanes.

chlorination with potassium hydroxide but in the second step the chlorine is removed from the β-carbon rather than the α-carbon (Eq. 12). The intermediate III then loses the second molecule of hydrogen chloride at random to produce the equimolar mixture of 2,3- and 2,4-dichlorothiophene.

B. Chlorine Substitution Products of Thiophene

Only two major studies of the chlorination of thiophene have been undertaken. Steinkopf and Kohler[2] made an extensive study of this field. Their work indicated that only 2-chloro-, 2,5-dichloro-, 2,3,5-trichloro-, and 2,3,4,5-tetrachlorothiophene were formed by direct substitution of the nucleus. It was later shown that 2-chloro-, 2,5-dichloro-, 2,3,4-trichloro-, and 2,3,4,5-tetrachlorothiophene were the major products obtained by the method of Steinkopf and Kohler and that all the possible chlorination isomers existed in the reaction mixtures.[7] The 2,4- and 3,4-dichlorothiophene isomers were shown to arise from dehydrochlorination of addition products. This was also the source of 2,3,4-trichloro- and tetrachlorothiophenes. Substitution of the 3,4-hydrogens in 2,5-dichlorothiophene took place very slowly even at high temperatures and the tri- and tetrachlorothiophenes were believed, therefore, to arise almost entirely from the addition products when reaction temperatures were maintained below 100° and no catalyst was used.

In order to establish that the dichlorothiophene isomers other than 2,5-dichlorothiophene did not arise through an unpredictable substitution in the thiophene nucleus, thiophene and 2-chlorothiophene were chlorinated under identical conditions at 50° and the proportion of isomers was determined by infrared analysis. Thiophene gave 99.7% yield of 2-chlorothiophene and 0.3% of 3-chlorothiophene. 2-Chlorothiophene gave 99% of 2,5-dichlorothiophene and only 1% of 2,3-dichlorothiophene.[7]

Since the chlorination of thiophene appears to be so rapid even in the dark at $-30°$, the influence of catalysts is difficult to ascertain. The distribution of the mono and dichloro substitution products is not noticeably affected by use of a chlorination catalyst such as iodine.[4] The formation of 2,2,3,4,5,5-hexachloro-3-thiolene from the exhaustive chlorination of thiophene or from the addition of chlorine to 2,3,4,5-tetrachlorothiophene with this catalyst indicates that substitution is the principal reaction even after 2,5-dichlorothiophene is formed and that the hydrogens of the 3,4-positions are replaced at a rate faster than the rate of chlorine addition to the double bonds. Unfortunately, no study has been made of the yields of trichlorothiophenes with iodine as a catalyst. If iodine increases the rate of substitution of the 3,4-hydrogens, 2,3,5-trichlorothiophene would be the anticipated trichlorothiophene isomer rather than the 2,3,4-isomer normally obtained in noncatalytic chlorination. The use of iron as a chlorination catalyst produces resinous products from thiophene.[4]

Table VII-2 summarizes the established reactions of chlorine and thiophene. A typical chlorination of thiophene gives a wide distribution

TABLE VII-2. Established Chlorination Reactions of Thiophene

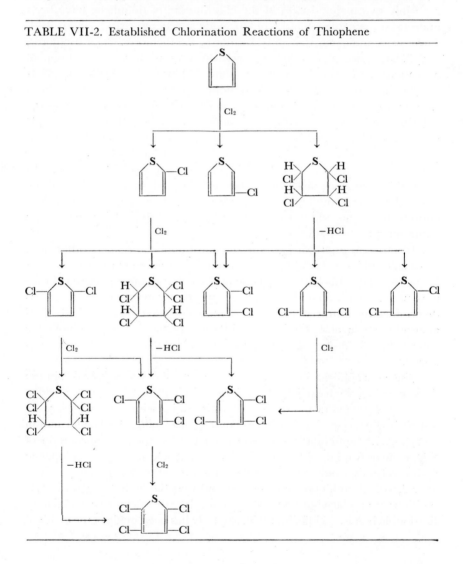

of products. For example, the products from 25 moles each of thiophene (2100 g.) and chlorine after dehydrochlorinating with solid caustic (NaOH-KOH) are listed in Table VII-3.[7]

TABLE VII-3. Distribution of the Chlorothiophenes from Chlorination of Thiophene

Derivative	Amount, g.	% Yield based on Cl
2-Chloro-............................	1055	36.8
3-Chloro-............................	3.3	0.1
2,5-Dichloro-........................	519	27.1
2,3-Dichloro-........................	63	3.3
2,4-Dichloro-........................	64	3.3
3,4-Dichloro-........................	113	5.9
2,3,4-Trichloro-.....................	120	7.3
2,3,5-Trichloro-.....................	2.5	0.2
		84.0

Methods other than direct substitution with elementary chlorine have been used in the preparation of various chlorothiophenes and a brief discussion with appropriate references will be found under specific compounds below.

1. 2-Chlorothiophene

2-Chlorothiophene is the main product (37% yield) resulting from treatment of one mole of thiophene with one mole of chlorine.[1,2,7] A somewhat higher yield (43%) is obtained when thiophene is chlorinated with sulfuryl chloride.[8,9] It is produced by the action of aqueous nitrosyl chloride[10] or hypochlorous acid [11-13] on thiophene. Chlorination with N-chloroacetamide gives 33% 2-chlorothiophene and some 2,5-dichlorothiophene[14].

2. 3-Chlorothiophene

This product is formed only in trace amounts in the direct chlorination of thiophene[7] but is best formed by the synthesis of Steinkopf and Kohler[2] (Eq. 13).

[8] Tohl and Eberhard, *Ber.*, **26**, 2945 (1893).
[9] Campaigne and Le Suer, *J. Am. Chem. Soc.*, **70**, 415 (1948).
[10] Datta and Fernandes, *J. Am. Chem. Soc.*, **36**, 1007 (1914).
[11] Ardagh and Bowman, *J. Soc. Chem. Ind.*, **54**, 267T (1935).
[12] Ardagh, Bowman, and Weatherburn, *J. Soc. Chem. Ind.*, **59**, 27 (1940).
[13] Dutt and Hamer, Brit. Pat. 117,683 (1917).
[14] Steinkopf and Otto, *Ann.*, **424**, 68 (1921).

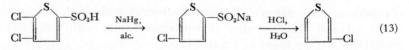

$$(13)$$

Coffman[15] reported the formation of 3-chlorothiophene by a ring closure procedure in which a stream of gaseous chloroprene was passed through molten sulfur (Eq. 14).

$$(14)$$

3. 2,5-Dichlorothiophene

2,5-Dichlorothiophene is the major dichlorothiophene isomer obtained by the direct chlorination of thiophene.[1,2,7-14]   It can be obtained in high yields from the chlorination of 2-chlorothiophene.[7]   The product distribution obtained from 2-chlorothiophene (809 g.) and an equimolar amount of chlorine at 50° is of interest in comparison with the distribution of products from thiophene previously listed (see Table VII-4).

TABLE VII-4. Distribution of the Chlorothiophenes from the Chlorination of 2-Chlorothiophene

Derivatives	Amount, g.	% Yield based on Cl
2-Chloro- (recovered)	201	—
2,5-Dichloro-	507	48.7
2,3-Dichloro-	5	0.5
2,3,5-Trichloro-	65	9.9
2,3,4-Trichloro-	116	17.3
2,3,4,5-Tetrachloro-	Present but not determined	
		76.4

4. 2,3-Dichlorothiophene

This isomer is formed in the direct chlorination of thiophene and 2-chlorothiophene[7] and in the dehydrochlorination of the α-2,3,4,5-tetra-chlorothiolane.[3]   The best method is from the chlorination of 2-thio-phenecarboxylic acid (Eq. 15).[7]   This method is an adaptation of Stein-kopf and Kohler who originally prepared the 4,5-dichloro-2-thiophene-carboxylic acid by direct chlorination of the 4,5-dibromo-2-thiophene-carboxylic acid[2] (Eq. 16).

[15] Coffman, U. S. Pat. 2,410,401 (1946).

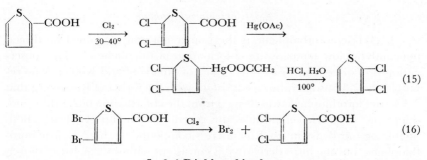

$$(15)$$

$$(16)$$

5. 2,4-Dichlorothiophene

This compound is one of the major products in the dehydrohalogenation of α-tetrachlorothiolane[3] and therefore arises in direct chlorination procedures from that source.   The compound has also been prepared by treating the sodium 4-chloro-2-thiophenesulfonate with phosphorus pentachloride[2] (Eq. 17).

$$(17)$$

6. 3,4-Dichlorothiophene

This isomer, the highest boiling of the four dichlorothiophenes, can be separated from chlorination mixtures by precise fractionation.[7]   It is formed from the alcoholic potassium hydroxide dehydrochlorination of the tetrachlorothiolanes.[3]   3,4-Dichlorothiophene has been synthesized in the following manner[2] (Eq. 18).

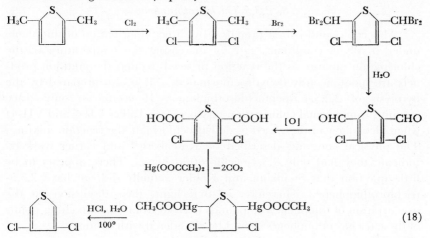

$$(18)$$

7. 2,3,4-Trichlorothiophene

2,3,4-Trichlorothiophene is the isomer normally obtained by direct, noncatalytic, low temperature chlorination of thiophene.[3,7] This observation is in direct contrast to the report of Steinkopf and Kohler[2] who reported the 2,3,5-isomer, but is consistent with the report of Rosenberg that 2,3,4-trichlorothiophene was formed from the chlorination of 2,5-dibromothiophene.[16] The mechanism of this reaction is not entirely clear. Both Steinkopf and Beilstein list Rosenberg's compound as the 2,3,5-trichlorothiophene, but the nitro derivative is consistent with the 2,3,4-trichloro-5-nitrothiophene of Steinkopf and Kohler.[2] It is most difficult to predict the formation of 2,3,4-trichlorothiophene from the chlorination of 2,5-dibromothiophene. Since Rosenberg did not fully describe his source of dibromothiophene, it may be assumed that he had a mixture of isomeric dibromothiophenes and the trichlorothiophene might have arisen from isomers other than the 2,5-isomer, or some 2-bromothiophene may have been present in the chlorination mixture.

Steinkopf and Kohler prepared 2,3,4-trichlorothiophene in the following manner[2] (Eq. 19).

$$\text{(19)}$$

Chlorination of 3,4-dichlorothiophene at 100° gives good yields of 2,3,4-trichlorothiophene and a small amount of 2,3,4,5-tetrachlorothiophene.[7]

8. 2,3,5-Trichlorothiophene

This compound is best prepared by direct chlorination of thiophene under pyrolytic conditions, i.e., by increasing the temperature of the chlorination mixture as the reaction proceeds so that the addition products are spontaneously dehydrochlorinated.[7] It is also prepared by the pyrolysis of 2,2,3,4,5-pentachlorothiolane.[3] It occurs in only trace amounts from normal chlorination mixtures (see Tables VII-3 and VII-4) when alcoholic caustic is used to dehydrochlorinate the reaction mixture. The physical constants described by Rosenberg[16] and earlier workers[2] indicate they had only 2,3,4-trichlorothiophene. There appears to be little question that Steinkopf and Kohler actually did not have 2,3,5-trichlorothiophene. Therefore, in that light, their discussion on the isomorphism of thiophene compounds derived from mixed melting points of these trichlorothiophenes should be considered with caution.

[16] Rosenberg, Ber., 19, 650 (1886).

9. 2,3,4,5-Tetrachlorothiophene

This product was first prepared by Weitz[1] from the chlorination of 2,5-dibromothiophene. It was later prepared by direct chlorination of thiophene,[2,7] by the dechlorination of 2,2,3,4,5,5-hexachloro-3-thiolene,[4] and by dehydrochlorination of 2,2,3,4,5,5-hexachlorothiolane.[3] The melting point reported by Weitz was 36° but has been more accurately determined and found to be 29.09°.[7] Reinvestigation of the product of Weitz from 2,5-dibromothiophene and chlorine indicated that a product melting at 42° could be obtained but the compound contained bromine that could not be removed by continued chlorination.[17]

High yields of 2,3,4,5-tetrachlorothiophene of the order of 70% are obtained by direct chlorination of thiophene under pyrolytic conditions.[7] A small amount of 2,2′,3,3′,4,4′-hexachloro-5,5′-dithienyl was obtained from the chlorination residues. This product could be isolated from other chlorination mixtures[7] and lower chlorinated dithienyls were also found to be present.[17] Eberhard reported formation of dichloro-dithienyl by action of sulfuric acid on 2-chlorothiophene.[18]

Steinkopf and Kohler[2] apparently were mistaken in their conclusion that the trichlorothiophene was formed in low yields because it was rapidly converted by chlorine into tetrachlorothiophene. A tenfold excess of chlorine with 2,3,5-trichlorothiophene gave only a 40% yield of tetrachlorothiophene.[7]

C. Chlorination of Alkylthiophenes

Chlorination of alkylthiophenes has been investigated to a lesser extent than has thiophene. In this series it has been found that nuclear substitution predominates over side chain chlorination even under conditions considered most favorable for side chain chlorination. The nucleus chlorinates with the same ease as thiophene and multiple substitution of the nucleus is the general rule.

Bonz, in 1885, reported the formation of a dichloroethylthiophene from chlorination of 2-ethylthiophene in the cold.[19] Opolski studied the chlorination of 2- and 3-methylthiophenes, 2-ethyl- and 2-butylthiophene and reported constants for the monochloro derivatives.[20,21] The sulfuryl chloride method has been applied to 2- and 3-methylthiophene with yields of the monochloro product ranging from 75–80% of theory.[9] In the latter case only the 2-chloro-3-methylthiophene isomer is reported.

[17] Coonradt and Hartough, unpublished work.
[18] Eberhard, Ber., 28, 2385 (1895).
[19] Bonz, Ber., 18, 549 (1885).
[20] Opolski, Anz. Akad. Wiss. Krakau, 1904, 730; Chem. Zentr., 1905, I, 1255.
[21] Opolski, Anz. Akad. Wiss. Krakau, 1905, 548; Chem. Zentr., 1905, II, 1796.

Chlorination of 2,5-dimethylthiophene gives 2,5-dimethyl-3,4-dichloro-thiophene.[2]

4,5-Dichloro-3-methylthiophene has been prepared in the manner as shown in equation 20.[22]   It was also noted that chlorination of methyl-

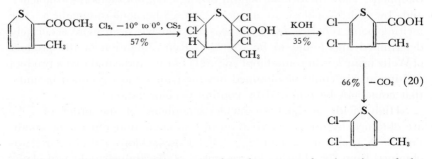

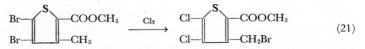

4,5-dibromo-3-methyl-2-thiophenecarboxylate caused migration of the bromine to the methyl group (Eq. 21).

4,5-dibromo-3-methyl-2-thiophenecarboxylate caused migration of the bromine to the methyl group (Eq. 21).

Table VII-8 (Section F) lists the physical constants of the chloro derivatives of the alkylthiophenes.

D. Introduction of the Halogens into an Alkylthiophene Side Chain

Several attempts have been made to halogenate alkylthiophenes in the alkyl group by methods normally used in the benzene series.   Opolski[20,21] states that 2-alkylthiophenes chlorinate almost entirely in the nucleus.   Voerman has chlorinated 3-methylthiophene in the side chain with phosphorus trichloride in the sunlight, but concurrent ring chlorination predominates.[23]

Buu-Hoï and Lecocq[24] found that bromosuccinimide, when warmed with 2,5-dimethylthiophene, gave 5-methyl-2-thenyl bromide.   Later this method was adapted and improved by Campaigne and Le Suer[25,26] and by Dittmer and co-workers[27] for the preparation of 3-thenyl bromide

[22] Steinkopf and Nitschke, *Ann.*, **536,** 135 (1938).
[23] Voerman, *Rec. trav. chim.*, **26,** 293 (1907).
[24] Buu-Hoï and Lecocq, *Compt. rend.*, **222,** 1441 (1946).
[25] Campaigne and Le Suer, *J. Am. Chem. Soc.*, **70,** 1555 (1948).
[26] Campaigne and Le Suer, *J. Am. Chem. Soc.*, **71,** 333 (1949); U. S. Pats. 2,471,090 and 2,471,091 (1949).
[27] Dittmer, Martin, Herz, and Cristol, *J. Am. Chem. Soc.*, **71,** 1201 (1949).

and found to give much higher yields when catalyzed by peroxides (Eq. 22). This development is of especial interest since it provides a conven-

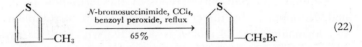

$$\text{(22)}$$

The reaction: thiophene–CH₃ with N-bromosuccinimide, CCl₄, benzoyl peroxide, reflux, 65% → thiophene–CH₂Br

ient synthesis for an intermediate through which many new 3-substituted thiophenes can be conveniently prepared (see Chapter V for more specific comments).

Side chain chlorination of 2-acetylthiophene can be accomplished by chlorinating the ketone in the vapor phase.[28] 2-Chloroacetylthiophene is produced in this manner. It is also formed by direct chlorination of 2-acetylthiophene in the presence of light[29] (Eq. 22a). In a somewhat

$$\text{(22a)}$$

thiophene–COCH₃, Cl₂, 65–75°, light, 77% → thiophene–COCH₂Cl

similar manner, it was found that 2-(bromoacetyl)thiophene could be prepared from 2-acetylthiophene in 80% yields by bromination in carbon tetrachloride solution if the reaction was catalyzed by iron.[30]

Chloromethylation of thiophene was first developed in 1942 by Blicke and Burckhalter[31] (Eq. 23). Attempts to improve this synthesis

$$\text{(23)}$$

thiophene + CH₂O + HCl, 0° → thiophene–CH₂Cl (40%) + thiophene–CH₂–thiophene (40%)

by blocking one of the reactive α-positions with halogens have been very successful; the yields are improved and formation of the dithienylmethanes is not reported[32] (Eq. 24). The chloromethylation of many alkyl-

$$\text{(24)}$$

Cl–thiophene + CH₂O + HCl, 70% → Cl–thiophene–CH₂Cl

thiophenes[33] has been reported but no yields or physical constants were given. 2,5-Dimethylthiophene is chloromethylated in the 3-position in

[28] Peter, *Ber.*, **18**, 537 (1885).
[29] Emerson and Patrick, *J. Org. Chem.*, **13**, 729 (1948).
[30] Kipnis, Soloway, and Ornfelt, *J. Am. Chem. Soc.*, **71**, 10 (1949).
[31] Blicke and Burckhalter, *J. Am. Chem. Soc.*, **64**, 477 (1942).
[32] Clapp, *et al.*, *J. Am. Chem. Soc.*, **69**, 1549 (1947).
[33] Blicke, U. S. Pats. 2,425,721–3, August 19, 1947.

low yield.[34]   The major product of this reaction was di-(2,5-dimethyl-3-thienyl)methane.

Griffing and Salisbury[35] reported the formation of 2,5-bis(chloromethyl)thiophene by direct chloromethylation of thiophene.   Aqueous 37% formaldehyde (28 moles) is saturated with gaseous hydrogen chloride, cooled to 30°, and thiophene (8 moles) is added.   The yield of crude product is 79%.   In this form it can be used directly for various replacement reactions.   The product is unstable and must be stored in the cold, although it can be distilled *in vacuo* without decomposition.   It is a lachrymator and a vesicant.   It polymerizes at room temperature with evolution of hydrogen chloride.

Chloroethylation of thiophene, 2-chloro- and 2-bromothiophene with acetaldehyde and hydrochloric acid has been effected but the products are too unstable to be isolated.[29]   They can be dehydrochlorinated with pyridine to produce the corresponding vinylthiophenes.

Chloromethylation of the halothiophenes can be carried out as shown in equation 25.[36,37]   The 3,4-hydrogens of both 2,5-dichloro- and 2,5-

$$\text{Br-}\underset{\text{S}}{\bigcirc}\text{-Br} + CH_2O \text{ (aq.)} \xrightarrow[53\%]{\substack{\text{6 moles HCl (aq.),} \\ 60°, \text{ 2 hrs.}}} \text{Br-}\underset{\text{S}}{\bigcirc}\text{-Br, } -CH_2Cl \qquad (25)$$

dibromothiophene are comparable to the hydrogens of mesitylene in activity and some small amounts of a dichloromethylated product were detected.[36]   The 4-hydrogen in 2,3,5-trichlorothiophene is less active and consequently lower yields of the 2,3,5-trichloro-4-thenylchloride (less than 20%) were obtained in a similar experiment.[36]

Side chain bromination of alkylthiophenes having a completely substituted nucleus has been carried out successfully[2,22] (see Eq. 18).

The 2-thenyl halides can be prepared from the 2-thenyl alcohols by treatment with hydrohalic acids or phosphorus trihalides.[31,38-41]

2-Acetylthiophene chloromethylates on the β-methyl group of the acetyl moiety in direct contrast to acetophenone.[42]   A mixture of a mono- and dichloromethylated ketone is obtained (Eq. 26).

[34] Buu-Hoï and Nguyen-Hoan, *Rec. trav. chim.*, **68**, 5 (1949).
[35] Griffing and Salisbury, *J. Am. Chem. Soc.*, **70**, 3416 (1948).
[36] Norris and Hartough, unpublished work.
[37] Clark, *et al.*, *J. Org. Chem.*, **14**, 216 (1949).
[38] Biedermann, *Ber.*, **19**, 636 (1886).
[39] Gomberg and Jickling, *J. Am. Chem. Soc.*, **35**, 446 (1913)
[40] Minnis, *J. Am. Chem. Soc.*, **51**, 2143 (1929).
[41] Braun, Fussgangen, and Kuhn, *Ann.*, **445**, 201 (1925).
[42] Hartough, unpublished work.

$$(26)$$

Thienylmethanes of the DDT type are produced by condensation of thiophene with chloral. This reaction was reported first by Peter in 1884[43] (Eq. 27). Bromination of this compound gave the 1,1,1-trichloro-

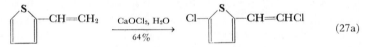

$$(27)$$

2-bis(3,4,5-tribromo-2-thienyl)ethane. Many varieties of this synthesis have been carried out by later investigators.[44-47] Physical constants of the DDT isologs and other side chain halogenated thiophenes appear in Table VII-9 (Section F).

2-Vinylthiophene reacts with calcium hypochlorite to give 5,β-dichloro-2-vinylthiophene[29] (Eq. 27a).

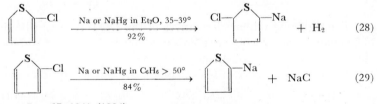

$$(27a)$$

E. Reactions of Chloro- and Halomethylthiophenes

The reactions of the chlorothiophenes have not been too fully investigated, but some unique reactions have been found. For example, 2-chlorothiophene can be metalated directly with sodium in ether solution and hydrogen is evolved (equation 28), but in benzene solution the replacement of the chlorine by sodium occurs[48] (equation 29).

$$(28)$$

$$(29)$$

[43] Peter, *Ber.*, **17**, 1341 (1884).
[44] Nahke, *Ber.*, **30**, 2041 (1897).
[45] Metcalf and Gunther, *J. Am. Chem. Soc.*, **69**, 2579 (1947).
[46] Truitt, Mattison, and Richardson, *J. Am. Chem. Soc.*, **70**, 79 (1948).
[47] Feeman, Dove, and Amschutz, *J. Am. Chem. Soc.*, **70**, 3136 (1948).
[48] Schick and Hartough, *J. Am. Chem. Soc.*, **71**, 286 (1948).

2-Chlorothiophene is not reported to undergo Grignard formation. It undergoes standard reactions slower than thiophene but acylates, mercurates,[2] and aminoalkylates[48a] normally.

2,5-Dichlorothiophene does not form a thienylsodium with sodium, but instead produces resins.[49]   With aluminum chloride and acetyl chloride, it acylates normally in the 3-position.[2,50]   Acylation with acetic anhydride using phosphoric acid as the catalyst causes replacement of the chlorine by an acetyl group[51] (Eq. 30).   2,5-Dichlorothiophene can be iodinated or brominated in the 3,4-positions.[2]

$$Cl-\langle S \rangle-Cl \xrightarrow{(CH_3CO)_2O, \ H_3PO_4, \ 110^\circ} Cl-\langle S \rangle-COCH_3 \qquad (30)$$

Chloromethylation of halogenated thiophenes can be carried out more efficiently than chloromethylation of thiophene (see discussion under chloromethylation) due to the lower reactivity of the nucleus.

2-Thenyl chloride is a rather unstable chemical and is best stored in a loosely stoppered bottle in a cool place.[52]   In a tightly stoppered bottle it has a tendency to decompose with some violence.   The best procedure for use of this material in further syntheses is to use freshly distilled material or to use the chloromethylation reaction mixture directly. Recent patents describe the stabilization by addition of small amounts of heterocyclic amines.[53]   The material is a lachrymator with an odor similar to benzyl chloride.

Lecocq[54] has shown that the bromine in 5-methyl-2-thenylbromide rearranges quantitatively to the nucleus when warmed with cuprous cyanide while attempting to prepare 5-methyl-2-thenylnitrile (Eq. 31).

$$H_3C-\langle S \rangle-CH_2Br \xrightarrow[100\%]{CuCN, \ heat} H_3C-\langle S \rangle \begin{matrix} -CH_3 \\ -Br \end{matrix} \qquad (31)$$

The dithienyl ethane derivatives of the **DDT** type can be dehydro-halogenated with alcoholic potassium hydroxide.[45,46]   Oxidation with chromic oxide gives 2-(2-thenoyl)thiophene.[46]

The thiophene derivatives of chloral are not as effective toward the

[48a] Hartough, Lukasiewicz, and Murray, *J. Am. Chem. Soc.*, **70**, 1146 (1948).
[49] Schick and Hartough, unpublished work.
[50] Hartough and Conley, *J. Am. Chem. Soc.*, **69**, 3096 (1947).
[51] Hartough and Kosak, *J. Am. Chem. Soc.*, **69**, 3093 (1947).
[52] Dunn, Waugh, and Dittmer, *J. Am. Chem. Soc.*, **68**, 2118 (1946).
[53] Zienty, U. S. Pats. 2,457,079–081 (1948).
[54] Lecocq, *Ann. chim.*, **3**, 62 (1948).

common fly as DDT and γ-hexane,[45,46] but they are as effective toward cockroaches as DDT.

F. Physical Properties

Table VII-6 lists the physical properties of the substituted chlorothiophenes. Vapor pressure data for 2-chloro- and 2,5-dichlorothiophene are listed in Table VII-5. Table VII-7 lists the properties of the chlorine-addition products of thiophene. The addition products are mild vesicants and lachrymators but do not show insecticidal activity of the order of γ-hexane. The chlorine substitution products of thiophene are effective soil fumigants and are especially toxic to nematodes.

TABLE VII-5. Vapor Pressure Measurements of 2-Chlorothiophene and 2,5-Dichlorothiophene[55]

2-Chlorothiophene		2,5-Dichlorothiophene	
Temp., °C.	Pressure, mm. Hg	Temp., °C.	Pressure, mm. Hg
32.6	21.5	42.4	11.0
42.4	36.0	56.4	19.0
51.0	51.0	82.8	59.0
56.6	66.0	91.8	84.0
60.8	78.0	99.0	111.0
65.0	92.5	102.0	125.0
68.0	103.0	109.4	161.0
70.6	115.0	114.6	191.0
76.0	141.0	117.8	211.0
81.2	161.0	122.0	233.0
85.8	201.0	130.6	311.7
89.0	221.0	142.0	435.7
91.8	233.0	150.2	557.7
104.2	377.7	157.8	665.7
115.4	529.7	163.2	765.7
117.8	561.7		
120.2	604.7		
128.6	765.7		
Heat of vaporization, cal./gram mole	8945		9605

$$\log P_{mm.} = \frac{-A}{T^\circ_k} + B = \frac{-1954}{T^\circ_k} + 7.75 \qquad\qquad = \frac{-2082}{T^\circ_k} + 7.64$$

[55] Private communication to the author from D. J. Crowley, these Laboratories. The vapor pressures were determined in a Cottrell-type apparatus, temperature measured by Anschütz thermometers, pressures determined by conventional laboratory mercury manometer.

TABLE VII-6. Physical Constants of the Chlorothiophenes[a]

Chloro isomer:	2-	3-	2,3-	2,4-	2,5-	3,4-	2,3,4-	2,3,5-	2,3,4,5-
Boiling point, °C	128.32	136–137	172.70	167.58	162.08	182.01	209.60	198.66	233.39
Freezing point, °C	−71.91	−63–62	−37.3	−37.2	−40.46 −50.92	−0.54	−2.76	−16.06	+29.09
Refractive indices									
n_D^{20}	1.5487	1.5532 (22°)	1.5651	1.5560	1.5626	1.5762	1.5861	1.5791	—
n_e^{20}	1.5530	—	—	—	1.5672	—	—	1.5837	—
n_g^{50}	1.5726	—	—	—	1.5880	—	—	1.6046	—
n_D^{20}	1.5450	—	—	—	1.5572	—	—	1.5741	1.5915
$\Delta n_D/\Delta t$	−0.00057	—	—	—	−0.00054	—	—	−0.00050	—
Density									
d_4^{20}	1.2863	—	1.4605	1.4553	1.4422	1.4867	1.6125	1.5856	1.7036
d_4^{80}	1.2737	—	—	—	1.4288	—	—	1.5724	—
$\Delta d_4/\Delta t$	−0.00126	—	—	—	−0.00134	—	—	−0.00132	—
Viscosity, centipoises, 30°..	0.803	—	—	1.091	0.997	1.465	2.181	1.464	3.318
Surface tension, dynes/cm., 30°	34	—	—	—	35.5	—	—	38	40
Molar refraction									
R_D^{20}	29.32	—	34.14	34.30	34.44	34.07	39.02	39.30	—
R_D^{30}	29.34	—	—	—	34.49	—	—	39.35	44.05
Molecular weight	118.58	—	153.03	153.03	153.03	153.03	187.48	187.48	221.93
Molecular volume, 20°	92.19	—	104.78	105.15	106.11	102.93	116.27	118.24	—
30°	93.10	—	—	—	107.14	—	—	119.23	130.27

[a] With the exception of 3-chlorothiophene[2] all constants are those of footnote 7.

The physical constants, the alkylchlorothiophenes, and the haloalkyl-thiophenes are listed in Tables VII-8 and VII-9, respectively.

Spectrochemical properties of various halogenated thiophenes are discussed by Auwers and Kohlhass.[63] The Raman spectra of 2,3,5-

TABLE VII-7. Physical Constants of Chlorine-Addition Products of Thiophene

Compound	B.p., °C. (mm.)	M.p., °C.	$n_D^{(t)}$	Ref.
2,3,4,5-Tetrachlorothiolane	—	—	—	3
α-Isomer	111.5 (3.4)	111.5–113.5	—	—
β-Isomer	110–118 (5)	44.5–46	1.5688 (50°)	—
2,2,3,4,5-Pentachlorothiolane	—	31–32	1.5755 (35°)	3
2,2,3,4,5,5-Hexachlorothiolane	100–105 (1)	45–46	1.5590 (50°)	3
2,2,3,4,5,5-Hexachloro-3-thiolene	89 (2)	40–41	1.5757 (50°)	4
Octachlorothiolane	—	217–218.5	—	4,6
Heptachloro-3-methylthiolane	—	217–218.5	—	2
3,4-Dichloro-3-methylthiolane	68–70 (3)	—	—	5
3,4-Dichloro-3,4-dimethylthiolane	—	174	—	5
2,3,4,5-Tetrachloro-3-methyl-2-thiolanecarboxylic acid, methyl ester	—	52.5–53.5	—	22

TABLE VII-8. Physical Constants of the Alkylchlorothiophenes[67]

Compound	B.p., °C. (mm.)	n_D^{20}	$d_4^{(t)}$	Ref.
5-Chloro-2-methylthiophene	154–155 (742)	1.5372	1.2147 (25)	9,20
	55 (19)	—	—	—
2-Chloro-3-methylthiophene	154–155 (742)	1.5408	1.2281 (25)	9,21
2,5-Dichloro-3-methylthiophene	65 (11)	1.5560	—	26
4,5-Dichloro-3-methylthiophene	96.5 (31)	—	—	22
2,4,5-Trichloro-3-methylthiophene	115–116 (23)	1.5662 (21.5)	—	2
3,4-Dichloro-2,5-dimethylthiophene	—	—	—	2
5-Chloro-2-ethylthiophene	175.5 (737)	1.5330	1.1629 (12.3)	21
	85–88 (37)	—	—	21
3(4),5-Dichloro-2-ethylthiophene	235–237 (760)	—	—	19
5-Chloro-2-butylthiophene	117–118 (88)	1.5162	1.0842 (17)	21

[56] Fredga and Palm, *Arkiv. Kemi. Mineral. Geol.*, **A26**, No. 26 (1949); *Chem. Abstr.*, **43**, 6611 (1949).

[57] Steinkopf, *Ann.*, **513**, 281 (1934).

[58] Cagniant, Cagniant, and Deluzarche, *Bull. soc. chim.*, **15**, 1083 (1948).

[59] Gerlach, *Ann.*, **267**, 145 (1892).

[60] Paal, *Ber.*, **18**, 2253 (1885).

[61] Messinger, *Ber.*, **18**, 563 (1885).

[62] Griskevich-Trokhimovskii and Mazurewitsch, *J. Russ. Phys.-Chem. Soc.*, **44**, 570 (1911); *Chem. Abstr.*, **6**, 2406 (1912).

[63] Auwers and Kohlhass, *J. prakt. Chem.*, [2] **108**, 321 (1924).

trichloro-[64] and tetrachlorothiophene[65] have been determined. All of the infrared spectrograms of the chlorothiophenes and the chlorine-thiophene addition products are to be found in Chapter IV. The dipole moments of some of the halothiophenes have recently been determined and it is reported that the values show general resemblance to the structures of the corresponding benzene derivatives.[66]

TABLE VII-9. Physical Constants of Haloalkylthiophenes[67]

Compound	B.p., °C. (mm.)	M.p., °C.	Ref.
thiophene—CH₂Cl	80–81 (18)	—	31,52,56
thiophene—CH₂Br	80–82 (15)	−10	27,41
thiophene—CH₂Br	75–78 (1)	− 9	25,27
H₃C—thiophene—CH₂Br	90 (13)	—	24,54
(CH₃)₃C—thiophene—CH₂Cl	67–71 (1)	—	37
H₃C—thiophene—CH₃, —CH₂Cl	110–115 (13)	—	34
ClCH₂—thiophene—CH₂Cl	106–108 (5)	36–37	35
Cl—thiophene—CH₂Cl	67–68 (1)	—	32
	90 (20)	—	36
Cl—thiophene—CH₂Cl, —Cl	125–128 (30)	—	37

Table Continued

[64] Bonino and Manzoni-Ansidei, *Z. physik. Chem.*, **B25**, 327 (1934).
[65] Simon and Kirret, *Naturwissenschaften*, **28**, 47 (1940).
[66] Keswani and Freiser, *J. Am. Chem. Soc.*, **71**, 218 (1949).
[67] Thiocyanates and isothiocyanates are included as halogens.

TABLE VII-9 (*Continued*)

Compound	B.p., °C. (mm.)	M.p., °C.	Ref.
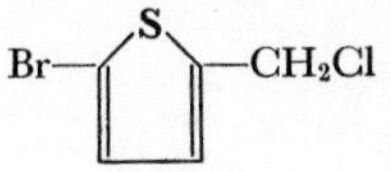 Br—[thiophene]—CH$_2$Cl	82–83 (1)	—	32
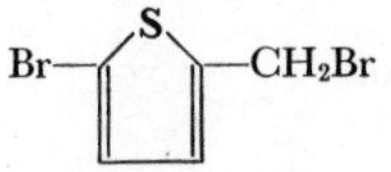 Br—[thiophene]—CH$_2$Br	71 (1.2)	—	27,37
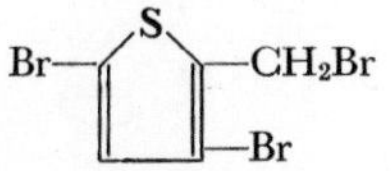 Br—[thiophene]—CH$_2$Br, —Br	104–108 (1)	—	37
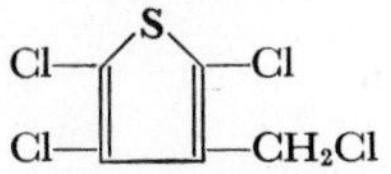 Cl—[thiophene]—Cl, Cl—[thiophene]—CH$_2$Cl	108 (4)	—	36
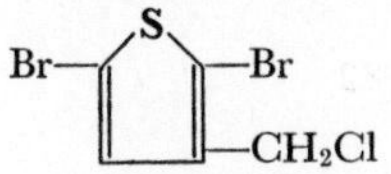 Br—[thiophene]—Br, —CH$_2$Cl	110–113 (3)	—	36
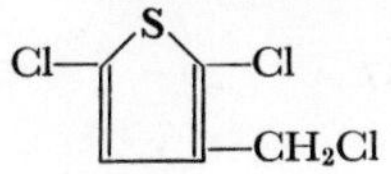 Cl—[thiophene]—Cl, —CH$_2$Cl	109–110 (15)	—	36,37
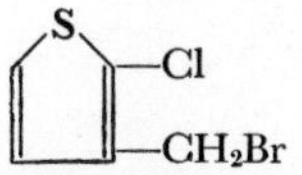 [thiophene]—Cl, —CH$_2$Br	85–92 (1–2)	—	26
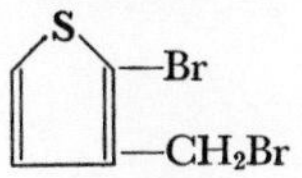 [thiophene]—Br, —CH$_2$Br	113 (7)	—	26,27
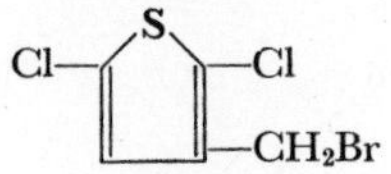 Cl—[thiophene]—Cl, —CH$_2$Br	104.5–106 (4)	—	26
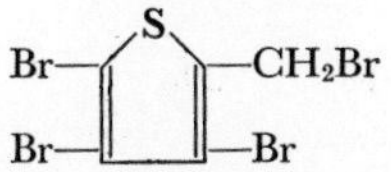 Br—[thiophene]—CH$_2$Br, Br—[thiophene]—Br	—	86	57
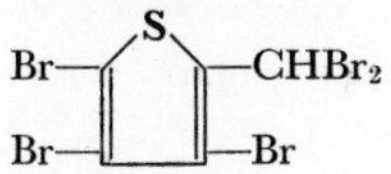 Br—[thiophene]—CHBr$_2$, Br—[thiophene]—Br	—	60–61	57
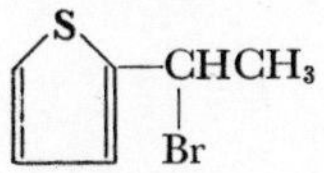 [thiophene]—CHCH$_3$, Br	Unstable	—	58
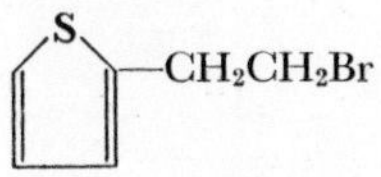 [thiophene]—CH$_2$CH$_2$Br	100–102 (15)	—	58

Table Continued

TABLE VII-9.   Physical Constants of Haloalkylthiophenes (*Continued*)

Compound	B.p., °C. (mm.)	M.p., °C.	Ref.
$\text{CH—C}_3\text{H}_7$, Br (thiophene)	63 (3)	—	37
Br—, Br—, CBr_2CH_3, —Br (thiophene)	—	86	59
CHBrCH_2Br (thiophene)	—	47–50	29
Cl—, CHBrCH_2Br (thiophene)	—	76	29
Br—, CHBrCH_2Br (thiophene)	—	80–82	29
CHCH_2SCN, SCN (thiophene)	—	87	29
Cl—, CHCH_2SCN, SCN (thiophene)	—	99	29
Cl—, CHCH_2SCN, CNS (thiophene)	—	65	29
Br—, CHCH_2SCN, SCN (thiophene)	—	96	29
Cl—, $\text{CH}=\text{CHCl}$ (thiophene)	116–118 (18)	16–18	29
H_3C—, CH_2Br, Br—, —Br (thiophene)	—	142–144	60
Cl_2CH—, CHCl_2, Cl—, —Cl (thiophene)	—	80	2
Br_2CH—, CHBr_2, Cl—, —Cl (thiophene)	—	112	2

TABLE VII-9 (*Continued*)

Compound	B.p., °C. (mm.)	M.p., °C.	Ref.
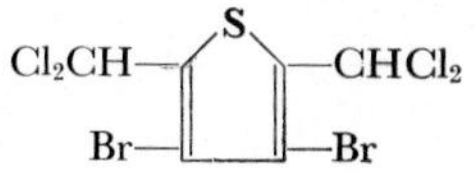 Cl_2CH—S—$CHCl_2$, Br—Br	—	103	2
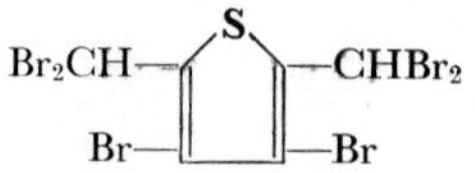 Br_2CH—S—$CHBr_2$, Br—Br	—	132	2
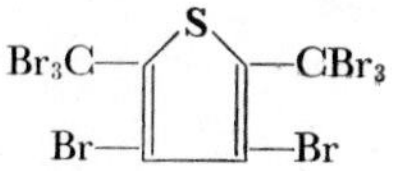 Br_3C—S—CBr_3, Br—Br	—	114	61
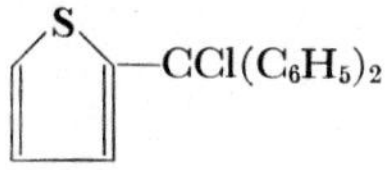 S—$CCl(C_6H_5)_2$	—	81	39,40
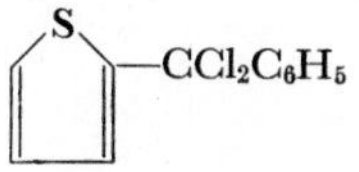 S—$CCl_2C_6H_5$	Dec.	—	39,40
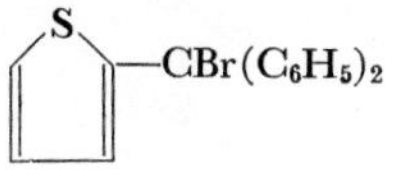 S—$CBr(C_6H_5)_2$	—	110–111	40
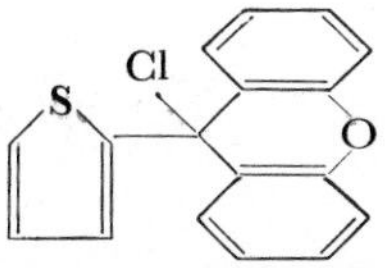 S, Cl (xanthene O)	—	—	40
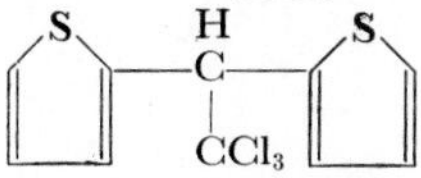 S—C(H)(CCl_3)—S	—	78.4–79.2	43,45,46, 47
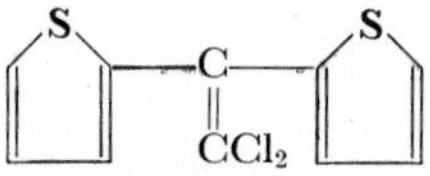 S—C(CCl_2)—S	208–210 (6)	—	43,46
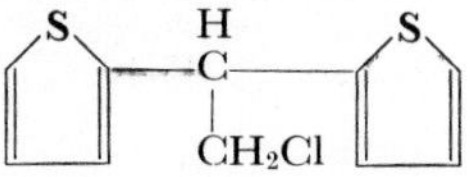 S—C(H)(CH_2Cl)—S	200–205 (25)	—	44
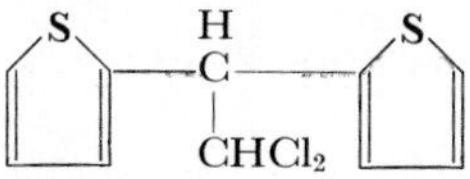 S—C(H)($CHCl_2$)—S	190–195 (18)	—	44
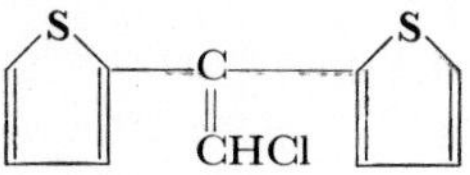 S—C(=$CHCl$)—S	170–180 (23)	—	44

Table Continued

TABLE VII-9.   Physical Constants of Haloalkylthiophenes (*Continued*)

Compound	B.p., °C. (mm.)	M.p., °C.	Ref.
(thienyl)–CH(CH₂Br)–(thienyl), H on C, CH₂Br below	200–210 (30)	—	44
(thienyl)–C(Br)(CH₂Br)–(thienyl), Br above, CH₂Br below	—	128 (dec.)	44,62
(thienyl)–CHBrCHBr—C₆H₅	—	113 (dec.)	62
Br,Br-dibromothienyl–C(CCl₃)(H)–Br,Br-dibromothienyl, each ring Br substituted, –Br	—	176	29
Cl–(thienyl)–C(H)(CCl₃)–(thienyl)–Cl	—	65–66	45,46,47
Cl–(thienyl)–C(H)(CHCl₂)–(thienyl)–Cl	208—210 (6)	—	45,46
Br–(thienyl)–C(H)(CCl₃)–(thienyl)–Br	—	94–94.7	45,46,47
I–(thienyl)–C(H)(CCl₃)–(thienyl)–I	—	94.8–95.1	46
(thienyl, CH₃)–C(CCl₃)(H)–(thienyl, CH₃)	—	124–125	45
H₃C–(thienyl)–C(H)(CCl₃)–(thienyl)–CH₃	—	72.2	45,46
(CH₃)₃C–(thienyl)–C(H)(CCl₃)–(thienyl)–C(CH₃)₃	—	90.5–91	47
Cl,Cl-dichlorothienyl–C(H)(CCl₃)–Cl,Cl-dichlorothienyl	—	109.5–109.7	47

TABLE VII-9 (*Continued*)

Compound	B.p., °C. (mm.)	M.p., °C.	Ref.
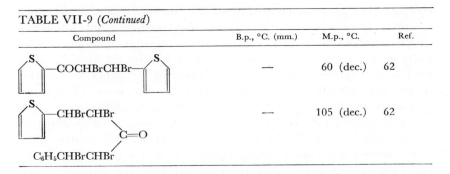	—	60 (dec.)	62
	—	105 (dec.)	62

III. The Bromothiophenes

Bromination of thiophene was the first chemical reaction of thiophene to be reported by Victor Meyer.   Since 1883, a large amount of research has been carried out in this field and a considerable number of bromo derivatives of thiophene have been reported.   Unfortunately, factors influencing substitution in the thiophene ring were not well understood in the early days so that it is difficult to verify exactly which isomers were actually prepared.   In some cases in Tables VII-10 and VII-11 (Section F) the author has assigned positions to the substituents in derivatives prepared by some of the early experimenters on the basis of orientation in the chlorination of thiophene.

Apparently no attempt has ever been made to isolate the bromine addition products of thiophene.   It appears that they must be present, since brominated thiophene mixtures must be stabilized with alcoholic potassium hydroxide in much the same manner as the chlorinated thiophene mixtures.   In regard to their relative stability, it can be predicted that the addition products would not be as stable as those isolated from the chlorination of thiophene, but their anticipated higher melting points might make them easier to separate from the reaction mixtures as crystalline products.

There has been no detailed study of the bromination products of thiophene and one can only refer to the chlorinated thiophenes where all the possible isomers were shown to occur in the reaction mixture and predict that all isomers of brominated thiophene probably are present in the reaction mixture.

A. Bromination of Thiophene

Victor Meyer's procedure for the bromination of thiophene consisted of adding an equimolar amount of bromine to thiophene with efficient cooling.   This step was followed by washing the heavy oil with water and caustic.[1]   Fractionation of the product yielded predominantly a dibromothiophene (2,5-) and a minor amount of a monobromothiophene (2-). Later in the same year, 1883, Meyer and Kreis[2] reported the isolation of tetrabromothiophene from the products obtained by further bromination of the polybromothiophenes from Meyer's earlier work.   Exhaustive bromination of thiophene gives 2,3,4,5-tetrabromothiophene.[3]

A tribromothiophene (presumably the 2,3,5-isomer) is obtained by further bromination of dibromothiophene.[4]   Meyer and Stadler found that benzene containing thiophene could be brominated and pure mono- and dibromothiophenes could be separated from the mixture.[5]   This method was later applied to a study of thiophene compounds in Russian shale oil.[6]   Better yields of 2-bromothiophene are obtained by brominating thiophene in glacial acetic acid[7,8] or in benzene.[9]

Small amounts of a dibromothiophene are produced when 2-bromothiophene is treated with fuming sulfuric acid,[6] but the main product is a mixture of mono- and dibromodithienyl.   Tribromothiophene is obtained by treating dibromothiophene with fuming sulfuric acid.   Tetrabromothiophene is formed by the same method from the tribromothiophene. 2,5-Dibromothiophene, a tribromothiophene (presumably, the 2,3,5-isomer), and tetrabromothiophene are produced from the action of bromine on an aqueous solution of 2,5-thiophenedimercurichloride.[10,11]

The best yield of 2-bromothiophene (77%) is obtained by refluxing thiophene with N-bromosuccinimide.[11a]

2-Bromothiophene (52%) is obtained by the action of N-bromoacetamide on thiophene in acetone at $-5°$.[12]   When an excess of the brominating agent (2.5 moles) is employed, a 65% yield of 2,5-dibromothiophene results.[12]   Cyanogen bromide, when heated at 45–50° with thiophene, gives 2-bromothiophene (45%) and a small amount of 2,5-dibromothiophene.[13]

[1] V. Meyer, *Ber.*, **16**, 1465 (1883).
[2] V. Meyer and Kreis, *Ber.*, **16**, 2172 (1883).
[3] Volhard and Erdmann, *Ber.*, **18**, 454 (1885).
[4] Rosenberg, *Ber.*, **18**, 1773 (1885).
[5] Meyer and Stadler, *Ber.*, **18**, 1488 (1885).
[6] Dodonov and Soshestvenska, *Ber.*, **B59**, 2202 (1926).
[7] Tohl and Schultz, *Ber.*, **27**, 2834 (1894).
[8] Krause and Renwanz, *Ber.*, **B62**, 1710 (1929).
[9] Mozingo, *et al.*, *J. Am. Chem. Soc.*, **67**, 2092 (1945).
[10] Steinkopf and Bauermeister, *Ann.*, **403**, 62 (1914).
[11] Briscoe, Peel, and Young, *J. Chem. Soc.*, **1929**, 2589.
[11a] Buu-Hoï, *Ann.*, **556**, 1 (1944).
[12] Steinkopf and Otto, *Ann.*, **424**, 64 (1919).
[13] Steinkopf, Augestad-Jensen, and Donat, *Ann.*, **430**, 78 (1922).

The relative rates of bromination of thiophene have been determined by Lauer in glacial acetic acid and benzene.[14] The reaction rate increases with the increasing dielectric constant of the solvent. A comparison of Lauer's rate constants indicates that thiophene is brominated about 20,000 times faster than benzene when using acetic acid as a solvent.

3-Bromothiophene is best prepared by reacting 2,3-dibromothiophene with methylmagnesium bromide[15] (Eq. 1). 2,3-Dibromothiophene is

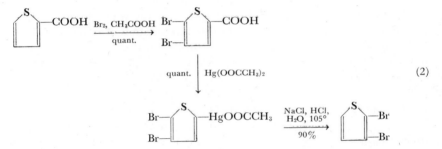

prepared by brominating 2-thiophenecarboxylic acid in glacial acetic acid. The brominated acid is decarboxylated with mercuric acetate:[16,16a]

(2)

A mixture of 2,3- and 2,4-dibromothiophene is obtained by treatment of 2,3,5-tribromothiophene with methylmagnesium bromide in the method demonstrated in equation 1.[17] 2,3,4-Tribromothiophene is prepared in 50% yields from tetrabromothiophene in the same manner. 3,4-Dibromothiophene is then prepared from the 2,3,4-tribromothiophene by removal of the other reactive α-bromine. 3,4-Dibromothiophene results in small quantities when 3,4-dibromo-2,5-thiophenedialdehyde is subjected to the Cannizzaro reaction. Presumably the diacid formed in the reaction is decarboxylated.[18]

B. Bromination of Alkyl- and Arylthiophenes

In general the same methods employed with thiophene are used with minor variations in techniques. Aliphatic side chain bromination with

[14] Lauer, *Ber.*, **B69**, 2618 (1936).
[15] Steinkopf, *Ann.*, **543**, 128 (1940).
[16] Steinkopf and Kohler, *Ann.*, **532**, 250 (1937).
[16a] P. D. Caesar, these Laboratories, private communication to the author.
[17] Steinkopf, Jacob, and Penz, *Ann.*, **512**, 136 (1934).
[18] Steinkopf and Eger, *Ann.*, **533**, 270 (1938).

elementary bromine occurs only after complete substitution of the nucleus has been effected (see Section II above).

1. The Methylthiophenes

The methylthiophenes in coal tar toluene were first separated by preferential bromination.[19,20]   The two isomeric methylthiophenes form tribromo derivatives that first appeared to form a mixed crystalline product (m. 74°). Investigation of this product revealed that it consisted of the 2,4,5-tribromo-3-methylthiophene (m. 34°) and the 3,4,5-tribromo-2-methylthiophene (m. 91°).[20] Controlled preferential bromination of alkylthiophenes in coal tar fractions has proved to be a convenient method of separation of these compounds, but it is difficult to assign structures to the mono-, di-, and tribromothiophenes prepared.[21—23]

2-Methylthiophene is brominated with bromine water to give 3,4,5-tribromo-2-methylthiophene.[24]   Selective bromination of both 2- and 3-methylthiophenes under a variety of conditions has been investigated by a number of workers.[16,25—28]   The isomeric products obtained are listed in Table VII-11.   From the data presented, it would appear that 3-methylthiophene monobrominates exclusively in the 2-position.   N-Bromo-succinimide[28a,b] with 2- and 3-methylthiophene in the presence of peroxides gives both nuclear and side chain bromination, the latter reaction predominating.

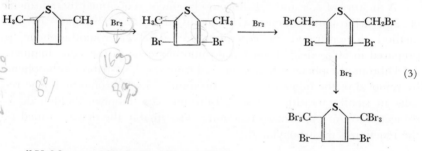

$$(3)$$

[19] V. Meyer and Kreis, *Ber.*, **17**, 787 (1884).
[20] Gattermann, Kaiser, and Meyer, *Ber.*, **18**, 3005 (1885).
[21] Keiser, *Ber.*, **28**, 1804 (1895).
[22] Keiser, *Ber.*, **29**, 2560 (1896).
[23] Challenger, *et al.*, *J. Inst. Petroleum Technol.*, **12**, 106 (1926).
[24] Egli, *Ber.*, **18**, 544 (1885).
[25] Opolski, *Anz. Akad. Wiss. Krakau*, **1904**, 728; *Chem. Zentr.*, **1905**, I, 1255.
[26] Opolski, *Anz. Akad. Wiss. Krakau*, **1905**, 550; *Chem. Zentr.*, **1905**, II, 1796.
[27] Steinkopf, *Ann.*, **513**, 281 (1934).
[28] Steinkopf and Nitschke, *Ann.*, **536**, 135 (1938).
[28a] Campaigne and Le Suer, *J. Am. Chem. Soc.*, **70**, 1555 (1948).
[28b] Dittmer, Martin, Herz, and Cristol, *J. Am. Chem. Soc.*, **71**, 1201 (1949).

2,5-Dimethylthiophene gives the corresponding 3,4-dibromothiophene.[29] With an excess of bromine, a tribromo derivative[29] and an octabromo derivative[30] are formed (Eq. 3).

Exhaustive bromination of alkylthiophenes substituted in the 2-position causes cleavage of the alkyl group. Thus, excess bromine with 2-methylthiophene[16,31] or 2-propylthiophene[31a] yields 2,3,4,5-tetrabromothiophene.

2. The Ethylthiophenes

Bromination of 2-ethylthiophene yields 5-bromo-2-ethylthiophene if bromine water is used.[32] Pure bromine yields the 3,4,5-tribromo-2-ethylthiophene.[33]

3-Ethylthiophene can be brominated to yield a monobromo (probably the 2-isomer), a dibromo (2,5-derivative), and a tribromo derivative.[34] Perbromination yielded a pentabromo derivative to which Gerlack assigned the structure of 2,4,5-tribromo-3-(α,α-dibromoethyl)thiophene:[34]

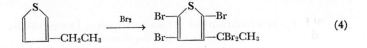

(4)

3. The Phenylthiophenes

Although thiophene brominates much more readily than benzene,[14] bromination of 2-phenylthiophene could not be directed exclusively to the thiophene nucleus.[35] Perbromination yielded the 2-(p-bromophenyl)-3,4,5-tribromothiophene (Eq. 5).

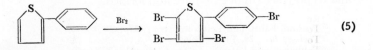

(5)

The use of cyanogen bromide as a brominating agent with 2-phenylthiophene gives the 5-bromo derivative in 90% yields[36] (Eq. 6).

[29] Messinger, *Ber.*, **18**, 563 (1885).
[30] Paal, *Ber.*, **18**, 2251 (1885).
[31] R. Meyer and Wesche, *Ber.*, **50**, 422 (1917).
[31a] Ruffi, *Ber.*, **20**, 1740 (1887).
[32] Demuth, *Ber.*, **19**, 679 (1886).
[33] Schleicher, *Ber.*, **18**, 3015 (1885).
[34] Gerlack, *Ann.*, **267**, 145 (1892).
[35] Kues and Paal, *Ber.*, **19**, 3141 (1886).
[36] Steinkopf, Petersdorfl, and Gording, *Ann.*, **527**, 272 (1937).

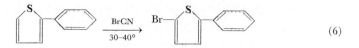

$$(6)$$

Tetrabromo derivatives have been prepared from 2,4- and 2,5-diphenylthiophene but no attempt was made to determine the position of the bromine atoms.[37] Judging from the work of Kues and Paal[35] it can be assumed that the third and fourth bromines are in the p,p'-positions of the phenyl radicals.

A monobromo derivative of triphenyl-2-thienylmethane can be prepared but the position of the bromine atom was not determined.[38]

4. Alkenylthiophenes

Bromination of 5-chloro (or bromo)-2-vinylthiophene yields the corresponding ethylene bromide derivative, 5-Cl(Br)-2-CH$_2$BrCHBr—C$_4$H$_2$S.[38a] Bromination of 2-allylthiophene is reported but the products were not investigated for ring or side chain substitution.[39]

C. Bromination of Thianaphthene, Thiophthene, and Bithiophenes

Bromination of the di- and polythienyls is accomplished in a manner similar to that of thiophene.[7,40–47] 3-Bromothianaphthene results from the direct bromination of thianaphthene.[48] A tetrabromothianaphthene is also reported but the structure was not determined.[81] Capelle has reported a dibromothiophthene derivative, m.p. 122.5°, by brominating thiophthene in carbon disulfide.[49] A tetrabromothiophthene (m.p. 172°) and its polymer (m.p. 223°) are also formed.

[37] Fromm, Fantl, and Leibsohn, *Ann.*, **457**, 267 (1927).
[38] Weisse, *Ber.*, **29**, 1402 (1896).
[38a] Emerson and Patrick, *J. Org. Chem.*, **13**, 729 (1948).
[39] Grishkevich-Trokhimovskii, *J. Russ. Phys.-Chem. Soc.*, **43**, 201 (1911); *Chem. Abstr.*, **6**, 223 (1912).
[40] Nahnsen, *Ber.*, **17**, 2197 (1884).
[41] Renard, *Compt. rend.*, **112**, 49 (1891).
[42] Tohl and Eberhard, *Ber.*, **26**, 2945 (1893).
[43] Tohl and Eberhard, *Ber.*, **26**, 2947 (1893).
[44] Tohl, *Ber.*, **27**, 665 (1894).
[45] Clark *et al.*, *J. Org. Chem.*, **14**, 216 (1949).
[46] Auwers and Bredt, *Ber.*, **27**, 1741 (1894).
[47] Eberhard, *Ber.*, **28**, 2385 (1895).
[48] Davies and Smith, *Nature*, **139**, 154 (1937).
[49] Capelle, *Bull. soc. chim.*, (4) **3**, 154 (1908).

D. Bromination of Thiophene Derivatives Containing Electron-Withdrawing Groups

In certain instances, members of this class of bromo derivatives are discussed in more detail in the respective chapters on various functional groups.

Bromination of 2-thiophenecarboxylic acid gives the 4,5-dibromo derivative.[16,17,50] 2-Thiophenealdehyde gives a dibromo derivative, presumably the 4,5-dibromo-2-thiophenealdehyde.[51] Bromination of thienyl ketones has been studied only to a limited extent.[52,53] 2-Benzoyl-thiophene with excess bromine gives only a dibromo derivative but in a sealed tube at 100° tetrabromothiophene is formed.[52] The bromination of nitrothiophene[54] is discussed elsewhere (see Chapter VIII).

E. Reactions of the Bromothiophenes

The reactions of the bromothiophenes are comparable to those of the chlorothiophenes only in certain respects. In general, the comparable reactions are mercuration,[55] metalation with sodium,[56] nitration,[57,58] sulfonation to produce the bromodithienyls,[41–43] and acylation which replaces a bromine atom by an acyl group.[59]

The bond energy of the bromine-carbon bond in the 2- or 5-position is lower than that of the corresponding chlorine-carbon bond. The 2-bromothiophenes, therefore, undergo Grignard reactions with ease.[16–18,27,60,61] 3-Bromothiophene does not undergo Grignard formation with magnesium in ether.[17] While typical Wurtz syntheses are not reported with the chlorothiophenes, 2-bromothiophene undergoes this reaction with sodium and ethyl bromide to give a product described as impure 2-ethylthiophene.[33] However, Eberhard[62] pointed out later that 2-bromo-thiophene with sodium in ether solvent failed to give the expected 2,2′-

[50] Peter, *Ber.*, **18**, 542 (1885).
[51] Rojohn and Schulten, *Arch. Pharm.*, **264**, 348 (1926).
[52] Marcusson, *Ber.*, **26**, 2457 (1893).
[53] Kitt, *Ber.*, **28**, 1807 (1895).
[54] Babasinian, *J. Am. Chem. Soc.*, **60**, 2906 (1938).
[55] Steinkopf, Rosler, and Setzer, *Ann.*, **522**, 35 (1936).
[56] Schick and Hartough, *J. Am. Chem. Soc.*, **70**, 286 (1948).
[57] Kreis, *Ber.*, **17**, 2073 (1884).
[58] Babasinian, *J. Am. Chem. Soc.*, **57**, 1763 (1935).
[59] Gattermann and Romer, *Ber.*, **19**, 688 (1886).
[60] Steinkopf, *Ann.*, **543**, 128 (1940).
[61] Steinkopf and Jacob, *Ann.*, **515**, 273 (1935).
[62] Eberhard, *Ber.*, **27**, 2919 (1894).

dithienyl.   In view of this observation and the more recent synthesis of 5-bromo-2-thienylsodium from 2-bromothiophene and sodium in ether solvent,[56] Schleicher's product[33] should be reinvestigated.   Since Schleicher admitted that his 2-ethylthiophene was no more than 80% pure as shown by analysis, the product may have contained substantial amounts of 5-bromo-2-ethylthiophene which formed as shown in equation 7.

$$Br-\overset{S}{\underset{}{\bigcirc}}-H \xrightarrow{Na,\ Et_2O} Br-\overset{S}{\underset{}{\bigcirc}}-Na\ +\ H_2 \xrightarrow{C_2H_5Br} Br-\overset{S}{\underset{}{\bigcirc}}-C_2H_5 \tag{7}$$

2-Bromothiophene undergoes normal metathetical replacement reactions.   Thus, 2-thiophenecarboxylic acid is obtained by treatment of 2-bromothiophene with cuprous cyanide and potassium cyanide[63] under conditions favoring hydrolysis (Eq. 8).   With piperidine in a sealed tube at 240°, 2-bromothiophene gives an unidentified amine.[64]

$$\overset{S}{\underset{}{\bigcirc}}-Br\ +\ KCN\ +\ CuCN \xrightarrow[\text{in sealed tube}]{H_2O,\ EtOH,\ 200°} \overset{S}{\underset{}{\bigcirc}}-COOH \tag{8}$$

Replacement of nuclear bromine by chlorine takes place spontaneously,[16,17,65-67] but replacement from the thiophene nucleus[67] is not complete.   Replacement of a nuclear bromine by hydrogen is accomplished in very high yields by reduction with sodium amalgam in alcohol[16,17,68-70] and by hydrogen in the presence of palladium.[9]   Rinkes[70] reported that reduction of a methyldibromothiophenecarboxylic acid with sodium amalgam gives a dihydromethylthiophenecarboxylic acid.   Replacement of the bromine by nitro groups can be effected easily in high yields through the action of nitric acid,[71] nitrogen trioxide,[72] or nitric acid in sulfuric acid.[73]   Equations 9–11 represent the three modes of replacement.

$$Br-\overset{S}{\underset{Br}{\bigcirc}}\overset{-Br}{\underset{-CH_3}{}} \xrightarrow{\text{concd. HNO}_3} O_2N-\overset{S}{\underset{Br}{\bigcirc}}\overset{-NO_2}{\underset{-CH_3}{}} \tag{9}$$

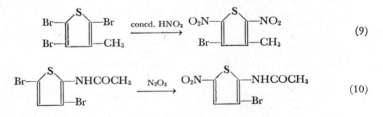

$$Br-\overset{S}{\underset{}{\bigcirc}}\overset{-NHCOCH_3}{\underset{-Br}{}} \xrightarrow{N_2O_3} O_2N-\overset{S}{\underset{}{\bigcirc}}\overset{-NHCOCH_3}{\underset{-Br}{}} \tag{10}$$

[63] Rosenmund and Struck, *Ber.*, **52**, 1749 (1919).
[64] Tohl, *Ber.*, **28**, 2217 (1895).

$$Br-\overset{S}{\underset{Br}{\bigcirc}}-SO_2Cl \quad \xrightarrow{HNO_3-H_2SO_4} \quad O_2N-\overset{S}{\underset{Br}{\bigcirc}}-NO_2 \qquad (11)$$

Oxidation of tetrabromothiophene with fuming nitric acid gives dibromomaleic acid[74,75] (Eq. 12). In a similar manner tribromo-2-

$$Br-\overset{S}{\underset{Br}{\bigcirc}}-Br \quad \xrightarrow{\text{fuming } HNO_3,\ 0-10°} \quad \begin{array}{c} Br-C-COOH \\ \parallel \\ Br-C-COOH \end{array} \qquad (12)$$

methylthiophene and tribromo-3-methylthiophene oxidize to compounds which are indicative of the original structure (Eqs. 13 and 14).

$$Br-\overset{S}{\underset{Br}{\bigcirc}}-CH_3 \quad \xrightarrow{\text{fuming } HNO_3,\ 0-10°} \quad \begin{array}{c} Br-C-COOH \\ \parallel \\ Br-C-COCH_3 \end{array} \qquad (13)$$

$$Br-\overset{S}{\underset{CH_3}{\bigcirc}}-Br \quad \xrightarrow{\text{fuming } HNO_3,\ 0-10°} \quad \begin{array}{c} H_3C-C-COOH \\ \parallel \\ Br-C-COOH \end{array} \qquad (14)$$

F. Physical Properties

The physical constants of the bromothiophenes are listed in Table VII-10. Those of the bromo derivatives of alkyl- and arylthiophenes are found in Table VII-11. Bromine derivatives of thiophene compounds containing a functional group, such as —COOH or —SO$_2$Cl, are recorded in their respective chapters.

Spectrochemical properties of 2-bromo- and 2,5-dibromothiophene have been investigated and various refractive indices reported.[76] Raman spectra data for 2-bromothiophene,[77] 2,5-dibromothiophene,[78] 2,3,4-tribromothiophene,[77] and 2,3,5-tribromothiophene have been reported. See compiled data on Raman spectra (Chapter IV). Infrared absorption

[65] Weitz, *Ber.*, **17**, 792 (1884).
[66] Rosenberg, *Ber.*, **19**, 650 (1886).
[67] Coonradt, Hartough, and Johnson, *J. Am. Chem. Soc.*, **70**, 2567 (1948).
[68] Langer, *Ber.*, **17**, 1566 (1884).
[69] Bonz, *Ber.*, **18**, 549 (1885).
[70] Rinkes, *Rec. trav. chim.*, **54**, 940 (1935).
[71] Muhlert, *Ber.*, **18**, 3003 (1885).
[72] Priestley and Hurd, *J. Am. Chem. Soc.*, **69**, 1173 (1947).
[73] Rosenberg, *Ber.*, **18**, 3027 (1885).
[74] Angeli and Ciamician, *Ber.*, **24**, 74 (1891).
[75] Ciamician and Angeli, *Ber.*, **24**, 1347 (1891).
[76] Auwers and Kohlhass, *J. prakt. Chem.*, [2] **108**, 321 (1924).
[77] Simon and Kirret, *Naturwissenschaften*, **28**, 47 (1940).
[78] Bonino and Manzoni-Ansidei, *Z. physik. Chem.*, **B25**, 327 (1934).

spectra of 2-bromothiophene have been determined.[79,80]   These are reported in Chapter IV.

TABLE VII-10. Physical Constants of Bromothiophenes

Derivative	B.p., °C. (mm.)	M.p., °C.	n_D^{20}	d_4^{20}	Ref.
2-Bromo-.........	149–151	—	1.5866	1.684	1,5,7–9,12, 76,81,82, 85
			n_{He}^{20} 1.587	—	76
3-Bromo-.........	157–158	—	1.5861	—	15,17
2,3-Dibromo-.......	212–213	−15.5	1.6309	—	85
			1.6304 (22.8°)	—	16,17
2,4-Dibromo-.......	210	−30 to −25	—	—	17
2,5-Dibromo-.......	210.3	−6.0	1.6288	—	1,5,7,9,12, 16,17,68, 69,85
			n_{He}^{20} 1.630	2.141	76
3,4-Dibromo-.......	221–222	4.5	—	—	17,18
2,3,4-Tribromo-....	Above 260	43–46	—	—	17,82
2,3,5-Tribromo-....	259–260	29	—	—	4,7,17
2,3,4,5-Tetrabromo-.	326	114	—	—	2,3,6,7,11, 17
	170–173 (13)				

TABLE VII-11. Physical Properties of Brominated Alkyl- and Arylthiophenes

Thiophene derivative	B.p., °C. (mm.)	M.p., °C.	n_D^{20}	d_4^{20}	Ref.
5-Bromo-2-methyl-..........	177	—	1.5673	1.5529	13,25,27, 28b
	29 (1.8)				
3-Bromo-2-methyl-..........	174–176	—	—	—	27,45
3,4-Dibromo-2-methyl-......	237–237.5	9	—	—	27
3,5-Dibromo-2-methyl-......	227.5–230	−13	—	—	27,45
3,4,5-Tribromo-2-methyl-....	—	91	—	—	19,20,24, 25,27

[79] Garach and Lecomte, *Compt. rend.*, **222**, 74 (1946).
[80] Lecomte, *Bull. soc. chim.*, **1946**, 415.
[81] Steinkopf, *Ann.*, **430**, 78 (1923).
[82] Steinkopf and Hanske, *Ann.*, **532**, 236 (1937).
[83] von Schweinitz, *Ber.*, **19**, 644 (1886).
[84] Lecocq, *Ann. chim.*, **3**, 85 (1948).
[85] Hartough and Dickert, unpublished work, determined refractive indices of 2-bromo-, 2,3-dibromo-, and 2,5-dibromothiophene on samples distilled through 12-plate fractionating column.

Table VII-11 (*Continued*)

Thiophene derivative	B.p., °C. (mm.)	M.p., °C.	n_D^{20}	d_4^{20}	Ref.
2-Bromo-3-methyl-..........	175 (729)	—	1.5731	1.571 $^{20}_{20}$	26,61,28*b*
	27 (1.8)				
4-Bromo-3-methyl-..........	180–182	—	—	—	61
2,4-Dibromo-3-methyl-......	105 (13.5)	—	—	—	28
2,5-Dibromo-3-methyl-......	226–230	—	1.6126	1.972 $^{20}_{20}$	61,28*b*
	55 (2)				
4,5-Dibromo-3-methyl-......	109.5	—	—	—	28,61
	–111 (14.5)				
	234.5–235.5	—	—	—	—
2,4,5-Tribromo-3-methyl-....	—	34	—	—	3,19,20,61
5-Bromo-2-ethyl-............	199.2	—	1.5576	1.4642	25,32
3(4),5-Dibromo-2-ethyl-.....	—	Oil	—	—	69
3,4,5-Tribromo-2-ethyl-......	—	108	—	—	69
5-Bromo-2-propyl-..........	189	—	—	—	31*a*
5-Bromo-2-butyl-...........	138.5 (42)	—	1.5398	1.3369	26
5-Bromo-2-octyl-............	285–290	5	—	—	83
3-Bromo-2,5-dimethyl-.......	195–198	—	—	—	84
	96 (13)				
3,4-Dibromo-2,5-dimethyl-...	128 (15)	47–50	—	—	29,30,84
3-Bromo-2,5-dipropyl-.......	130–132.5	—	—	—	13,81
	(10)				
3(4)-Bromo-2-ethyl-5-isoamyl-	122–127 (14)	—	—	—	13,81
3(4)-Bromo-2-methyl-5-octyl-.	—	20	—	—	83
Tetrabromo-2,5-diphenyl-....	—	203	—	—	37
Tetrabromo-2,4-diphenyl-...	—	150	—	—	37
5-Bromo-2-phenyl-..........	—	85–86	—	—	36
3,4,5-Tribromo-2-*p*-bromo-phenyl-.................	—	145–146	—	—	35
2-Bromo-3-ethyl-............	180–190	—	—	—	34
2,5-Dibromo-3-ethyl-........	215–225	—	—	—	34
2,3,5-Tribromo-3-ethyl-......	272–280	—	—	—	34

IV. Iodothiophenes and Mixed Halothiophenes

The earliest method for the direct iodination of thiophene, developed in Victor Meyer's laboratory, still stands today as the best method of preparing iodothiophenes. This method, involving the use of iodine and mercuric oxide, is very convenient and gives a higher yield of the mono-substituted derivative than can be obtained with any other halogen. The ease with which 2-iodo- and 3-iodothiophene undergo the Grignard reaction has made them suitable starting materials for a great number of thiophene derivatives. Iodine addition products are unknown.

Since mixed halogen compounds of thiophene have received only limited attention they are included as a basic portion of this section—due to their relationship to the iodothiophenes.

A. Preparation of the Iodothiophenes

1. 2-Iodothiophene

Direct iodination of the thiophene nucleus can be accomplished in high yields, 70–80%, by iodinating thiophene in the presence of mercuric oxide[1,2] (Eq. 1). This method can be widely adapted to thiophene

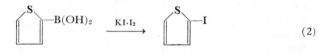

$$\text{(thiophene)} + I_2 \xrightarrow[70-80\%]{\text{HgO, benzene, 10-25°}} \text{(2-iodothiophene)} + HgI_2 \qquad (1)$$

homologs and derivatives and direct iodination of compounds such as 2,5-dialkylthiophenes proceeds smoothly. Without the mercuric oxide, the hydrogen iodide liberated polymerizes the thiophene and causes ring rupture with evolution of hydrogen sulfide. Other references to this method are numerous and only the most pertinent are listed.[3-6]

While cyanogen bromide gives good yields of 2-bromothiophene, cyanogen iodide fails to give 2-iodothiophene.[7]

2-Iodothiophene has been prepared by the action of potassium triiodide $(KI \cdot I_2)$ on 2-thiopheneboronic acid[8] (Eq. 2).

$$\text{(thiophene)}-B(OH)_2 \xrightarrow{KI \cdot I_2} \text{(2-iodothiophene)}-I \qquad (2)$$

2. 3-Iodothiophene

This compound has been prepared in good yields (62%) by the method of Rinkes[9, 10] (Eq. 3) through the reduction of tetraiodothiophene

[1] V. Meyer and Kreis, *Ber.*, **17**, 1558 (1884).
[2] Minnis, *Org. Syntheses*, Coll. Vol. II, p. 357.
[3] Curtius and Thyssen, *J. prakt. Chem.*, [2] **65**, 5 (1902).
[4] Krause and Renwanz, *Ber.*, **62**, 1710 (1929).
[5] Schlenk and Ochs, *Ber.*, **48**, 678 (1915).
[6] Grischkevitsch-Trokhimovskii, *J. Russ. Phys.-Chem. Soc.*, **43**, 204 (1911); *Chem. Abstr.*, **6**, 223 (1912).
[7] Steinkopf, Augestad-Jensen, and Donat, *Ann.*, **430**, 78 (1922).
[8] Johnson, Van Campen, and Grummitt, *J. Am. Chem. Soc.*, **60**, 111 (1938).
[9] Rinkes, *Rec. trav. chim.*, **55**, 991 (1936).
[10] Steinkopf, Schmitt, and Fiedler, *Ann.*, **527**, 237 (1937).

with aluminum amalgam (see Appendix I for detailed preparation).

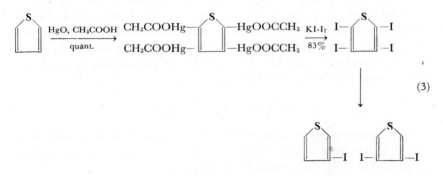

$$(3)$$

3. 2,5-Diiodothiophene

2,5-Diiodothiophene is conveniently prepared in high yields through the method of Meyer and Kreis[1] by reacting one mole of thiophene with two moles of iodine in the presence of one mole of mercuric oxide.

Volhard prepared 2,5-diiodothiophene by reacting iodine with 2,5-thiophenedimercurichloride but no yields were given.[11] Steinkopf and Bauermeister carried out the reaction stepwise isolating the intermediate, 2-iodo-5-thiophenemercurichloride.[12] Iodine and the 2,5-thiophenedimercuriacetate also give 2,5-diiodothiophene[13] (Eq. 4).

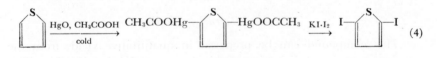

$$(4)$$

4. 2,3-Diiodothiophene

2,3-Diiodothiophene has been prepared by an indirect procedure[10] which involves Volhard's original technique (Eq. 5).

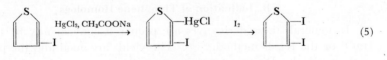

$$(5)$$

5. 2,4-Diiodothiophene

This compound is not reported in the literature.

[11] Volhard, *Ann.*, **267**, 180 (1892).
[12] Steinkopf and Bauermeister, *Ann.*, **403**, 69 (1914).
[13] Paolini and Silberstrom, *Gazz. chim. ital.*, **55**, 388 (1915).

6. 3,4-Diiodothiophene

This diiodo derivative is prepared in the same reaction with 3-iodothiophene by the reductive action of aluminum amalgam on tetraiodothiophene.[10]   The yields are very good if proper proportions of the amalgam are employed.   Rinkes,[9] in using larger proportions of amalgam, failed to find the 3,4-diiodothiophene.

7. 2,3,4-Triiodothiophene

Preparation of this compound has been reported by the reduction of the tetraiodothiophene with sodium amalgam in dioxane and with sodium in amyl alcohol.[10]   No yields are reported.

8. 2,3,5-Triiodothiophene

2,3,5-Triiodothiophene has been prepared by a direct process involving iodination of 3-iodothiophene[10] (Eq. 6).   It has also been prepared by

$$\text{[structure]} \xrightarrow{2I_2,\ HgO} \text{[structure]} + HgI_2 + H_2O \qquad (6)$$

the action of concentrated sulfuric acid on 2,5-diiodothiophene.   This disproportionation method also yields tetraiodothiophene.[14]

9. 2,3,4,5-Tetraiodothiophene

This compound can be prepared in quantitative yields from the tetraacetoxymercury derivative of thiophene and $KI \cdot I_2$.[10,12,13,15,16]   This method has been used for the quantitative determination of thiophene in benzene.[14]   It is also prepared by the action of concentrated sulfuric acid on 2,5-diiodothiophene.[14]

B. Iodination of Thiophene Homologs

In general, these derivatives are prepared conveniently by the I_2—HgO[1] or the $KI \cdot I_2$ method.[16-18]   The yields are good and the products easily purified.   Direct reference to specific compounds can be found in Table VII-13.

[14] Steinkopf, Petersdorff, and Gording, *Ann.*, **527**, 278 (1937).
[15] Briscoe, Peel, and Young, *J. Chem. Soc.*, **1929**, 2589.
[16] Steinkopf and Hanske, *Ann.*, **527**, 264 (1937).
[17] Steinkopf and Hanske, *Ann.*, **532**, 236 (1937).
[18] Steinkopf, Merckoll, and Strauch, *Ann.*, **545**, 45 (1940).

TABLE VII-12. Physical Constants of the Iodothiophenes

Derivative	B.p., °C. (mm.)	M.p., °C.	Ref.
2-Iodo-.....................	73 (15)	−40 to −41	1–6,10
	80–81 (20)	—	—
	90–94 (34–38)	—	—
	66.5 (9)	—	—
3-Iodo-.....................	68 (12)	−13.4	9,10
2,3-Diiodo-..................	138.5 (12)	−10	10
2,5-Diiodo-..................	139–140 (15)	40.5–41.5	1,10,11,12, 27,36
3,4-Diiodo-..................	142–143 (12)	4.5	10
2,3,4-Triiodo-...............	—	116	10
2,3,5-Triiodo-...............	—	87–88	10,14
2,3,4,5-Tetraiodo-............	—	199	9,10,13–16

TABLE VII-13. Physical Constants of the Iodoalkylthiophenes

Thiophene derivative	B.p., °C. (mm.)	M.p., °C.	Ref.
3-Iodo-2-methyl-.............	78–79 (10)	−17 to −15.6	16
4-Iodo-2-methyl-.............	86–87.5 (11)	−6.5 to −5.5	16
5-Iodo-2-methyl-.............	88.8–89 (14)	−28 to −25.4	16,43,60
3,5-Diiodo-2-methyl-	103–105 (2)	6.5 to 8.0	16
3,4-Diiodo-2-methyl-.........	—	44–45	16
4,5-Diiodo-2-methyl-	—	37.5–38.5	16
3,4,5-Triiodo-2-methyl-.......	—	100–101.5	16
2-Iodo-3-methyl-.............	84.5–85.5 (11)	−45.9 to −43.7	17,28,55
4-Iodo-3-methyl-.............	88 (12)	−25 to −24.5	17
5-Iodo-3-methyl-.............	86.5–87.5 (12)	−61	17
2,4-Diiodo-3-methyl-.........	—	56.5–57.5	17
2,5-Diiodo-3-methyl-.........	120.8–121 (2.5)	10.5–12	17
4,5-Diiodo-3-methyl-.........	98.5 (0.5)	15–17	17
2,4,5-Triiodo-3-methyl-.......	—	75–76	17
5-Iodo-2-ethyl-	Dec.	—	61
5-Iodo-2,4-dimethyl-.........	119.5–120.5 (20)	—	33
3-Iodo-2,5-dimethyl-.........	99–100 (11.5)	—	23,56
3,4-Diiodo-2,5-dimethyl-......	—	—	56,62
5-Iodo-2-methyl-3-ethyl.......	103–103.5 (4)	—	18
5-Iodo-2,3,4-trimethyl-	Dec.	—	31
5-Iodo-2-octyl-..............	—	0	29
5-Iodo-2-phenyl-.............	—	76–77	57
5-Iodo-2-benzyl-.............	—	55–57	43
5,5′-Diiodo-2,2′-dithienyl.....	—	164	58
5 - Iodo - 2 - thienyltriphenyl- methane................	— 184–185	59
Di-(5-iodo-2-thienyl)phenyl- methane.................	—	89	50

C.   Preparation of Iodonitrothiophenes

Apparently no attempt has been made to iodinate 2-nitrothiophene directly but 3-nitrothiophene has been iodinated in the following way:[19]

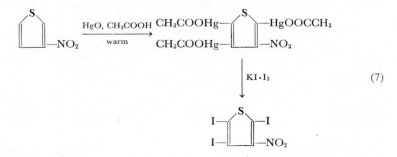

$$\tag{7}$$

2-Iodo-5-nitrothiophene is prepared from 2-iodothiophene by nitration with acetyl nitrate.[20,21]

In general, compounds such as 5-iodo-2-thiophenecarboxylic acid and 5-iodo-2-acetylthiophene are prepared by direct substitution reactions rather than by iodination of the acid or ketone.

D.   Reactions of the Iodothiophenes

The bond energy of the C—I linkage in the thiophene nucleus is so low that any simple hydrogenation process removes the iodine radical easily and the reduction products are received in excellent yields.   The usual reductive methods involve sodium amalgam[9,10,22] with alcohol or water, sodium in alcohol, or aluminum amalgam.[9,22,23]

The easy replacement of the iodine radical by the —CN group is effected with potassium and cuprous cyanides[10] (Eq. 8).   Dann prepared

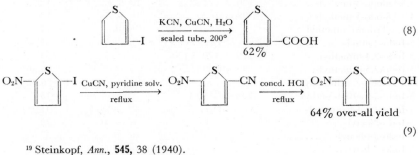

$$\tag{8}$$

$$\tag{9}$$

[19] Steinkopf, *Ann.*, **545**, 38 (1940).
[20] Rinkes, *Rec. trav. chim.*, **53**, 648 (1934).
[21] Dann, *Ber.*, **76**, 419 (1943).
[22] Steinkopf, Jacob, and Penz, *Ann.*, **512**, 136 (1934).
[23] Messinger, *Ber.*, **18**, 563 (1885).

5-nitro-2-thiophenecarbonitrile from the reaction of 5-nitro-2-iodothiophene and cuprous cyanide in pyridine[21] (Eq. 9).

Only one attempt to replace the iodine radical by an amine has been reported and the reaction was unsuccessful although rather interesting. 2-Iodothiophene in a sealed tube with piperidine was reported to give a sulfur-free diamine[24] (Eq. 10). The product was reported to polymerize

$$\text{(structure)} \quad \xrightarrow[\text{sealed tube}]{2C_5H_{10}NH,\ 200°} \quad HI + H_2S + C_5H_{10}N-CH=C=C=CH-NC_5H_{10} \quad (10)$$

rapidly in air. It was reduced with sodium amalgam to a compound tentatively identified as tetramethylenedipiperidide. This work has not been repeated and definite proof that such a compound is formed in the ring scission is lacking. It should, therefore, be viewed with some skepticism until further substantiating evidence is presented.

Cleavage of an iodine radical during acylation of thiophene when the 2,5-positions were filled was found to take place in high yields[25] (Eq. 11).

$$I\text{—}\text{(structure)}\text{—}I \quad \xrightarrow[\text{AlCl}_3]{\text{CH}_3\text{COCl}} \quad I\text{—}\text{(structure)}\text{—COCH}_3 \qquad (11)$$

The iodothiophenes undergo a Wurtz reaction readily but no yields are reported in any of the references listed below. In some cases, yields are referred to as rather poor. The reaction has been used with ethyl chloroformate[26-28] to produce the thiophenecarboxylic acids. With alkyl bromides or iodides[1,29-31], the corresponding aklylthiophenes are produced.

2-Iodothiophene reacts with sodium in ether to give the intermediate 5-iodo-2-thienylsodium which, when carbonated, gives 5-iodo-2-thiophenecarboxylic acid,[32] behaving in this respect like the 2-chloro- and 2-bromothiophene.

The Grignard reaction takes place easily with the iodothiophenes. In contrast to 3-bromothiophene, 3-iodothiophene forms the Grignard in

[24] Tohl, Ber., 28, 2217 (1885).
[25] Gattermann and Romer, Ber., 19, 693 (1886).
[26] Nahnsen, Ber., 17, 2192 (1884).
[27] Nahnsen, Ber., 18, 2304 (1885).
[28] Levi, Ber., 19, 656 (1886).
[29] von Schweinitz, Ber., 19, 644 (1886).
[30] Demuth, Ber., 19, 1857 (1886).
[31] Zelinsky, Ber., 21, 1835 (1888).
[32] Schick and Hartough, J. Am. Chem. Soc., 70, 286 (1948).

high yields.[9,15]   The 2-thienylmagnesium iodide appears to undergo all of the typical Grignard syntheses in yields comparable to those of the alkyl or aryl isologs.   Typical references are listed.[8,14,17,32a−45]

The iodothiophenes can be coupled readily with powdered silver[46] or with copper bronze[14,47,48] (Eq. 12).   The coupling of 2-iodothiophene

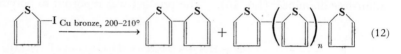

$$\tag{12}$$

gives low yields of product where $n = 1$ or 3.   Where $n = 2$ and 4 the products are formed by treating 2,5-diiodothiophene with copper bronze (for further details, see Chapter XV).

Exhaustive chlorination of 2-iodothiophene yields the perchlorothiophene, octachlorothiolane[49] (Eq. 13).   The lower chlorination products of this reaction have not been investigated.

$$+ \; ICl_3 \tag{13}$$

Introduction of nuclear substituents can be accomplished without cleavage of the iodine radical if a 2- or 5-position is to be substituted.   For example, 2-iodothiophene can be condensed with benzaldehyde to form di-(5-iodo-2-thienyl)phenylmethane[50]; it can be nitrated[20,21,51]; it can be mercurated[14,16,17] and the 5-iodo-2-thiophenemercurichloride exchanged with arsenic trichloride and the arsonic acids prepared.[52]   Sul-

[32a] Grischkevich-Trokhimoviskii, *J. Russ. Phys.-Chem. Soc.*, **43**, 201 (1911); *Chem. Abstr.*, **6**, 223 (1912).

[33] Grischkevich-Trokhimoviskii, *J. Russ. Phys.-Chem. Soc.*, **48**, 901 (1916); *Chem. Abstr.*, **11**, 787 (1917).

[34] Thomas and Couderc, *Bull. soc. chim.*, [4] **23**, 326 (1918).

[35] Thomas and Couderc, *Bull. soc. chim.*, [4] **23**, 288 (1918).

[36] Thomas, *Compt. rend.*, **181**, 218 (1925).

[37] Krauze and Renwanz, *Ber.*, **B60**, 1582 (1927).

[ɛ] Chichibabin and Gavrilov, *J. Russ. Phys.-Chem. Soc.*, **46**, 1614 (1914); *Chem. Abstr.*, **9**, 2069 (1915).

[39] Schneider and Wilmanns, Ger. Pat. 629,196 (1936).

[40] Steinkopf and Gording, *Biochem. Z.*, **292**, 368 (1937).

[41] Steinkopf and Killingstad, *Ann.*, **532**, 288 (1937).

[42] Steinkopf and Schmitt, *Ann.*, **533**, 264 (1938).

[43] Steinkopf and Hanske, *Ann.*, **541**, 238 (1939).

[44] Steinkopf, *Ann.*, **543**, 128 (1940).

[45] Putokhin and Egorova, *J. Gen. Chem. (U. S. S. R.)*, **10**, 1873 (1940).

[46] Eberhard, *Ber.*, **27**, 2919 (1894).

[47] Steinkopf, Leitsmann, and Hofmann, *Ann.*, **546**, 180 (1941).

[48] Sease and Zechmeister, *J. Am. Chem. Soc.*, **69**, 271 (1947).

[49] Willgerodt, *J. prakt. Chem.*, [2] **33**, 150 (1886).

[50] Nahke, *Ber.*, **30**, 2037 (1897).

[51] Kreis, *Ber.*, **17**, 2073 (1884).

[52] Finzi, *Gazz. chim. ital.*, **55**, 824 (1925).

fonation of 2-iodothiophene gives a variety of products[22] (Eq. 14). Cleavage

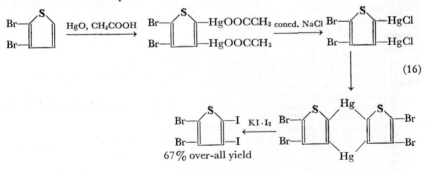

(I)   (14)

of the 5-iodo group in the sulfonyl chloride (I) appears to be more difficult and reaction 15 takes place.   Reduction of II with sodium amalgam

$$ \text{I} \xrightarrow{\text{SO}_3,\ \text{H}_2\text{SO}_4} \quad (\text{II}) \tag{15} $$

causes replacement of the iodine radical by hydrogen without reduction
of the sulfonic acid groups.[22]

Tetraiodothiophene decomposes without boiling and at 450° loses
three atoms of iodine.[53]   The fourth atom of iodine is lost by heating at
red heat in an inert atmosphere.   The product was described as "thiophene graphite" and appeared to have the empirical formula, $(C_4S)_n$.

E. Preparation of Mixed Halogen Derivatives of Thiophene

As pointed out previously, direct chlorination of bromo- or iodothiophenes gives only chlorinated thiophenes.   The best approach to compounds of this kind appears to be the method represented in equation
16.[10,22,42,54]   Limited bromination of 2,3-diiodothiophene gave only 2,4,5-
tribromo-3-iodothiophene.[10]

$$ \text{(16)} $$

67% over-all yield

In general, those compounds listed in Table VII-14 have been prepared by the method listed in equation 16 above or by replacement of the
—HgCl or —HgOOCCH₃ with iodine by the methods listed in equations 6
and 7.   Table VII-14 follows on page 218.

[53] Cuisa, *Gazz. chim. ital.*, **52**, II, 130 (1922).
[54] Steinkopf, Rosler, and Setzer, *Ann.*, **522**, 35 (1936).

TABLE VII-14. Physical Constants of Mixed Halothiophenes

Thiophene derivative	B.p., °C. (mm.)	M.p., °C.	Ref.
2-Chloro-5-iodo-....................	95–96 (14)	−25 to −24	62
2-Chloro-5-bromo-.................	69.5–70.0 (18)	−22 to −20	63
2-Chloro-3,4,5-tribromo-...........	—	91	62
2-Chloro-3,4,5-triiodo-.............	—	126	62
3-Chloro-2,4,5-tribromo-...........	—	91	62
3-Chloro-2,4,5-triiodo-.............	—	121	62
2,3-Dichloro-5-bromo-.............	212–214	6	62
2,3-Dichloro-5-iodo-...............	—	27	62
2,3-Dichloro-4,5-dibromo-..........	—	65–66	62
2,3-Dichloro-4,5-diiodo-............	—	72	62
2,4-Dichloro-3,5-dibromo-	—	72	62
2,5-Dichloro-3,4-dibromo-..........	—	65	62
2,5-Dichloro-3,4-diiodo-............	—	83	62
3,4-Dichloro-2,5-dibromo-..........	—	75	62
3,4-Dichloro-2,5-diiodo-............	—	106	62
2,3,4-Trichloro-5-bromo-...........	—	50.5	62
2,3,4-Trichloro-5-iodo-.............	—	50–51	62
2-Bromo-5-iodo-...................	116 (13)	—	22
2-Bromo-3,4,5-triiodo-.............	—	170	54
3-Bromo-2,5-diiodo-...............	—	55–56	44
3-Bromo-2,4,5-triiodo-.............	—	156–157	44
2,3-Dibromo-5-iodo-	—	59	22,44
2,3-Dibromo-4,5-diiodo-...........	—	142	54
2,5-Dibromo-3,4-diiodo-...........	—	141–142 (147)	10,54
3,4-Dibromo-2-iodo-...............	—	60	22
3,4-Dibromo-2,5-diiodo-...........	—	145	54
2,3,4-Tribromo-5-iodo-.............	—	126	22
2,3,5-Tribromo-4-iodo-.............	—	111–112	10
5-Iodo-2-bromo-3-methyl-...........	131–135 (14)	−3 to −2	55

[55] Steinkopf and Jacob, *Ann.*, **515,** 273 (1935).
[56] Steinkopf, Poulsson, and Herdey, *Ann.*, **536,** 138 (1938).
[57] Chrzaszczewska, *Roczniki Chem.*, **5,** 1, 33 (1925); *Chem. Abstr.*, **20,** 1078 (1926).
[58] Steinkopf and Kohler, *Ann.*, **522,** 17 (1936).
[59] Weisse, *Ber.*, **29,** 1402 (1896).
[60] Vlastelitza, *J. Russ. Phys.-Chem. Soc.*, **46,** 790 (1914); *Chem. Abstr.*, **9,** 1750 (1915).
[61] Bonz, *Ber.*, **18,** 549 (1885).
[62] Steinkopf and Kohler, *Ann.*, **532,** 250 (1937).
[63] Bachman and Heisey, *J. Am. Chem. Soc.*, **70,** 2379 (1948).

CHAPTER VIII

The Nitro- and Aminothiophenes

I. The Nitrothiophenes

When thiophene was first discovered by Victor Meyer in 1882, nitration techniques similar to those used in the benzene series were applied to thiophene. Many difficulties were encountered and no nitrothiophenes were obtained until it was found that when air saturated with thiophene was passed through fuming red nitric acid low yields of nitro- and dinitrothiophenes were formed. Later, when the acetyl nitrate technique for the nitration of aromatic hydrocarbons was developed, it was discovered that this new process could be applied to thiophene with marked success in comparison to prior methods. Babasinian, in studying the results of earlier workers, developed the best set of conditions known at the present time for the preparation of 2-nitrothiophene and 2,5-dinitrothiophene in high yields.

Several attempts by the author and co-workers to nitrate thiophene have been carried out in an effort to circumvent the acetyl nitrate procedures. The work was significantly unsuccessful and extremely hazardous. There appeared to be an induction period during which little reaction took place. Only when some critical point was reached in the mixing of reactants or in adjusting the temperature a sudden, rather violent, uncontrollable reaction set in which caused profound decomposition of the thiophene or alkylthiophene.

A. Preparation of the Nitrothiophenes

1. 2- and 3-Nitrothiophenes

After a considerable number of unsuccessful attempts to nitrate thiophene by standard nitration methods, Victor Meyer and Stadler[1] in 1884 reported that they could successfully obtain nitro- and dinitrothiophenes by passing a vigorous stream of air saturated with thiophene through fuming red nitric acid. Later, in 1906, it was found that benzoyl nitrate, when added to cold thiophene, gave 2-nitrothiophene in nearly quantita-

[1] V. Meyer and Stadler, *Ber.*, **17**, 2648 (1884).

tive yields.[2]   Later methods used acetyl nitrate[3] and thiophene dissolved in acetic acid.[4,5]   These later methods gave yields of about 70% of 2-nitrothiophene with minor amounts of the dinitrothiophenes.

The method of Babasinian,[6] which is an adaptation of prior methods,[2-5] is an excellent and easy one to carry out in the laboratory.   Babasinian states that the yields are above 80%, no 3-nitrothiophene is formed (see footnote 9 below), and very little dinitrothiophene is obtained.   The essential modification consists of slowly adding thiophene dissolved in acetic anhydride to a solution of nitric acid in glacial acetic acid with careful control of the temperature at 10°.

Another method consists of nitrating thiophene in carbon tetrachloride solution with nitrogen tetroxide, but the products are difficult to purify.[7]   In the presence of light, thiophene and nitrogen tetroxide react to give nitro- and dinitrothiophene.[8]   In the absence of light a violent reaction sets in and only resins are formed.

3-Nitrothiophene is reported to be formed in about 5% yields by the acetyl nitrate method, although Babasinian failed to isolate the material.[9] The compound is isolated from the mother liquor after separating the 2-nitrothiophene.

3-Nitrothiophene is best prepared by nitration of 2-thiophenesulfonyl chloride in the following manner[9,10] (Eq. 1).   I and II can be separated

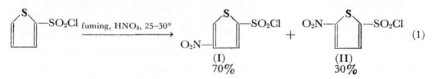

$$\text{(1)}$$

(I)   (II)
70%   30%

by fractional distillation[10] or the mixture may be subjected to a fractional hydrolysis in sulfuric acid.[9]   At 130–145°, I is hydrolyzed to 3-nitrothiophene and, at 150–160°, II gives 2-nitrothiophene.

2. The Dinitrothiophenes

Only 2,4- and 2,5-dinitrothiophene are known.   They are prepared by the direct nitration of the mononitrothiophenes with nitric and sulfuric acids[1,5,9] (Eqs. 2 and 3).   In nitration of the 3-nitrothiophene, the addi-

[2] Francis, *Ber.*, **39**, 3801 (1906).
[3] Pictet and Khotinsky, *Ber.*, **40**, 1163 (1907).
[4] Steinkopf, *Ann.*, **403**, 17 (1914).
[5] Steinkopf and Lutzkendorf, Ger. Pat. 255,394 (1912).
[6] Babasinian, *J. Am. Chem. Soc.*, **50**, 2748 (1928); *Org. Syntheses*. Coll. Vol. II, p. 466.
[7] Schaarschmidt, Balzerkiewicz, and Gante, *Ber.*, **B58**, 499 (1925).
[8] Schorigin and Topchiev, *Ber.*, **B67**, 1362 (1934).
[9] Steinkopf and Hopner, *Ann.*, **501**, 174 (1933).
[10] Burton and Davy, *J. Chem. Soc.*, **1948**, 525.

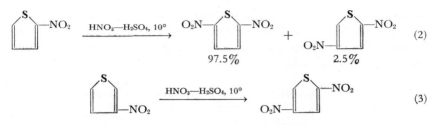

$$(2)$$

97.5%   2.5%

$$(3)$$

tive directing effects of the sulfur and nitro group so greatly activate the 5-position that no isomers are formed.[9] Babasinian reported that the acetyl nitrate method for the preparation of 2-nitrothiophene[5] would not further nitrate 2-nitrothiophene to produce the dinitrothiophenes. Also, he reported that ring oxidation was inhibited almost entirely in 2-nitrothiophene.

Meyer and Stadler[1,11] reported conversion of a dinitrothiophene (m.p. 52°) into another isomer (m.p. 78°) by steam distillation. The 52° isomer was later shown to be a mixture of 2,4- and 2,5-dinitrothiophene.[11] The 78° isomer is 2,5-dinitrothiophene. 2,4-Dinitrothiophene melts at 56°.

3. Tri- and Tetranitrothiophenes

This group of compounds is unknown. Trinitro-2-thienylacetamides are produced from the reaction of N_2O_3 on the triiodo- or tribromo-2-thienylacetamides (see aminothiophenes below for further references and discussion).

B. Nitration of Thiophene Homologs

2-Methylthiophene can be nitrated by the acetyl nitrate method.[12] Only the 5-nitro-2-methylthiophene can be isolated from the reaction mixture.

3-Methylthiophene gave two isomers, but the principal product was 2-nitro-3-methylthiophene[13] (Eq. 4). It appears that nitration with

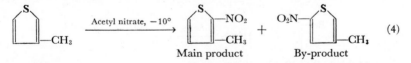

$$(4)$$

Main product   By-product

acetyl nitrate is the only procedure effective in this series, since the method of Meyer and Stadler[1] gives only a little dinitroethylthiophene when air saturated with ethylthiophene is blown through nitric acid.[14]

[11] Stadler, *Ber.*, **18**, 532 (1885).
[12] Rinkes, *Rec. trav. chim.*, **51**, 1134 (1932).
[13] Rinkes, *Rec. trav. chim.*, **52**, 1052 (1933).
[14] Bonz, *Ber.*, **18**, 549 (1885).

Diethylthiophene gave a compound of unknown structure.[15]   2,5-Dimethylthiophene gave resinous products.[16,17]   The latter compound can be nitrated in fair yields with dilute nitric acid liberated from potassium nitrate and sulfuric acid[17] (Eq. 5).   Fuming nitric acid produces side

$$\xrightarrow[\text{30\%}]{\text{KNO}_3,\ \text{H}_2\text{SO}_4,\ \text{H}_2\text{O}}$$

(5)

chain nitration of the 2,5-dimethyl-3,4-dinitrothiophene[17] (Eq. 6).

$$\xrightarrow{\text{fuming HNO}_3,\ 70°}$$

(6)

Nitration of a compound listed as "triphenyl-2-thienylmethane" is reported to give a trinitro derivative.[18]

C. Nitration of Halothiophenes

The nitration of 2-chlorothiophene is not reported.   2,3-Dichlorothiophene can be nitrated by the acetyl nitrate method[19] (Eq. 7).   2,5-

$$+\ \text{HNO}_3 \xrightarrow[\text{37\%}]{\text{Ac}_2\text{O, 60°}}$$

(7)

Dichlorothiophene[20,21] and 2,3,4-trichlorothiophene[20,22] can be nitrated easily in nitric acid–sulfuric acid mixture to give high yields.   (*Author's note:*   The compound reported as 2,3,5-trichloro-4-nitrothiophene by Steinkopf[20,23] is actually the 2,3,4-trichloro-5-nitrothiophene.   See section on 2,3,4-trichlorothiophene in Chapter VII).

A considerable amount of research has been carried out on the nitration of the bromothiophenes.   Babasinian[24] found that 2-bromothiophene is very susceptible to side reactions during nitration and recommended that the compound be nitrated by the acetyl nitrate method (Eq. 8).

$$+\ \text{HNO}_3 \xrightarrow[\text{66\%}]{\text{Ac}_2\text{O, }-5°}$$

(8)

[15] Muhlert, *Ber.*, **19,** 635 (1886).
[16] Messinger, *Ber.*, **18,** 1639 (1885).
[17] Steinkopf, Poulsson, and Herdey, *Ann.*, **536,** 128 (1938).
[18] Weisse, *Ber.*, **29,** 1402 (1896).
[19] Steinkopf and Kohler, *Ann.*, **532,** 273 (1937).
[20] Steinkopf, Jacob, and Penz, *Ann.*, **512,** 136 (1934).
[21] Coonradt and Hartough, unpublished work.
[22] Rosenberg, *Ber.*, **19,** 651 (1886).
[23] Steinkopf, Die Chemie des Thiophens.   Steinkopff, Dresden, 1941, p. 58.
[24] Babasinian, *J. Am. Chem. Soc.*, **57,** 1763 (1935).

Babasinian's technique for the nitration of thiophene,[5] *i.e.*, use of acetic acid solvent, gives lower yields than the technique of equation (8). The use of pure nitric acid with 2-bromothiophene led to explosive mixtures.[25] Products of this violent reaction are tars and sulfuric acid. Further indications of the oxidative action of nitric acid on the thiophene nucleus are demonstrated by the action of nitric acid on tetrabromothiophene, which results in the formation of dibromomaleic acid.[25,26] This degradative oxidation of the nucleus is an excellent method by which the structure of various thiophene compounds can be deduced. For example, 2,2,3,4,5,5-hexachloro-3-thiolene is oxidized to dichloromaleic acid by this method[27] (Eq. 9).

$$\underset{Cl-\underset{Cl}{\overset{S}{\diagup}}\overset{Cl_2}{\diagdown}}{Cl_2} + HNO_3 \text{ (fuming)} \xrightarrow{10°} \begin{array}{c} Cl-C-COOH \\ \parallel \\ Cl-C-COOH \end{array} \qquad (9)$$

3-Bromothiophene can be mononitrated by the acetyl nitrate method but the position of the nitro group has not been established.[20] Continued nitration with HNO_3—H_2SO_4 gives two isomeric dinitro-3-bromo-thiophenes.

Nitration of bromothiophenes with both the 2- and 5-positions blocked is usually carried out by the HNO_3—H_2SO_4 method. From the reaction of 2,5-dibromothiophene the main product is 3,4-dinitro-2,5-dibromothiophene.[28-30] It should be noted at this point that substitution of the 3,4-positions in 2,5-dichlorothiophene,[20,21] in 2,5-dibromothiophene,[28-30] and in 2,5-dimethylthiophene[17] proceeds with considerable ease. This is so contradictory to benzene chemistry, in which *ortho*-nitro groups are formed by substitution only in minute traces or not at all, that special attention should be focused upon this reaction. Steinkopf[31] considered that these 3,4-positions should be compared to *meta* positions in the benzene nucleus. It appears likely, however, that the 2,5-dihalo-3,4-dinitrothiophenes form by an addition reaction of a nitrogen oxide to the double bonds of this nucleus. It has been shown that the double bonds of the thiophene nucleus of 2,5-dichlorothiophene are more similar to olefinic double bonds than to the double bonds of an aromatic compound since chlorine adds to these bonds rather than substituting the nucleus.

[25] Angeli and Ciamician, *Ber.*, **24**, 75 (1891).
[26] Ciamician and Angeli, *Ber.*, **24**, 1347 (1891).
[27] Coonradt, Hartough, and Norris, unpublished work.
[28] Rosenberg, *Ber.*, **18**, 3028 (1885).
[29] Steinkopf and Bauermeister, *Ann.*, **403**, 63 (1914).
[30] Mozingo, *et al.*, *J. Am. Chem. Soc.*, **67**, 2092 (1945).
[31] Steinkopf, *Die Chemie des Thiophens*. Steinkopff, Dresden, 1941, p. 26.

Thus, 2,2,3,4,5,5-hexachlorothiolane results from the addition of chlorine to 2,5-dichlorothiophene[21,32] (see further discussion under chlorination of thiophene, Chapter VII).   The addition of nitrogen trioxide, nitrogen tetroxide, and nitrosyl chloride to olefinic double bonds is an established reaction.

Published literature indicates migration of a nitro group during bromination of 2-nitrothiophene which yields a variety of brominated nitrothiophenes[33] (Eq. 10).   A trace of 2,3,5-tribromothiophene was also

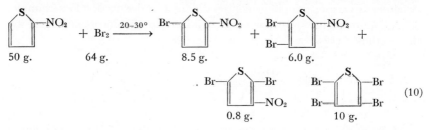

indicated.   A considerable amount of unreacted 2-nitrothiophene was recovered.   Since Babasinian was generally unaware that 3-nitro-thiophene was a contaminant in his starting material, the 2,5-dibromo-3-nitrothiophene may have arisen from that source.   The bromination of 3-nitrothiophene proceeds smoothly to give only this product.[20]   While the 2-nitro group appears to be easily cleaved by bromine, the 3-nitro group is stable to excess bromine.   Although no actual thermodynamic studies have been made this is another indication that 3-substituted thiophenes are more stable thermodynamically than their 2-substituted isomers.   Other indications of this fact are brought out in the discussion on 3-bromothiophene.

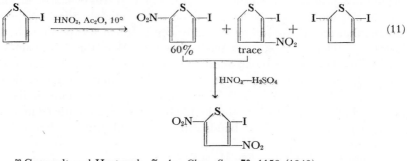

[32] Coonradt and Hartough, *J. Am. Chem. Soc.*, **70**, 1158 (1948).
[33] Babasinian, *J. Am. Chem. Soc.*, **60**, 2906 (1938).
[34] Rinkes, *Rec. trav. chim.*, **53** [4], 643 (1934).
[35] Dann, *Ber.*, **76**, 419 (1943).

2-Iodothiophene is nitrated easily by the acetyl nitrate technique[34,35] (Eq. 11). Nitration of 2-iodothiophene with excess nitric acid gives only oxidation products, but slow addition of the nitric acid to the 2-iodothiophene, with strong cooling, yields 5-nitro-2-iodothiophene.[36] 3,4-Diiodo- and 2,3,4-triiodothiophene are nitrated in the 5-position with acetyl nitrate.[37]

D. Nitration of Thiophenes Substituted with an Electron-Withdrawing Group

The nitration of this group of compounds, *i.e.*, the acylthiophenes, the thiophenecarboxylic acids, and thiophenesulfonic acids, has been thoroughly studied. The classical work of Rinkes in the early 1930's showed without doubt that "a typical *meta*-directing group of the benzene series" did not control further substitution in the "*meta* position" as had been previously held. It was shown by Rinkes[12,13,38] that nitration of 2-acetylthiophene, 2-thiophenecarboxylic acids, and the methyl-2-thiophenecarboxylic acids gave the typical 5-substitution that was controlled by the hetero atom, sulfur, rather than by the —$COCH_3$ or —$COOH$ groups, *i.e.*, they normally substituted in the 5-position rather than in the 4-position. This phase of orientation in the thiophene nucleus is discussed in more detail elsewhere (see Chapter V).

For all rules of orientation there are glaring exceptions and this is typified by the nitration of 2-thiophenesulfonyl chloride,[9,10] which results in the formation of approximately eight parts of 4-nitro-2-thiophenesulfonyl chloride to three parts of 5-nitro-2-thiophenesulfonyl chloride.

Nitration of 4,5-dibromo-2-benzoylthiophene with fuming nitric acid causes cleavage of the ketone linkage.[39] When the 4-position is un-

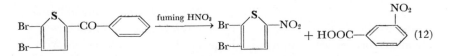

$$(12)$$

occupied, *e.g.*, 5-ethyl-2-benzoylthiophene and 5-iodo-2-benzoylthiophene, the material nitrates normally in the 4-position without cleavage of the ketone linkage.[39,40] Splitting of the halogenated thienyl ketones with nitric

[36] Kreis, *Ber.*, **17**, 2073 (1884).
[37] Steinkopf, Schmitt, and Fiedler, *Ann.*, **527**, 237 (1937).
[38] Rinkes, *Rec. trav. chim.*, **52** [4], 538 (1933).
[39] Marcusson, *Ber.*, **26**, 2460 (1893).
[40] Weitkamp and Hamilton, *J. Am. Chem. Soc.*, **59**, 2699 (1937).

acid is directly contrasted by replacement of the halogens by the nitro group in the 2-acetamidothiophene series.[41]

Replacement of the carboxyl group by the nitro group takes place during nitration of thiophenecarboxylic acids, but the reaction is secondary to nuclear nitration[12] (Eq. 13).

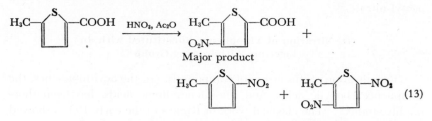

E. Chemical Properties of the Nitrothiophenes

The introduction of a nitro group into the thiophene nucleus creates the same type of reactive structure as found in the benzene series.   For example, the methyl group of 5-methyl-2-thiophenecarboxylic acid is quite unreactive, but introduction of a 4-nitro group creates a system with enough reactivity to condense quantitatively with benzaldehyde[38] (Eq. 14).   The free acid is quite easily decarboxylated with copper chromite in quinoline.

Reduction of nitrothiophenes is discussed in some detail in Section II on aminothiophenes.   The isologs of the intermediate reduction products of nitrobenzene (azo-, hydrazo-, azoxy-, and nitrosobenzene and phenylhydroxylamine) are unknown in the thiophene series.

There are only a few known properties of 2- and 3-nitrothiophene. These available data indicate a close resemblance to nitrobenzene in chemical properties.   Aqueous alkali produces a rust color with 2-nitrothiophene, but 2,5-dinitrothiophene produces a violet color with a trace of alkali in alcohol.   Excess alkali or acid destroys the color.[42] The mono- and dinitrothiophenes closely resemble trinitrobenzene in their ability to form molecular complexes with alcohols,[43] polynuclear aromatic hydrocarbons,[42,44] and alkali salts.[43]   Steinkopf[43,45] presented the follow-

[41] Priestley and Hurd, *J. Am. Chem. Soc.*, **69**, 1173 (1947).
[42] V. Meyer and Stadler, *Ber.*, **17**, 2778 (1884).
[43] Steinkopf, *Ann.*, **513**, 285 (1934).
[44] Rosenberg, *Ber.*, **18**, 1773 (1885).
[45] Steinkopf, *Die Chemie des Thiophens.*   Steinkopff, Dresden, 1941, p. 57.

ing speculative formula (15) for the purple potassium methylate complex with 2-nitrothiophene. With sodium ethylate a tan compound is formed.

$$\qquad (15)$$

2,4-Dinitrothiophene gives a bronze-colored amorphous powder with potassium methylate. Complexes of 2,4- and 2,5-dinitrothiophene and naphthalene, anthracene, and dibenzothiophene form in equimolar proportions.[44]

F. Physical Properties of the Nitrothiophenes

2- and 3-Nitrothiophene are light yellow solids and have an odor similar to nitrobenzene. They are mild vesicants[5] and continued breathing of the vapor should be avoided. 2 - Nitrothiophene has a very high vapor pressure and its crystals evaporate rapidly in a stream of air.

The vapor pressures of 2-nitrothiophene and 2,5-dinitrothiophene have been determined by Babasinian and Jackson.[46] These investigators claim that these materials do not behave as normal liquids due to their anomalous entropy of vaporization. It is well to point out that the purity of their starting products is in considerable doubt since Babasinian persistently refused to recognize the formation of the 3-nitrothiophene isomer by his method of nitration. Instead of the pure 2,5-dinitrothiophene, m.p. 78–79°, the workers used a dinitrothiophene, m.p. 52°. Stadler[11] had previously shown that the product of the nitration of 2-nitrothiophene melted at 52° and was a mixture of 2,4- and 2,5-dinitrothiophene.

Babasinian[6] reported that huge crystals of 2,5-dinitrothiophene (probably mixed crystals of the 2,4- and 2,5-isomers) five to eight inches in length have been grown by slow evaporation from solutions in ligroin or light naphthas.

The color of nitrobenzene is reported to deepen rapidly when a trace of 2-nitrothiophene is present.[47] Reduction products of nitrothiophene are reported to be prooxidants in the oxidation of aniline.[48]

The dipole moment of 2-nitrothiophene,[49] 4.12 D, indicates contributions of polar structures such as (16).

[46] Babasinian and Jackson, *J. Am. Chem. Soc.*, **51**, 2147 (1929).
[47] Bidet, *Compt. rend.*, **108**, 520 (1889).
[48] Vorozhtsov and Strel'tsova, *J. Chem. Soc.* (*U. S. S. R.*), **9**, 1015 (1939); *Chem. Abstr.*, **33**, 8581 (1939).
[49] Oesper, Lewis, and Smyth, *J. Am. Chem. Soc.*, 64, 1130 (1942).

TABLE VIII-1. Melting Points of the Nitro Derivatives of Thiophene and Substituted Thiophenes

Thiophene derivative	M.p., °C.	Ref.
2-Nitro-.....	46.5	1,4,6,10,12,44
3-Nitro-.....	78–79	9,10,12,13,38,50
2,4-Dinitro-.....	56	1,6,9,38
2,5-Dinitro-.....	80–82	1,6,9
2-Methyl-3-nitro-.....	45	12,38
2-Methyl-5-nitro-.....	27.4	12,38
3-Methyl-2-nitro-.....	63	13
3-Methyl-5-nitro-.....	Liquid	13
2-Methyl-3,5-dinitro-.....	100	12,38
3-Methyl-2,5-dinitro-.....	58	13
3-Methyl-2,4-dinitro-.....	96	13
2-Styryl-3-nitro-.....	87–88	38
2-Styryl-3,5-dinitro-.....	205	38
2-Ethyl-3,5-dinitro-.....	Liquid	14
2-Propyl-3,5-dinitro-.....	Semi-liquid	52
2,5-Dimethyl-3,4-dinitro-.....	118–119	17
5-Methyl-3,4-dinitro-2-thenylnitrate.........	83.5–85	17
2-Phenyl-5-nitro-.....	74	51
3-Phenyl-2(5)-nitro-.....	141	51

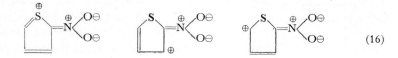

$$\tag{16}$$

Table VIII-1 above lists the physical properties of the nitrothiophenes and nitroalkylthiophenes, and Table VIII-2 lists the constants of the halonitrothiophenes. Other nitro derivatives, such as the carboxylic acids or acylthiophenes, will be found in the tables of their respective chapters.

II. The Aminothiophenes

Despite the potential importance of the aminothiophenes in pharmaceuticals and dyestuffs, only a few investigators have been active in this field. Perhaps potential investigators have been discouraged by earlier literature. The tendency of these compounds to decompose in air is well recognized. The compounds are stable only as the stannic chloride

[50] Steinkopf, *Ann.*, **545**, 42 (1940).
[51] Chrazaszczewska, *Roczniki Chem.*, **5**, 33 (1925); *Chem. Abstr.*, **20**, 1078 (1926).
[52] Ruffi, *Ber.*, **20**, 1742 (1887).

TABLE VIII-2. Melting Points of the Nitro Derivatives of the Halothiophenes

Thiophene derivative	M.p., °C.	Ref.
2,3-Dichloro-5-nitro-..........................	55–56	19
2,5-Dichloro-3,4-dinitro-......................	88–91	20,21
2,3,4-Trichloro-5-nitro-.......................	70(86)	19,20,22
2,3,5-Trichloro-4-nitro-.......................	See discussion	
2-Bromo-5-nitro-..............................	48–49	20,24,33
3-Bromo-2-nitro-..............................	81–83	20
3-Bromo-2,4(5)-dinitro-.......................	167	20
3-Bromo-2,5(4)-dinitro-.......................	110–111	20
2,3-Dibromo-5-nitro-..........................	75.5–76	20,33
2,4-Dibromo-5-nitro-..........................	79–80	20
2,4-Dibromo-3,5-dinitro-......................	102	20
2,5-Dibromo-3-nitro-..........................	60–61	20,33,36
2,5-Dibromo-3,4-dinitro-......................	139–140	28–30,33,36
3,4-Dibromo-2-nitro-..........................	115–116	20
3,4-Dibromo-2,5-dinitro-......................	128	20
2,3,4-Tribromo-5-nitro-.......................	96–98	20
2,3,5-Tribromo-4-nitro-.......................	106	28
2-Iodo-3-nitro-...............................	131	34
2-Iodo-5-nitro-...............................	75	34,36,53
3-Iodo-2-nitro-...............................	131–134	34,50
2-Iodo-3,5-dinitro-...........................	148	34
3-Iodo-2,3(4)-dinitro-........................	187–188	37
3-Iodo-2,4(3)-dinitro-........................	119–120	37
2,3-Diiodo-5-nitro-...........................	79–80	37
2,5-Diiodo-3-nitro-...........................	108.5–110	50
3,4-Diiodo-2-nitro-...........................	163–164	37
3,4-Diiodo-2,5-dinitro-.......................	148–151	37
2,3,4-Triiodo-5-nitro-........................	203–204	37
2,3,5-Triiodo-4-nitro-........................	169.5–170.5	50

[53] Dann and Moller, *Chem. Ber.*, **80**, 23 (1947).

double salts, the hydrochlorides or as the acetamidothiophenes.   The free bases are unstable unless stored under an inert atmosphere.   In order to analyze these amines or to isolate them in a form suitable for storage, it has been necessary to convert them to stable derivatives.

The instability of this class of compounds is comparable to that of the hydroxythiophenes.   In the latter case, migration of the hydroxyl hydrogen to the nucleus is known to take place and it may be that a similar situation exists here where an unstable imine structure forms and polymerizes in alkali to the "gummy mass" described below.

The aminothiophenes have not been diazotized and coupled.   Introduction of strong electron-withdrawing groups such as carboxyl or acetyl into the thiophene nucleus has led to aminothiophenes of higher stability which can be diazotized and coupled with other organic compounds.

A. Preparation of 2-Aminothiophenes

2-Aminothiophene was prepared as the stable double salt of stannic chloride in 1885 when Stadler[1] reduced 2-nitrothiophene with tin and alcoholic hydrogen chloride (Eq. 1).   Stadler[1] reported that reductions

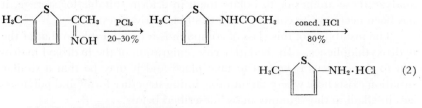

$$\text{(I)} \qquad\qquad\qquad\qquad \text{(II)} \qquad\qquad\qquad (1)$$

other than this failed to give the desired product and that the reduction failed in media other than alcohol.   In the words of Stadler, "Reductions with tin and concentrated hydrochloric acid, stannous chloride and hydrochloric acid, ferrous sulfate and ammonia, ammonium sulfide, sodium amalgam, zinc and acetic acid, zinc and ammonia, and hydrosulfurous acid give no reaction or the reagents are too strong as reducing agents and give decomposition with evolution of hydrogen sulfide."

Steinkopf and Lutzkendorf[2] found that compound I could be reduced to II in 68% yield by the use of tin or stannous chloride and aqueous hydrochloric acid despite Stadler's failure.   The free amine was obtained by treatment of II with alkali in an inert atmosphere and was reported to boil at 77–79° at 11 mm.   The free amine "polymerized" to a gummy mass very rapidly in an ordinary atmosphere.

The only C-substituted homolog of 2-aminothiophene reported is 5-methyl-2-aminothiophene, which was prepared by Beckmann rearrangement of the oxime of 5-methyl-2-acetylthiophene.   The acetamido derivative was converted to stable crystalline 5-methyl-2-aminothiophene hydrochloride by hydrolysis of the amide in concentrated hydrochloric acid[3] (Eq. 2).

$$\text{(2)}$$

[1] Stadler, *Ber.*, **18**, 1490 (1885).
[2] Steinkopf, *Ann.*, **403**, 17 (1914).   Steinkopf and Lutzkendorf, Ger. Pat. 257,462 (1913); *Chem. Zentr.*, **1913**, I, 1155.
[3] Chabrier, Tchoubar, and Le Tellier-Dupre, *Bull. soc. chim. France*, **1946**, 332.

The preparation of amino-2-acetylthiophenes,[4] 5-amino-2-thio-phenecarboxylic acid[5,6] and 5-amino-2-thiophenearsonic acids[7,8] is described in their respective chapters and below in Sections C and D.

B. Preparation of the 3-Aminothiophenes

3-Aminothiophene has been prepared by the method of Steinkopf[2] and was reported to be less stable than the isomeric 2-aminothiophene.[9]

2,5-Dimethyl-3-aminothiophene hydrochloride has been prepared through Beckmann rearrangement of 2,5-dimethyl-3-acetylthiophene oxime by the method shown in equation (2). The yield is not reported.[3]

3,4-Diaminothiophene has been prepared by a unique method[10] (Eq. 3). The product was too unstable in air to be isolated and was con-

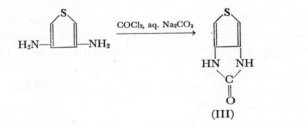

$$(3)$$

verted to the diacetamido and dibenzamido derivatives for characterization. 3,4-Diaminothiophene can be converted in low yields to 2,3-dihydro-2-oxo-1-thieno-(3,4)-imidazole (III) by the action of phosgene (Eq. 4). III is of interest since its skeletal structure is related to the cyclic structure in the biotin molecule.

$$(4)$$

(III)

Recent patents[11] describe the preparation of compounds of the following formula:

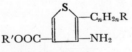

[4] Steinkopf and Jaffe, *Ann.*, **413**, 333 (1917).
[5] Dann, *Ber.*, **76**, 419 (1943).
[6] Steinkopf and Muller, *Ann.*, **448**, 210 (1926).
[7] Finzi and Furlotti, *Gazz. chim. ital.*, **45**, II, 290 (1915).
[8] Finzi, *Gazz. chim. ital.*, **60**, 159 (1930).
[9] Steinkopf and Höpner, *Ann.*, **501**, 178 (1933).
[10] Mozingo, Harris, Wolf, Hoffhine, Easton, and Folkers, *J. Am. Chem. Soc.*, **67**, 2092 (1945).
[11] Cheney and Piening, U. S. Pat. 2,443,598 (1948); U. S. Pat. 2,466,004 (1949); *J. Am. Chem. Soc.*, **67**, 729, 731 (1945).

where R' is a saturated alkyl group, n an integer between 1 and 8, and R is a radical of the class —COOH, —COOR', aryloxy, aralkoxy, or alkoxy. These compounds are formed as in equation 5.   The free base of IV is

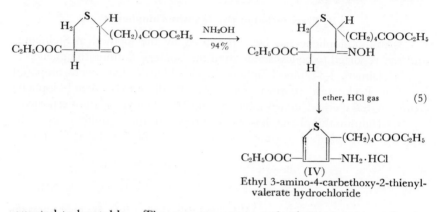

ether, HCl gas   (5)

(IV)
Ethyl 3-amino-4-carbethoxy-2-thienyl-
valerate hydrochloride

reported to be stable.   The rearrangement and subsequent conversion to 2-oxo-3,4-imidazolido-2-thiophenevaleric acid are described in Chapter XII, Section II.

C. Preparation of N-Substituted 2-Aminothiophenes

2-Acetamidothiophene can be prepared from the action of acetic anhydride on 2-aminothiophene.[2]   It can also be prepared by a Beckmann rearrangement of the oxime of 2-acetylthiophene[2,12] (Eq. 6).   The

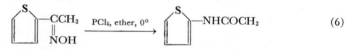

oximes of 5-methyl-2-acetylthiophene and 2,5-dimethyl-3-acetylthiophene undergo this reaction[3]; the oximes of 4- and 5-nitro-2-acetylthiophene are reported to be inactive.[4]

The Curtius reaction yields ethyl N-2-thienylcarbamate[13] (Eq. 7). Water converts 2-thenoylazide to N,N'-di-(2-thienyl)urea[13] (Eq. 8). In the presence of aniline, N-phenyl-N'-(2-thienyl)urea is formed.

[12] Rimini, *Chem.-Ztg.*, **23**, 266 (1889).
[13] Curtius and Thyssen, *J. prakt. Chem.*, **65**, 5 (1902).

$$\text{(thiophene)}\text{—CON}_3 \xrightarrow{\text{H}_2\text{O, 100}^\circ} \text{(thiophene)}\text{—NHCONH—}\text{(thiophene)} \qquad (8)$$

Reduction of ethyl 5-nitro-2-thiophenecarboxylate with aluminum chips in wet ether gives a good yield of the 5-amino derivative, easily converted to its acetamide[5] (Eq. 9). If the free acid of V is reduced with tin in acetic acid, 5-acetamido-2-thiophenecarboxylic acid is obtained directly.[6]

$$\text{O}_2\text{N—}\text{(thiophene)}\text{—COOEt} \xrightarrow[78\%]{\text{ether, H}_2\text{O, Al}} \text{H}_2\text{N—}\text{(thiophene)}\text{—COOEt} \xrightarrow{\text{Ac}_2\text{O}}$$

(V)

$$\text{CH}_3\text{CONH—}\text{(thiophene)}\text{—COOEt} \quad (9)$$

N-Alkylaminothiophenes[2] are prepared as shown in equation 10. Tohl attempted to prepare 2-thienylpiperidine by condensing 2-halo-

$$\text{(thiophene)}\text{—NHCOCH}_3 \xrightarrow[45\%]{\text{RI, Na, xylene soln.}} \text{(thiophene)}\text{—N(R)COCH}_3 \xrightarrow{\text{saponify}} \text{(thiophene)}\text{—NHR} \quad (10)$$

thiophenes with piperidine in a sealed tube.[14] The reaction with 2-bromothiophene gives only a trace of an amine, but 2-iodothiophene gives a product whose formula was $\text{C}_5\text{H}_{10}\text{N—CH}{=}\text{C}{=}\text{C}{=}\text{CH—NC}_5\text{H}_{10}$, according to Tohl's rather inadequate proof. The N-alkylamino-thiophenes appear to be as unstable as the parent compound.

Stadler[15] reported an attempt to form N,N-dimethylaminothiophene hydrochloride by heating 2-aminothiophene hydrochloride with methanol in a sealed tube at 250–280°. A considerable amount of material decomposed and the investigator did not isolate the expected product.

D. Reactions of the Aminothiophenes

Although the instability of 2-aminothiophene as the free base in air was early recognized by Stadler,[1,15] Steinkopf[2] found that the free base was stable and derivatives could be prepared in an inert atmosphere such as nitrogen.

The stannic chloride double salt of 2-aminothiophene hydrochloride (II) yields 2-aminothiophene hydrochloride (VI), when treated with

[14] Tohl, *Ber.*, **28**, 2217 (1895).
[15] Stadler, *Ber.*, **18**, 2316 (1885).

hydrogen sulfide.[15] Treatment of VI with potassium carbonate gives a partially crystalline "gummy mass."[15] II reacts with acetyl chloride at 100° to give a dark red powder containing 7.2% chlorine and 15.19% sulfur. An attempt to diazotize VI with potassium nitrite is reported to have given a compound corresponding to 5-nitro-2-hydroxythiophene, m.p. 115–116°.[15]

Nuclear substitution of 2-aminothiophene has been carried out successfully. VI reacts with concentrated sulfuric acid to give 2-amino-5-thiophenesulfonic acid hydrochloride (VII).[15,16] With diazonium compounds, VI couples in the 5-position to give "azodyestuffs"[15] (Eq. 11).

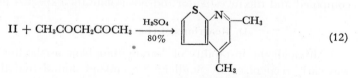

$$\text{(VI)} \qquad\qquad\qquad\qquad\qquad \text{(VIII)} \tag{11}$$

VIII was described as a "crystalline yellow precipitate." Treatment of VI with benzenesulfonic acid diazonium chloride gave a "yellow dyestuff."[15]

Reactions involving the nitrogen of the aminothiophenes are somewhat like those of aniline. The principal exception is the failure of aminothiophene to undergo diazotization and subsequent coupling. The free base reacts with ethyl chloroformate to give ethyl 2-thienylcarbamate and with acetic anhydride to give 2-acetamidothiophene.[2] Acetic anhydride reacts with ethyl 5-amino-2-thiophenecarboxylate to give the corresponding acetamido derivative (see Eq. 9).

Ring closure can be effected with acetylacetone and II in the presence of sulfuric acid and excellent yields of 4,6-dimethylthieno[2,3-b]pyridine, b.p. 103–108° (4 mm.), d_{20}^{20} 1.152, n_D^{20} 1.6230 are obtained[17] (Eq. 12). Unfortunately, this method cannot be applied generally to α,γ-diketones, and resinification products are normally obtained.

$$\text{II} + CH_3COCH_2COCH_3 \xrightarrow[80\%]{H_2SO_4} \tag{12}$$

The Skraup synthesis was investigated, but because of the sensitivity of 2-aminothiophene to oxidizing agents low yields were obtained[18] (Eq. 13).

[16] Hurd and Priestley, *J. Am. Chem. Soc.*, **69**, 859 (1947).
[17] Emerson, Holly, and Klemm, *J. Am. Chem. Soc.*, **63**, 2569 (1941).
[18] Steinkopf and Lutzkendorf, *Ann.*, **403**, 45 (1914).

$$\text{II} + \underset{\text{S}}{\boxed{}}\!\!\!-NO_2 \quad \xrightarrow[5\%]{\text{glycerine, concd. } H_2SO_4,\ 150°} \quad \underset{\text{Thieno [2,3-}b\text{]pyridine}}{\boxed{}\!\!\!\boxed{N}} \qquad (13)$$

Unlike the parent compound, aminothiophenes substituted with electron-withdrawing substituents are easily diazotized and coupled. 5-Amino-2-thiophenecarboxylic acid hydrochloride and its esters have been diazotized and coupled with β-naphthol[6,19] (Eq. 14). According to Ben-

$$C_2H_5OOC\!\!-\!\!\underset{S}{\boxed{}}\!\!\!-N_2\cdot HSO_3 \quad \xrightarrow{\beta\text{-naphthol}} \quad C_2H_5OOC\!\!-\!\!\underset{S}{\boxed{}}\!\!\!-N{=}N{-}\overset{OH}{\boxed{}} \qquad (14)$$

ary and Bavarian,[20] ethyl 2-methyl-4-amino-3-thiophenecarboxylate cannot be diazotized and coupled. It did couple with benzenediazonium chloride, but the product was not characterized. 2-Amino-5-thiophenesulfonic acid, prepared by the action of fuming sulfuric acid on II, can be diazotized and coupled with β-naphthol to form an intensely red dye.[16] Diazotized 2-amino-5-thiophenearsonic acids are also capable of coupling.[7,8]

During the last decade interest in sulfanilamides as therapeutic agents brought about the almost simultaneous synthesis of 2-sulfanilamidothiophene by three different groups of investigators. The synthesis was effected by condensation of p-acetamidobenzenesulfonyl chloride with 2-aminothiophene, its hydrochloride salt, or the stannic chloride double salt.[21-23]

E. Reactions of the Acetamidothiophenes

2-Acetamidothiophene (IX) reacts with alkyl iodides to produce N-substituted-2-acetamidothiophenes. Subsequent hydrolysis yields the N-substituted aminothiophenes[2] (see Eq. 10). Nitrous fumes (N_2O_3) with acetanilide produce N-nitrosoacetanilide. When 2-acetamidothiophene is so treated nuclear substitution occurs with the introduction of a nitro group.[2,24] Blocking the reactive 3,5-positions with halogen atoms failed to permit the formation of the N-nitroso derivative (see discussion below).[24]

[19] Dann, *Chem. Ber.*, **82**, 72 (1949).
[20] Benary and Bavarian, *Ber.*, **48**, 596 (1915).
[21] Berlin, Laudon, Sjörgen, *Svensk Kem. Tid.*, **53**, 372 (1941).
[22] Seemann and Lucas, *Can. J. Research*, **B19**, 291 (1941).
[23] Bost and Starns, *J. Am. Chem. Soc.*, **63**, 1885 (1941).
[24] Priestley and Hurd, *J. Am. Chem. Soc.*, **69**, 1173 (1947).

TABLE VIII-3. Physical Constants of 2- and 3-Aminothiophenes and Miscellaneous Derivatives

Compound	B.p., °C. (mm.)	M.p., °C.	Ref.
2-Aminothiophene.....................	61–62 (1)	—	2
	77–79 (11)	—	2
2-Aminothiophene hydrochloride..........	—	Very hygroscopic	14
2-Methylaminothiophene.................	88–92 (15)	—	2
2-Ethylaminothiophene..................	85–89 (12–13)	—	2
3-Aminothiophene.....................	—	—	9
2,5-Dimethyl-3-aminothiophene hydrochloride...........................	—	205–206	3
2-Acetamidothiophene..................	—	160–161	2,12,16,24
2-Bromoacetamidothiophene.............	—	160	2
2-Propionamidothiophene...............	—	110–110.5	2
2-Butyramidothiophene.................	—	129.5	2
2-Isovaleramidothiophene...............	—	130–131	2
2-Benzamidothiophene..................	—	172–173	2
2-Toluamidothiophene..................	—	183–184	2
N-Methyl-2-acetamidothiophene..........	123.5–124.5 (13)	60	2
N-Ethyl-2-acetamidothiophene............	121–123 (15)	—	2
3-Acetamidothiophene..................	—	145–148	2
2,5-Dimethyl-3-acetamidothiophene.......	—	105	3
3-Benzamidothiophene..................	—	153–155	2
Ethyl 2-thienylcarbamate...............	—	52	2,13
2-Sulfanilamidothiophene...............	—	156.5–157.5	21–23
3-(N-Acetylsulfanilamido)-2,5-dimethylthiophene..........................	—	125	3
N-Acetyl-2-sulfanilamidothiophene........	—	196	21–23
3,4-Diaminothiophene..................	—	Unstable liquid	10
3,4-Diacetamidothiophene...............	—	207–208	10
3,4-Dibenzamidothiophene..............	—	268–269	10
2,3-Dihydro-2-oxo-1-thieno(3,4)imidazole..	—	200	10
N-Phenyl-N′-2-thienylurea	—	215	13
N,N′-Di-2-thienylurea..................	—	224	13
N-(2,5-Dimethyl-3-thienyl)urea..........	—	181	3

IX is nitrated easily with acetyl nitrate[2] to give a mixture of two isomeric mononitro derivatives (X), m.p. 165.5–166.5°, and XI, m.p. 222–223°. Further nitration yields a single isomer (XII), m.p. 182°, later shown to be 3,5-dinitro-2-acetamidothiophene.[24] In the present author's opinion, it seems logical to assume that X and XI are represented in equation (15). In addition to nitration, 2-acetamidothiophene (IX)

TABLE VIII-4. Nuclear Substituted Derivatives of *N*-(2-Thienyl)acetamide

N-(2-Thienyl)-acetamide	M.p., °C. (uncorr.)	Ref.
5-Methyl-	167	3
3-Bromo-	—	16
4-Bromo-	160	16,24
3,5-Dibromo-	142	16,24
3,4,5-Tribromo-	210	16,24
3,5-Diiodo-	172	16,24
3,4,5-Triiodo-	225	16,24
3-Bromo-5-iodo-	159	16,24
4-Bromo-5-iodo-	170	16,24
5-HgCl	222 (dec.)	16
3,5-Di-HgCl	>280	16
3,4,5-Tri-HgCl	250 (dec.)	16
3-Bromo-5-HgCl	222 (dec.)	16
4-Bromo-5-HgCl	245 (dec.)	16
3,5-Dinitro-	180	2,16
3,4,5-Trinitro-	140 (explodes)	24
3-Bromo-5-nitro-	206 (dec.)	16
3,4-Dibromo-5-nitro-	206 (dec.)	24
3,4-Diiodo-5-nitro-	260 (dec.)	24
4-Iodo-3,5-dinitro-	195	24

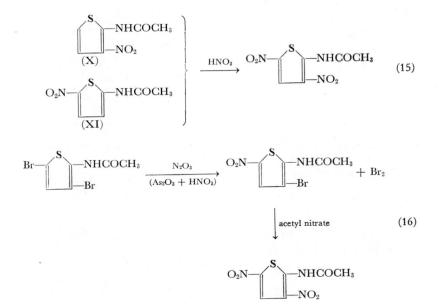

TABLE VIII-5. Diazo Derivatives of Thiophene

Formula	M.p., °C.	Color	Ref.
naphthalene—N=N—thiophene—COOEt, with —OH on naphthalene	165–166.5	Red-brown	19
naphthalene—N=N—thiophene—SO₃H, with —OH on naphthalene	—	Intensely red	16
naphthalene—N=N—thiophene—NHCOCH₃, with COOEt on naphthalene	215–217	Red	19
phenyl—N=N—thiophene—NHCOCH₃, with COOEt on phenyl	233	Red-orange	19
EtOOC—thiophene—N=N—thiophene—NHCOCH₃	248 (dec.)	Purple	19
EtOOC—thiophene—N=N—furan—NHCOCH₃	191–192 (dec.)	Dull red	19
phenyl—N=N—thiophene—NHCOCH₃, with NO₂ on phenyl	262	Dark red	16
phenyl—N=N—thiophene(—Br)—NHCOCH₃, with NO₂ on phenyl	235 (dec.)	Red	16

TABLE VIII-5. (*continued*)

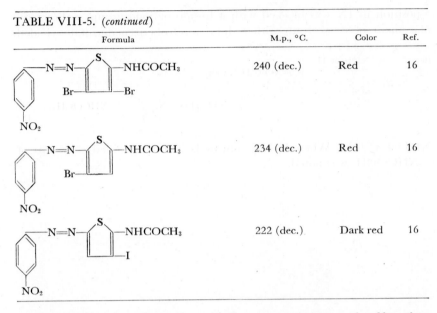

Formula	M.p., °C.	Color	Ref.
	240 (dec.)	Red	16
	234 (dec.)	Red	16
	222 (dec.)	Dark red	16

has been shown to undergo bromination, mercuration, and sulfonation; primary substitution occurs at the 5-position. A second substituent enters at the 3-position.[16,24] In the case of nitration, a portion of the primary substitution also occurs at this position.[2] Trisubstitution occurs in bromination and mercuration with excess reagents. 3,4,5-Trinitro-2-acetamidothiophene is not prepared by direct nitration but is obtained by a replacement reaction of 3,4,5-triiodo-2-acetamidothiophene. This reaction is partially demonstrated in equation 16 on page 237.

The action of nitrogen trioxide (Eq. 16) or acetyl nitrate on halo-2-acetamidothiophenes causes loss of the halo groups and replacement by nitro groups.[24] Mixed melting points showed this product to be identical with Steinkopf's dinitro derivative (XII).[2] A stepwise replacement of the iodine in 3,4,5-triiodo-2-acetamidothiophene indicated that replacement took place in the following order: (*1*) 5-iodo; (*2*) 3-iodo; (*3*) 4-iodo.

IX has been found to couple quite easily with diazonium compounds,[16,19,24] whereas acetanilide is not known to undergo such coupling. In acid solution the following reaction takes place[16] (Eq. 17). When the

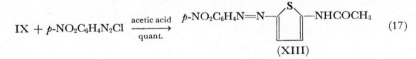

$$\text{IX} + p\text{-NO}_2\text{C}_6\text{H}_4\text{N}_2\text{Cl} \xrightarrow[\text{quant.}]{\text{acetic acid}} p\text{-NO}_2\text{C}_6\text{H}_4\text{N}=\text{N} \text{—} \boxed{} \text{—NHCOCH}_3 \qquad (17)$$

(XIII)

5-position in IX was blocked with a bromo or iodo group, a direct replacement of that group with sodium p-nitrobenzenediazotate yielded

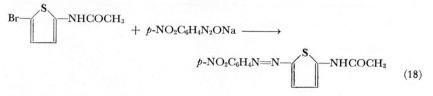

$$+ \; p\text{-NO}_2\text{C}_6\text{H}_4\text{N}_2\text{ONa} \; \longrightarrow$$

$$(18)$$

XIII (Eq. 18).   When XIII is nitrated, XII is obtained.   No loss of —NHCOCH$_3$ was noted.

CHAPTER IX

Thiophene Compounds Containing Nitrogen in the Side Chain

The aminoalkylthiophenes have, until the past few years, received relatively little attention because of the difficulties of synthesis. As a consequence, only isolated syntheses of aminoalkylthiophenes were reported before 1940.

The synthesis of 2-thenyl chloride by chloromethylation in the early 1940's renewed interest in this field among pharmacologists, and various thenylamines were prepared and tested for a variety of uses. From that work stems the discovery of the activity of thiophene in antihistaminic drugs. At the present time, three types of thenylamine derivatives are available in commercial form under the names of "Thenylene," "Histadyl," "Diatrin," and "Tagathen."

During 1947–1949 the author and his co-workers published six articles concerning a type of Mannich reaction specifically designated below as the Aminomethylation Reaction (see Section I."B"). This reaction, that of thiophene, formaldehyde, and ammonium halides or hydroxylamine salts, offers a convenient synthesis for many new thenylamines and thenylhydroxylamines. This reaction also produces a new class of intermediates, the N-(2-thenyl)formaldimines, which undergo many unique reactions.

The difunctional characteristics of thiophene (*i.e.*, the high reactivities of the 2,5-positions) make possible resin formation through the aminomethylation reaction. The resins obtained by the reaction are water soluble as the hydrochlorides and the aqueous solutions of the reaction mixtures can be used directly for the impregnation of wood, paper, and textile fabrics. They impart a definite water-repellency to paper and textiles when deposited in concentrations from 2–6% by weight. As far as textile uses are concerned, their tendency to yellow in ultraviolet light has been a deterrent to commercial development. In special instances, where color stability is no prime factor, they could easily be adapted to large-scale use in current processes for conferring water-repellency.

241

The N-(2-thenyl)formaldimines have been subjected only to a preliminary study and their reactions have been found to be unique. They appear to couple with considerable ease with acetone, aniline, hydrogen cyanide, urea, styrene, and phenol, but the structure of the resultant products has not been studied. Other reactions are given in Section I.B.2 below.

Nomenclature

The complexity of some of the nomenclature used in this chapter makes it necessary to indicate the kind to be used. In all cases given below, the first name listed will be used as standard nomenclature in the remaining portion of the chapter. For simplicity, the term *thenyl*, C_4H_3S—CH_2—, is employed as much as possible. This nomenclature is based on the analogy to the benzyl radical and offers considerable convenience, as will be seen in Figure IX-1.

Di-(5-methyl-2-thenyl)amine
N,N-Bis-(5-methyl-2-thenyl)amine

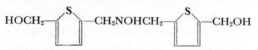

Di-(5-hydroxymethyl-2-thenyl)hydroxylamine
N,N-Bis-(5-hydroxymethyl-2-thenyl)hydroxylamine

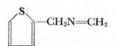

2-(2'-Thienyl)ethylamine
1-Amino-2-(2-thienyl)ethane
β-(2-Thienyl)ethylamine

N-(2-Thenyl)formaldimine
2-(Methyleneiminomethyl)thiophene

N-(2-Thenyl)aminomethylsulfonic acid
N-(2-Thienyl)methylaminomethylsulfonic acid

Figure IX-1

I. Preparation of Thienylalkylamines

A. Reduction of Oximes

2-Thenylamine was first prepared by reduction of 2-thiophenealdoxime with sodium amalgam in unspecified yield[1] (Eq. 1). Later the

$$\text{[S]}-CH{=}NOH \xrightarrow{\text{NaHg}} \text{[S]}-CH_2NH_2 \qquad (1)$$

same workers indicated that 2-tetrahydrothenylamine (2-aminomethylthiolane) could be prepared by this method if the reaction was carried out with 2.5% amalgam with water at 80°.[1a] 2-Aminomethylthiolane boils at 69.5° at 10 mm., d_4^{15} 1.0920, n_D^{15} 1.5399.

The oximes of 2-acetylthiophene[2] and various substituted 2- and 3-acetylthiophenes[3] have been reduced to 1-(2' or 3'-thienyl)ethylamines. Zinc and hydrochloric acid can also be used for this reduction.[1a] Barger and Easson reduced 2-(isonitrosoacetyl)thiophene to 2-thenoylmethylamine using stannous chloride[4] (Eq. 2). Reduction of the oxime of 2-

$$\text{[S]}-COCH{=}NOH \xrightarrow[48\%]{\text{SnCl}_2, \text{HCl}} \text{[S]}-COCH_2NH_2 \cdot HCl \qquad (2)$$

thiopheneglyoxylic acid with tin and hydrochloric acid gave 2-thienylglycine[5] (Eq. 5). Sodium amalgam reduction of 2-thenylhydroxylamine

$$\text{[S]}-\underset{\underset{NOH}{\|}}{C}-COOH \xrightarrow{\text{Sn, HCl}} \text{[S]}-\underset{NH_2 \cdot HCl}{CHCOOH} \qquad (3)$$

gave a low yield of 2-thenylamine[6] (Eq. 4). Stannous chloride was

$$\text{[S]}-CH_2NHOH \xrightarrow[20\%]{\text{NaHg, alc.}} \text{[S]}-CH_2NH_2 \qquad (4)$$

effective for this reduction and also in reducing di-(2-thenyl)hydroxylamine. The yields were considerably higher than with sodium amalgam

[1] Putokhin and Egorova, *J. Gen. Chem.* (*U. S. S. R.*), **10**, 1873 (1940); *Chem. Abstr.*, **35**, 4377 (1941).
[1a] Putokhin and Egorova, *J. Gen. Chem.* (*U. S. S. R.*), **18**, 1866 (1948); *Chem. Abstr.*, **43**, 3816 (1949).
[2] Goldschmidt and Schulthess, *Ber.*, **20**, 1700 (1887).
[3] Chabrier, Tchoubar, and Le Tellier-Dupre, *Bull. soc. chim. France*, **1946**, 332.
[4] Barger and Easson, *J. Chem. Soc.*, **1938**, 2100.
[5] Bradley, *Ber.*, **19**, 2122 (1886).
[6] Hartough and Conley, unpublished work.

but decomposition of the stannic chloride double salts gave considerable trouble.

Di-2,5-(3-aminobutyl)thiophene is prepared by reduction of the corresponding oxime with hydrogen and Raney nickel.[7]

B. The Aminomethylation Reaction

1. Reaction of Thiophenes, Formaldehyde, and Ammonium Chloride

Thiophene, 2-alkylthiophenes, and 2-halothiophenes react with ammonium chloride and formaldehyde to give N-(2-thenyl)formaldimines.[8-13] The reaction was found to proceed as shown in equation (5).[10] Compound I was also formed in quantitative yield when 2-thenyl-

$$\text{thiophene} + 2CH_2O + NH_4Cl \xrightarrow[50-65\%]{65°} \text{thiophene}-CH_2N=CH_2 \cdot HCl \quad (5)$$

(I)

amine (II) was treated with formaldehyde. Originally,[8,9] II was thought to be the primary product of the reaction but it was subsequently shown to form from the reaction of I with thiophene.[10] The secondary amine, di-(2-thenyl)amine, and di-(2-thienyl)methane are also formed by a secondary reaction (Eq. 6).

$$\text{thiophene} + I \xrightarrow{70°} \text{thiophene}-CH_2NH_2 \cdot HCl + \left(\text{thiophene}-CH_2\right)_2 NH \cdot HCl + \left(\text{thiophene}-\right)_2 CH_2 \quad (6)$$

2- and 3-Methylthiophene react rapidly with ammonium chloride and formaldehyde without application of heat. With 2-methylthiophene at 30–35°, almost equimolar quantities of di-(5-methyl-2-thenyl)amine hydrochloride and N-(5-methyl-2-thenyl)formaldimine hydrochloride are obtained. At 55°, the yield of the former increases at the expense of the latter. At 88°, about 20% of tri-(5-methyl-2-thenyl)amine, along with the primary and secondary amines and some di-(5-methyl-2-thienyl)-methane, is formed, but no formaldimine products were isolated.

[7] Griffing and Salisbury, *J. Am. Chem. Soc.*, **70**, 3416 (1948).
[8] Hartough, Lukasiewicz, and Murray, *J. Am. Chem. Soc.*, **68**, 1139 (1946).
[9] Hartough, *et al.*, *J. Am. Chem. Soc.*, **70**, 1146 (1948).
[10] Hartough, Meisel, Koft, and Schick, *J. Am. Chem. Soc.*, **70**, 4013 (1948).
[10a] Hartough and Schick, unpublished work.
[11] Hartough and Dickert, *J. Am. Chem. Soc.*, **71**, 3922 (1949).
[12] Hartough and Meisel, *J. Am. Chem. Soc.*, **70**, 4018 (1948).
[12] Hartough, Schick, and Dickert, *J. Am. Chem. Soc.*, **72**, 1572 (1950).

Further proof that the formaldimines were the intermediates in the aminoalkylation reaction was provided by reaction (7).[10]

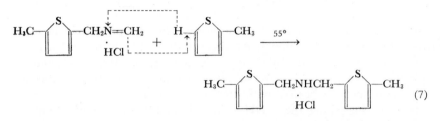

$$(7)$$

The halothiophenes, *e.g.*, 2-chlorothiophene, will not react with aqueous formaldehyde and ammonium chloride.   The reaction can be carried out conveniently using paraformaldehyde and a little acetic acid.[9]

The aminomethylation reaction proceeds well when the source of ammonia is ammonium halides.   Other ammonium salts fail to react. The lower alkylamines, such as methyl and dimethylamines, react to a lesser extent and the main reaction consists of a coupling of two thienyl radicals with a methylene bridge, *e.g.*, 2-methylthiophene, formaldehyde, and dimethylamine hydrochloride give a 45% yield of di-(5-methyl-2-thienyl)methane.   Octylamine, dodecylamine, and octadecylamine as their hydrochlorides condense with thiophene and formaldehyde slowly. They condense rapidly with the use of sulfurous acid to give resinous amines.   The structures of these amines have not been investigated.

When, in lieu of ammonium chloride, ethylenediamine, aniline, or urea is used in the presence of hydrochloric acid, a very rapid, uncontrollable reaction ensues with the formation of powdery, nonfusible resinous amines.[9]

Resins are also obtained from polymeric formaldehyde (paraformaldehyde or trioxymethylene), ammonium chloride, and thiophene.   With a mole ratio of formaldehyde to thiophene above 2:1, resins are formed by continued boiling of the reaction mixture.   These resinous amines, as their hydrochlorides, are soluble in water in concentrations as high as 80%.

These resins normally contain about one nitrogen atom per sulfur atom (or thiophene radical).   A study of the monomeric, dimeric, and trimeric thenylformaldimines has suggested two possible structures for these resins.[13]   The first form may arise through interaction of *N*-(2-thenyl)formaldimine with the reactive 5-position (8).   The second form may arise by polymerization through the formaldimine linkage, giving resins of the type shown in (9).   The latter appears to be the only likely

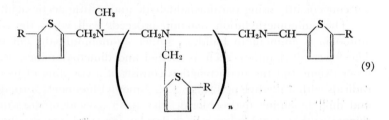

$$(8)$$

structure in the case of 2-methylthiophene.   Further proof that the latter structure exists in the thiophene resins is indicated by formation of 1–2% of 2-thiophenealdehyde by strong acid hydrolysis.   When subresinous, plastic amines obtained by the sulfurous acid method, described in section 2.C, are further treated with formaldehyde, further resinification is observed, suggesting the —NH— linkage of (8).   It appears from extended study that the resins obtained from thiophene are mixtures of the above two types (8 and 9).

$$(9)$$

tert-Butyl 3-thienyl sulfide, and di-2,4-(2-thienyl)thiolane undergo the aminomethylation reaction but the products are complex and the amine hydrochlorides are for the most part insoluble in water.[10a]

2. Reactions of the N-(2-Thenyl)formaldimines

When N-(2-thenyl)formaldimine hydrochloride is neutralized it can be distilled to give a product that corresponds in molecular weight to a dimer.   Subsequent redistillations of this dimeric material give a crystalline trimeric formaldimine.   On the basis of its chemical reactions, this dimeric formaldimine was assigned the structure of N,N'-bis-(2-thenyl)-1,3-diazocyclobutane.   The trimeric material is then N,N',N''-tris-(2-thenyl)hexahydro-1,3,5-triazine.   There is further evidence that the dimeric form exists in aqueous solution above pH 3, since it undergoes reactions (10) to form 2-thiophenealdehyde and N-methyl-2-thenyl-amine.[11]   In this manner, 95% of the original thiophene was accounted for in the hydrolysis products.   The trimeric triazine resinifies under similar conditions.

Other reactions investigated, and the products obtained, are represented in equations (11)–(14).[10,12]   The diazocyclobutane derivative reacts rapidly with urea, aniline, and styrene in 1:1 molar ratios.   Reduction with zinc and hydrochloric acid gives N-methyl-2-thenylamine.[10]   Re-

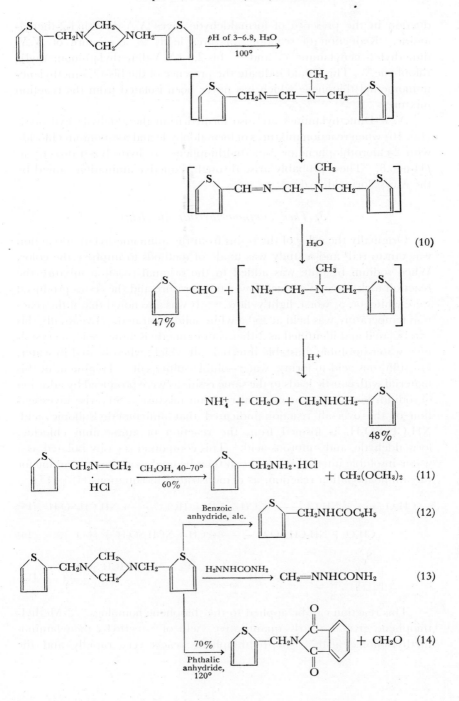

$$\xrightarrow[100°]{p\text{H of } 3\text{-}6.8, \text{H}_2\text{O}}$$

(10)

47%

48%

$$\xrightarrow[60\%]{CH_3OH, \ 40\text{-}70°} \quad + \ CH_2(OCH_3)_2 \quad (11)$$

$$\xrightarrow[\text{anhydride, alc.}]{\text{Benzoic}} \quad (12)$$

$$\xrightarrow{H_2NNHCONH_2} \quad CH_2\!=\!NNHCONH_2 \quad (13)$$

$$\xrightarrow[\substack{\text{Phthalic} \\ \text{anhydride,} \\ 120°}]{70\%} \quad + \ CH_2O \quad (14)$$

duction in the presence of formaldehyde gives *N,N*-dimethyl-2-thenyl-amine.   Reduction of reaction mixtures leads to a mixture of *N,N*-dimethyl-2-thenylamine   and   bis-2,5-(*N,N*-dimethylaminomethyl)-thiophene.[10]   This would indicate the presence of the bis-(2,5-methylene-iminomethyl)thiophene which has never been isolated from the reaction mixtures.

N,N'-Dimethylamines are also formed from the aldehyde hydrolysis (Eq. 10) when reaction mixtures of formaldehyde and ammonium chloride with 2-chlorothiophene or 3-methylthiophene are hydrolyzed directly at *p*H 6–6.8.   These probably arise through reductive amination caused by the excess formaldehyde.

3. *Thenylaminomethylsulfonic Acids*

Originally the color of the resins from the aminomethylation reaction was tan to red[9] and a study was made of methods to improve the color. When sodium bisulfite was added to the original reaction mixture the reaction took place at a much lower temperature and the resins produced were white, or, at worst, light yellow.[13]   It was also noted that if the reaction temperature was held at 35° a white solid separated.   Eventually this was isolated and identified as 2-thenylaminomethylsulfonic acid, a crystalline, water-insoluble, unstable internal salt which, when heated in water, lost sulfurous acid to form a water-soluble sulfite salt.   Treatment of this material with caustic leads to the same resins as were produced by addition of sodium bisulfite to the original reaction mixture.   Stepwise investigation of the over-all reaction indicated that aminomethylsulfonic acid, $NH_2CH_2SO_3H$, is formed from the reaction of ammonium chloride, formaldehyde, and sulfurous acid.   This compound is easily isolated as a water-insoluble internal salt and can then be used as a source of amine for the aminoalkylation reaction, as demonstrated in equations (15)–(17).

$$CH_2O \text{ (aq.)} + NH_4Cl \xrightarrow{55°} CH_2{=}NH + HCl \xrightarrow[80\%]{H_2SO_3} NH_2CH_2SO_3H \quad (15)$$

$$CH_2O + NH_2CH_2SO_3H \longrightarrow CH_2{=}NCH_2SO_3H + H_2O \quad (16)$$

$$(17)$$

This reaction can be applied to the thiophene homologs.   2-Methyl-thiophene gives a nearly quantitative yield of 5-methyl-2-thenylamino-methylsulfonic acid.   3-Methylthiophene reacts very rapidly and the product is almost exclusively 3-methyl-2-thenylaminomethylsulfonic acid, since no thiophenecarboxylic acid corresponding to 3-methyl-5-thenyl-aminomethylsulfonic acid is found upon oxidation. 2-Chlorothiophene forms the 5-chloro-2-thenylaminomethylsulfonic acid by reaction with aminomethylsulfonic acid and aqueous formaldehyde.

Reaction (18) occurs in hot alcohol or water. When the amino-

$$\text{[thiophene]}-CH_2NHCH_2SO_3H \xrightarrow[\text{quant.}]{60-100°} \left(\text{[thiophene]}-CH_2N{=}CH_2\right)_2 H_2SO_3 + SO_2 + H_2O$$

(18)

methylsulfonic acids are treated with caustic, the N-(2-thenyl)formaldi-mines are obtained in improved yields over the prior method (see section B.1 above). The reaction is reversible, and thenylaminomethylsulfonic acids are obtained by treatment of the dimeric or trimeric N-(2-thenyl)-formaldimines with sulfurous acid or by treating the thenylamines with formaldehyde and sulfurous acid. The thenylformaldimines dissolve in concentrated sodium bisulfite solutions, and acidification yields the aminomethylsulfonic acids but in considerably lower yields.

Continued heating of these salts in water at 70–80° causes polymer-ization, and subsequent decomposition with caustic gives white resins rather than the N-(2-thenyl)formaldimines.

4. Reaction of Thiophenes, Formaldehyde, and Hydroxylamine Salts

Thiophene reacts rapidly with aqueous formaldehyde and hydroxyl-amine salts to give 2-thenylhydroxylamines.[14] As in the case of thiophene, formaldehyde, and ammonium chloride, resinous amines are obtained along with primary and secondary thenylhydroxylamines. It was found that the best way to prepare and isolate the relatively unstable 2-thenyl-hydroxylamine was to carry out the reaction stepwise (Eqs. 19 and 20).

$$CH_2O + NH_2OH \cdot HCl \longrightarrow CH_2{=}NOH + HCl$$ (19)

$$\text{[thiophene]} + CH_2{=}NOH \xrightarrow[78\%]{HCl, 30-55°} \text{[thiophene]}-CH_2NHOH \cdot HCl$$ (20)

A 9% yield of di-(2-thenyl)hydroxylamine hydrochloride was also ob-tained. The latter product is obtained in improved yields, along with resinous amines, by a different procedure (Eq. 21). If the reagents are mixed together and heated under reflux, instead of di-(2-thenyl)hydroxyl-

[14] Hartough, *J. Am. Chem. Soc.*, **69**, 1355 (1947).

$$\text{[thiophene]} + NH_2OH \cdot HCl \xrightarrow[48\%]{\substack{CH_2O \text{ added} \\ \text{dropwise, } 65°}} \left(\text{[thiophene]}-CH_2- \right)_2 NOH \cdot HCl \qquad (21)$$

amine hydrochloride a new product, di-(5-hydroxymethyl-2-thenyl)hydroxyl amine hydrochloride, crystallizes from the reaction mixture. This may be an intermediate in the resinification of these amines but the free base was too unstable to allow investigation.

When 2-chlorothiophene is employed, 5-chloro-2-thenylhydroxylamine hydrochloride precipitates from the reaction mixture. *tert*-Butylthiophene appears to give a mixture of primary and secondary amines.

Oxidation of the resinous products produced from this reaction was found to give 2-thiophenecarboxylic acid, 2-thiophenealdehyde, and 2,5-thiophenedicarboxylic acid when oxidized with alkaline permanganate. The structure was then deduced accordingly (22).

$$\text{[thiophene]}\left(CH_2NOHCH_2-\text{[thiophene]}- \right)_n CH_2NOHCH_2-\text{[thiophene]} \qquad (22)$$

All free bases of this class of compounds are thermally unstable. At 100° they lose water and slowly polymerize into light yellow, thermoplastic resins. They decompose with near-explosive violence at 150° and thus cannot be distilled. For the most part, the isolation of pure chemicals depends upon crystallization from the reaction mixture or by induced crystallization from solvents such as thiophene or benzene by addition of paraffinic antisolvents.

As in the case of ammonium chloride, the molar ratio of formaldehyde and hydroxylamine salts can be varied and a great variety of polymeric amines can be obtained.

5. Catalysis and Inhibition of the Aminomethylation Reaction

Sulfurous acid, acetic acid, and phosphoric acid catalyze the reaction of thiophene, formaldehyde, and ammonium chloride.[13] Sulfurous acid definitely enters into the reaction but the course of reaction involved with the other two materials has not been determined. Acetic acid induces high yields of di-(2-thenyl)amine[12] when thiophene reacts with polymeric formaldehyde and ammonium chloride, probably by interaction of N-(2-thenyl)formaldimine and thiophene. Orthophosphoric acid may enter into the reaction in a manner analogous to that by which sulfurous acid acts but the intermediates could not be isolated. A salt of orthophosphoric acid and N-(2-thenyl)formaldimine has been observed, but attempts to purify it for characterization led to decomposition.

In the course of the above work, Sections I.B.1–4, aqueous formaldehyde containing 2–6% methanol was employed. Careful investigation of the reaction indicated that the products were more resinous when 30% methanol-free formaldehyde was used. Subsequent studies indicated that methanol, ethanol, and n-butanol, when employed as solvents, inhibited the reaction completely and formed formals, $CH_2(OR)_2$, presumably by interaction of the alcohols with the formaldimine intermediate, $CH_2{=}NH$. The removal of the methylene group from $C_4H_3S{-}CH_2N{=}CH_2$ with methanol[12] is further evidence for such a mechanism.

C. Reaction of Thenyl Halides with Amines

Condensation of thenyl halides with aminopyridines or aniline gives compounds possessing excellent "antihistaminic" activity. Their syntheses are exemplified by equation (23).[15–17,17a,17c] The isomeric 3-substituted derivatives are also prepared by this method.[17b]

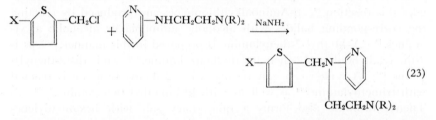

$$\text{(23)}$$

The X may be a halogen, methyl, or hydrogen, and R is methyl or ethyl. The physical properties of these amines are listed in Table IX-2 (page 268). When R is a methyl group and X hydrogen the compound is sold commercially under the name "Thenylene" by Abbott Laboratories. Eli Lilly markets this compound under the name of "Histadyl." When X is chlorine and R a methyl group, the compound is known as "Tagathen" and is thus marketed by Lederle. Warner Laboratories' "Diatrin" is N,N-dimethyl-N'-phenyl-N'-(2-thenyl)ethylenediamine.

The current pharmaceutical interest in these types of compounds has been responsible for a great variety of new thenylamine and thienylalkylamine derivatives somewhat similar to those represented by the above formula. Those appearing in the literature too late for inclusion in the text are to be found in the tables at the end of this chapter (see pages 275 to 279). Current data indicate that the antihistaminic effect of the

[15] Weston, *J. Am. Chem. Soc.*, **69**, 980 (1947).
[16] Clapp *et al.*, *J. Am. Chem. Soc.*, **69**, 1549 (1947).
[17] Kyrides, Meyer, and Zienty, *J. Am. Chem. Soc.*, **69**, 2239 (1947). Kyrides and Zienty, U. S. Pat. 2,457,048 (1948).
[17a] Leonard and Solmssen, *J. Am. Chem. Soc.*, **70**, 2064 (1948).
[17b] Campaigne and Le Suer, *J. Am. Chem. Soc.*, **71**, 333 (1949).
[17c] Clark *et al.*, *J. Org. Chem.*, **14**, 216 (1949).

3-thenyl analogs is about one and one-half times as active as the 2-thenyl compounds. A similar increase in activity is noted when a 5-halogen group is introduced into the 2-thenyl nucleus. The physiological activity of these compounds is discussed in more detail in Chapter II.

The addition product of thenyl bromide and hexamethylene tetramine can be successfully degraded with hydrogen chloride to give high yields of 2-thenylamine hydrochloride as demonstrated in equation (24).[18] The

$$\text{—CH}_2\text{Br} \cdot (\text{CH}_2)_6\text{N}_4 \xrightarrow[\text{80\%}]{\text{HCl gas, alcohol}}$$

$$\text{—CH}_2\text{NH}_2 \cdot \text{HCl} \quad + \text{ CH}_2(\text{OC}_2\text{H}_5)_2 + \text{NH}_4\text{Cl} \quad (24)$$

2-thenyl chloride hexamethylenetetramine addition product also undergoes this reaction.[19] β-Aminoalkylthiophenes are produced by reacting the corresponding halides with alcoholic ammonia or alcoholic alkylamines.[18] N-Methyl-2-thenylamine is prepared in this manner,[10,18] as is 2-thenylallylaniline, 2-thenylmethylbenzylamine,[19a] and di-(2-thenyl)-amine.[19b] A quaternary salt results when 2-thenyl bromide is reacted with trimethylamine[19a] as well as with hexamethylenetetramine.[18,19] 3-Thenyl bromide also forms a quaternary salt with hexamethylenetetramine.[19c]

D. Leuckhardt Reaction

The Leuckhardt synthesis, comprising the interaction of 2-acetylthiophene and ammonium formate, yields 1-(2-thienyl)ethylamine [2-(α-aminoethyl)thiophene][18,20] (Eq. 25). This reaction has also been

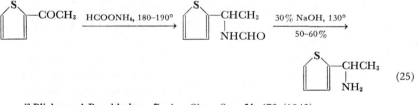

$$(25)$$

[18] Blicke and Burckhalter, *J. Am. Chem. Soc.*, **64**, 478 (1942).
[19] Hartough, unpublished work.
[19a] von Braun, Fussganger, and Kühn, *Ann.*, **445**, 218 (1945).
[19b] Lincoln, Heinzelmann, and Hunter, *J. Am. Chem. Soc.*, **71**, 2902 (1949).
[19c] Long, Miller, and Chen, *J. Am. Chem. Soc.*, **71**, 669 (1949).
[20] Schick and Crowley, Socony-Vacuum Laboratories, unpublished work.

applied to 3-(2-thienyl)-2-butanone, and 3-(2-thienyl)-2-butylamine was obtained.[21] 2-(2-Thienyl)cyclopentanone and 3-(2-thienyl)-2-propanone were also reported to undergo this reaction. Yields of amine from these reactions were not reported.

E. Miscellaneous Methods

2-(2-Thienyl)ethylamine has been prepared by Barger and Easson[4] from 3-(2-thienyl)propionamide by means of the Hoffman reaction (Eq. 26).

$$\text{(thienyl)}-CH_2CH_2CONH_2 \xrightarrow[63\%]{NaOCl} \text{(thienyl)}-CH_2CH_2NH_2 \qquad (26)$$

Acid hydrolysis of methyl 2-(5-phenyl-2-thienyl)ethyl carbamate (Eq. 27) is reported to form 2-(5-phenyl-2-thienyl)ethylamine[22].

$$C_6H_5-\text{(thienyl)}-CH_2CH_2COOH \cdot H_2NNH_2 \xrightarrow[\substack{NaNO_2, CH_3OH}]{ether, HCl,}$$

$$C_6H_5-\text{(thienyl)}-CH_2CH_2NHCOOCH_3 \qquad (27)$$

The condensation of methylolchloroacetamide and 2-thiophenecarboxylic acid gives 2-carboxy-5(4?)-thenylchloroacetamide[23,24] (Eq. 28). A similar condensation was carried out by the author with thiophene

$$\text{(thienyl)}-COOH + HOCH_2NHCOCH_2Cl \xrightarrow{H_2SO_4}$$

$$HOOC-\text{(thienyl)}-CH_2NHCOCH_2Cl + H_2O \quad (28)$$

and methylolacetamide using equimolar amounts of reagents and orthophosphoric acid[19] (Eq. 29).

$$\text{(thienyl)} + HOCH_2NHCOCH_3 \xrightarrow[50-60\%]{85\% H_3PO_4, 70-80°} \text{(thienyl)}-CH_2NHCOCH_3 \qquad (29)$$

[21] Van Zoeren, U. S. Pat. 2,367,702 (1945).
[22] Robinson and Todd, J. Chem. Soc., **1939**, 1743.
[23] Cinneide, Proc. Royal Irish Acad., **B42**, 359 (1935); Chem. Abstr., **29**, 7326 (1935).
[24] See author's note on this compound under thiophenecarboxylic acids; Cinneide reports this compound to be 2-carboxy-4-thenylchloroacetamide.

A recent synthesis of N-n-butyl-1-(2′-thienyl)propylamine was effected by the addition of ethylmagnesium iodide to N-n-butyl-2-the-naldimine[24a] (Eq. 30).

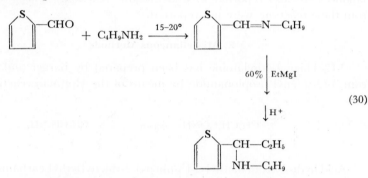

$$(30)$$

II. Preparation of Thiophene Compounds Containing Nonfused Nitrogen Rings

For convenience, this series of compounds has been broken down into simple ring systems.   The five-membered C_4N, C_3NO, C_3NS, and C_3N_2 rings, the six-membered C_5N, C_4N_2, and C_3N_3 rings, and bicyclic six-membered C_6—C_5N rings are discussed below.   The four-membered C_2N_2 system and the six-membered C_3N_3 system arising from the aminomethyl-ation reaction (see Section I.2.B) will not be discussed again.   In general, the methods used for ring closure are standard techniques; no new syn-thetic methods are involved.

A. The C₄N Systems

Thienylpyrroline and Thienylpyrrolidine

Kirchner and Johns[25] have synthesized 2-(2′-thienyl)pyrroline and 2-(2′-thienyl)pyrrolidine by the methods shown in equation (31).

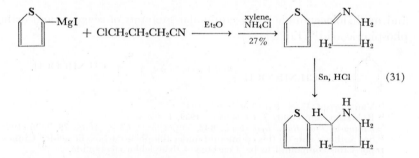

$$(31)$$

[24a] Emling, Beatty, and Stevens, *J. Am. Chem. Soc.*, **71**, 703 (1949).
[25] Kirchner and Johns, *J. Am. Chem. Soc.*, **62**, 2183 (1940).

The insecticidal activity of these compounds was found to be less than that of nicotine.[26]

2-Thenalpyrrole

H. Fischer and Schormüller[27] condensed 2-thiophenealdehyde with kryptopyrrole with formation of the following compound:

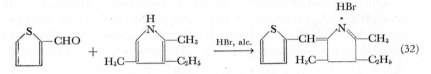

$$(32)$$

B. The C_3NO Systems

Isoxazoles

Angeli[28] condensed hydroxylamine with ethyl 2-thenoylmethyl-glyoxylate, $2\text{-}C_4H_3SCOCH_2COCOOC_2H_5$, to obtain a product, m.p. 48°, represented by one or both of the formulas of (33).

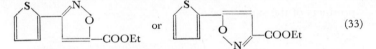

$$(33)$$

Homeyer[29] has condensed hydroxylamine with ethyl 2-thenoylacetate to obtain 3-(2-thienyl)isoxazol-5-one.

Oxazoles

Yuan and Li[30] condensed diethyl-2-thiophenealdehyde acetal with hippuric acid to obtain 2-phenyl-4-(2'-thenal)oxazolone. Crowe and Nord[30a] extended this reaction to the homologs of 2-thiophenealdehyde (Eq. 34). 2-Phenyl-4-(3'-thenal)oxazolone (63.5% yield) has been pre-

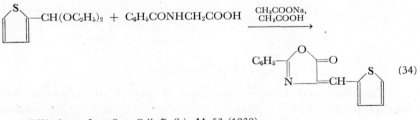

$$(34)$$

[26] Kirchner, Iowa State Coll. J. Sci., 14, 53 (1939).
[27] H. Fischer and Schormüller, Ann., 482, 248 (1930).
[28] Angeli, Ber., 24, 232 (1891); J. Chem. Soc., 60, 550 (1891).
[29] Private communication to the author. Products prepared according to method of Wallingford, Homeyer, and Jones, J. Am. Chem. Soc., 63, 2252 (1941).
[30] Yuan and Li, J. Chinese Chem. Soc., 5, 214 (1937); Chem. Abstr., 32, 496 (1938).
[30a] Crowe and Nord, Nature, 163, 876 (1949).

pared by condensation of the 3-thiophenealdehyde with hippuric acid in the same manner as described above.[19c]

C.   The C₃NS Systems

Thienylmercaptothiazoles

Emerson and Patrick[31] condensed 2-chloroacetylthiophene with ammonium dithiocarbamate.   The main product was 2-mercapto-4-(2-thienyl)thiazole;   2'-thenoylmethyl-4-(2-thienyl)-2-thiazolyl sulfide was obtained as a by-product (Eq. 35).   The products were separated by

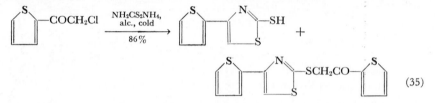

(35)

means of 5% sodium hydroxide.   5-Chloro-2-chloroacetylthiophene gave products of the same type.[31]

Thenalaminothiazoles

2-Thiophenealdehyde gives two products when condensed with aminothiazole: 2-thenaliminothiazole and 2-thenal-bis-aminothiazole[32] (Eq. 36).   2-Thenaliminothiazole exists in two forms, one melting at 109–110° and another at 47–48°.

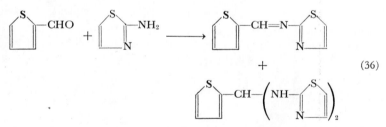

(36)

Thienylthiazolidone

Troutman and Long[32a] condensed N-methyl-2-thenaldimine with methyl thioglycolate to produce 2-(2'-thienyl)-3-methyl-4-thiazolidone (Eq. 37).

[31] Emerson and Patrick, J. Org. Chem., **13,** 722 (1948).
[32] Hantzsch and Witz, Ber., **34,** 845 (1901).
[32a] Troutman and Long, J. Am. Chem. Soc., **70,** 3436 (1948).

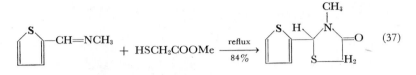

$$(37)$$

Thenalrhodanines

Both 2-thenalrhodanine[32b] and 3-thenalrhodanine[32c] have been prepared by condensation of the respective thiophenealdehyde with rhodanine in glacial acetic acid (for example, see Eq. 38).

$$(38)$$

D. The C₃N₂ Systems

Pyrazolines

Harradence and Lions[33] condensed phenylhydrazine with 2-(3-morpholinopropanoyl)thiophene to give 1-phenyl-3-(2-thienyl)pyrazoline (Eq. 39).

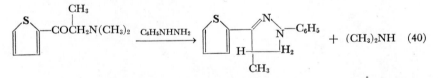

$$(39)$$

Blicke and Burckhalter[18] condensed phenylhydrazine with 2-(N,N-dimethylaminopropanoyl)thiophene with identical results. With 2-(3-N,N-dimethylamino-2-methylpropanoyl)thiophene, the corresponding 4-methylpyrazoline was obtained (Eq. 40).

$$(40)$$

Homeyer[29] has condensed phenylhydrazine with ethyl 2-thenoyl-acetate to produce 1-phenyl-3-(2-thienyl)-5-pyrazolone (Eq. 41). None of the physical constants were communicated to the author.

[32b] Libermann, Himbert, and Hengl, *Bull. soc. chim. France*, [5] **15**, 1124 (1949).
[32c] Campaigne and Le Suer, *J. Am. Chem. Soc.*, **70**, 1555 (1948); U. S. Pat. 2,471,-090 (1949).
[33] Harradence and Lions, *J. Proc. Roy. Soc. N.S. Wales*, **72**, 233 (1939); *Chem. Abstr.*, **33**, 5855 (1939).

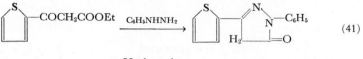

$$(41)$$

Hydantoins

5-(2-Thenal)hydantoin (thenylidenehydantoin) has been prepared as shown in equation (42).[4]   Reduction of this product with 3% sodium amalgam gives 5-(2-thenyl)hydantoin (75% yield).

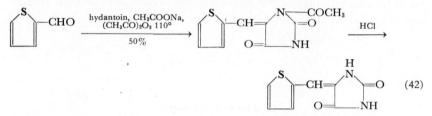

$$(42)$$

More recently, the 1-alkyl-5-(2-thienyl)hydantoins have been prepared by condensation of N-R-2-thenaldimines with hydrogen cyanide and treatment of the resultant product with potassium cyanate in acetic acid solvent to effect conversion to the hydantoin[19c] (Eq. 43).   The respective substituted hydantoins are recorded in Table IX-5 with their melting points and the yields obtained by the above method.   5,5-Di-(2-thienyl)hydantoin has been prepared by condensing 2-(2'-thenoyl)-thiophene with potassium cyanide, ammonium carbonate, and acetamide.[33a]

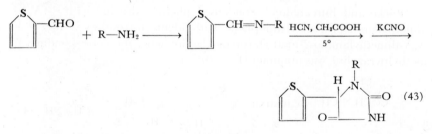

$$(43)$$

Imidazolines

2-[N-(2'-Thenyl)-anilinomethyl]-2-imidazoline is prepared by the following condensations[17] (Eq. 44).   The condensation of methyl 2-thienylacetate and ethylenediamine yields 2-(2'-thenyl)-4,5-dihydro-imidazole.[33b] o-Phenylenediamine and 2-thiophenecarboxylic acid condense to give 2-(2'-thienyl)benzimidazole.[33c]

[33a] Bywater and Coleman, U. S. Pat. 2,468,168 (1949).
[33b] Kyrides, U. S. Pat. 2,457,047 (1948).
[33c] Buu-Hoï and Nguyen-Hoan, *Rec. trav. chim.*, **68**, 5 (1949).

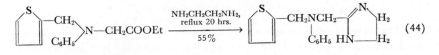

$$(44)$$

E. C₅N Systems

Blicke[34] describes the preparation of various thienyl- and alkylthienyl-piperidines by condensation of 2-thenylcyanides with β,β'-dihaloalkyl-amines in the presence of sodamide (Eq. 45). R is a hydrogen atom or an

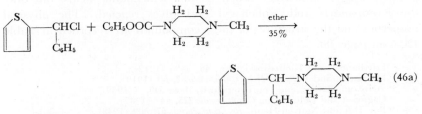

$$(45)$$

alkyl radical, R_1 is hydrogen or methyl, and R_2 is hydrogen, halogen, or alkyl. The physical constants of these compounds were not reported.

The pyridyl type compounds, namely those of the antihistaminic type, are discussed in Section I.C above. Other thienylpyridines are listed in Chapter XV.

F. C₄N₂ Systems

The only compound reported before 1949 is 5-ethyl-5-(2'-thienyl)-barbituric acid. It was prepared by the standard reaction of urea with the proper diethyl malonates[35] (Eq. 46). Recently, the preparation of 1-

$$+ 2EtOH \qquad (46)$$

methyl-4-(2-thienylphenylmethyl)piperazine has been described:[35a]

$$(46a)$$

[34] Blicke, U. S. Pats. 2,425,721–3 (1947).
[35] Blicke and Zienty, *J. Am. Chem. Soc.*, **63**, 2945 (1941).
[35a] Hamlin, *et al.*, *J. Am. Chem. Soc.*, **71**, 2731 (1949).

G. C_6—C_4N Systems

This class of compounds is prepared only through the condensation of the *keto* form of 5-phenyl-3-hydroxythiophene with isatin[36] and its members are not strictly thiophene derivatives.   The reactions to form the two isomeric indole derivatives were carried out in the manner shown in equation (47).

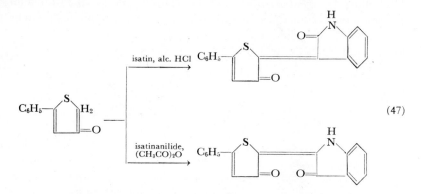

(47)

H. C_6—C_5N Systems

The condensation of isatin with 2-acetylthiophene gave 2-(2′-thienyl)cinchoninic acids[37] in an application of the well-known Pfitzinger reaction to acylthiophenes (Eq. 48).   This synthesis was applied subse-

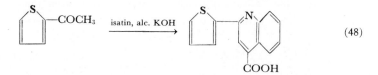

(48)

quently to various 2-alkanoylthiophenes, and 3-alkyl-2-thienylcinchoninic acids resulted.[33c,38,39]   Buu-Hoï and Nguyen-Hoan[40] have attempted to condense a variety of 2,5-dimethyl-3-alkanoylthiophenes with isatin to produce 2-(2′,5′-dimethyl-3′-thienyl)-3-alkylcinchoninic acids, but only the 3-propanoyl- and 3-phenacyl derivatives reacted.   The physical properties and the structures of these compounds are recorded in Table IX-6 on page 286.

[36] Friedlander and Kielbasinski, *Ber.*, **45**, 3396 (1912).
[37] Hartmann and Wybert, *Helv. Chim. Acta*, **2**, 60 (1919).
[38] Steinkopf, Barlag, and von Petersdorff, *Ann.*, **540**, 7 (1939).
[39] Cagniant and Deluzarche, *Compt. rend.*, **225**, 447 (1947).
[40] Buu-Hoï and Nguyen-Hoan, *Rec. trav. chim.*, **67**, 309 (1948).

These cinchoninic acids can easily be decarboxylated to give high yields of the corresponding 2-(2'- or 3'-thienyl)quinolines.   Decarbonylation to the 4-hydroxyquinolines also can be carried out.[39]

2-(2-Thienyl)quinoline has been prepared from quinoline[40a] (Eq. 48a).   The 2-(5-triphenylsilyl-2-thienyl)quinoline was prepared by the same method.[40b]   Subsequent treatment of 2-(2-thienyl)quinoline with butyllithium followed by carbonation yielded 2-(5-carboxy-2-thienyl)-quinoline.[40a]   2-(2-Thienyl)-4,7-dichloroquinoline (m.p. 200–203°) was prepared by the method demonstrated in equation (48a).

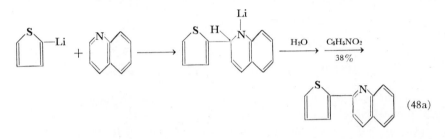

$$(48a)$$

I. C_6—C_4N_2 Systems

Only the quinoxaline derivatives are known.   They are prepared in high yields by condensation of 2,2'-thenil[41] or 2-thienyl phenyl diketone[42] with o-phenylenediamine (Eq. 49).   2-(5-Bromo-2-thienyl)-3-phenyl-

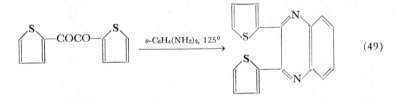

$$(49)$$

quinoxaline and 2-(5'-bromo-2'-thienyl)-3-phenyl-5,6,7,8-dibenzoquin-oxaline are also prepared by this method.[33c]

J. C_6—C_6—C_5N and C_6—C_6—C_6—C_5N Systems

9-(2-Thienyl)phenanthridine has been prepared by effecting a ring closure of the amide of o-aminodiphenyl and 2-thiophenecarboxylic

[40a] Gilman and Shirley, *J. Am. Chem. Soc.*, **71**, 1870 (1949).
[40b] Gilman and Plunkett, *J. Am. Chem. Soc.*, **71**, 1117 (1949).
[41] Deschamps, King, and Nord, *J. Org. Chem.*, **14**, 184 (1949).
[42] Steinkopf and Bokor, *Ann.*, **540**, 21 (1939).

acid[33c] (Eq. 49a). Similarly, 10-(2-thienyl)-3,4-benzacridine has been prepared from the amide of β-phenylnaphthylamine and 2-thiophene-carboxylic acid.[33c]

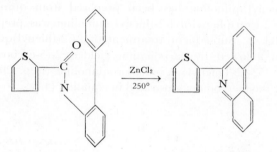

$$\xrightarrow[250°]{ZnCl_2}$$

(49a)

III. Preparation of the Thienylalanines

Yuan and Li[30] first prepared β-(2-thienyl)alanine from 2-phenyl-4-(2′-thenal)oxazolone (Section II.B) in the series of steps shown in equation (50). No yields were given in the *Chemical Abstracts* reference.

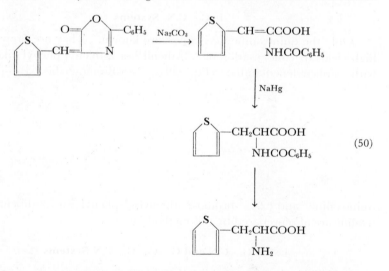

(50)

The compound was synthesized independently by the same method by Barger and Easson[4] in low yields. These investigators also prepared this amino acid in 45% yield by barium hydroxide hydrolysis of the 2-thienyl-hydantoin (Section II.D.).

The activity of β-(2-thienyl)alanine as a "phenylalanine anti-metabolite" with yeast has been described in detail.[43–45] See Chapter II for further details.

The synthesis of β-(3-thienyl)-alanine was carried out almost simultaneously by three independent groups.[46,47,47a] The syntheses were effected by condensation of 3-thenyl bromide with diethyl sodioacetamidomalonate as demonstrated in equation (51). β-(2-Thienyl)-

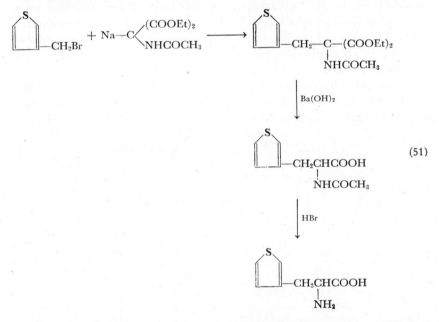

(51)

alanine has been prepared by another modification of this synthesis.[48] 2-Thenyl chloride is reacted with diethyl sodioformylaminomalonate to give diethyl 2-thenylformylaminomalonate (m.p. 112.5°), which is subsequently hydrolyzed to the barium salt and hydrolyzed to the β-(2-thienyl)alanine by $2N$ sulfuric acid. The over-all yield is about 45% of theory.

[43] duVigneaud et al., *J. Biol. Chem.*, **159**, 385 (1945).
[44] Dittmer et al., *J. Biol. Chem.*, **164**, 761 (1946).
[45] Herz, Dittmer, and Cristol, *J. Biol. Chem.*, **171**, 383 (1947).
[46] Dittmer, Paper presented before the 113th meeting of the A.C.S., April, 1948, *J. Am. Chem. Soc.*, **71**, 1205 (1949).
[47] Campaigne et al., *J. Am. Chem. Soc.*, **70**, 2611 (1948).
[47a] Garst, Gaebler, and Harmon, *J. Biol. Chem.*, **180**, 1013 (1949).
[48] Koster and Krol, *Coll. Czeck. Chem. Comm.*, **14**, 263 (1949).

IV. Chemical Properties of Thienylalkylamines and Thenylhydroxylamines

A. Thenylamines and Thienylalkylamines

2-Thenylamine is relatively stable in comparison with 2-amino-thiophene and will not polymerize in air as the latter is prone to do.   Because of their basicity, members of this class of amines pick up carbon dioxide from the air very rapidly.   A thin layer of 2-thenylamine on a watch glass completely solidifies to the carbamic acid in a few minutes.[12] 2-Thenylamine and the 3-methyl- and 5-methylthenylamines are soluble in water in all proportions but are conveniently salted out with salt or sodium hydroxide.

2-Thenylamine forms amides with acid anhydrides, or acid chlorides, or with acids in boiling toluene or xylene.[9]   With dibasic anhydrides such as phthalic anhydride, both the diamide and the imide are formed[9] (Eq.

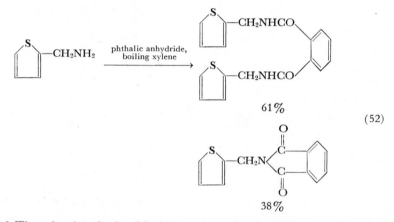

$$(52)$$

52).   2-Thenylamine hydrochloride reacts with urea in the following manner[9] (Eq. 53).

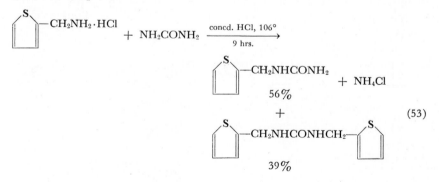

$$(53)$$

2-Carboxy-5(4?)-thenylamine hydrochloride can be diazotized and hydrolyzed with aqueous potassium nitrite to produce 2-carboxy-5-thenyl alcohol.[23,24]

2-Thenylamine is easily oxidized with alkaline potassium permanganate to 2-thiophenecarboxylic acid.[9]   The thenylamines, as well as the N-methyl-2-thenylamines, form phenylthioureas, picrates, and hydrochlorides with ease and are thus conveniently characterized.   Physical properties of these amines and their derivatives are listed in the tables at the end of this chapter.

2-(2-Thienyl)ethylamine reacts with formaldehyde to form a red "semi-solid" product; it forms a carbamic acid in air and gives a crystalline hydrochloride.[4]

B. Thenylhydroxylamines

These compounds are unstable and polymerize rapidly at 100° with loss of water to clear light yellow thermoplastic resins.[14]   They are dehydrated or decomposed rapidly at 150° with near-explosive violence.

In general, it is difficult to obtain crystalline derivatives other than hydrochlorides, and these are isolated directly from the reaction mixtures. Phenyl isothiocyanate gives crystalline derivatives at −15 to 0°, but above that temperature range the products decompose with gas evolution.[14]   Attempts to prepare the benzoate and 3,5-dinitrobenzoate esters lead only to decomposition products.

The most stable of this class of compounds is di-(2-thenyl)hydroxylamine.   It does not lose water in boiling benzene or in the presence of catalytic amounts of iodine in boiling benzene.[14]   It forms an O-acetate ester which can be pyrolyzed at 150–160° with loss of acetic acid to give N-(2-thenyl)-2'-thenaldimine.   The latter can be hydrolyzed to its components, 2-thenylamine and 2-thiophenealdehyde, in 2 N hydrochloric acid (Eq. 54).

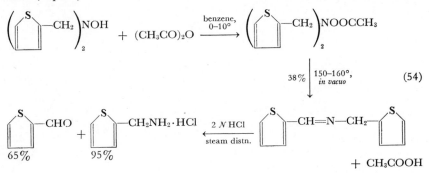

$$\left(\overset{S}{\bigsqcup}-CH_2\right)_2 NOH \; + \; (CH_3CO)_2O \;\xrightarrow[\text{0–10°}]{\text{benzene,}}\; \left(\overset{S}{\bigsqcup}-CH_2\right)_2 NOOCCH_3$$

$$38\% \Big\downarrow \begin{array}{l} 150\text{–}160°, \\ \textit{in vacuo} \end{array} \qquad (54)$$

$$\overset{S}{\bigsqcup}-CHO \; + \; \overset{S}{\bigsqcup}-CH_2NH_2 \cdot HCl \;\xleftarrow[\text{steam distn.}]{2\,N\,HCl}\; \overset{S}{\bigsqcup}-CH=N-CH_2-\overset{S}{\bigsqcup}$$

$$65\% \qquad\qquad 95\% \qquad\qquad\qquad\qquad\qquad\qquad + \; CH_3COOH$$

Both 2-thenylhydroxylamine and di-(2-thenyl)hydroxylamine can be reduced to the corresponding amines with sodium amalgam.[6]

Tables 1–6 follow on pages 267–286.

[49] Campbell, Ackerman, and Campbell, *J. Am. Chem. Soc.*, **71**, 2905 (1949).
[50] Denton, *et al.*, *J. Am. Chem. Soc.*, **71**, 2048 (1949).
[51] Spielman, Geiszler, and Close, *J. Am. Chem. Soc.*, **70**, 4189 (1948).
[52] Dunn and Waugh, *J. Am. Chem. Soc.*, **68**, 2118 (1946).
[53] Brit. Pat. 606,181 (1948).
[54] Biel, *J. Am. Chem. Soc.*, **71**, 1306 (1949).
[55] Brown, Cook, and Heilbron, *J. Chem. Soc.*, **1949**, S113.
[56] Benkeser and Landesman, *J. Am. Chem. Soc.*, **71**, 2493 (1949).

TABLE IX-1. Physical Properties of Thenylamines and Their Derivatives

Structure: R, S, CH_2NH_2, R'

Nuclear substituents	Ref.	B.p., °C. (mm.)	n_D^{20}	Derivative	M.p., °C.	Ref.
R = R′ = H	1,9,18	82 (17)	1.5615	HCl	188–189	9,18
				Phenylthiourea	123.5–124	9,12,19a
				Benzamide	121–122	9,10
				Stearamide	92.5–93	9
				Phthalimide	126–127	9,10
				Phthalamide(di)	169–169.5	9
				2-Thenylurea	129.5–130.5	9
				N,N′-Di-(2-thenyl)-urea	164–165	9
				Picrate	181–182	12
				Carbamate	83–85	12
R = H; R′ = CH₃	12	78 (4)	1.5606	HCl	224–226	12
				Phenylthiourea	137–138	12
				Picrate	Decomp. above 200°	12
R = CH₃; R′ = H	9,12	67–68 (3)	1.5514	HCl	197–198	12
				Phenylthiourea	133–134	9,12
				Picrate	201–202 (dec.)	12
				Phthalimide	123–124	10
R = Cl; R′ = H	12	69–71 (2)	1.5630	HCl	280–282 (dec.)	12
				Phenylthiourea	119.5–120	12
				Picrate	201–202 (dec.)	12
R or R′ = tert-C₄H₉	12	75–82 (2)	1.5048	Phenylthiourea	129–130	12
				α-Naphthylurea	185–186	12
R = COOH	23,24	—	—	HCl	242	23
				Benzamide	177	23

TABLE IX-2. N-Substituted Thenylamines

Substituents	Ref.	B.p., °C. (mm.)	n_D^{20}	Derivative	M.p., °C.	Ref.
R = CH₃	10,11,19	67 (11)	1.5371	HCl	195.5–196 (dec.)	11
				Phenylthiourea	127–128	10,11
R = R″ = CH₃	11	—	—	Picrate	181.5–182 (dec.)	11
				HCl	196–199 (dec.)	11
				Phenylthiourea	148–149	11
R″ = —CH₂OH; R = CH₃	12	123–124 (2)	1.5578 (30°)	Phenylthiourea	100–101	12
R = R′ = CH₃	10	60–61 (10)	1.5188	Methiodide	152.5–153	10
R = R′ = R″ = CH₃	11	61 (2.5)	1.5386	Methiodide	179.5–180.5	11
R″ or R‴ = tert-C₄H₉—; R = R′ = CH₃	11	—	—	Methiodide	193–194 (dec.)	11
R = R′ = CH₃; R‴ = (CH₃)₂NCH₂—	10	134–138 (10)	1.5453	Dimethiodide	248–250 (dec.)	10
R‴ = Cl; R = R′ = CH₃	11	42–44 (0.5)	1.5335	Methiodide	193.5–194.5	11
R = C₆H₅	17,17a	174–177 (12) m. 37–39	1.6295	HCl	170–171	17a
R = C₆H₅; R′ = CH₂ = CHCH₂	19a	161–165 (14)	—	—	—	—
R = C₆H₅; R′ = CH₂COOC₂H₅	17	155–165 (0.3)	—	—	—	—
R = C₆H₅; R′ = (CH₃)₂NCH₂CH₂	17,17a	185–186 (8)	1.5902 (25°)	HCl	183–184	17
				HCl	186–187	17a
R = C₆H₅; R′ = (C₂H₅)₂NCH₂CH₂	17	157–160 (2)	—	HCl	144–145	17
R = C₆H₅; R′ = (CH₃)₂NCH(CH₃)CH₂	17a	164–171 (3)	—	Bisuccinate	99–100	17a
				Picrate	139–140	17a
R = C₆H₅; R′ = (CH₃)₂NCH₂CH₂CH₂	17a	158–161 (3)	—	HCl	138–139	17a
R = C₆H₅; R′ = C₅H₁₀NCH₂CH₂	17a	215–218 (5)	—	HCl	187–188	17a
R = C₆H₅CH₂	49	145–147 (2)	1.5900	HCl	248–250 (dec.)	49
				Phenylthiourea	105–106	49

Substituents	Ref.	B.p., °C. (mm.)	n_D^{20}	Derivative	M.p., °C.	Ref.
R = $C_6H_5CH_2$; R′ = CH_3	19a	148–152 (12)	—	Picrate	95	19a
				Methiodide	165	19a
R = $C_6H_5CH_2$; R′ = $HOCH_2CH_2$	49	135–145 (0.07)	1.5738	HCl	146–147	49
R = $C_6H_5CH_2$; R′ = $ClCH_2CH_2$	49	—		HCl	177–178 (dec.)	49
R = $(CH_3)_2NCH_2CH_2$; R″ = Cl	17c	105–107 (2)	1.5250 (28)	HCl	199–201 (dec.)	17c
R = $(CH_3)_2NCH_2CH_2$; R″ = Br	17c	93–96 (0.2–0.3)	1.5395 (29)	HCl	191–217 (dec.)	17c
R = $2\text{-}C_5H_4N$	17a	m. 78–80		—	—	
R = $2\text{-}C_5H_4N$; R″ = Cl	17c	m. 71–74		HCl	125–127	17c
R = $2\text{-}C_5H_4N$; R″ = Br	17c	m. 81–83		HCl	151–153.5	17c
R = $2\text{-}C_5H_4N$; R′ = $(CH_3)_2NCH_2CH_2$	15,17a,17c	173–175 (3)		HCl	161–162	15,17a
		166–168 (2)		Methiodide	156–157 (dec.)	15
R = $2\text{-}C_5H_4N$; R′ = $(CH_3)_2NCH_2CH_2$; R″ = $tert\text{-}C_4H_9$	17c	185–190 (3.5)		HCl	145–146	17c
R = $2\text{-}C_5H_4N$; R′ = $(CH_3)_2NCH_2CH_2$; R″ = Cl	16,17c	155–156 (1)		HCl	106–108	16,17c
				Methiodide	159–160	17c
				Dihydrogen phosphate	105–106	17c
				Dihydrogen citrate	115–118	17c
R = $2\text{-}C_5H_4N$; R′ = $(CH_3)_2NCH_2CH_2$; R″ = Br	17c	—		HCl	184–185	17c
R = $2\text{-}C_5H_4N$; R′ = $(CH_3)_2NCH_2CH_2$; R″ = Br	16,17c	173–175 (1)		HCl	124–126	16,17c
R = $2\text{-}C_5H_4N$; R′ = $(CH_3)_2NCH_2CH_2$; R″ = R″ = Br	17c	150–160 (0.001)		HCl	208–209	17c
R = $2\text{-}C_5H_4N$; R′ = $(CH_3)_2NCH_2CH_2$; R″ = COOH	17c	—		Dipicrate	199–200	17c

Table continued

TABLE IX-2 (*Continued*)

Substituents	Ref.	B.p., °C. (mm.)	n_D^{20}	Derivative	M.p., °C.	Ref.
R = 2-C₅H₄N; R′ = (CH₃)₂NCH₂CH₂CH₂	17a	171–174 (4)	—	HCl	122–124	17a
R = 2-C₅H₄N; R′ = (CH₃)₂NCH(CH₃)CH₂	17a	162–169 (1.5)	1.5755 (25°)	Bisuccinate	101–102	17a
				Dipicrate	136–138	17a
R = 2-C₆H₄N; R′ = C₅H₁₀NCH₂CH₂	17a	189–194 (1)	—	HCl	135–136	17a
R = 2-C₅H₄N; R′ = (CH₃)₂NCH₂CH(CH₃); R″ = Br	17c	164–168 (0.1)	—	—	—	—
R = 5-Br-2-C₅H₃N; R′ = (CH₃)₂NCH₂CH₂	17c	175–185 (0.6)	—	HCl	140–141	17c
R = 5-Br-2-C₅H₃N; R′ = (CH₃)₂NCH₂CH₂; R″ = tert-C₄H₉	17c	—	—	HCl	175–176	17c
R = 5-Br-2-C₅H₃N; R′ = (CH₃)₂NCH₂CH₂; R″ = Cl	17c	—	—	HCl	136–137	17c
R = 5-Br-2C₆H₃N; R′ = (CH₃)₂NCH₂CH₂; R″ = Br	17c	175–190 (0.0001)	—	HCl	140–141	17c
R = —CH₂SO₃H	13	m. 135–136 (dec.)	—	—	—	—
R = —CH₂SO₃H; R″ = CH₃	13	m. 140–141 (dec.)	—	—	—	—
R = —CH₂SO₃H; R′″ = CH₃	13	m. 138–140 (dec.)	—	—	—	—
R = —CH₂SO₃H; R′″ = Cl	13	m. 141–142 (dec.)	—	—	—	—
R = —CH₂SO₃H; R′″ = (CH₃)₃CCH₂C-(CH₃)₂	13	m. 140–142 (dec.)	—	—	—	—
R = 2-C₄H₃S-CH₂	8,9,12	134–135 (3)	1.6032	HCl	252–253 (dec.)	9
R′″ = CH₃; R = 5-CH₃-2-C₄H₂SCH₂	9,10	161–162 (4)	1.5832	HCl	216–217	9,10
R′″ = CH₃; R = R′ = 5-CH₃-2-C₄H₂SCH₂	9	207–214 (3) m. 81–81.5	—	—	—	—
R′″ = tert-C₄H₉; R = R′ = 5-tert-C₄H₉-2-C₄H₂SCH₂	9	—	—	HCl	204–206	9
R′″ = Cl; R = 5-Cl-2-C₄H₂SCH₂	9	—	—	HCl	240–242	9

TABLE IX-3. Miscellaneous *N*-Substituted Thenylamines and Thienylalkylamines

Formula	Ref.	B.p., °C.	M.p., °C.	Derivative	M.p., °C.	Ref.
(thienyl)—CH$_2$NHOH	14	—	58–60	—	—	—
(thienyl)—CH$_2$NCH$_2$—OH	14	—	60–62	HCl	171–172 (dec.)	14
HOCH$_2$—(thienyl)—CH$_2$NCH$_2$—OH, —CH$_2$OH	14	—	—	HCl	157–160 (dec.)	14
Cl—(thienyl)—CH$_2$NHOH	14	—	—	HCl	—	14
piperazine structure (H$_2$C, N—CH$_2$, C·H$_2$, CH$_2$N)	10	115–125 (3)	—	—	—	—
triazine structure (H$_2$C, N—CH$_2$, H$_2$C—N, CH$_2$)	10	—	55.5–56	—	—	—

Table continued

TABLE IX-3 (*Continued*)

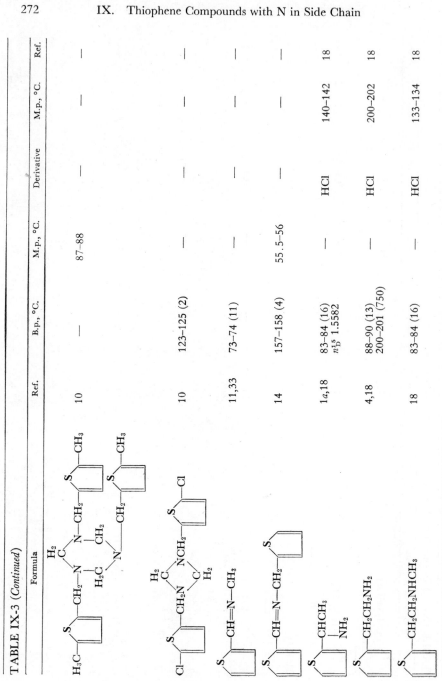

Formula	Ref.	B.p., °C.	M.p., °C.	Derivative	M.p., °C.	Ref.
	10	—	87–88	—	—	—
	10	123–125 (2)		—	—	—
	11,33	73–74 (11)	—	—	—	—
	14	157–158 (4)	55.5–56	—	—	—
	14,18	83–84 (16) n_D^{15} 1.5582	—	HCl	140–142	18
	4,18	88–90 (13) 200–201 (750)	—	HCl	200–202	18
	18	83–84 (16)	—	HCl	133–134	18

Formula	Ref.	B.p., °C.	M.p., °C.	Derivative	M.p., °C.	Ref.
S⟩—CHCH$_2$CH$_3$ —NH$_2$	18	89–91 (13)	—	HCl	173–175	18
S⟩—CH$_2$CHCH$_3$ —NH$_2$	18,21	95–97 (20) 85–88 (14)	—	HCl	133–135	18
S⟩—CHCH$_2$CH$_3$ —NHCH$_3$	18	90–92 (12)	—	HCl	121–122	18
S⟩—CH CH$_2$CH$_3$ —NH C$_4$H$_9$	24a	84 (3)	—	—	—	—
S⟩—CH$_2$CH$_2$CH$_2$NH$_2$	18	110–112 (19)	—	HCl	194–195	18
S⟩—CHCHCH$_3$ CH$_3$ —NH$_2$	21	91–92 (11)	—	—	—	—
CH$_3$CHCH$_2$CH$_2$—S⟩—CH$_2$CH$_2$CH$_2$CHCH$_3$ NH$_2$ ... NH$_2$	6	133–135 (2)	—	—	—	—
C$_6$H$_5$—S⟩—CH$_2$CH$_2$NH$_2$	22	—	—	HCl Picrate Acetamide Benzamide Ethylcarbamate	226 217 128 141 100	22 22 22 22 22

Table continued

TABLE IX-3 (Continued)

Formula	Ref.	B.p., °C.	M.p., °C.	Derivative	M.p., °C.	Ref.
p-CH₃OC₆H₄ thiophene —CH₂CH₂NH₂	22	—	—	HCl Acetamide	283 145	22 22
(methylenedioxyphenyl)thiophene —CH₂CH₂NH₂	4	—	57–58	—	—	—
thiophene —CH₂CH₂N(CH₃)₃I	4	—	236–238	—	—	—
thiophene —CH—COOH, NH₂	5	—	235–240 (dec.)	Benzamide	95	5
thiophene —CH₂CHCOOH, NH₂	4,30	—	246–246.5 274–275	—	—	—
thiophene —CH₂CHCOOH, NH₂	46,47	—	265–267	—	—	—
thiophene —COCH₂NH₂	4	—	—	HCl	215–218	4
thiophene —COCH₂CH₂N(CH₃)₂	18,50	—	—	HCl	178–179	18

Formula	Ref.	B.p., °C	M.p., °C	Derivative	M.p., °C	Ref.
S—$COCH_2CH_2N(C_2H_5)_2$	18	—	—	HCl	116–117	18
S—$COCH_2CH_2NC_5H_{10}$	18,50	—	—	HCl	201–202	18
S—$COCH_2CH_2NC_4H_8O$	34,50	—	—	HCl / Picrate	194 / 189–190	34 / 34
S—$COCH\!\!<^{CH_3}_{CH_2N(CH_3)_2}$	18	—	—	HCl	154–156	18
S—$COCH_2CH_2NCH_2CH_2CO$— (CH₃, thienyl)	18	—	146–148	HCl	185–186	18
S—CONH— (pyridyl)	17	165–170 (2)	—	HCl	215–217	17
S—$CH_2CONHCONH_2$	51	—	203–204	—	—	—
Hexamine salt of 2-thenyl chloride	52	—	Not given	—	—	—
Hexamine salt of 2-thenyl bromide	18	—	160–161	—	—	—
Hexamine salt of 3-thenyl bromide	32c	—	150	—	—	—
Hexamine salt of 2-chloro-3-thenyl bromide	17b	—	165	—	—	—
Hexamine salt of 2-bromo-3-thenyl bromide	17b	—	171–172	—	—	—
Hexamine salt of 2,5-dichloro-3-thenyl bromide	17b	—	178–180 (dec.)	—	—	—

Table continued

TABLE IX-3 (*Continued*)

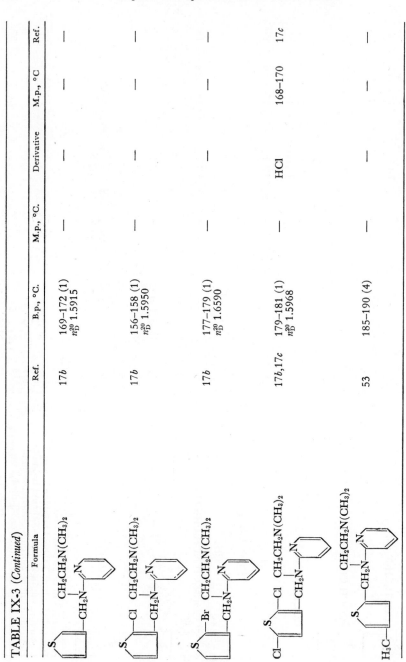

Formula	Ref.	B.p., °C.	M.p., °C.	Derivative	M.p., °C	Ref.
	17*b*	169–172 (1) n_D^{20} 1.5915	—	—	—	—
	17*b*	156–158 (1) n_D^{20} 1.5950	—	—	—	—
	17*b*	177–179 (1) n_D^{20} 1.6590	—	—	—	—
	17*b*,17*c*	179–181 (1) n_D^{20} 1.5968	—	HCl	168–170	17*c*
	53	185–190 (4)	—	—	—	—

Formula	Ref.	B.p., °C.	M.p., °C.	Derivative	M.p., °C.	Ref.
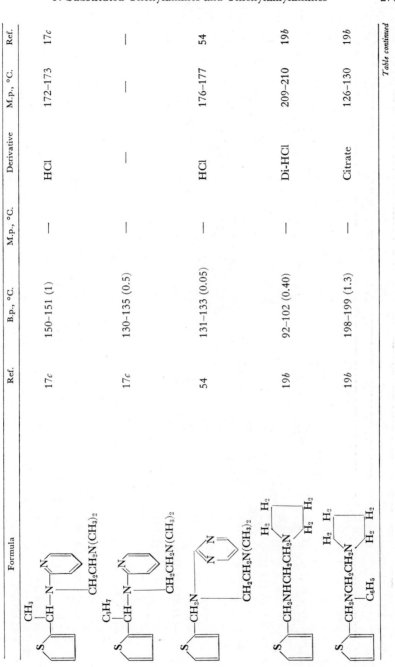	17c	150–151 (1)	—	HCl	172–173	17c
	17c	130–135 (0.5)	—	—	—	—
	54	131–133 (0.05)	—	HCl	176–177	54
	19b	92–102 (0.40)	—	Di-HCl	209–210	19b
	19b	198–199 (1.3)	—	Citrate	126–130	19b

Table continued

TABLE IX-3 (*Continued*)

Formula	Ref.	B.p., °C.	M.p., °C.	Derivative	M.p., °C.	Ref.
	19b	152–153 (0.2)	—	Citrate	95–97	19b
	19b	167–170 (0.25)	—	Citrate Dipicrate	97–100 176–177	19b 19b
	—	155–160 (0.2)	—	HCl	246.5–247.5	19b
	—	168–172 (0.1)	—	Citrate	117–118	19b
	55	155–157 (0.1)	—	—	—	—

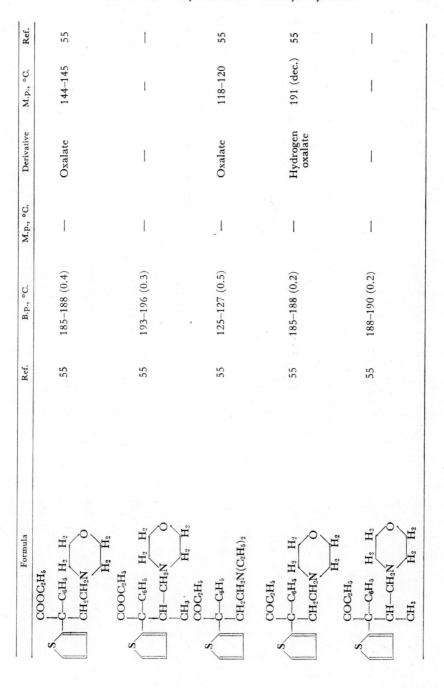

Formula	Ref.	B.p., °C.	M.p., °C.	Derivative	M.p., °C.	Ref.
$COOC_2H_5$, S—C—C$_6$H$_5$, CH$_2$CH$_2$N-morpholine	55	185–188 (0.4)	—	Oxalate	144–145	55
$COOC_2H_5$, S—C—C$_6$H$_5$, CH—CH$_2$N-morpholine, CH$_3$	55	193–196 (0.3)	—	—	—	—
$COOC_2H_5$, S—C—C$_6$H$_5$, CH$_2$CH$_2$N(C$_2$H$_5$)$_2$	55	125–127 (0.5)	—	Oxalate	118–120	55
COC_2H_5, S—C—C$_6$H$_5$, CH$_2$CH$_2$N-morpholine	55	185–188 (0.2)	—	Hydrogen oxalate	191 (dec.)	55
COC_2H_5, S—C—C$_6$H$_5$, CH—CH$_2$N-morpholine, CH$_3$	55	188–190 (0.2)	—	—	—	—

TABLE IX-4. Thiophene Compounds Containing Nonfused Nitrogen Rings

Compound	B.p., °C. (mm.)	M.p., °C.	Derivative	M.p., °C.	Ref.
	111.1–112.1 (4)	57	Picrate	197.7	25
	88–89 (3)	—	Picrate	187.6	25
	—	—	HBr	133	27
	—	173–174	—	—	30,30a
	—	151–152	—	—	30a
	—	152–153	—	—	30a
	—	107.5–109	—	—	30a
	—	97–98.5	—	—	30a

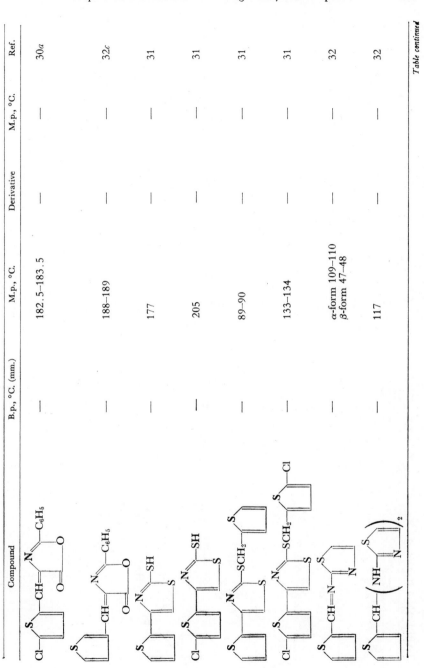

Compound	B.p., °C. (mm.)	M.p., °C.	Derivative	M.p., °C.	Ref.
	—	182.5–183.5	—	—	30a
	—	188–189	—	—	32c
	—	177	—	—	31
	—	205	—	—	31
	—	89–90	—	—	31
	—	133–134	—	—	31
	—	α-form 109–110 β-form 47–48	—	—	32
	—	117	—	—	32

Table continued

TABLE IX-4 (Continued)

Compound	B.p., °C. (mm.)	M.p., °C.	Derivative	M.p., °C.	Ref.
(structure)	—	65–66	—	—	32a
(structure)	—	243	—	—	32b
(structure)	—	212–213	—	—	32c
(structure)	—	102–103	—	—	18,34
(structure)	—	81–83	—	—	18
(structure)	—	253–255	Monoacetyl	214–216	4
(structure)	165–170 (9)	—	—	—	33b

Compound	B.p., °C. (mm.)	M.p., °C.	Derivative	M.p., °	Ref.
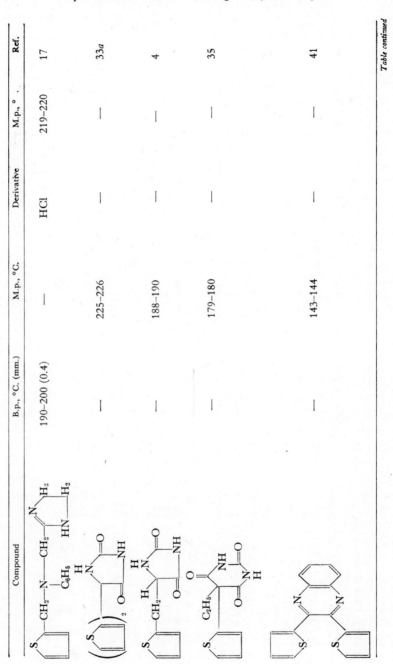	190–200 (0.4)	—	HCl	219–220	17
	—	225–226	—	—	33a
	—	188–190	—	—	4
	—	179–180	—	—	35
	—	143–144	—	—	41

Table continued

TABLE IX-4 (*Continued*)

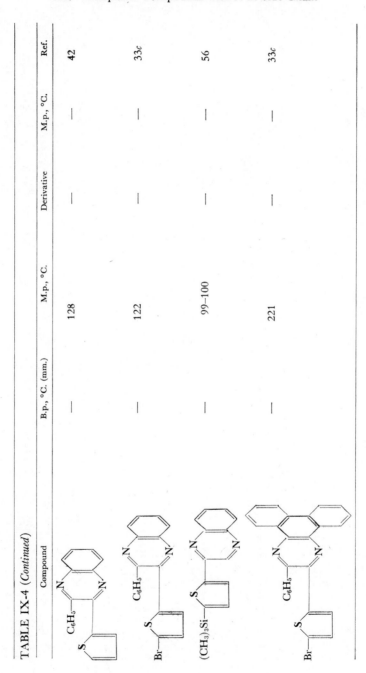

Compound	B.p., °C. (mm.)	M.p., °C.	Derivative	M.p., °C.	Ref.
	—	128	—	—	42
	—	122	—	—	33c
	—	99–100	—	—	56
	—	221	—	—	33c

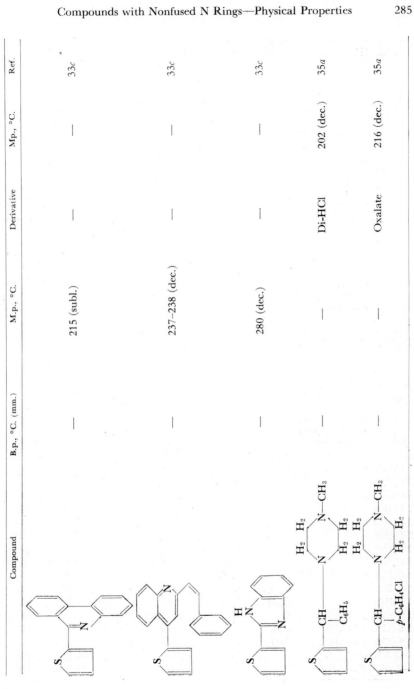

Compound	B.p., °C. (mm.)	M.p., °C.	Derivative	Mp., °C.	Ref.
	—	215 (subl.)	—	—	33c
	—	237–238 (dec.)	—	—	33c
	—	280 (dec.)	—	—	33c
	—	—	Di-HCl	202 (dec.)	35a
	—	—	Oxalate	216 (dec.)	35a

TABLE IX-5. 1-Substituted-5-(2-thienyl)-hydantoins[19c]

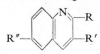

R	M.p., °C.	% Yield
CH$_3$—	163–164	38
C$_2$H$_5$—	163–165	49
C$_3$H$_7$—	109–110	47
iso-C$_3$H$_7$—	173–174	28
CH$_2$=CHCH$_2$—	105–106	48
n-C$_4$H$_9$—	123–125	47
sec.-C$_4$H$_9$—	148–150	7
CH$_3$CH$_2$CH$_2$CH(CH$_3$)—	136–137	14
Cyclohexyl-	181–183	2
C$_6$H$_5$CH$_2$—	191–193	35
C$_6$H$_5$CH$_2$CH$_2$—	156–157	61

TABLE IX-6. 2-(2′- and 3′-Thienyl)cinchoninic Acids and Quinolines

Cinchoninic acid

Quinoline

R	R′	R″	M.p., °C.	Ref.	M.p., °C.	Ref.
2-C$_4$H$_3$S	H	H	211	37	132–133	38,40a
3-CH$_3$-2-C$_4$H$_2$S	H	H	202	33c	—	—
5-CH$_3$-2-C$_4$H$_2$S	H	H	227–228	38	122–123	38
2-C$_4$H$_3$S	H	OCH$_3$	—	—	227–228	40b
2-C$_4$H$_3$S	C$_4$H$_9$	CH$_3$	238	39	81	39
2-C$_4$H$_3$S	C$_5$H$_{11}$	CH$_3$	182	39	65	39
2-C$_4$H$_3$S	C$_6$H$_{13}$	CH$_3$	212	39	34	39
2-C$_4$H$_3$S	C$_7$H$_{15}$	CH$_3$	152	39	52	39
2-C$_4$H$_3$S	C$_8$H$_{17}$	CH$_3$	153	39	50	39
2-C$_4$H$_3$S	C$_9$H$_{19}$	CH$_3$	143	39	67	39
2-C$_4$H$_3$S	C$_{10}$H$_{21}$	CH$_3$	152	39	68	39
2,5-(CH$_3$)$_2$-3-C$_4$HS	H	H	214–215	38	Oil	38
2,5-(CH$_3$)$_2$-3-C$_4$HS	CH$_3$	H	315	40	182	40
2,5-(CH$_3$)$_2$-3-C$_4$HS	C$_6$H$_5$	H	285	40	—	—
5-COOH-2-C$_4$H$_2$S	H	H	—	—	206–207	40a
5-(C$_6$H$_5$)$_3$Si-2-C$_4$H$_2$S	H	H	—	—	168–170	40b

CHAPTER X

Hydroxythiophenes, Thienylalkanols, Alkoxythiophenes, and Thienylalkyl Ethers

Introduction

The synthesis of 2- and 3-hydroxythiophene in 1948 has at last completed the series of the simple substituted thiophenes. Since the discovery of thiophene, all attempts to obtain these compounds were unsuccessful. Their syntheses were accomplished in fair yields by treating thienylmagnesium halides and isopropylmagnesium bromide in ether solution with oxygen. This is the only known method for preparing the hydroxythiophenes from thiophene. All other methods involve ring closure.

The hydroxythiophenes are inherently unstable and decompose rapidly in air to unstable tars. This characteristic may be due, in part, to the ability of compounds of this class to undergo a rearrangement to a keto-form, *i.e.*, to exist in two tautomeric forms. This tendency has been clearly demonstrated with 5-methyl-2-hydroxythiophene which appears to be in equilibrium with the keto form, 5-methyl-4-thiolen-2-one. This form undergoes definite reactions which are listed below. There is no proof that 3,4-dihydroxythiophene exists in the 3,4-thiolanedione form, but, presumably, it does, since 3,4-thiolanedithione (see Chapter XIII) has been shown to exist almost entirely in that form.

The chemistry of the thienylalkanols and ethers is more complete, since they can be prepared by typical Grignard or other well-established reactions. 2-Thenyl alcohol (2-thiophenecarbinol) is relatively unstable in the presence of acids and polymerizes rapidly to give typical thiopheneformaldehyde resins. The other alcohols of this series are quite similar to their respective benzene isologs in activity.

I. Nomenclature

The nomenclature to be used in this chapter is listed below in the form of examples. Alternative names follow the preferred name. Nomenclature previously used in the literature is not systematic and appears in some cases to be incorrect.   In the case of 5-methyl-4-thiolen-2-one and other thiolenones, this is the first instance in which this form of nomenclature appears but it is believed to be more systematic than that listed in the alternate names.

A. Hydroxythiophenes.   2-Hydroxy-5-methyl-
   thiophene.   Thiotenol (hydroxy-form).
   5-Methylthiophene-2-ol.

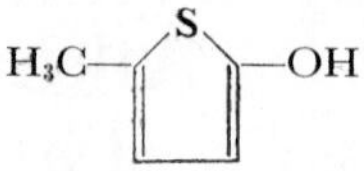

H_3C—⟨S⟩—OH

B. Thiolenones.   5-Methyl-4-thiolen-2-one.
   Thiotenol (keto-form)

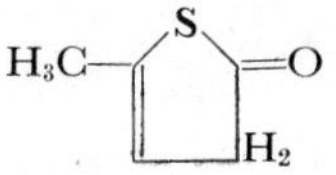

H_3C—⟨S⟩=O
      H_2

Bis-$\Delta^{3,3'}$-(5-methyl-4-thiolen-2-one).
   Bis-(5-methylthiophene) - 3 - indigo

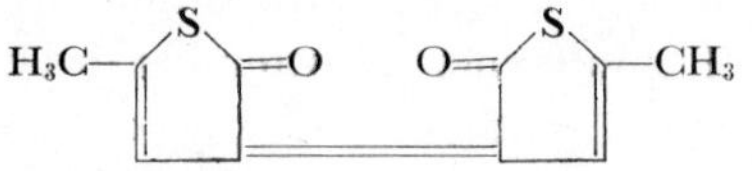

H_3C—⟨S⟩=O   O=⟨S⟩—CH_3

C. Thienylalkanols.   2-Thenyl alcohol.   2-
   Thienylcarbinol.   2-(Hydroxymethyl)-thio-
   phene

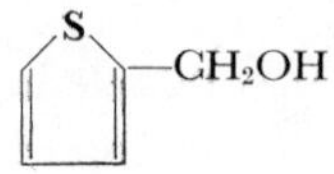

⟨S⟩—CH_2OH

2-(2-Thienyl)-ethanol. β-(2-Thienyl)-ethanol

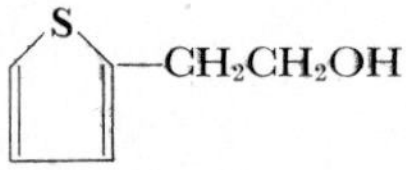

⟨S⟩—CH_2CH_2OH

II. Preparation of the Hydroxythiophenes

A. 2- and 3-Hydroxythiophene

Although many attempts were made to prepare 2-hydroxythiophene, its synthesis was not completed until 1948.   Kruez and Hurd[1] have synthesized this compound by the action of oxygen on 2-thienylmagnesium bromide admixed with isopropylmagnesium bromide (Eq. 1).   The func-

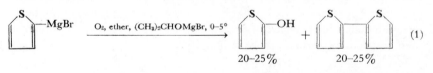

$$⟨S⟩—MgBr \xrightarrow{\text{O}_2, \text{ ether, } (CH_3)_2CHOMgBr, \, 0–5°} ⟨S⟩—OH \;+\; ⟨S⟩⟨S⟩ \qquad (1)$$

20–25%   20–25%

[1] Kruez and Hurd, private communication to the author.   Data used herein were announced at the 113th meeting of the American Chemical Society at Chicago, April, 1948.   A portion of these data was later published; see Hurd and Kreuz, *J. Am. Chem. Soc.*, **72**, 5543 (1950).

tion of the isopropylmagnesium bromide is to prevent formation of the peroxide, C_4H_3S—O—O—MgBr. Without the application of this mixed Grignard reaction, no 2-hydroxythiophene is obtained.[2]

There has been no reported attempt to prepare 2-hydroxythiophene by caustic fusion of sodium 2-thiophenesulfonate, but it would not appear that this synthesis would be effective since Kruez and Hurd[1] reported that the sodium salt of 2-hydroxythiophene gradually underwent decomposition on standing in excess alkali, hydrogen sulfide being evolved on acidification.

It was reported that this compound in storage rapidly assumed a red color but when stored in the frozen state did not change appreciably. It gives a red color with dilute ferric chloride, it reduces ammoniacal silver nitrate immediately at room temperature, and in alkaline solution can be coupled with diazotized aniline or p-nitroaniline to yield intensely colored red and violet solids.

3-Hydroxythiophene was prepared from 3-thienylmagnesium iodide by the method described above (see equation 1).[1] This compound is even less stable than 2-hydroxythiophene, being polymerized in an inert atmosphere by heat with loss of water. Thus it cannot be distilled and purified.

B. Methyl-2-hydroxythiophenes

5-Methyl-2-hydroxythiophene has been prepared by the method of Paal[3] through the action of phosphorus tri- or pentasulfide on levulinic acid[4,4a] (Eq. 2).

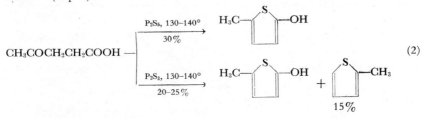

$$CH_3COCH_2CH_2COOH \quad \tag{2}$$

The same method was adapted to the synthesis of 4,5-dimethyl-2-hydroxythiophene[3] by the action of phosphorus pentasulfide on β-methyl-levulinic acid.

[2] Thomas, *Compt. rend.*, **146**, 642 (1908).
[3] Paal, *Ber.*, **19**, 551 (1886).
[4] Kues and Paal, *Ber.*, **19**, 556 (1886).
[4a] Mentzer and Billet, *Bull. soc. chim. France*, **12**, 292 (1945).

C. Nitro-2-hydroxythiophenes

Stadler reported the synthesis of 5-nitro-2-hydroxythiophene by diazotization of 2-aminothiophene hydrochloride with potassium nitrite[5] (Eq. 3).   Some doubt has been cast upon the existence of this compound since attempts to reproduce this synthesis were unsuccessful.[6]

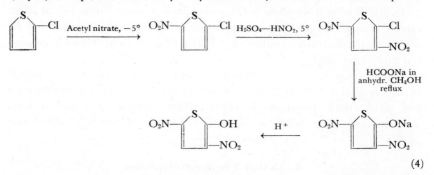

$$\tag{3}$$

Kruez and Hurd[1] have prepared 3,5-dinitro-2-hydroxythiophene (Eq. 4).   Aqueous caustic hydrolysis of the 3,5-dinitro-2-chlorothiophene

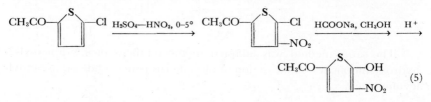

$$\tag{4}$$

gives rise to resinous materials.   3,5-Dinitro-2-hydroxythiophene is reported to decompose rapidly on standing at room temperature, and decomposes violently at 50–52°.   It can be stored for several days at $-10°$ without appreciable change.   It is more conveniently stored in solution in ether or water, in which it is readily soluble.   Like picric acid, it is an extremely strong acid having an ionization constant of about 3×10^{-2}. 5-Acetyl-3-nitro-2-hydroxythiophene has been prepared as shown in equation (5).[1]   This compound was reported to be a somewhat weaker

CH₃CO—[structure]—Cl →(H₂SO₄—HNO₃, 0–5°) CH₃CO—[structure]—Cl, —NO₂ →(HCOONa, CH₃OH) →(H⁺) CH₃CO—[structure]—OH, —NO₂

$$\tag{5}$$

acid than 3,5-dinitro-2-hydroxythiophene and had an ionization constant of about 5×10^{-3}.

[5] Stadler, *Ber.*, **18,** 2316 (1885).
[6] Steinkopf, *Die Chemie des Thiophens*.   Steinkopff, Dresden, 1941, p. 62, footnote 5.

These investigators[1] also studied the activity of the chlorine atom in 2-chloro-3-nitrothiophene and 2-chloro-5-nitrothiophene toward alcoholic alkali. The latter was found to be slightly more active. With piperidine in benzene 2-chloro-3-nitrothiophene showed the greater reactivity. In this respect, the relationship is precisely the same as that known to exist with the *o*- and *p*-chloronitrobenzenes, although the benzene compounds are of a lower order of reactivity.

D. 5-Phenyl-3-hydroxythiophene

Baumann and Fromm[7] prepared a 5-phenyl-1,2-dithiacyclopenten-3-one from the action of sulfur and ethyl cinnamate. This compound, when treated with chloroacetic acid in the presence of sodium sulfide, gives the acetate ester of 5-phenyl-3-hydroxythiophene[8] (Eq. 6). Hydrolysis with caustic yielded 5-phenyl-3-hydroxythiophene.[8]

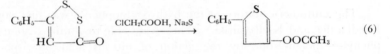

$$\text{(6)}$$

E. 3,4-Dihydroxythiophenes

A considerable number of 3-hydroxy- and 3,4-dihydroxythiophene-dicarboxylic acids have been prepared by the ring closure method of Hinsberg[9] and are discussed more thoroughly in the section on hydroxy-thiophenecarboxylic acid in Chapter XII.

3,4-Dihydroxythiophene is obtained in nearly quantitative yield by decarboxylation of 3,4-dihydroxy-2,5-thiophenedicarboxylic acid in refluxing pyridine. The synthesis is carried out by the ring closure method of Hinsberg (see Chapter XII) in the following manner[10,10a] (Eq. 7).

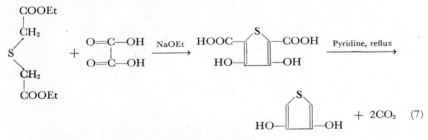

$$\text{(7)}$$

[7] Baumann and Fromm, *Ber.*, **30**, 111 (1897).
[8] Friedländer and Kielbasinski, *Ber.*, **45**, 3389 (1912).
[9] Hinsberg, *Ber.*, **45**, 2413 (1912).
[10] Turnbull, U. S. Pat. 2,453,103 (1948).
[10a] Fager, *J. Am. Chem. Soc.*, **67**, 2217 (1945).

Karrer and Kehrer[11] have prepared 3,4-dihydroxy-2-thiophene-propionic acid (see Eq. 8).   The product is reported to give a green color

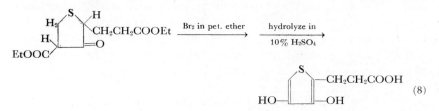

(8)

with dilute ferric chloride.   It will not react with hydroxylamine as a ketone, an observation indicating a low degree of tautomerism in this compound.

III. Reactions of the Hydroxythiophenes

The tautomeric nature of the hydroxythiophenes was first noted by Friedländer and Kielbasinski.[8]   They were able to obtain 2-isonitroso-5-phenyl-4-thiolen-3-one by the action of nitrous acid on 5-phenyl-3-hydroxythiophene, I (Eq. 9).   Compounds of the indigo type (10) are

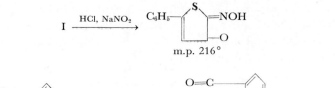

(9)

m.p. 216°

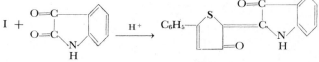

(9) reference label position

m.p. 281° (dec.)
Δ^5-(2-phenyl-2-thiolen-4-one)-Δ^2-indole

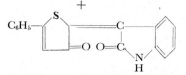

(10)

Δ^5-(2-phenyl-2-thiolen-4-one)-Δ^3-indole

---

[11] Karrer and Kehrer, *Helv. Chim. Acta*, **27**, 150 (1944).   Karrer *et al.*, *ibid.*, **27**, 242 (1944).

obtained by coupling with isatin (see Chapter IX).   Oxidation of I with
potassium ferricyanide gave brown-red crystals of structure (11).

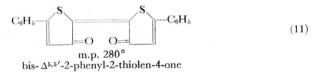

$$(11)$$

m.p. 280°
bis- $\Delta^{5,5'}$-2-phenyl-2-thiolen-4-one

Steinkopf and Thormann[12] investigated the chemical reactions of 5-
methyl-2-hydroxythiophene and found it to exist in both the enol and keto
forms (Eq. 12).   The product forms the conventional esters with benzoyl

$$(12)$$

(II)   (IIa)

chloride and with acetic anhydride,[3] but most of the chemical reactions
reported by these authors[12] involve the keto form (IIa).   They are listed
in Scheme I on the following page.   II is reported not to undergo the
Liebermann reaction.[3]   With isatin in sulfuric acid, a "Bordeau red" color
forms slowly in the cold and rapidly when warmed.

2-Hydroxythiophene is also reported to undergo readily a condensation with benzaldehyde to give a product which may be one or both of the
compounds of equations (13) and (14), depending upon the tautomeric

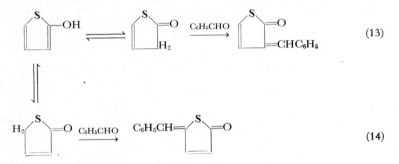

$$(13)$$

$$(14)$$

form of 2-hydroxythiophene.[1]   The benzylidene derivative melts at 97–
98°.

The physical constants of the hydroxythiophenes and their derivatives
are listed in Table X-1 on page 303.

[12] Steinkopf and Thormann, *Ann.*, **540**, 1 (1939).

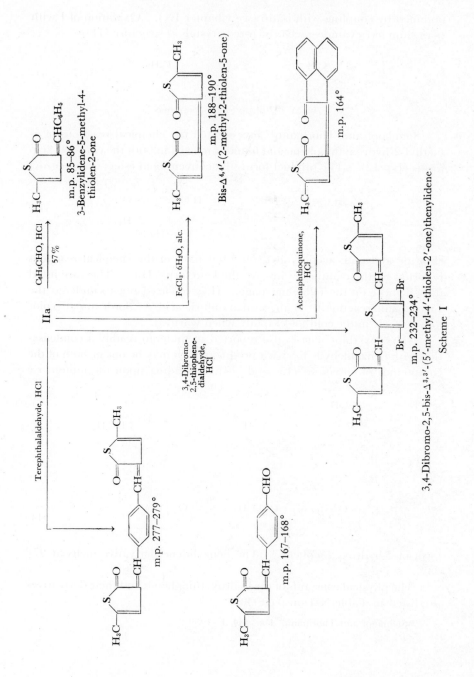

Scheme I

IV. Preparation of the Thienylalkanols

A. Thenyl Alcohols

Steinkopf and Bokor[13] added monomeric anhydrous formaldehyde to 2-thienylmagnesium iodide to obtain a relatively high yield of 2-thenyl alcohol (Eq. 15).   Blicke and Burckhalter[14] repeated this experiment with similar results.

$$(15)$$

2-Thenyl alcohol is conveniently prepared by the Cannizzaro reaction by the action of potassium hydroxide on 2-thiophenealdehyde.[15, 16] Formaldehyde has been used to improve the yield of 2-thenyl alcohol[17] (Eq. 16).   Dunn and Dittmer[17] also reported a microbiological synthesis

$$(16)$$

of 2-thenyl alcohol (33% yield) effected by the fermentation action of Budweiser strain yeast on 2-thiophenealdehyde.

Diazotization of 2-thenylamine gives 2-thenyl alcohol and a product reported as hydroxythiapyran[18] (Eq. 17).   The basis of this conclusion on

$$(17)$$

ring expansion of thiophene was the observation that 2-thenyl alcohol could easily be oxidized to 2-thiophenecarboxylic acid while the hydroxythiapyran resisted oxidation with alkaline permanganate.   Such an explanation might account for the reaction of ethyl diazoacetate with thiophene observed by Steinkopf and Augestad-Jensen[19] wherein they reported the structure of the compound to be as shown in formula (18).

$$(18)$$

[13] Steinkopf and Bokor, *Ann.*, **540**, 23 (1939).
[14] Blicke and Burckhalter, *J. Am. Chem. Soc.*, **64**, 477 (1942).
[15] Biedermann, *Ber.*, **19**, 639 (1886).
[16] von Braun, Fussgänger, and Kühn, *Ann.*, **445**, 218 (1925).
[17] Dunn and Dittmer, *J. Am. Chem. Soc.*, **68**, 2561 (1946).
[18] Putokhin and Egorova, *J. Gen. Chem. (U. S. S. R.)*, **10**, 1873 (1940).
[19] Steinkopf and Augestad-Jensen, *Ann.*, **428**, 154 (1922).

However, if ring expansion occurred in this case the compound would, by analogy,[18] be a thiapyrancarboxylic acid (19).

$$(19)$$

A number of attempts were made in the author's laboratory to prepare 2-thenyl alcohol by direct condensation of thiophene with formaldehyde. At best the yields were low.   The primary cause for failure appears to be in the fact that the catalysts (such as dilute sulfuric acid or hydrochloric acid, dilute calcium chloride or zinc chloride solutions, and acetic acid) cause condensation of 2-thenyl alcohol with itself or thiophene at a rate much faster than the rate of the primary condensation between thiophene and formaldehyde.   Thus the main products of the reaction were dithienylmethane and higher thiophene-formaldehyde polymers.

Bis-2,5-(hydroxymethyl)thiophene has been prepared in a 33% overall yield from thiophene by acetylation and saponification of the bis-2,5-(chloromethyl)thiophene[19a] (Eq. 20).

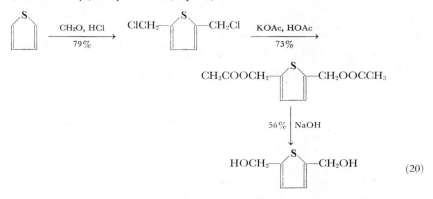

$$(20)$$

Steinkopf and Eger[20] attempted to prepare 3,4-dibromo-2,5-di-(hydroxymethyl)thiophene by a double Cannizzaro reaction with 3,4-dibromo-2,5-thiophenedialdehyde.   The end products, which are surprising in some cases, are listed in Scheme II (page 297).

3,4,5-Tribromo-2-thenyl alcohol has been prepared by the Cannizzaro method[21] by the action of 50% alcoholic potassium hydroxide on 3,4,5-tribromo-2-thiophenealdehyde.

    [19a] Griffing and Salisbury, *J. Am. Chem. Soc.*, **70**, 3416 (1948).
    [20] Steinkopf and Eger, *Ann.*, **533**, 273 (1938).
    [21] Steinkopf, *Ann.*, **513**, 293 (1934).

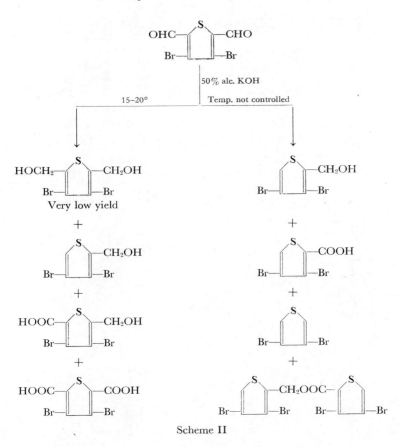

Scheme II

4,5-Dichloro-3-hydroxymethyl-2-thiophenecarboxylic acid has been prepared as demonstrated in equation (21).[22]

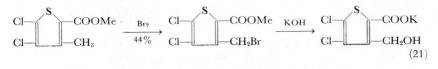

$$(21)$$

B. Thienylalkanols

The greatest number of these compounds have been prepared from ketones, aldehydes, or epoxides with thienyl magnesium halides. For example, ethylene oxide and propylene oxide react with 2-thienylmag-

[22] Steinkopf and Nitschke, *Ann.*, **536**, 135 (1938).

nesium bromide to give 2-(2-thienyl)ethanol[14,22a] and 1-(2-thienyl)-2-propanol[14] in yields of about 60%. The preparation of 2-thienylchloro-alkanols is described by Van Zoeren[23] by condensation of 2-thienyl-magnesium bromide with chloroketones. Thomas[2] has found that alkyl ketones such as acetone condense with 2-thienylmagnesium bromide, but the tertiary alcohols are very unstable and lose water spontaneously. Compounds prepared by these methods are listed in Table X-2 (p. 304).

A direct synthesis of the 2-thienylethanols has recently been described. It consists of condensation of 2-thienylsodiums with ethylene oxide[24] (Eq. 22), where R is a hydrogen, methyl, tert-butyl, or chloro

$$R-\overset{S}{\underset{}{\bigcirc}}\xrightarrow{Na,\ C_6H_5Br,\ C_6H_6} R-\overset{S}{\underset{}{\bigcirc}}-Na \xrightarrow[50-70\%]{C_2H_4O} R-\overset{S}{\underset{}{\bigcirc}}-CH_2CH_2ONa \qquad (22)$$

group. A similar reaction takes place with butyllithium and the halo-thiophenes, e.g., 2-chlorothiophene gives 5-chloro-2-thienyllithium. When treated with acetaldehyde, 1-(5-chloro-2-thienyl)ethanol (81% yield) is obtained. With 2-bromothiophene, butyllithium, and acetone, 2-(5-bromo-2-thienyl)isopropanol (61% yield) results.[24a]

The aluminum isopropoxide reduction of 2-acylthiophenes (the Meer-wein-Pondorff-Verley reaction) has been used successfully in the thiophene series[25-28] (Eq. 23). R may be an alkyl[25-28] or an aryl group.[28a] Side

$$\overset{S}{\underset{}{\bigcirc}}-COR \xrightarrow[50-90\%]{Al(OCH(CH_3)_2)_3,\ reflux} \overset{S}{\underset{}{\bigcirc}}-\underset{OH}{\underset{|}{CH}}-R + CH_3COCH_3 \qquad (23)$$

products of this reaction are 1-(2-thienyl)ethyl isopropyl ether[25-27] and 1,1'-di-(2-thienyl)ethyl ether[25] when 2-acetylthiophene is employed.

1-(2-Thienyl)ethanol has been prepared by the diazotization of 1-(2-thienyl)ethylamine with silver nitrite in neutral solution.[28b] Ring expansion similar to that described by thenylamine is not reported (see Eq. 17).

[22a] P. Cagniant, D. Cagniant, and Deluzarche, Bull. soc. chim. France, **15**, 1083 (1948).
[23] Van Zoeren, U. S. Pat. 2,367,702 (1945).
[24] Schick and Hartough, J. Am. Chem. Soc., **70**, 1646 (1948).
[24a] Bachman and Heisey, J. Am. Chem. Soc., **70**, 2378 (1948).
[25] Kuhn and Dann, Ann., **547**, 293 (1941).
[26] Mowry, Renoll, and Huber, J. Am. Chem. Soc., **68**, 1105 (1946).
[27] Nazzaro and Bullock, J. Am. Chem. Soc., **68**, 2121 (1946).
[28] Campaigne and Diedrick, J. Am. Chem. Soc., **70**, 391 (1946).
[28a] Dahlbom, Acta Chem. Scand., **3**, 93 (1949); Chem. Abstr., **43**, 6619 (1949).
[28b] Putokhin and Egorova, J. Gen. Chem. (U. S. S. R.), **18**, 1866 (1948); Chem. Abstr., **43**, 3816 (1949).

C. Arylthienylcarbinols

This series of compounds is best prepared by addition of aryl- or thienylmagnesium halides to a diaryl- or aryl thienyl or dithienyl ketone as illustrated in equation (24).

$$C_4H_3S\text{—}CO\text{—}C_4H_3S + C_4H_3SMgI \longrightarrow (C_4H_3S)_3COH \tag{24}$$

Pyridylthienylalkylcarbinols are conveniently prepared by condensation of acylthiophenes with pyridine[28c] (Eq. 25). The yield is somewhat

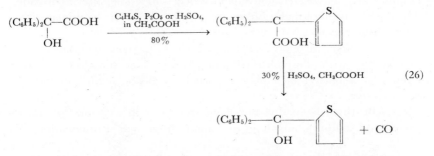

$$(25)$$

lower with 2-acetyl-5-chlorothiophene. It appears that the reaction (Eq. 25) could be carried out generally with alkanoylthiophenes, since alkanoylbenzenes, in general, can be utilized.

This class of compounds can also be prepared by direct condensation of thiophene with diarylglycollic acids[29] (Eq. 26).

Tri-(2-thienyl)carbinol is an unstable solid compound and has not been obtained in its pure state nor can any of the typical derivatives of this class of compounds be obtained in the pure form. It dissolves in dilute mineral acids, and in dilute acetic acid, and deposits deep green crystals. In concentrated hydrochloric acid it is converted to the chloride and forms double salts conveniently with zinc chloride. The fact that this compound is soluble in dilute acids indicated to the investigators[30] that, as a base (or a pseudo base), it occupies an intermediate position between triphenylcarbinol, which is soluble only in strong acids, and bases of the fuchsin type. In respect to the degree of hydrolysis in acid solution it

[28c] Tilford, Shelton, and Van Campen, *J. Am. Chem. Soc.*, **70**, 4001 (1948).
[29] Ancizar-Sordo and Bistrzycki, *Helv. Chim. Acta*, **14**, 141 (1931).
[30] Chichibabin and Gavrilov, *J. Russ. Phys.-Chem. Soc.*, **46**, 1614 (1914).

resembles the fuchsin bases more closely than triphenylcarbinol. With regard to the constitution of the trithienylchloromethane derivative, the investigators felt that the compound was either a *p*-quinoid compound or a carbonium salt and they stated that "at any rate we have a substance that is nearly related to the dyes, without containing any typical auxochrome groups."

Other arylthienylcarbinols, their physical constants, and appropriate references are listed in Table X-3 on page 305.

V. Reactions of the Thienylalkanols

2-Thenyl alcohol is quite stable in the absence of acid catalysts but in their presence condenses rapidly with itself, yielding resins. It is stable to heat and can be distilled at atmospheric pressure. The 2-(2-thienyl)-ethanols are similar in this respect. The 1-(2-thienyl)ethanols are quantitatively converted at the reflux temperature to the corresponding 2-vinyl thiophenes in the presence of 0.1% hydroquinone.[27] The 2-(2-thienyl)-ethanols are dehydrated conveniently over solid potassium hydroxide.[24] The phenyl- or naphthylurethans are normally used for the preparation of solid derivatives for characterization.

The primary alcohols can be converted to the corresponding thienyl-alkyl halides with phosphorus trihalides[16] or with the anhydrous hydrogen halides.[15] 2-Thenyl alcohol is reported by Biedermann[15] to form an acetate ester.

2,5-Bis-(hydroxymethyl)thiophene reacts with acrylonitrile in the presence of sodium ethoxide in the manner represented in equation (27).

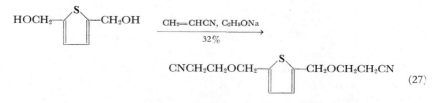

$$(27)$$

VI. Preparation of Alkoxythiophenes and Thienylalkyl Ethers

A. The Alkoxythiophenes

2-Methoxythiophene was prepared in high yield by the action of methyl sulfate on 2-hydroxythiophene.[1] 2-Methoxy-3,5-dinitrothiophene was prepared by the reaction of diazomethane with the corresponding hydroxythiophene.[1] This method was also used for the preparation of 3,4-dimethoxythiophene[10] (Eq. 28).

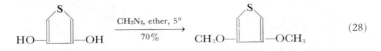

$$(28)$$

B. Thienylalkyl Ethers

Thienylalkyl ethers are best prepared by the classical Williamson synthesis, which involves interaction of thienylalkyl halides with alcohols in the presence of caustic. Thus, 2,5-di-(ethoxymethyl)thiophene results from 2,5-di-(chloromethyl)thiophene in the presence of sodium ethoxide in 77% yield.[19a] Two gram atoms of sodium dissolved in excess ethylene glycol react with the dichloromethylated thiophene in the following way:

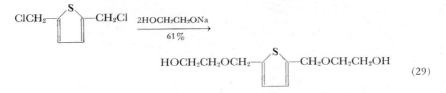

$$(29)$$

Buu-Hoï and Le Cocq[31] found that attempts to prepare 5-methyl-2-thenyl cyanide from 5-methyl-2-thenyl bromide in alcoholic potassium cyanide resulted in 5-methyl-2-thenyl ethyl ether (Eq. 30).

$$H_3C-\text{thiophene}-CH_2Br \xrightarrow{\text{KCN, } C_2H_5OH} H_3C-\text{thiophene}-CH_2OC_2H_5 \qquad (30)$$

Thiophene recovered from the aminoalkylation reaction (thiophene, CH_2O, and NH_4Cl) has been found to contain small amounts (1–5%) of 2-thenyl methyl ether, which presumably arose as shown in equation (31).[32] Its structure was ascertained by oxidation to 2-thiophene-carboxylic acid, by splitting the ether linkage with zinc chloride and identifying methanol, and by determining that the compound had no active hydrogen.

The aluminum isopropoxide reduction of 2-acetylthiophene gives rise to 1-(2-thienyl)ethyl isopropyl ether and 1,1'-di-(2-thienyl)ethyl ether as

[31] Buu-Hoï and Le Cocq, *Compt. rend.*, **222**, 1441 (1946).
[32] Hartough and Meisel, unpublished work.

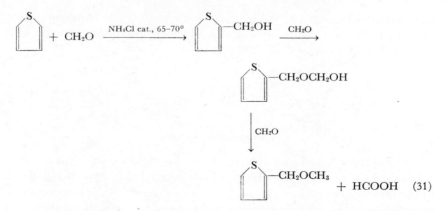

$$+ \ HCOOH \quad (31)$$

by-products of the reaction.[25-27] When 1-(2-thienyl)ethyl chloride is treated with ethanol and sodium hydroxide, 1-(2-thienyl)ethyl ethyl ether and 1,1'-di-(2-thienyl)ethyl ether result.[33] Recently a series of ethers having structures related to various classes of antihistaminic drugs have been prepared.[28a, 34, 35] The method of synthesis involved the classical Williamson reaction of alkyl halides and sodium alkoxides. The physical constants of the thienylalkyl ethers are listed in Table X-4.

Tables 1 to 4 follow on pages 303–306.

[33] Emerson and Patrick, *J. Org. Chem.*, **13**, 729 (1948).
[34] Sperber *et al.*, *J. Am. Chem. Soc.*, **71**, 887 (1949).
[35] Wright, Kollof, and Hunter, *J. Am. Chem. Soc.*, **70**, 3098 (1948).

TABLE X-1. Physical Constants of Hydroxythiophenes

Compound	Ref.	B.p., °C. (mm.)	M.p., °C.	Deriv.	B.p., °C. (mm.)	M.p., °C.
2-Hydroxythiophene............	1,36	217–219 (760)	7–9	Methoxy	153–155 (760)	—
				Acetate	96 (25)	—
				Benzoate	—	44–45
5-Methyl-2-hydroxythiophene........	3,4,4a	85 (40) / 97–105 (18)	—	Acetate	208–212 (?)	—
			—	Benzoate	—	47–47.5
5-Nitro-2-hydroxythiophene........	5	—	115–116	—	—	—
3,5-Dinitro-2-hydroxythiophene........	1	—	52–54 (dec. violently)	Methoxy	—	137–139
3-Nitro-5-acetyl-2-hydroxythiophene........	1	—	65	Methoxy	—	158–159
5-Phenyl-3-hydroxythiophene	7	—	78	Acetate	—	75
3,4-Dihydroxythiophene........	10,10a	—	90–91.5	Diacetate	Liquid	—
				Dimethoxy	100–101.5 (11)	—
				Dibenzoate	—	108–110
3,4-Dihydroxy-2-thiophenepropionic acid...	11	—	194–197	—	—	—
3,4-Dihydroxy-2-thiophenebutyric acid.....	11	—	183	—	—	—
3,4-Dihydroxy-2-thenoylpropionic acid.....	10a	—	—	Dimethoxy	—	134.5–135.5

TABLE X-2. Physical Constants of Thienylalkanols

Compound	Ref. B.p. °C. (mm.)	n_D^{20}	Deriv.	M.p. °C.	Ref.
2-Thenyl alcohol.............	13,15–17 / 207 (760) / 74.5–76 (12)	—	Phenylurethan / α-Naphthylurethan / 5-HgCl	72.3–74 / 148 / 183–185	13 / 17 / 17
3,4-Dibromo-2-thenyl alcohol....	20 / m.p. 84	—			
3,4,5-Tribromo-2-thenyl alcohol...	21 / m.p. 127–128				
3,4-Dibromo-2,5-di-(hydroxymethyl)thio-phene.........	20 / m.p. 174				
2,5-Di-(hydroxymethyl)thiophene.........	19a / 162–166 (0.25)	1.5690 (25)	Diethoxy ether / Di-(CNCH₂CH₂O—) / Di-(HOCH₂CH₂O—) / Diacetate	b.p. 124–126 (13) / b.p. 210–212 (0.45) / b.p. 210–220 (1) / b.p. 140–142 (2)	19a / 19a / 19a / 19a
1-(2'-Thienyl)ethanol.........	24–27, 28b, 37 / 88–89 (6)	1.5422 (25)	Phenylurethan / 5-HgCl	85 / 157	25 / 25
2-(2-Thienyl)ethanol.........	14,24, 22a / 99–100 (7)	1.5478	Phenylurethan	52–53 / 57–58	24 / 14
2-(4-Methyl-2-thienyl)ethanol....	24 / 87–89 (2)	1.5397	Phenylurethan	68–69	24
2-(tert-Butyl-2-thienyl)ethanol....	24 / 115–116 (3)	1.5198	Phenylurethan	73–74	24
2-(5-Chloro-2-thienyl)ethanol....	24 / 98.5–100 (1–2)	1.5576	Phenylurethan	57–58	24
1-(5-Chloro-2-thienyl)ethanol....	24a / 85–87 (2)	1.5556 (25)			
1-(2,5-Dichloro-3-thienyl)ethanol....	24a / 95–97 (1)	1.5630 (25)			
1-(3,4,5-Trichloro-2-thienyl)ethanol....	24a / 109–112 (2)				
1-(2'-Thienyl)-2-propanol.........	14 / m.p. 52.5–53.5 / 106–109 (13)		Phenylurethan	62–63	24
2-(5-Chloro-2-thienyl)-2-propanol......	24a / 83–85 (1)	1.5362 (25)			
2-(2,5-Dichloro-3-thienyl)-2-propanol......	24a / 104–105 (2)	1.5560 (25)			
2-(3,4,5-Trichloro-2-thienyl)-2-propanol...	24a / 118–122 (2)				
1-(5-Chloro-2-thienyl)propanol.........	24a / m.p. 78.5–79.5 / 100–101 (1)	1.5408 (25)			
1-(2-Thienyl)butanol.........	37 / 84–86 (3)				
1-(2-Thienyl)hexanol.........	28 / 110–112 (1)	1.5155			
1-(2-Thienyl)octanol.........	28 / 133–135 (1)	1.5203			
1-(2-Thienyl)nonanol.........	28 / 149–152 (1)	1.4902			
1-(2-Thienyl)trichloroethanol.........	38 / 140–142 (10)		Acetate ester / Benzoate ester	m. 63.5, b. 138 (8) / 74.5	38 / 38
1-(2-Thienyl)-2,2,3-trichloro-1-butanol ...	38 / 152–155 (4)		Acetate ester / Benzoate ester	b. 138–142 (3) / 102	38 / 38

TABLE X-3. Physical Constants of Thienylcarbinols $\begin{matrix} R \\ R' \\ R'' \end{matrix} {>} COH$

Substituents	B.p., °C.	M.p., °C.	Ref.
$R = R' = R'' = 2\text{-}C_4H_3S\text{---}$	—	Unstable solid	30,39
$R = R' = 2\text{-}C_4H_3S$; $R'' = C_6H_5$	—	90	40,41
$R = R' = C_6H_5$; $R'' = 2\text{-}C_4H_3S$	—	128	29,40,42
$R = 2\text{-}C_4H_3S$; $R' = C_6H_5$; $R'' = H$	—	57–58	28a,35, 43,44
$R = 2\text{-}C_4H_3S$; $R' = p\text{-}ClC_6H_4\text{---}$; $R'' = H$	157–158 (0.3)	59.5– 60	44
$R = 2\text{-}C_4H_3S$; $R' = C_6H_5CO$; $R'' = H$	—	56	41
$R = 5\text{-}Me\text{-}2\text{-}C_4H_2S$; $R' = C_6H_5CO$; $R'' = H$ ...	—	78–79	45
$R = 5\text{-}Br\text{-}2\text{-}C_4H_2S$; $R' = C_6H_5CO$; $R'' = H$	—	99.5– 100.5	45
$R = 2\text{-}C_4H_3S$; $R' = CH_3CO$; $R'' = H$	82 (10)	—	45
$R = 2\text{-}C_4H_3S$; $R' = R''$ and biphenylene........	—	168–169	43
$R = 2\text{-}C_4H_3S$; $R' = R''$ and xanthydrol.........	—	63–64	29
$R = 2\text{-}C_4H_3S$; $R' = R'' = CH_3$.................	—	33	42
$R = 2\text{-}C_4H_3S$; $R' = R'' = C_2H_5$	116–117 (18)	—	46
$R = 2\text{-}C_4H_3S$; $R' = R'' = C_3H_7$	160–163 (45)	—	42
$R = 2\text{-}C_4H_3S$; $R' = C_6H_5$; $R'' = CH_3$	—	50	42
$R = 2\text{-}C_4H_3S$; $R' = CH_3$; $R'' = 1\text{-}C_{10}H_6\text{-}2\text{-}$ COOH, lactone.......................	—	109–110	47
$R = 2\text{-}C_4H_3S$; $R' = C_6H_5$; $R'' = COOC_2H_5$	—	59.5	45
$R = 2\text{-}C_4H_3S$; $R' = CH_3$; $R'' = COOC_2H_5$	134.5 (13)	—	48
$R = 2\text{-}C_4H_3S$; $R' = 2\text{-}C_5H_4N$; $R'' = H$	139 (1)	—	34
$R = 2\text{-}C_4H_3S$; $R' = CH_3$; $R'' = 2\text{-}C_5H_4N$	130–136 (0.5) m. 49–50	—	28c 34
$R = 5\text{-}Cl\text{-}2\text{-}C_4H_2S$; $R' = CH_3$; $R'' = 2\text{-}C_5H_4N$ ..	138–142 (0.2)	—	28c

[36] Footnote 1 describes 2-hydroxythiophene as "a colorless liquid, b.p. 217–219° (corr.), d_4^{20} 1.255, n_D^{20} 1.5644 having a characteristic nonphenolic odor."
[37] Clark *et al.*, *J. Org. Chem.*, **14**, 216 (1949).
[38] Floutz, *J. Am. Chem. Soc.*, **71**, 2859 (1949).
[39] Schlenk and Ochs, *Ber.*, **48**, 676 (1915).
[40] Gomberg and Jickling, *J. Am. Chem. Soc.*, **35**, 446 (1913).
[41] Thomas and Couderc, *Bull. soc. chim.*, [4] **23**, 326 (1928).
[42] Thomas, *Compt. rend.*, **146**, 643 (1908); *Bull. soc. chim.*, [4] **5**, 730 (1909).
[43] Minnis, *J. Am. Chem. Soc.*, **51**, 2143 (1929).
[44] Hamlin *et al.*, *J. Am. Chem. Soc.*, **71**, 2731 (1949).
[45] Steinkopf and Hanske, *Ann.*, **541**, 238 (1939).
[46] Domracheva, *J. Russ. Phys.-Chem. Soc.*, **46**, 864 (1914).
[47] Sandin and Feiser, *J. Am. Chem. Soc.*, **62**, 3098 (1940).
[48] Steinkopf and Wolfram, *Ann.*, **437**, 22 (1924).

TABLE X-4. Physical Constants of the Thienylalkyl Ethers

$$R—O—R'$$

Substituents	B.p., °C. (mm.)	n_D (°C.)	Ref.
R = 2-$C_4H_3SCH_2$; R' = CH_3	65–68 (18)	1.538 (20)	32
R = 5-CH_3-2-$C_4H_2SCH_2$; R' = CH_3CH_2	86 (15)	1.5615 (17)	31
R = 2-$C_4H_3SCH(CH_3)$; R' = CH_3CH_2	78–79 (16)	1.4963 (25)	33
R = 2-$C_4H_3SCH(CH_3)$; R' = $(CH_3)_2CH$	73–74 (11)	1.5018 (25)	25–27
R = R' = 2-$C_4H_3SCH(CH_3)$	121–122 (3)	1.5580 (20)	25
		1.5754 (25)	33

2-C_4H_3S

R =   CH; R' = $(CH_3)_2NCH_2CH_2$ ..   132–134 (0.25)   —   35
    /   HCl m. 119–
 C_6H_5 121
                           Methiodide m.
                           176.5–177

2-C_4H_3S H_2 H_2

R =   CH; R' = [ring with N]NCH_2CH_2 ..   180–185 (0.5)   —   35
    /   Methiodide m.
 C_6H_5 H_2 H_2 133–134

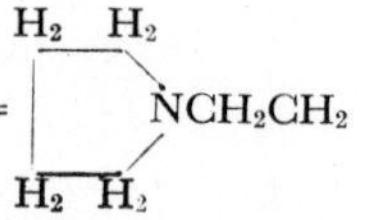

2-C_4H_3S H_2 N

R =   CH; R' = [ring]—CH_2— ...   Dioxalate m.   —   28a
    /   155–156.5
 C_6H_5 H_2 N   Picrate m.
                     H   179–179.5

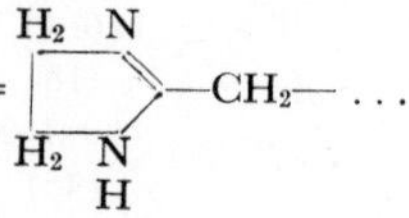

2-C_4H_3S

R =   CH; R' = $(CH_3)_2NCH_2CH_2$ ..   145 (1)   —   34
    /
 2-C_5H_4N

CHAPTER XI

Aldo and Keto Derivatives of Thiophene

I. The Thiophenealdehydes

This potentially important class of thiophene derivatives has been neglected in the past because of the difficulties incurred in preparation. Typical syntheses used for the benzene isologs are not always applicable. The Gattermann and Rosenmund syntheses fail or produce extremely low yields of aldehyde. In the past, syntheses that yielded the aldehydes involved several steps and over-all yields were no higher than 10%. The cost of thiophene derivatives before 1943 made extended study in this field prohibitively expensive.

Very recently, two satisfactory syntheses have been developed in which the 2-thiophenealdehydes are formed directly from thiophene in a single step reaction in yields of 45–85%. These two processes should make the aldehydes easily available in all laboratories and extended studies will now be possible.

3-Thiophenealdehyde was practically unknown until 1948 when Campaigne and Le Suer developed a method for the preparation of 3-thenyl bromide from 3-methylthiophene. The aldehyde was then easily available through the Sommelet reaction.

A. Preparation of the Thiophenealdehydes

1. 2- and 3-Thiophenealdehydes

Peter first prepared 2-thiophenealdehyde in 1885 by decarboxylating heated 2-thienylglyoxylic acid in a stream of hydrogen[1] (Eq. 1). This

$$\text{S}\text{—COCOOH} \xrightarrow{\Delta,\ H_2} \text{S}\text{—CHO} + CO_2 \qquad (1)$$

method later became known as the Biedermann synthesis,[2] but the latter's only refinement was in changing the hydrogen atmosphere to carbon

---

[1] Peter, *Ber.*, **18**, 537 (1885).
[2] Biedermann, *Ber.*, **19**, 636 (1886).

dioxide.   Barger and Easson found that 45% over-all yield of (I) from thiophene could be obtained by carrying out the decarboxylation in acetic acid at 200°.[3,4]

The Gattermann synthesis, involving the use of aluminum chloride catalyst with hydrogen cyanide[5] or carbon monoxide,[3] gives very low yields.   The Rosenmund synthesis, *i.e.*, reduction of the thiophenecarbonyl chloride with hydrogen using palladium catalyst, is reported to give low yields of (I).   The principal product is 2-thiophenecarboxylic anhydride, a rather surprising product in view of the reagents.[3,6]

Compound I is prepared from 2-thienylmagnesium bromide and *N*-methylformanilide.[3,7]   The yields by this method are controversial, but Gattermann has reported yields as high as 70% (Eq. 2).   The Grignard

$$
\text{(thienyl)}-\text{MgBr} \; + \; \underset{\text{OHC}}{\overset{\text{H}_3\text{C}}{>}}\text{N}-\text{C}_6\text{H}_5 \; \xrightarrow{70\%} \; \text{(thienyl)}-\text{CHO} \tag{2}
$$

(I)

intermediates can be condensed with ethyl orthoformate[8–11] or ethyl formate[3,12] to give yields of (I) that normally are in the range of 10–20%.

The method of King and Nord[13,13a–b] appears to be a superior one. It also involves the use of *N*-methylformanilide, but the condensation is directly with thiophene using phosphorus oxychloride as catalyst rather than through a Grignard intermediate (Eq. 3).   R is H, CH$_3$, C$_2$H$_5$, C$_3$H$_7$,

$$
\text{R}-\text{(thienyl)} \; + \; \underset{\text{OHC}}{\overset{\text{H}_3\text{C}}{>}}\text{N}-\text{C}_6\text{H}_5 \; \xrightarrow[45-85\%]{\text{POCl}_3} \; \text{R}-\text{(thienyl)}-\text{CHO} \tag{3}
$$

Cl, or Br.   When R is Br the final product is 5-chloro-2-thiophenealdehyde, the bromine being replaced by the chlorine in the phosphorus oxychloride.   To prepare 5-bromo-2-thiophenealdehyde by this method it is necessary to employ phosphorus oxybromide as the condensing agent.

[3] Barger and Easson, *J. Chem. Soc.*, **1938**, 2100.
[4] DuVigneaud *et al.*, *J. Biol. Chem.*, **159**, 385 (1945).
[5] Reichstein, *Helv. Chim. Acta*, **13**, 349 (1930).
[6] Rojahn and Schulten, *Arch. Pharm.*, **264**, 348 (1926).
[7] Gattermann, *Ann.*, **393**, 230 (1912).
[8] Griskevich-Trokhimovskii, *J. Russ. Phys.-Chem. Soc.*, **43**, 204 (1911).
[9] Griskevich-Trokhimovskii, *J. Russ. Phys.-Chem. Soc.*, **43**, 803 (1911).
[10] Vlastelitza, *J. Russ. Phys.-Chem. Soc.*, **46**, 790 (1914).
[11] Putokhin and Egorova, *J. Gen. Chem. (U. S. S. R.)*, **10**, 1873 (1940).
[12] Steinkopf and Schmitt, *Ann.*, **533**, 264 (1938).
[13] King and Nord, *J. Org. Chem.*, **13**, 635 (1948).
[13a] King and Nord, *J. Org. Chem.*, **14**, 638 (1949).
[13b] King and Nord, *J. Org. Chem.*, **14**, 405 (1949).

Hantzsch[14] prepared 2-thiophenealdehyde in quantitative yield by cyclization of 1,2-diketo-3-chlorocyclopentane and hydrogen sulfide. Dieckmann reported that this synthesis proceeded well with potassium hydrosulfide.[15] The following mechanism involving the opening and closing of the ring was proposed by Hantzsch[14] (Eq. 4).

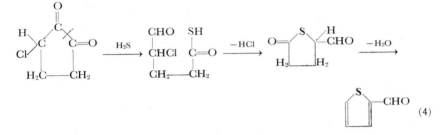

$$(4)$$

Biedermann found that the phenylhydrazone of 2-thienylglyoxylic acid was quantitatively decarboxylated, but hydrolysis gave only poor yields of the aldehyde[16] (Eq. 5).

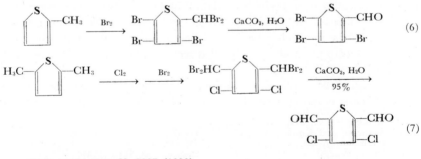

$$(5)$$

Normally, chlorination of the methylthiophenes leads to complete chlorination of the nucleus before chlorination of the methyl group begins, but Voerman[17] has prepared 3-thenylidene dichloride by the chlorination of 3-methylthiophene with phosphorus pentachloride in light. This dichloride was subsequently hydrolyzed to 3-thiophenealdeyhde. No yield

$$(6)$$

$$(7)$$

[14] Hantzsch, *Ber.*, **22**, 2827 (1889).
[15] Dieckmann, *Ber.*, **35**, 3201 (1902).
[16] Biedermann, *Ber.*, **19**, 1853 (1886).
[17] Voerman, *Rec. trav. chim.*, **26**, 293 (1907).

was reported and Voerman admitted to large quantities of nuclear substituted products. Halogenated thiophenealdehydes are prepared by perhalogenation of the methylthiophenes[18,19] (Eqs. 6 and 7, p. 309).

2-Thiophenealdehyde is conveniently prepared from di-(2-thenyl)-hydroxylamine by dehydration to 2'-thenyl-2-thenaldimine which is then hydrolyzed to the aldehyde and 2-thenylamine[20] (Eq. 8).

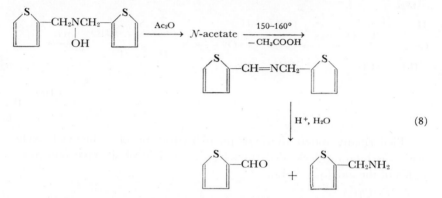

$$\text{(8)}$$

The Sommelet reaction has been applied to the synthesis of 2-thiophenealdehyde,[21,22] 3-thiophenealdehyde,[23] and the halo-3-thiophenealdehydes.[23a] (Eq. 9). 2-Thiophenealdehyde, prepared from 2-thenyl

$$\text{(9)}$$

chloride in the same manner, was obtained in 51% yield. Since 2-thenyl chloride decomposes to some extent on distillation or on storage it has been found that a 50% overall yield based on thiophene of 2-thiophenealdehyde can be obtained if the crude, freshly chloromethylated reaction mixture obtained by the method of Blicke and Burckhalter[24] is treated with hexamethylenetetramine and hydrolyzed directly without intermediate purification.[25]

Another direct synthesis of 2-thiophenealdehydes has been developed. This synthesis employs a combination of the Mannich reaction and the

[18] Steinkopf, *Ann.*, **513**, 281 (1934).
[19] Steinkopf and Kohler, *Ann.*, **532**, 250 (1937).
[20] Hartough, *J. Am. Chem. Soc.*, **69**, 1355 (1947).
[21] Dunn, Waugh, and Dittmer, *J. Am. Chem. Soc.*, **68**, 2118 (1946).
[22] Blicke and Leonard, *J. Am. Chem. Soc.*, **68**, 1934 (1946).
[23] Campaigne and Le Suer, *J. Am. Chem. Soc.*, **70**, 1555 (1948); U. S. Pat. 2,471,092 (1949).
[23a] Campaigne and Le Suer, *J. Am. Chem. Soc.*, **71**, 333 (1949).
[23b] Campaigne and Le Suer, U. S. Pat. 2,471,093 (1949).
[24] Blicke and Burckhalter, *J. Am. Chem. Soc.*, **64**, 477 (1942).
[25] Hartough, unpublished work.

Sommelet reaction.[26] Thiophene is reacted with ammonium chloride and formaldehyde and the N-(2-thenyl)formaldimine is hydrolyzed as demonstrated in equation (10).   3-Methylthiophene gives a 47% yield of

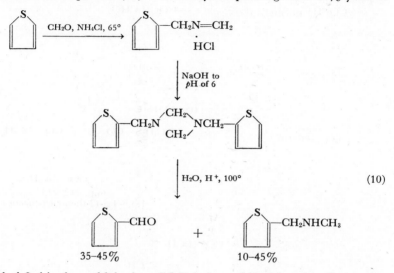

$$(10)$$

35–45%   10–45%

3-methyl-2-thiophenealdehyde.   2-Methyl- and 2-chlorothiophene give somewhat lower yields (35–40%).

2. Keto Aldehydes of Thiophene

2-Thienylglyoxal has been prepared in 40% yield by hydrolysis of 2-(isonitrosoacetyl)thiophene prepared from the action of amyl nitrite and 2-acetylthiophene.[3,27]   It was also prepared by the interaction of 2-bromoacetylthiophene with pyridine; the pyridinium salt was condensed with p-nitrosodimethylaniline and hydrolyzed in acid.[28]   The most convenient method to prepare this compound is by direct oxidation of 2-acetylthiophene with selenium dioxide[28a] (Eq. 11).   5-Trimethylsilyl-2-thienylglyoxal was prepared by the same method.[29]

$$\text{—COCH}_3 + SeO_2 \xrightarrow[43\%]{\text{dioxane, } H_2O, 55°} \text{—COCHO} + Se \qquad (11)$$

2-Thenoylacetaldehyde (β-keto-2-thiophenepropionaldehyde) is prepared from 2-acetylthiophene by the action of sodium methoxide and

[26] Hartough and Dickert, *J. Am. Chem. Soc.*, **71**, 3922 (1949).
[27] Fujise, *Biochem. Z.*, **236**, 241 (1931).
[28] Kröhnke and Börner, *Ber.*, **69**, 2006 (1936).
[28a] Kipnis and Ornfelt, *J. Am. Chem. Soc.*, **68**, 2734 (1946).
[29] Benkeser and Landesman, *J. Am. Chem. Soc.*, **71**, 2493 (1949).

ethyl formate.[29a]   The aldehyde is unstable and readily trimerizes into 1,3-5-tri-(2-thenoyl)benzene (scheme 12).   It forms a monooxime of un-

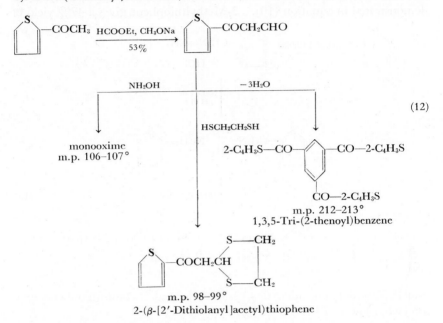

(12)

m.p. 212–213°
1,3,5-Tri-(2-thenoyl)benzene

m.p. 98–99°
2-(β-[2′-Dithiolanyl]acetyl)thiophene

known structure.   With ethylene mercaptan the cyclic 2-(β-[2′-dithiol-anyl]-acetyl)thiophene is formed.

B. Chemical Properties of the Thiophenealdehydes

In general, the thiophenealdehydes undergo the usual reactions of their benzene isologs.   Nuclear substitution of these aldehydes has not been studied.   The odors of 2-thiophenealdehyde and benzaldehyde are quite similar.   While no physical measurements have been made, 2-thiophenealdehyde does not appear to be as easily oxidized in air as benzaldehyde.   But 2-thiophenealdehyde, prepared by the Sommelet reaction[25] and from the aminomethylation reaction,[26] develops color more rapidly than benzaldehyde when stored in a brown bottle, or even in the presence of hydroquinone.   It is more like furfural in color stability.   3-Methyl-2-thiophenealdehyde prepared from the aminomethylation reaction[26] does not develop color in a clear bottle after twelve months' storage.

[29a] Kelber and Schwarz, *Ber.*, **45,** 2484 (1912).

These aldehydes form oximes, semicarbazones, phenylhydrazones, anils, and other derivatives with ease. Hantzsch[30,31] studied the structures of some of these derivatives from the standpoint of stereoisomerism and came to the conclusion that the distribution of their isomers, especially the oxime, is the converse of that of the benzaldehyde isologs. For example, the ease with which the normal oxime from 2-thiophenealdehyde is converted to 2-thiophenecarbonitrile is in direct contrast to benzaldoxime. Hantzsch[30] therefore assigned the *syn* form to the 2-thiophenealdoxime melting at 128°. It would appear, however, from the later classical work of Meisenheimer and of Brady, that this is the *anti* form. The *syn* form is an oil.[32] The *syn* form is then the normal form for both 2-thiophenealdehyde and benzaldehyde and it is converted to the *anti* form with hydrochloric acid.[32] The *anti* form reacts with phenyl cyanate to give a product, m.p. 69–70°, while the product from the *syn* form melts at 144°.

2-Thiophenealdehyde condenses with aminothiazole to give various products assumed to be structural isomers and/or stereoisomers.[33] 2-Thiophenealdehyde condenses with kryptopyrrole (2,4-dimethyl-3-ethyl-pyrrole)[34] (Eq. 13). A somewhat similar condensation takes place with

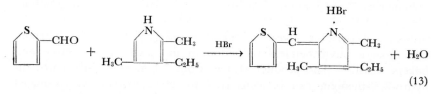

$$(13)$$

3-hydroxythianaphthene. With 3,4-dibromo-2,5-thiophenedialdehyde compound (14) is formed.[35] 5-Methyl-2-hydroxythiophene (thiotenol) condenses with the aldehyde in a similar manner.

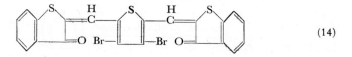

$$(14)$$

Thiophenealdehydes undergo a typical Cannizzaro reaction with strong alkali; the thiophenecarbinols and thiophenecarboxylic acids

[30] Hantzsch, *Ber.*, **24**, 47 (1891).
[31] Hantzsch, *Ber.*, **34**, 841 (1901).
[32] Goldschmidt and Zanoli, *Ber.*, **25**, 2588 (1892).
[33] Pascal, *Bull. soc. chim.*, [4] **15**, 451 (1914).
[34] Fischer and Schormuller, *Ann.*, **482**, 248 (1930).
[35] Steinkopf and Thormann, *Ann.*, **540**, 1 (1939).

result.[2,19,36,37] When the reaction is carried out in the presence of form-aldehyde, increased yields of carbinols are obtained[37] (Eq. 15).   The di-

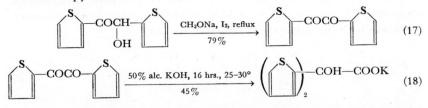

aldehydes, when treated with strong caustic, give a wide variety of prod-ucts, including dicarbinols, mono- and di-acids and esters[38] (see p. 296).

Dunn and Dittmer[37] have reduced 2-thiophenealdehyde to 2-thio-phenecarbinol with Budweiser yeast.

Very recently, both 2-thiophenealdehyde[39,39a] and 3-thiophenealde-hyde[23,23b] have been shown to undergo the benzoin condensation (Eq. 16).

A 33% yield of 3,3'-thenoin was obtained.   It had previously been re-ported that potassium cyanide caused complete resinification of the thi-ophene ring.[40]   Oxidation of 2,2'-thenoin with iodine in sodium methox-ide gives 2,2'-thenil[39] (Eq. 17).   Oxidation with copper sulfate in the presence of pyridine gives 2,2'-thenil in 33% yield.[39a]   2,2'-Thenoin undergoes a phytochemical reduction in the presence of sucrose and bakers' yeast.[39]   The product (1.3 g. from 3.1 g. of 2,2'-thenoin), di-hydro-2,2'-thenoin, can be converted to its dibenzoate with benzoyl chloride in pyridine.

2,2'-Thenil undergoes the benzilic acid rearrangement with alcoholic potassium hydroxide[39a] to give 2,2'-thenilic acid [di-(2-thienyl)glycolic acid] (Eq. 18).

When 2-thiophenealdehyde is treated with hydrogen sulfide in alco-holic hydrogen chloride an α- and β-form of the trimer of 2-thiophenethio-

[36] Braun, Fussganger, and Kuhn, *Ann.*, **445**, 201 (1925).
[37] Dunn and Dittmer, *J. Am. Chem. Soc.*, **68**, 2561 (1946).
[38] Steinkopf and Eger, *Ann.*, **533**, 270 (1938).
[39] Deschamps, King, and Nord, *J. Org. Chem.*, **14**, 184 (1949).
[39a] Cardon and Lankelma, *J. Am. Chem. Soc.*, **70**, 4248 (1948).
[40] Griskevich-Trokhimovskii and Matzurevich, *J. Russ. Phys.-Chem. Soc.*, **44**, 570 (1912).

aldehyde can be isolated.[41]   These compounds, when treated with copper powder, are converted into 1,2-di-(2-thienyl)ethylene.[41]

2-Thiophenealdehyde condenses with 2-iodothiophene or thiophene in the presence of phosphorus pentoxide to yield a tri-(2-thienyl)methane.[42] Tri-(5-methyl-2-thienyl)methane has been prepared by the condensation of 5-methyl-2-thiophenealdehyde in the presence of an activated montmorillonite clay in boiling toluene.[43]   2-Thiophenealdehyde fails to react under similar conditions, whereas benzaldehyde reacts quantitatively with 2-methylthiophene to form di-(5-methyl-2-thienyl)phenylmethane.

2-Thiophenealdehyde, its homologs, and its halo derivatives undergo condensation with malonic acid in pyridine solution to give the 2-thienyl-acrylic acids.[13b,44]   Condensation with ethyl acetate in the presence of sodium ethoxide yields the ethyl 2-thienylacrylates.[13b]   2-Thiophenealdehyde and malonylnitrile condense in the presence of a trace of piperidine to give a good yield of 2-thenalmalonylnitrile, $2\text{-}C_4H_3SCH\!\!=\!\!C(CN)_2$, m.p. 95–96°.[45]

The phenylhydrazone of 2-thiophenealdehyde condenses with maleic anhydride to give a product, $C_{15}H_{12}N_2O_3S$, said by Herz[46] to be 2-thiophenealdehyde-1-maleyl-phenylhydrazone.   The anil of 2-thiophenealdehyde and p-toluidine gives only the p-toluidine condensation product of maleic anhydride liberating the 2-thiophenealdehyde from the anil.

C. Preparation of Dyestuffs from Thiophenealdehydes

This particular phase of thiophene chemistry has received only a limited amount of attention although a "leucothiophene green" (from the condensation of 2-thiophenealdehyde with dimethylaniline in the presence of zinc chloride) was reported many years ago[1,47] (Eq. 19).   The color

$$\text{(19)}$$

base is obtained by oxidation with manganese dioxide.   A similar intense green dye is obtained from 5-methyl-2-thiophenealdehyde.[10]

Steinkopf and co-workers[35,38,48] have made a study of the comparative colors of various dyestuff derivatives of typical dialdehydes (e.g., terephthalaldehyde) with those of the 3,4-dibromo-2,5-thiophenedialdehyde.

[41] Steinkopf and Jacob, Ann., 501, 188 (1933).
[42] Nahke, Ber., 30, 2037 (1897).
[43] Hartough, unpublished work.
[44] Barger and Easson, J. Chem. Soc., 1938, 2100.
[45] Sturz and Noller, J. Am. Chem. Soc., 71, 2949 (1949).
[46] Herz, J. Am. Chem. Soc., 71, 2929 (1949).
[47] Levi, Ber., 20, 513 (1887).
[48] Steinkopf, Leitsmann, Müller, and Wilhelm, Ann., 541, 260 (1939).

From their work it was concluded that substituting the thiophene ring for a benzene ring intensified the colors.   A definite shading from yellow to red was produced by the substitution.

When 3,4-dibromo-2,5-thiophenedialdehyde was condensed with dimethylaniline in the presence of zinc chloride an excellent yield of the leuco base of "dibromothiophene blue" was produced[48] (Eq. 20).   A

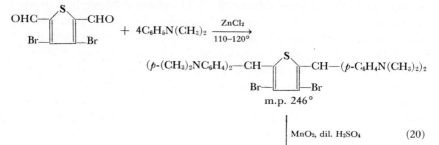

$$(p\text{-}(CH_3)_2NC_6H_4)_2\text{---}CH$$

m.p. 246°

MnO$_2$, dil. H$_2$SO$_4$ (20)

Carbinol base—brown

Concd. H$_2$SO$_4$, hot alc.

"Dibromothiophene Blue"

"tribromothiophene green" is obtained in a like manner from 3,4,5-tribromo-2-thiophenealdehyde.[48]

Color reactions of thiophenealdehydes with various reagents have been reported.[2, 10, 16]

D. Physical Properties of the Thiophenealdehydes

Table XI-1 lists the physical constants of 2- and 3-thiophenealdehydes and their derivatives.   Table XI-2 lists the physical constants of the other known thiophenealdehydes.

The thiophenealdehydes have odors very similar to those of their benzene isologs; 2-thiophenealdehyde like benzaldehyde has an odor of bitter almonds.   Its tendency to darken in light or in storage appears to be dependent upon traces of impurities.   Samples purified by sodium bisulfite complex formation and regeneration have a greater tendency to remain light colored on storage than samples purified by distillation.   The tendency to form 2-thiophenecarboxylic acid by oxidation in storage does not appear to be as great as with benzaldehyde.   No crystals of 2-thiophenecarboxylic acid were observed after one month in a loosely stoppered

TABLE XI-1. Physical Constants of 2- and 3-Thiophenealdehydes and Their Derivatives

Properties	2-Aldehyde	Ref.	3-Aldehyde	Ref.
B.p., °C. (mm.)	198 (760)	2	195–199 (744)	23,17
	187 (640)	21	78 (14)	12
	77 (12)	5	—	
	66–67 (4)	13	—	
n_D^{20}	1.5920	26	1.5860	23
$d(t/t)$	1.215 (21/21)	16	1.2800 (24/4)	23
Melting point of derivatives, °C.				
Oxime	128	16,30,32	111	12
Semicarbazone	223–224	5,13,20, 26,40	233–234	23
Phenylhydrazone	134–135	2,14	138	12
2,4-Dinitrophenylhydrazone	233–236	49	236–237	23
Thenoin	108–109	39,39a	116–117	23,23b
Thenoin oxime	142–143	39a	—	
Thenil	81–82	39,39a	—	
2,2'-Thenilic acid	80	39a	—	
Dihydrothenoin	90–91	39	—	
Anil	Oil	31	—	
p-Methylanil, α-form	36	31	—	
β-form	62	31	—	
p-Bromoanil	90	31	—	
Aminothiazole, α-form	109	31	—	
β-form	47–48	31	—	
Thienyl methylene bis-aminothiazole	117	31	—	
N-Thenal-N'-phenylurea, α-form	69–70	32	—	
β-form	144	32	—	
N-Thenal-N'-o-tolylurea, β-form	66	32	—	
Hydramide	11.5	8	—	
Azine	154	7,40	—	
Trimeric thiophenethioaldehyde,				
α-form	179	41	—	
β-form	221	41	—	
Diethyl thiophenal	Liquid, b.p. 222.5–223.5	8	—	
ω-Nitro-2-vinylthiophene	78–79	13b	—	
1-(2-Thienyl)-2-nitropropene	68.5	13b	—	

bottle. In a control experiment, benzaldehyde deposited a considerable amount of benzoic acid.

[49] Bredereck and Fritzsche, *Ber.*, **B70,** 802 (1937).

TABLE XI-2. Physical Constants of Substituted Thiophenealdehydes

Formula	Ref.	B.p., °C. (mm.)	n_D^{20}	Derivative Name[a]	Derivative M.p., °C.	Derivative Ref.
(thiophene)—CHO, CH₃	13,26	83–85 (5)	1.5860	Semicarbazone..... A[a].....	208–209 211–212 66–67	13 26 13b
H₃C—(thiophene)—CHO	13,26	81–82 (6)	1.5742	Semicarbazone..... A.....	207–208 79–81	13,26 13b
C₂H₅—(thiophene)—CHO	13	91–92 (5)	—	Semicarbazone..... A.....	194–195 56–57	13 13b
H₃C— H₃C—(thiophene)—CHO	13a	80–85 (3)	1.5770	Semicarbazone.....	222–225 (dec.)	13a
C₃H₇—(thiophene)—CHO	13	108–109 (5)	—	Semicarbazone..... A.....	186–187 36.5	13 13b
4 or 5-i-C₄H₉—(thiophene)—CHO	26	155–162 (1)	—	Semicarbazone.....	212–214	26

[a] The ω-nitrovinylthiophene derivatives are coded as "A" under derivatives.

Formula	Ref.	B.p., °C. (mm.)	n_D^{20}	Derivative		
				Name[a]	M.p., °C.	Ref.
(S, CHO, Cl)	13,26	89–90 (6.5)	1.5942	Semicarbazone.........	199–200	13
					218–219	26
				A..........	84.5–85	13b
(S, CHO, Br)	7,13b	80–83 (2)	—	Semicarbazone.........	200–201	7,13b
				Azine............	157–158	7
				Phenylhydrazone......	105	7
				A..........	91–92	13b
(S, CHO, Cl)	19	Solid, m.p. 72	—	—	—	—
(S, CHO, Br)	6	—	—	Oxime.........	139	6
				Semicarbazone.........	248	6
(S, CHO, Br, Br)	48	Solid, m.p. 141–142	—	—	—	—
(OHC, CHO, Cl, Cl)	19	Solid, m.p. 194	—	—	—	—

Table continued

TABLE XI-2 (Continued)

Formula	Ref.	B.p., °C. (mm.)	n_D^{20}	Derivative Name[a]	Derivative M.p., °C.	Derivative Ref.
OHC—S—CHO (Br, Br)	19,45	Solid, m.p. 227	—	Azines.................... Dianil................... Di-(o-hydroxyanil)	No m.p. 245 (dec.) 214 (dec.)	19 48 48
OHC—S—CHO / CH₂ (Cl, Cl, Cl)	48	Solid, m.p. 179	—	—	—	—
(thiophene, Cl, CHO)	23a	100–102 (1–2) m.p. 25	1.5908	2,4-Dinitrophenylhydrazone......	214	23a
(thiophene, Br, CHO)	23a	m.p. 34	—	2,4-Dinitrophenylhydrazone......	230.5	23a
H₃C—S—CHO (CH₃)	13a	77–82 (4)	1.5620	Semicarbazone............	228–230 (dec.)	13a
H₃C—S—CHO (CH₃, H₃C)	13a	87–91 (3)	1.5553	Semicarbazone............	179–180	13a

II. The Acylthiophenes

The acylation of thiophene and substituted thiophenes is the most extensively studied reaction in the thiophene series. The reaction proceeds with considerable ease, high yields of products are obtained, and the acylthiophenes are convenient intermediates for the production of alkylthiophenes, carboxylic acids of thiophene, etc.

In the past few years many new catalysts have been found to be specific for the acylation of the 5-membered heterocylics, thiophene, furan, and pyrrole.

Later, it will be more clearly indicated that the mechanism for acylation of thiophenes unsubstituted in the 2- or 5-position does not correspond in general to the mechanism for acylation of benzenoid hydrocarbons proposed by Groggins, Nagel, and Stirton.[1] Indeed, the use of catalytic quantities of such catalysts as iodine, hydriodic acid, zinc chloride, boron trifluoride complexes, activated clays and alumina-silica gels, strong inorganic oxyacids (H_3PO_4, H_2SO_4, etc.), and others indicates primarily that acylation proceeds in a manner similar to alkylation. Acylation with less than molar quantities of aluminum chloride (0.5 mole per mole of acetyl chloride) and stannic chloride indicates a mechanism of acylation alien to the concepts set forth in benzenoid hydrocarbon chemistry.

A. Preparation of Acylthiophenes

1. Aluminum Chloride Catalyst

In general, the use of aluminum chloride as an acylation catalyst has found wide application and this method has been used in the past to prepare a great many ketone derivatives of thiophene. Aluminum chloride rapidly polymerizes thiophene, forming an amorphous insoluble resin over its surface. Hence, in acylation reactions the order of addition of the reactants is quite important. In an example, the catalyst should be added to the acyl halide and the thiophene in an inert solvent such as petroleum ether.[2] Thus a 90% yield of 2-acetylthiophene can be obtained with a molar amount of aluminum chloride (Eq. 1). More recently it has been

$$\text{(thiophene)} + CH_3COCl \xrightarrow[90\%]{AlCl_3 \text{ in pet. ether, } 30\text{--}40°} \text{(2-acetylthiophene, } COCH_3) + HCl \qquad (1)$$

[1] Groggins, Nagel, and Stirton, *Ind. Eng. Chem.*, **26**, 1317 (1934).
[2] Biedermann, *Ber.*, **19**, 636 (1886).

found that as little as one mole of aluminum chloride ($AlCl_3$) can be used per mole of acetic anhydride and thiophene in nitrobenzene.[3] Yields are comparable to those by the original method.

Gattermann, the first investigator to use aluminum chloride in the acylation of thiophene, found that aromatic, aliphatic, and heterocyclic acid halides as well as phosgene reacted to produce ketones of thiophene.[4]

The monoalkyl- and monohalothiophenes have been acylated successfully by this method.[5-7] 2,5-Dichlorothiophene[8,9] and 2,5-dialkyl thiophenes[10,11] are normally acylated in the 3-position in yields of about 60–70% of theory. Apparently, substitution of thiophene in the 3-position when the 2- and 5-positions are blocked more closely resembles substitution of benzenoid hydrocarbons, since only the metal halides of the Friedel-Crafts type have been reported as applicable catalysts. The reported use of orthophosphoric acid catalyst in the acylation of 2,5-di-*tert*-butyl-thiophene[9] to give 41% of 2,5-di-*tert*-butyl-3-acetylthiophene may be in error, since the starting material probably contained nearly equimolar amounts of 2,5- and 2,4-di-*tert*-butylthiophenes and the 2,4-isomer may have reacted instead of the 2,5-isomer.

Replacement of halogen in 2,5-dibromo- and 2,5-diiodothiophene takes place to a major extent during acylation. The yields are not reported.[12] While 2,5-diiodothiophene gives only 2-acetyl-5-iodothiophene, 2,5-dibromothiophene gives a mixture of the normal 3-acetyl derivative and 2-acetyl-5-bromothiophene. Evolution of hydrogen sulfide normally accompanies this reaction when carried out with 2,5-dichlorothiophene using a mild catalyst such as orthophosphoric acid. The product is 5-chloro-2-acetylthiophene.[13]

Thiophene reacts with dibasic acid anhydrides in the presence of aluminum chloride to give the corresponding keto acids. With succinic anhydride, 3-(2-thenoyl)propionic acid is formed[14,15,15a] (Eq. 2).

[3] Weinmayr, U. S. Pat. 2,462,697 (1949).
[4] Gattermann, *Ber.*, **18**, 3013 (1885).
[5] Peter, *Ber.*, **17**, 2643 (1884).
[6] Comey, *Ber.*, **17**, 790 (1884).
[7] Chichibabin and Gavrilov, *J. Russ. Phys.-Chem. Soc.*, **46**, 1614 (1914).
[8] Steinkopf and Kohler, *Ann.*, **532**, 265 (1937).
[9] Hartough and Conley, *J. Am. Chem. Soc.*, **69**, 3096 (1947).
[10] Ruffi, *Ber.*, **20**, 1744 (1887).
[11] Buu-Hoï and Nguyen-Hoan, *Rec. trav. chim.*, **67**, 309 (1948).
[12] Gattermann and Römer, *Ber.*, **19**, 689 (1886).
[13] Hartough and Kosak, *J. Am. Chem. Soc.*, **69**, 3093 (1947); U. S. Pats. 2,458,513 and 2,458,520 (1949).
[14] Feiser and Kenneley, *J. Am. Chem. Soc.*, **57**, 1611 (1935).
[15] Steinkopf, Poulsson, and Herdey, *Ann.*, **536**, 128 (1938).
[15a] Kitchen and Sandin, *J. Am. Chem. Soc.*, **67**, 1645 (1945).

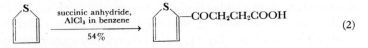

$$(2)$$

Glutaric anhydride or the monoethyl ester of glutaryl monochloride reacts similarly to give 4-(2-thenoyl)-butanoic acid.[15,16] Similar products are obtained from the dibasic fatty acid chlorides.[17,18] The yields range from 50 to 75%.

These thenoylalkanoic acids undergo normal Clemmensen reduction to the corresponding thienylalkanoic acids. Ring closure in the 3-position can be effected with thienylbutanoic and thienylpentanoic acids to give a fused 6-membered ring[14] and 7-membered ring,[16] respectively (Eq. 3).

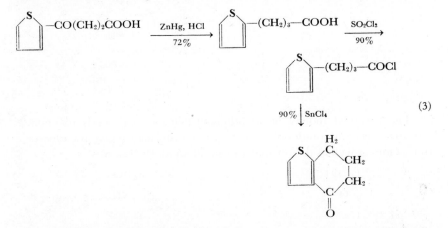

$$(3)$$

The corresponding 4-(2-thenoyl)-butanoic acid gives the 2,3-thiopheno-suberone[16] after reduction and ring closure.

Phthalic anhydride likewise reacts with thiophene to give o-(2-thenoyl)benzoic acid in 20–25% yields.[19] Ring closure to 4,9-thiophanthraquinone can be effected with phosphorus pentoxide, or with sulfuric acid

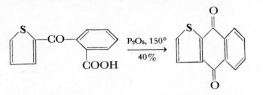

$$(4)$$

[16] Cagniant and Deluzarche, *Compt. rend.*, **222**, 1301 (1946).
[17] Papa, Schwenk, and Hankin, *J. Am. Chem. Soc.*, **69**, 3019 (1947).
[18] Billman and Travis, *Proc. Indiana Acad. Sci.*, **54**, 101 (1945).
[19] Steinkopf, *Ann.*, **407**, 94 (1915).

in somewhat lower yields (Eq. 4).   Steinkopf and co-workers[20] prepared 1,3-dimethyl-4,9-naphtho [2,3-*c*] thiophenequinone in a like manner from 2,5-dimethylthiophene (Eq. 5).   The isomeric dithiophanthraquinones are not reported in the literature.

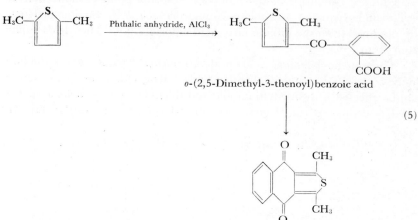

o-(2,5-Dimethyl-3-thenoyl)benzoic acid

(5)

The carbonyl moiety of *o*-(2-thenoyl)benzoic acid tends to enolize with the esters and amides of the orthocarboxylic acid to give pseudoesters and amides as well as the normal esters and amides[19] (Eq. 6).

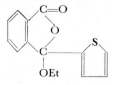   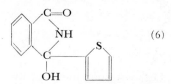

(6)

Dipropylmalonyl chloride reacts with thiophene to give two products,[21] the diketone and the product corresponding to decarboxylation of

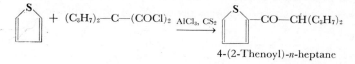

4-(2-Thenoyl)-*n*-heptane

+   (7)

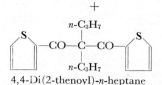

4,4-Di(2-thenoyl)-*n*-heptane

[20] Steinkopf, Barlag, and von Petersdorff, *Ann.*, **540**, 7 (1939).
[21] Freund and Fleischer, *Ann.*, **399**, 182 (1913).

the keto acid (Eq. 7).   Diketone formation from the dipropyl-malonyl dichloride is unexpected in view of the failure to form such products from other dibasic acid dichlorides in a single step.   Billman and Travis[18] were able to accomplish diketone synthesis only in a two-stage reaction and in rather poor yields.

Diacylation of thiophene with aluminum chloride is not reported, although it takes place to some extent with other catalysts (see Section A.3 below).   2-Octylthiophene, however, appears to give fair yields of 2-octyl-3,5-diacetylthiophene[22] with aluminum chloride.

2. Other Metallic Halides Required in Molar Quantities

Stadnikov and co-workers[23-27] and Steinkopf and Nitschke[28] reported that stannic chloride and titanium tetrachloride were efficient catalysts for the acylation of thiophene.   Better yields with fewer side reactions are obtained with these catalysts than with aluminum chloride.   Since these catalysts do not induce the acylation of benzene under the mild conditions used, benzene may be used to advantage as a solvent.   Titanium tetrachloride and 2-acetylthiophene form an exceptionally stable double salt which required boiling for some time with water in order to resolve it into its components.

Johnson and May[29] describe in detail the preparation of 2-acetylthiophene from thiophene and acetyl chloride with stannic chloride catalyst (Eq. 8).   Goldfarb[27] found that decreasing the amount of stannic

$$\text{[thiophene]} + CH_3COCl \xrightarrow[90\%]{SnCl_4,\ benzene,\ 0°} \text{[2-acetylthiophene]}-COCH_3 + HCl \qquad (8)$$

chloride from one mole to one-half mole per mole of acetyl chloride gave no decrease in the yield (96%) in benzene solvent.   Further reduction of the catalyst to 0.25 mole per mole of acetyl chloride gave only 49% of the theoretical 2-acetylthiophene.

[22] von Schweinitz, *Ber.*, **19**, 646 (1886).
[23] Stadnikov and Kaschtanov, *J. Russ. Phys.-Chem. Soc.*, **60**, 1117 (1928).
[24] Stadnikov and Kaschtanov, *Ber.*, **61**, 1389 (1928).
[25] Stadnikov and Rakowsky, *Ber.*, **61**, 268 (1928).
[26] Stadnikov and Goldfarb, *Ber.*, **61**, 2341 (1928).
[27] Goldfarb, *J. Russ. Phys.-Chem. Soc.*, **62**, 1073 (1930); *Chem. Abstr.*, **25**, 2719 (1931).
[28] Steinkopf and Nitschke, *Arch. Pharm. Ber.*, **278**, 360 (1940).
[29] Johnson and May, *Organic Synthesis*, Coll. Vol. II, **1943**, 8.

3. Catalysts Required in Less than Molar Quantities

Volhard[30] recorded that aliphatic or aromatic acyl halides and 2-thiophenemercurichloride gave the corresponding ketones of thiophene. Steinkopf and Bauermeister later found that catalytic amounts of 2-thiophenemercurichloride in the presence of acetyl chloride and thiophene gave 2-acetylthiophene[31] (Eq. 9).   The mercuric chloride generated re-

$$\text{(thiophene)} + CH_3COCl \xrightarrow[26\%]{2\text{-}C_4H_3S-HgCl,\ 65°,\ 16\ hrs.} \text{(thiophene)}-COCH_3 + HgCl_2 \qquad (9)$$

acted again to produce more catalyst, thus giving the first truly catalytic acylation of thiophene.   However, it is reported that catalytic amounts of mercuric chloride fail to catalyze the reaction between acetic anhydride and thiophene.[32]

Steinkopf[32a] has found that catalytic amounts of phosphorus pentoxide cause acylation of thiophene with acetic anhydride or acetyl chloride, but the yields normally are not above 50%.

It has been shown that catalytic amounts of zinc chloride (0.01 to 0.05 mole) give excellent yields of acylated thiophene and furan[32] (Eq. 10).

$$\text{(thiophene)} + (CH_3CO)_2O \xrightarrow[80-90\%]{0.03\ \text{mole}\ ZnCl_2,\ \text{reflux}} \text{(thiophene)}-COCH_3 + CH_3COOH \qquad (10)$$

Further acylation of 2-acetylthiophene or use of excess acetic anhydride gives small amounts of 2,5-diacetylthiophene (Eq. 11).

$$\text{(thiophene)}-COCH_3 + (CH_3CO)_2O \xrightarrow[5-6\%]{0.03\ \text{to}\ 0.05\ \text{mole}\ ZnCl_2,\ \text{reflux}}$$

$$CH_3CO-\text{(thiophene)}-COCH_3 + CH_3COOH \qquad (11)$$

Iodine and hydriodic acid in amounts of the order of 0.01 mole of iodine per mole of acetic anhydride cause smooth acylation of thiophenes (80–90% yields) and furan (60–75% yields).[33]   When larger amounts of catalyst are used, reactions too vigorous to control take place and the

[30] Volhard, *Ann.*, **267**, 172 (1892).
[31] Steinkopf and Bauermeister, *Ann.*, **403**, 57 (1914).
[32] Hartough and Kosak, *J. Am. Chem. Soc.*, **69**, 1012 (1947).
[32a] Steinkopf, *Ann.*, **413**, 343 (1916).
[33] Hartough and Kosak, *J. Am. Chem. Soc.*, **68**, 2639 (1946); U. S. 2,457,825 (1949).

products are tars rather than acylated thiophenes.   Stevens reported that acetyl iodide reacted vigorously with thiophene to produce a small amount of 2-acetylthiophene.[34]   The use of iodine as an acylation catalyst has been extended to the acylation of the 2-thienyltrimethylsilane[35] but the yield was low (13%).   With di-(2-thienyl)methane and acetic anhydride, this catalyst gave di-(5-acetyl-2-thienyl)methane (46% yield).[35a]   The latter can be oxidized quantitatively to di-(5-acetyl-2-thienyl) ketone by chromic acid.

Silica-alumina gels and naturally occurring montmorillonite clays of low calcium content are good catalysts for the acylation of thiophene[36] in both the liquid and the vapor phases.   A marine deposit, glauconite, also catalyzes the reaction.[36,37]   Phthalyl chloride with thiophene and a montmorillonite clay gives 3,3-bis(2-thienyl)phthalide rather than the diketone[36] (Eq. 12).

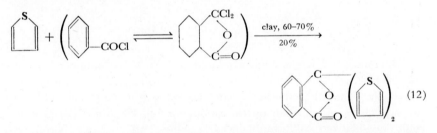

$$(12)$$

Three sets of independent investigators discovered almost simultaneously that boron trifluoride and its complexes in catalytic quantities induce acylation of thiophene with acid anhydrides and acyl halides.[38-41]

Levine and co-workers[41] postulate the following mechanism for the boron trifluoride-catalyzed acylation of thiophene (Eq. 13).

Since a molecular amount of acetic acid-boron trifluoride complex with thiophene yields 2-acetylthiophene (25%) in the absence of acetic anhydride, and the complex is effective when used in catalytic amounts with the anhydride, the postulated mechanism seems to have some basis in fact.

[34] Stevens, *J. Am. Chem. Soc.*, **56,** 450 (1934).
[35] Benkeser and Currie, *J. Am. Chem. Soc.*, **70,** 1780 (1948).
[35a] McKusick, U. S. Pat. 2,467,439 (1949).
[36] Hartough, Kosak, and Sardella, *J. Am. Chem. Soc.*, **69,** 1014 (1947).   Hartough and Kosak, U. S. Pats. 2,458,512 (1949), 2,458,519 and 2,458,521 (1949).
[37] Hartough and Sardella, U. S. Pat. 2,432,991 (1947).
[38] Given and Hammick, *J. Chem. Soc.*, **1947,** 1237.
[39] Hartough and Kosak, *J. Am. Chem. Soc.*, **70,** 867 (1948).
[40] Heid and Levine, *J. Org. Chem.*, **13,** 409 (1948).
[41] Levine, Heid, and Farrar, *J. Am. Chem. Soc.*, **71,** 1207 (1949).

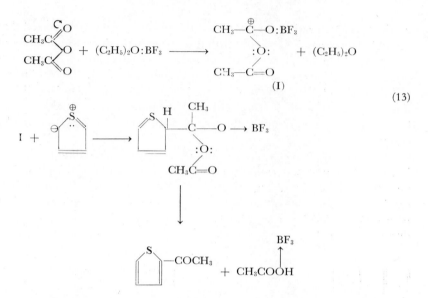

(13)

Hartough and Kosak[39] have isolated a "2-triacetylthiophene" of un-known structure from the further reaction of 2-acetylthiophene with acetic anhydride using BF_3· etherate. Acylation was assumed to take place in the side chain rather than on the thiophene nucleus, since the product could be oxidized to 2-thiophenecarboxylic acid. Because boron tri-fluoride complexes cause ring rupture and polymerization of thiophene their wide use is not to be recommended, particularly in view of the high yields obtained with orthophosphoric acid.

The best class of acylation catalysts consists of strong inorganic oxy-acids of sulfur and phosphorus.[13] The best single member of the class is orthophosphoric acid and consistent yields between 85 and 95% of theory can be expected (Eq. 14).

$$\text{(thiophene)} + (CH_3CO)_2O \xrightarrow[\substack{85-95\%}]{\substack{10 \text{ g. } 85\% \, H_3PO_4, \\ \text{reflux 3 hrs.}}} \text{(2-acetylthiophene)}{-}COCH_3 + CH_3COOH \quad (14)$$

3 moles   1 mole

Kellett and Rasmussen[42] have developed a continuous method for the production of 2-acetylthiophene employing orthophosphoric acid as a catalyst. Their technique consists of mixing a stream of acetic anhydride

[42] Kellett and Rasmussen, *Ind. Eng. Chem.*, **40**, 384 (1948).

and thiophene with a stream of 85% orthophosphoric acid and passing the mixture through a heated coil at 95–150°C. Yields are virtually quantitative when an excess of thiophene is used.

Attempts to acylate 2,5-dichlorothiophene in the 3-position, using orthophosphoric acid as a catalyst, result in the replacement of one of the chloro atoms with an acyl group. Some hydrogen sulfide is evolved during the process[13] (Eq. 15). While this class of catalysts produces 3,3-bis-

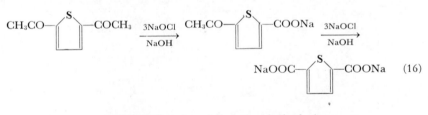

$$Cl-\underset{S}{\bigcirc}-Cl \quad + \quad (CH_3CO)_2O \quad \xrightarrow[20\%]{85\% \ H_3PO_4} \quad Cl-\underset{S}{\bigcirc}-COCH_3 \tag{15}$$

(2-thienyl)phthalide when phthalyl chloride is used and 5-(2-thenoyl)-pentanoic acid with adipyl chloride, they do not cause condensation of phthalic anhydride or succinic anhydride with thiophene. This condensation also fails with catalytic amounts of iodine, hydriodic acid, zinc chloride, activated clays, alumina-silica gels, and boron trifluoride complexes. The failure of dibasic acid anhydrides to undergo this reaction with the above catalysts is difficult to explain on the basis of the mechanism of Levine and coworkers.[40–41]

Minor amounts (3–6%) of 2,5-diacylthiophenes are formed during the acylation reaction when an excess of the respective anhydride is used with orthophosphoric acid[13] and zinc chloride[32] catalysts. Substitution in the 5-position was established by stepwise oxidation of 2,5-diacetylthiophene with sodium hypochlorite to 2-acetyl-5-thiophenecarboxylic acid and finally to 2,5-thiophenedicarboxylic acid[32] (Eq. 16).

$$CH_3CO-\underset{S}{\bigcirc}-COCH_3 \xrightarrow[NaOH]{3NaOCl} CH_3CO-\underset{S}{\bigcirc}-COONa \xrightarrow[NaOH]{3NaOCl}$$
$$NaOOC-\underset{S}{\bigcirc}-COONa \tag{16}$$

4. Miscellaneous Methods of Acylation

A method for the direct acylation of thiophene with carboxylic acids employs molecular amounts of phosphorus pentoxide.[43] Yields increase with the length of the alkyl chain of the carboxylic acid and vary from 40 to 95% from acetic to oleic acids (Eq. 17).

[43] Hartough and Kosak, *J. Am. Chem. Soc.*, **69**, 3098 (1947); U. S. Pat. 2,478,484 (1949).

$$\text{(thiophene)} + RCOOH + P_2O_5 \xrightarrow[\text{40-95\%}]{\text{benzene, reflux}} \text{(2-acylthiophene)}{-}COR + HPO_3 \qquad (17)$$

Diacylation of thiophene occurs in higher yields with this catalyst, particularly when the higher aliphatic acids are employed.   2,5-Didecanoylthiophene has been prepared in 20% yield in this manner (Eq. 18).

$$\text{(thiophene)} \xrightarrow[\text{P}_2\text{O}_5\text{, benzene}]{\text{capric acid,}} \underset{45\%}{\text{(thiophene)}{-}COC_9H_{19}} + \underset{20\%}{C_9H_{19}CO{-}\text{(thiophene)}{-}COC_9H_{19}} \qquad (18)$$

This method is to be recommended for the preparation of acylthiophenes directly from the higher fatty acids, since it is sometimes difficult or uneconomical to obtain the acyl halides or acid anhydrides in a reasonable state of purity.

Thiophene ketones are produced in yields of 20–55% by the action of nitriles on 2-thienylmagnesium iodide followed by hydrolysis.[44]   2-(2'-Thenoyl)thiophene can be prepared from the reaction of cyanogen chloride and 2-thienylmagnesium iodide (Eq. 19).

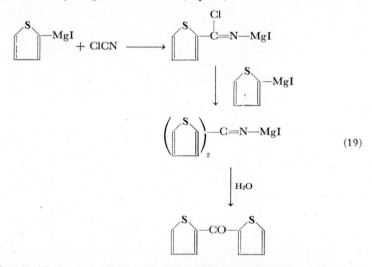

$$\qquad (19)$$

The dry distillation of calcium salts of thiophenecarboxylic acids gives low yields of the corresponding thenoylthiophenes.   2-(2'-Thenoyl)-thiophene[4] and 3-(3'-thenoyl)thiophene[45] are produced in this manner.

[44] Thomas and Couderc, *Bull. soc. chim. France*, [4] **23**, 288 (1918).
[45] Steinkopf and Schmitt, *Ann.*, **533**, 268 (1938).

The action of acyl halides on 2-thiophenemercurichloride yields the corresponding acylthiophenes.[30] This reaction provides a convenient method for making 2,5-diacylthiophene derivatives[46] (Eq. 20).

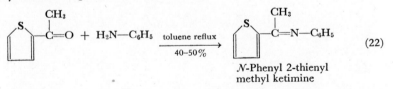

$$\text{ClHg-} \underset{S}{\bigsqcup} \text{-HgCl} \;+\; 2C_6H_5COCl \;\longrightarrow\; C_6H_5CO- \underset{S}{\bigsqcup} -COC_6H_5 \tag{20}$$

Preparation of β-ketones of thiophene appears to be difficult, but Nahke[47] has prepared 3,3-di-(2-thienyl)butan-2-one by the condensation of thiophene with diacetyl by means of phosphorus pentoxide (Eq. 21).

$$\underset{S}{\bigsqcup} \;+\; CH_3COCOCH_3 \;\xrightarrow[10\%]{P_2O_5,CHCl_3, \text{ reflux}}\; \underset{S}{\bigsqcup} \overset{COCH_3}{\underset{CH_3}{\overset{|}{\underset{|}{CH}}}} \underset{S}{\bigsqcup} \tag{21}$$

Phenyl-2-thienylmethyl ethyl ketone is prepared by condensation of 2-benzylthiophene and ethyl propionate in the presence of potassium amide.[47a]

Benzoyl chloride, when heated at the reflux temperature with thiophene, slowly yields 2-benzoylthiophene.[33] During a six-hour reflux period, only 6% of 2-benzoylthiophene was produced.

B. Chemical Properties of Acylthiophenes

Acylthiophenes undergo normal carbonyl reactions with hydroxylamine, the hydrazines, and semicarbazone. Preparation of these derivatives offers a convenient method for the identification of liquid acylthiophenes.

The carbonyl group in acylthiophenes is more reactive than that in the corresponding acylbenzenes, since they react directly with aniline or other primary amines to give Schiff bases[48] (Eq. 22).

$$\underset{S}{\bigsqcup}\overset{CH_3}{\underset{}{\overset{|}{C}}}{=}O \;+\; H_2N-C_6H_5 \;\xrightarrow[40-50\%]{\text{toluene reflux}}\; \underset{S}{\bigsqcup}\overset{CH_3}{\underset{}{\overset{|}{C}}}{=}N-C_6H_5 \tag{22}$$

N-Phenyl 2-thienyl
methyl ketimine

2-Acetylthiophene is soluble in all proportions in concentrated hydrochloric acid or 50% sulfuric acid. In this respect it is similar to aceto-

[46] Steinkopf and Killingstad, *Ann.*, **532**, 288 (1937).
[47] Nahke, *Ber.*, **30**, 2040 (1897).
[47a] Brown, Cook, and Heilbron, *J. Chem. Soc.*, **1949**, S113.
[48] Hartough, *J. Am. Chem. Soc.*, **70**, 1282 (1948).

phenone. The clear solution of 2-acetylthiophene and concentrated hydrochloric acid gradually turns red and within a few days a red organic layer settles out. The 2-acetylthiophene can be recovered to the extent of 95% from this lower layer.[49]

The normal reaction of the carbonyl moiety with hydroxylamine, semicarbazide, and the phenylhydrazines is hindered by β-substitution of alkyl ketones, e.g., 2-(2-ethylbutanoyl)thiophene and 2-(2-ethylhexanoyl)thiophene form oximes and semicarbazones only by the pyridine method, and the hydrazones cannot be formed.[43] The oxime and semicarbazone of 2-benzoylthiophene and 2-(2'-thenoyl)thiophene form easily but the 2,4-dinitrophenylhydrazone does not form at all. While 2,5-dichloro-3-acetylthiophene forms the semicarbazone readily, 2,5(4?)-di-tert-butyl-3(5?)-acetylthiophene does not form this derivative even by the pyridine method.[9]

Alkylthiophenes can be prepared by Clemmensen reduction in good yield (see Chapter VI). The attempted reduction to the corresponding pinacol with magnesium gives only tars.[50] Attempts to reduce 2-acylthiophenes to 2-thienylalkanols with zinc and sodium hydroxide have been unsuccessful.[50] The carbonyl group is best reduced to the carbinol by the aluminum isopropoxide method (see Chapter X).[51,52]

2-Acetylthiophene is converted to the 2-thioacetylthiophene by the action of hydrogen sulfide.[53] Phosphorus pentachloride converts 2-benzoylthiophene to 2-thienylphenyldichloromethane.[54] An attempt to convert 2-acetylthiophene to the corresponding dichloride by a similar method led to an uncontrollable reaction after which only tars were isolated.[50]

The acylthiophenes undergo the Pfitzinger reaction with isatic acid or isatin[11,20,55,55a] (Eq. 23). Pyrolysis of 2-(thienyl)cinchoninic acids gives

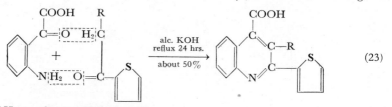

$$(23)$$

[49] Hartough, unpublished work.
[50] Hartough and Kosak, unpublished work.
[51] Mowry, Renoll, and Huber, J. Am. Chem. Soc., **68**, 1105 (1946).
[52] Nazzaro and Bullock, J. Am. Chem. Soc., **68**, 2121 (1946).
[53] Steinkopf and Jacob, Ann., **501**, 188 (1933).
[54] Minnis, J. Am. Chem. Soc., **51**, 2143 (1929).
[55] Cagniant and Deluzarche, Compt. rend., **225**, 455 (1947); **223**, 1148 (1946).
[55a] Hartmann and Wybert, Helv. Chim. Acta, **2**, 60 (1919).

2-(thienyl)quinolines.[11,55]   The major product of the pyrolysis is reported
to be 2-(2,5-dimethyl-3-thienyl)-4-hydroxy-3-methylquinoline when 2,5-
dimethyl-3-propanoylthiophene is condensed with isatin and pyrolyzed[11]
(Eq. 24).

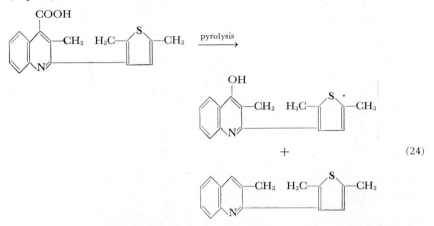

$$+ \qquad\qquad (24)$$

The acylthiophenes undergo the usual Grignard reactions but the
alcohols appear to dehydrate quite easily and the olefinic residue is
obtained in certain cases[11] (Eq. 25).   This general method has been used

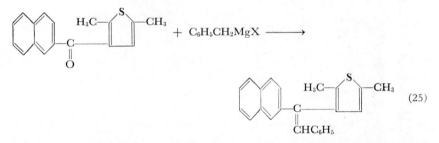

$$(25)$$

for the preparation of various secondary and tertiary alcohols (see Chapter
X for further references).

The reactions of the α-methylene hydrogens of alkanoylthiophenes
are similar to those of the corresponding atoms in the benzene isologs.
Steinkopf and Popp[56] obtained benzal-di-(2-acetylthiophene) and 1,3,5-
tri-(2-thenoyl)-2,4-diphenylpentane from the condensation of 2-acetyl-
thiophene and benzaldehyde (Eq. 26).   2-Acetylthiophene and furfural
were reported to give similar products in approximately the same yield.[56]

[56] Steinkopf and Popp, *Ann.*, **540**, 27 (1939).

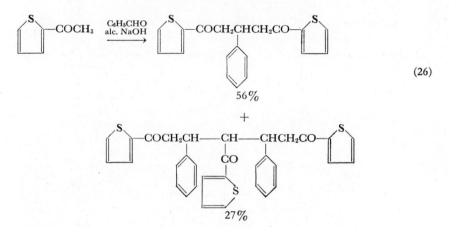

(26)

Brunswig[57] reported that this reaction proceeded normally to give the expected 1-(2-thenoyl)-2-phenylethylene (Eq. 27).

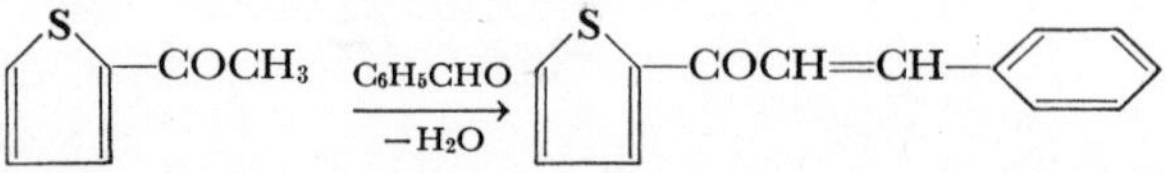

(27)

Cyanoethylation of 2-acetyl- and 2-propanoylthiophene takes place in the following manner[58,58a] (Eqs. 28 and 29).   This reaction can also be

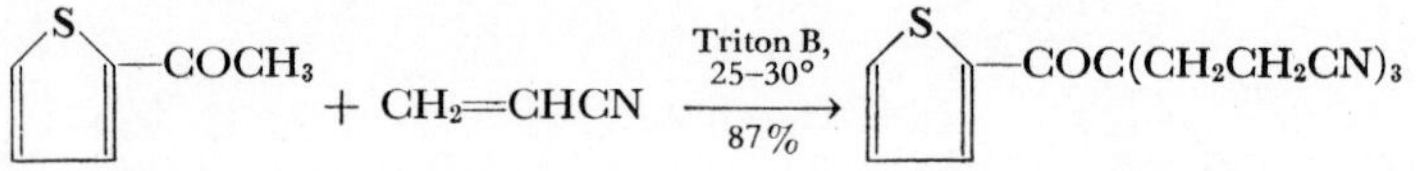

(28)

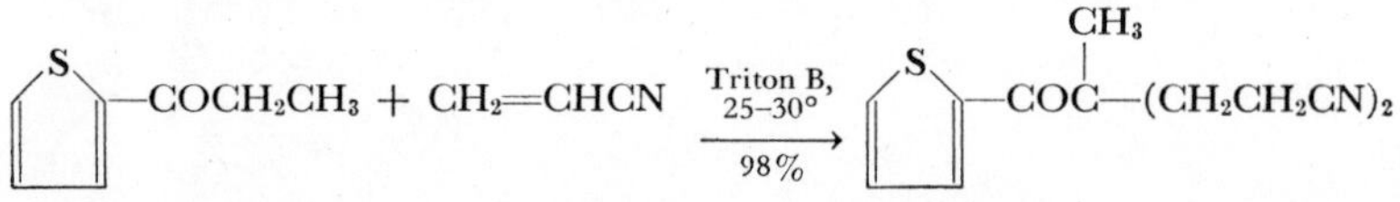

(29)

catalyzed with sodium hydroxide but the reaction is then sluggish and the yields are much lower.[50]   2-Thenoylacetone is cyanoethylated only at the methylene carbon atom.[58a]

2-Acetylthiophene can be chloromethylated to give 2-(β-chloro-propanoyl)thiophene[49] (Eq. 30).   With trioxane or paraformaldehyde

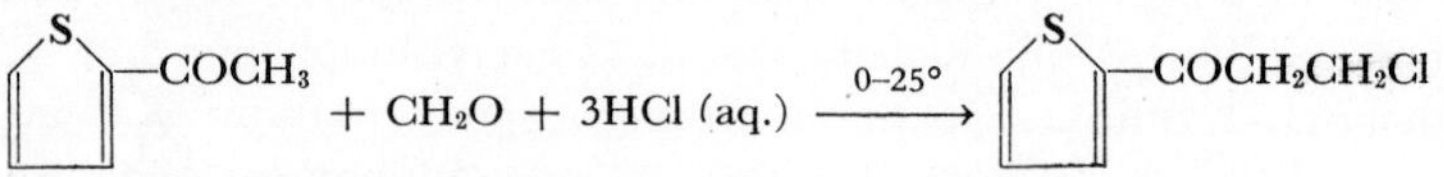

(30)

[57] Brunswig, *Ber.*, **19**, 2890 (1886).
[58] Bruson and Riener, *J. Am. Chem. Soc.*, **70**, 214 (1948).
[58a] Zellars and Levine, *J. Org. Chem.*, **13**, 911 (1948).

and acetic anhydride, 2-acetylthiophene reacts in the presence of a mont-morillonite clay or 85% orthophosphoric acid[49] (Eq. 31).

$$\text{S}\underset{}{\overset{}{\bigcirc}}-COCH_3 \ + \ (CH_2O)_x \ + \ (CH_3CO)_2O \ \xrightarrow[30\%]{\text{clay, 90-100°}}$$

$$\text{S}\underset{}{\overset{}{\bigcirc}}-COCH_2CH_2OCOCH_3 \tag{31}$$

2-Acetylthiophene undergoes a typical Mannich reaction with di-methylamine hydrochloride and paraformaldehyde[59,59a] to give 2-(β-N,N-dimethylaminopropanoyl)thiophene hydrochloride (Eq. 31a). For further discussion of this subject see Chapter IX.

$$\text{S}\underset{}{\overset{}{\bigcirc}}-COCH_3 \ + \ (CH_3)_2NH \cdot HCl \ + \ (CH_2O)_x \ \xrightarrow[50\%]{\text{alc. reflux}}$$

$$\text{S}\underset{}{\overset{}{\bigcirc}}-COCH_2CH_2N(CH_3)_2 \cdot HCl \tag{31a}$$

Amyl nitrite, in the presence of sodium ethoxide, reacts with 2-acetylthiophene to produce 2-(isonitrosoacetyl)thiophene[60,60a] (Eq. 32).

$$\text{S}\underset{}{\overset{}{\bigcirc}}-COCH_3 \ + \ C_5H_{11}ONO \ \xrightarrow[40\%]{C_2H_5ONa} \ \text{S}\underset{}{\overset{}{\bigcirc}}-COCH=NOH \ + \ H_2O \tag{32}$$

Hydrolysis of this compound with sodium bisulfite gives 2-thiophene-glyoxal.[60] The latter has also been prepared by the interaction of 2-bromoacetylthiophene with pyridine, condensation of the resulting pyridinium salt with p-nitrosodimethylaniline and hydrolysis in acid solu-tion.[61] Kipnis and Ornfelt[62] have prepared 2-thiopheneglyoxal by direct oxidation of 2-acetylthiophene with selenium dioxide (Eq. 33). 5-Trimethylsilyl-2-thienylglyoxal has been prepared by the same method.[62a]

$$\text{S}\underset{}{\overset{}{\bigcirc}}-COCH_3 \ + \ SeO_2 \ \xrightarrow[43\%]{\text{dioxane, H}_2O, 55°} \ \text{S}\underset{}{\overset{}{\bigcirc}}-COCHO \ + \ Se \tag{33}$$

[59] Blicke and Burckhalter, *J. Am. Chem. Soc.*, **64,** 478 (1942).
[59a] Levy and Nesbit, *J. Chem. Soc.*, **1938,** 1053.
[60] Fujise, *Biochem. Z.*, **236,** 241 (1931).
[60a] Barger and Easson, *J. Chem. Soc.*, **1938,** 2100.
[61] Kröhnke and Börner, *Ber.*, **69,** 2006 (1931).
[62] Kipnis and Ornfelt, *J. Am. Chem. Soc.*, **68,** 2734 (1946).
[62a] Benkeser and Landesman, *J. Am. Chem. Soc.*, **71,** 2493 (1949).

2-Acetylthiophene is nitrated easily and a mixture of 5-nitro- and 4-nitro-2-acetylthiophene results.[63]   The 5-isomer occurs in the major proportion.   Structure proof of the two isomers was carried out by synthesis through the ethyl acetoacetate reaction (Eq. 34).   Proof of the

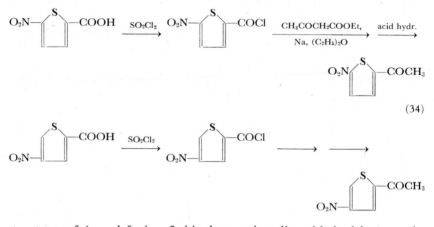

$$(34)$$

structures of 4- and 5-nitro-2-thiophenecarboxylic acids had been established before this synthesis by independent methods (see Chapters V and XII).

2-Acetylthiophene reacts rapidly with sodium in dry ether and only unidentified scission products have been obtained.   2-Benzoylthiophene reacts similarly and after carbonation only benzoic acid could be isolated.[64]

Oxidation of 2-acetylthiophene with potassium permanganate gives 2-thienylglyoxylic acid (see Chapter XII) in fair yields.   The conversion of 2-acetylthiophene and its homologs to 2-thiophenecarboxylic acids by sodium hypochlorite oxidation is reported to give yields of 80–95% of theory.[9]   This reaction has recently been extended to alkanoylthiophenes in general.[64a]   This is the best method for converting acetylthiophenes to the corresponding acids, since little or no oxidation of the thiophene nucleus takes place.   Other oxidizing agents readily attack the thiophene nucleus forming carbon dioxide and oxides of sulfur with only moderate yields of the corresponding acids.

The alkanoylthiophenes up to an alkyl chain of six carbon atoms can be detected by a color reaction with sodium nitroprusside.[50]   The test consists of placing one drop of the ketone to be tested in a test tube and

[63] Rinkes, *Rec. trav. chim.*, [4] **52,** 544 (1933).
[64] Schick and Hartough, unpublished work.
[64a] Farrar and Levine, *J. Am. Chem. Soc.*, **71,** 1496 (1949).

adding 2 ml. of a saturated methanol solution of sodium nitroprusside. This solution is diluted with 2 ml. of water and 3–10 drops of 10% methanolic potassium hydroxide are added. A deep purple to red coloration develops. If a few drops of glacial acetic acid are added to the deep purple test solution formed with 2-acetylthiophene, the color changes to deep blue. This is specific for the —COCH$_3$ group. 2-Propanoylthiophene does not change color on addition of glacial acetic acid.

2-Acetylthiophene can be carboxyethylated in the presence of sodamide and diethyl carbonate to give ethyl 2-thenoylacetate[65,65a] (Eq. 35). This compound easily forms a five-membered ring with hydroxyl-

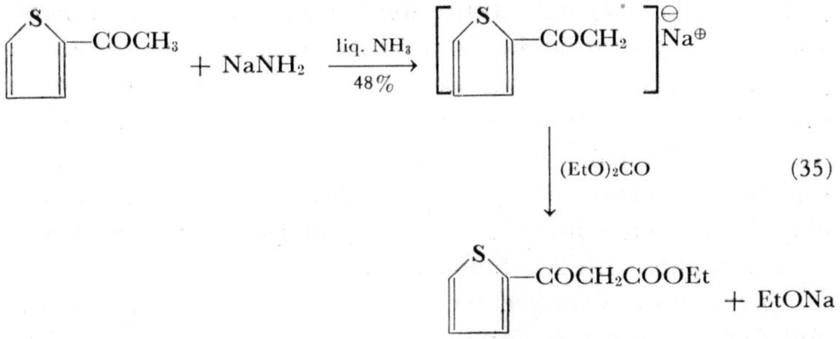

$$\text{(thienyl)}{-}COCH_3 + NaNH_2 \xrightarrow[48\%]{\text{liq. NH}_3} \left[\text{(thienyl)}{-}COCH_2 \right]^{\ominus} Na^{\oplus}$$

$$\Big\downarrow (EtO)_2CO \qquad\qquad (35)$$

$$\text{(thienyl)}{-}COCH_2COOEt + EtONa$$

amine or phenylhydrazine in the presence of sodium hydroxide to give 3-(2-thienyl)isoxazolone and the 1-phenyl-3-(2-thienyl)pyrazolone, respectively.[66]

2-Acetylthiophene forms crystalline complexes with aluminum chloride, titanium chloride, stannic chloride, and zinc chloride.[49] All are decomposed by water. Steinkopf[67] reports that the titanium chloride complex must be heated in water for some time to effect decomposition.

Upon warming a mixture of 2-acetylthiophene and orthophosphoric acid, a double salt, C_4H_3S—$COCH_3 \cdot H_3PO_4$ (m.p. 92–96°), separates from the mixture.[68] The complex is decomposed by water or alcohol but is stable in anhydrous ether in which it is very soluble.

2-Thenoyltrifluoroacetone is used to separate zirconium and hafnium salts.[68a,68b] Four moles of this ketone form a chelate with the ZrO^{++} ion having the following structure:

[65] Levine and Hauser, *J. Am. Chem. Soc.*, **66**, 1768 (1944).
[65a] Harris and Levine, *J. Am. Chem. Soc.*, **70**, 3360 (1948).
[66] Private communication from Homeyer, Mallinckrodt Laboratories.
[67] Steinkopf, *Die Chemie des Thiophens.* Steinkopff, Dresden, 1941, p. 72.
[68] Klages and Allendorf, *Ber.*, **31**, 1298 (1898).
[68a] Huffman and Beaufait, *J. Am. Chem. Soc.*, **71**, 3179 (1949).
[68b] Connick and McVey, *J. Am. Chem. Soc.*, **71**, 3182 (1949).

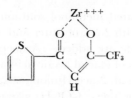

The zirconium chelate is soluble in benzene and can be extracted from aqueous solutions in that manner.

Nuclear substitution of acylthiophenes has not been thoroughly studied but it would appear that substitution takes place predominantly in the 5-position.   The normal substitution in the benzene series is *meta* to the acyl group, *i.e.*, 2-acylthiophenes would be expected to substitute in the 4-position.   Nuclear substitution in 2-benzoylthiophene occurs in the thiophene nucleus.[69]   Blocking of the 5-position with halogens does not inhibit this tendency and substitution takes place in the 4-position of the thiophene nucleus.   Attempts to sulfonate 2-isobutanoylthiophene gave only 2-thiophenesulfonic acid and isobutyric acid.[70]   Schleicher reported similar results with 2-heptanoylthiophene.[71]

Steinkopf has studied the reactions of the 2-thienyl phenyl diketones and their oximes.   A summary and comparison of their chemistry with that of benzil is given by Steinkopf.[72]

Benzil and 2-acetylthiophene react as shown in equation (36).[73]

$$\begin{matrix} C_6H_5-C=O \\ | \\ C_6H_5-C=O \end{matrix} \quad + \quad CH_3CO-\!\!\langle S \rangle \quad \xrightarrow[80-85\%]{CH_3ONa, \; CH_3OH} \quad \langle S \rangle\!-\!\begin{matrix} COCH=C-C_6H_5 \\ | \\ O=C-C_6H_5 \end{matrix} \tag{36}$$

2-Acetylthiophene and carbon disulfide react in the presence of potassium hydroxide to give a molecular compound,[74] C_4H_3S—$COCH_3 \cdot CS_2$ (m.p. 90–91°).   The compound reacts with methyl iodide in the presence of sodium hydroxide to form a dimethyl thioether and forms a dibenzoate ester in the Schotten-Baumann reaction.   Alcoholic potassium hydroxide at 125° cleaves the compound to 2-thiophenecarboxylic acid; alcoholic ammonia at 140° regenerates 2-acetylthiophene; alco-

[69] Weitkamp and Hamilton, *J. Am. Chem. Soc.*, **59**, 2699 (1937).
[70] Krekeler, *Ber.*, **19**, 677 (1886).
[71] Schleicher, *Ber.*, **19**, 660 (1886).
[72] See footnote 67, pp. 75 and 80.
[73] Allen and Hubbard, *J. Am. Chem. Soc.*, **52**, 384 (1930).
[74] Kelber and Schwarz, *Ber.*, **44**, 1693 (1911).

holic hydrochloric acid at 130° gives ethylmercaptan and 2-acetylthiophene along with unidentifiable products.   On the basis of these reactions, Kelber and Schwarz consider the formula to be $C_4H_3SCOCH:C(SH)_2$.

C. Physical Properties of Acylthiophenes

In general the ketones of thiophene and their derivatives resemble their benzene isologs closely in odor, color, boiling point, melting point, etc.   Their stability to storage is fair.   The liquid ketones discolor in ultraviolet light and from contact with oxygen, but samples of 2-acetylthiophene stored in the dark under nitrogen have not discolored in three years.   2-Acetylthiophene distilled at atmospheric pressure is a light yellow liquid, and under reduced pressure a water-white liquid.

Physical constants of 2-acetylthiophene are listed in Table XI-3. Tables XI-4 to XI-8 list the physical constants of all the other known ketones of thiophene and of some of the common derivatives used for identification.

TABLE XI-3.   Physical Properties of 2-Acetylthiophene[75]

Freezing point, °C.	10.45
Boiling point at 760 mm., °C.	213.9
Change in b.p. with pressure, °C./mm.	0.055
Refractive index, n_D^{20}	1.5667
n_E^{20}	1.5727
n_G^{20}	1.6017
Change in n_D per °C.	-0.00049
Density, g./ml. at 20°	1.1709
Change in d_4 per °C. (0–30°)	-0.00097
Viscosity at 30°, centipoises	2.32
Surface tension at 30°, dynes/cm.	44.5
Solubility characteristics	
grams sol. in 100 g. of water at 30°	1.4
grams water sol. in 100 g. 2-acetylthiophene at 30°	2.4

[75] Johnson, *J. Am. Chem. Soc.*, **69**, 150 (1947).   The data in this reference appear to supersede those of the references following: Peter, *Ber.*, **17**, 2643 (1884); **18**, 537 (1885); Biedermann, *Ber.*, **19**, 636 (1886); Volhard and Thiele, *Ann.*, **267**, 172 (1892); Nahke, *Ber.*, **30**, 2040 (1897); Voerman, *Rec. trav. chim.*, **26**, 295 (1907); Steinkopf and Bauermeister, *Ann.*, **403**, 50 (1914); Steinkopf, *Ann.*, **413**, 343 (1917); Auwers and Kohlhaas, *J. prakt. Chem.*, **108**, 321 (1924); Stadnikov and Rakowsky, *Ber.*, **61**, 268 (1928); Stadnikov and Goldfarb, *Ber.*, **61**, 2341 (1928); Goldfarb, *J. Russ. Phys.-Chem. Soc.*, **62**, 1073 (1930); Johnson and May, *Organic Syntheses*, Coll. Vol. II, Wiley, New York, 1943, p. 8.

TABLE XI-4. Physical Constants of 2-Acetylthiophenes

Ring structure:

```
        S
       / \
      /   COCH3
  R--|     |
  R'--\___/--R''
```

R	R'	R"	Ref.	B.p., °C. (mm.)	M.p., °C.	n_D^{20}	Key[a]	M.p., °C.	Ref.
H—	H—	H—	See Table XI-3	—	—	—	A	112–113	33,43,76
							B	191–192	9,33,77
							C	96	76
							D	181–182	77
							E	245	33
							F	83–83.5	77
H—	H—	CH₃—	13,28,78–80	216 (760) / 79 (4)	—	1.5618	A	85–86	13,79
							B	207–207.5	9,28
							D	193.5–194	28
H—	CH₃—	H—	9,13	86 (3)	—	1.5600	A	132.5–134	13
							B	219–220	9
CH₃—	H—	H—	9,13,78,81–83	232–233 (760) / 84.5 (2)	27–28	1.5622	A	125	13,78,81,83
							B	225	9,82,83
							C	127–128	78,81
							D	206.5–207	28,83
C₂H₅—	H—	H—	71,83,86	248–250 (760) / 116 (18)	—	—	A	110	83,85
							B	215	83,86
							C	68	71
							D	194–194.5	83,84
H—	H—	C₂H₅—	79	227	—	—	A	56	79
CH₃—	CH₃—	H—	28	131–133 (17)	—	—	B	245–245.5	28
							D	204–205	28
CH₃—	H—	CH₃—	87	226–228 (760)	—	—	A	About 70° / 70	87
							C	70	87
C₃H₇—	H—	H—	10,82,88	257–260 (760) / 125–126 (11)	—	1.5438	A	57	10,82,88
							C	60	10
							D	206	88

[a] A = oxime; B = semicarbazone; C = phenylhydrazone; D = p-nitrophenylhydrazone; E = 2,4-dinitrophenylhydrazone; F = aminoguanidine.

Substituents			Ref.	B.p., °C. (mm.)	M.p., °C.	n_D^{20}	Derivatives		
R	R'	R″					Key[a]	M.p., °C.	Ref.
(CH₃)₂CH—	H—	H—	88–90	130.5 (22)	—	1.5428	A	74	88,89
							D	198	88–90
H—	H—(n-C₃H₇—)	n-C₃H₇—(H—)	88,91	237–239	—	1.5426	A	108	88
				123–127 (22)	—	—	D	171	88
H—	H—((CH₃)₂CH—)	(CH₃)₂CH—(H—)	88	122–128 (15)	—	1.5392	D	141	88
C₂H₅—	CH₃—	H—	92	140–143 (14)	—	—	B	228.5–229	92
							D	186–187	92
CH₃—	C₂H₅—	H—	92	132–134 (16)	—	—	D	189.5	92
n-C₄H₉—	H—	H—	90	160–161 (25)	—	1.4914	D	164	90
H—	H—(n-C₄H₉—)	n-C₄H₉—(H—)	90	145–146 (25)	—	1.5069	D	146–147	90
tert-C₄H₉—(H—)	H—(tert-C₄H₉—)	H—	9	114 (4)	—	1.5343	B	209–210	9
C₂H₅—	C₂H₅—	H—	84	128–130 (12.5)	—	1.5448 (17°)	D	140	84
(CH₃)₂CHCH₂CH₂—	H—	H—	93	149–151 (13)	—	—	B	212	93
tert-C₅H₁₁—(H—) CH₃	H—(tert-C₅H₁₁—) CH₃	H—	9	111 (2)	—	1.5356	B	214–215	9
C₃H₇—CH—(H—) CH₃	H—(C₃H₇—CH—) H—	H—	9,36	121–125 (6)	—	1.5313	B	184–186	9
								167.5–168.5	36
n-C₈H₁₇—	H—	H—	22	350–355	—				
(CH₃)₃Si—	H—	H—	35,62a	104–105 (4)	—	1.5289	B	217–220	35
Cl—	H—	H—	9,12,13,36	73 (2.5)	46.5–47	—	A	159.5–160.5	13
							B	232.5–233.5	9
							C	108	12

Table continued

TABLE XI-4.   Physical Constants of 2-Acetylthiophenes (*Continued*)

R	R'	R"	Ref.	B.p., °C. (mm.)	M.p., °C.	n_D^{20}	Key[a]	M.p., °C.	Ref.
H—	Cl—	Cl—	8	—	56				
Cl—	Cl—	H—	8	—	68				
Cl—	Cl—	Cl—	8	—	80				
Br—	H—	H—	9,12,13	107.5–110 (5)	94–95	—	B	232–233	9
H—	H—	Br—	94	130 (11)	—	—	C	122	12
Br—	Br—	Br—	94	—	83–85				
Br—	H—	Br—	94	—	45				
Br—	Br—	H—	94	—	86–88				
Br—	Br—	Br—	8,94	—	131				
CH₃—	Br—	Br—	95	—	115				
Br—	CH₃—	H—	79	—	—	—	A	105	79
Br—	CH₃—	Br—	96	—	126–127				
I—	H—	H—	12,31	—	129–130	—	C	134	12
—COOH	H—	H—	32	—	142–143				
H—	—NO₂	H—	63	—	126–127	—	A	129	63
—NO₂	H—	H—	63	—	106–107	—	A	189	63
—NO₂	H—	—NO₂	76	—	166–167				
CH₃—	—NO₂	H—	78,81	—	120–121				
C₂H₅—	—NO₂	H—	85	—	71				
—NHCOCH₃	H—	H—	97	—					

[a] A = oxime; B = semicarbazone; C = phenylhydrazone; D = p-nitrophenylhydrazone; E = 2,4-dinitrophenylhydrazone; F = aminoguanidine.

TABLE XI-5. Physical Constants of 3-Acetylthiophenes

R, R', R''—thiophene—$COCH_3$

| Substituent | | | | | | | Derivatives | | |
R	R'	R''	Ref.	B.p., °C (mm.)	M.p., °C	n_D^{20}	Key[a]	M.p., °C	Ref.
H—	H—	H—	98	208–210 (748)	57	—	B	174–175	98
							E	265	98
CH₃—	H—	CH₃—	10,11,28,82,99	224 (760)	4.5	—	A	83	83,99
				125–126 (28)			B	213 (220)	82,83
				110 (13)			D	175–175.5	28,83
CH₃—	CH₃—	CH₃—	83,100	248–249	—	1.5454	B	157	100
							D	162.5–163	100
C₂H₅—	H—	C₂H₅—	84,101	126–128 (12)	—	1.5101	A	Liquid	101
							B	167	84
							D	153.5–154.5	92
C₂H₅—	C₂H₅—	C₂H₅—	67	125–130 (12)			D	151–152	67
tert-C₄H₉—	H—	tert-C₄H₉—	102	105 (3)	54–55	—	Steric hindered—no derivatives could be formed		
Cl—	H—	Cl—	8,9	87 (3)	38–38.5	—			
Br—	H—	Br—	96	—	55		B	212–213 (dec.)	9

[a] A = oxime; B = semicarbazone; C = phenylhydrazone; D = p-nitrophenylhydrazone; E = 2,4-dinitrophenylhydrazone; F = aminoguanidine.

TABLE XI-6. Physical Constants of 2-Acylthiophenes Other Than 2-Acetylthiophenes

Structure:

$$\text{R'} \;\; \overset{S}{\diagdown}\!\!\diagup \; \text{COR}$$
R''—, R'''

Substituents	Ref.	B.p., °C. (mm.)	M.p., °C.	Derivatives			
				n_D^{20}	Key[a]	M.p., °C.	Ref.
R=C₂H₅	13,36,44,70, 82,88	228 (760)	—	1.5540	A	55–56	70
		88 (7)	—	—	B	172–173	13,82
					F	215	82
R=C₂H₅—; R'=C₂H₅—	93	137–138 (19)	—	—	B	195–196	93
R=C₂H₅—; R'=n-C₃H₇—	93	137–138.5 (13)	—	—	B	174–175	93
R=C₂H₅—; R''=(CH₃)₂CH—	91	251 (760)	—	—			
R=n-C₃H₇—	13,82,88,90	118–121 (16)	—	1.5413	A	57	82
		87–92 (3)	—		B	176–176.5	13,82
R=(CH₃)₂CH—	70	232 (760)	—	—	A	107–108	70
R=CH₃CH=CH—	36,103	109–116 (5)	—	1.5949 (25°)	E	183–185	36
		134.5–135.5 (14)	—				
R=CH₃CH=CH—; R''=CH₃—	103	135–136.5 (14)	—	1.5836 (25)			
R=CH₃CH=CH—; R'=(CH₃)₃C—	103	168–169 (14)	—	1.5592 (25)			
R=CH₃CH=CH—; R'=Cl	103	—	72–73	—			
R=(CH₃)₂CHCH₂—	82	130.5–135.5 (22)	—	—	A	88	82
					B	168–169	82
					F	212	82
R=n-C₅H₁₁—	104,105	136 (11)	—	1.5301	A	53–54	105
		117–119 (1)	—		B	133–134	105
					E	152–153	105
R=(C₂H₅)₂CH—	43	91–93 (2)	—	1.5309 / 1.5268 (30°)	A	78–79	43
R=n-C₆H₁₃—	71,104	304 (760)	—	1.5265 (18°)	A	49	71
		152 (13)	—				
R=n-C₆H₁₃—; R'=C₂H₅—	71	329–330 (760)	—	—	A	38–39	71
R=n-C₇H₁₅—	104,105	181 (23.5)	—	1.5214	A	56–57	105
		140–143 (1)	—		B	127–129	105
					E	123–125	105
R=(n-C₄H₉)(C₂H₅)CH—	43	116–117 (4)	—	1.5176	A	53–55	43

[a] A = oxime; B = semicarbazone; C = phenylhydrazone; D = p-nitrophenylhydrazone; E = 2,4-dinitrophenylhydrazone; F = aminoguanidine.

Substituents	Ref.	B.p., °C. (mm.)	M.p., °C.	n_D^{20}	Derivatives		
					Key[a]	M.p., °C.	Ref.
R = (C₃H₇)₂CH—	21	158–163 (25)	—				
R = n-C₈H₁₇—	104,105	185 (18)	—	1.5150	A	Oil	105
		155–157 (1)	—	1.4917	B	134–135	105
					E	108–109	105
R = n-C₉H₁₉—	43,104	194 (17)	—	1.5083	B	110–110.5	43
		179–180 (6)	—	1.5120	E	119.5–120.5	43
R = n-C₁₀H₂₁—	104	205.5 (15.5)	—	1.5099			
R = n-C₁₁H₂₃—	104,106	190–195 (4)	—	1.5058			
		217 (17)					
		205–210 (4)					
R = n-C₁₃H₂₇—	106	—	48–49				
R = n-C₁₇H₃₅—	106	—	—				
R = CH₃(CH₂)₇CH=CH(CH₂)₇—	43	250–255 (2)	—	—	E	68–68.5	43
R = C₆H₅—	6,13,30–33,36, 43,44,46,82, 107–109	141–142 (3)	56.5–57	—	A	113–114	6,108,109
					A	92–93	33,108,109
R = p-C₆H₅—C₆H₄—	110	255–260 (13)	109				
R = (structure)	110	235–236 (13)					
R = (structure)	110	258 (13)	91				
R = (structure)	110	270–278 (13)	117				

Table continued

TABLE XI-6.   Physical Constants of 2-Acylthiophenes Other Than 2-Acetylthiophene (*Continued*)

Substituents	Ref.	B.p., °C. (mm.)	M.p., °C.	n_D^{20}	Derivatives		
					Key[a]	M.p., °C.	Ref.
R = (structure)	110	—	188				
R = H₃C (structure, CH₃, S)	110	189–190 (13)	77				
R = (structure)	110	208–210 (23)	75				
R = (structure)	110	—	181				
R = (structure, CH₃)	110	—	145				
R = C₆H₅—; R''' = CH₃—	96	—	Liquid				
R = p-C₆H₅—C₆H₄; R''' = CH₃—	110	274 (13)	123				

[a] A = oxime; B = semicarbazone; C = phenylhydrazone; D = *p*-nitrophenylhydrazone; E = 2,4-dinitrophenylhydrazone; F = aminoguanidine.

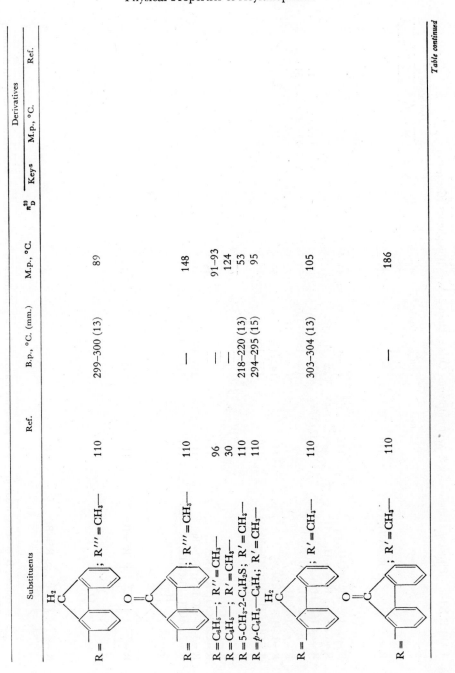

Substituents	Ref.	B.p., °C. (mm.)	M.p., °C.		Derivatives			
				n_D^{20}	Key[a]	M.p., °C.	Ref.
R = 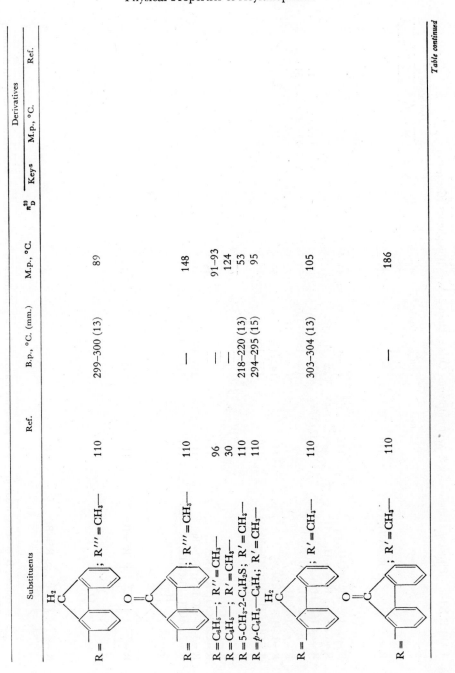; R''' = CH₃—	110	299–300 (13)	89				
R = 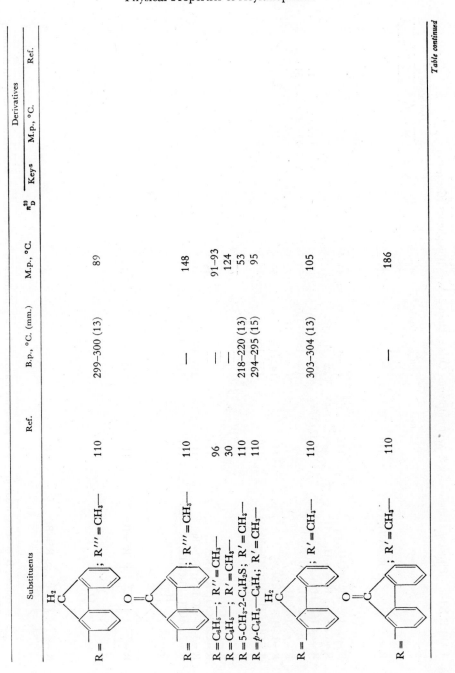; R''' = CH₃—	110	—	148				
R = C₆H₅—; R'' = CH₃—	96	—	91–93				
R = C₆H₅—; R' = CH₃—	30	—	124				
R = 5-CH₃-2-C₄H₂S; R' = CH₃—	110	218–220 (13)	53				
R = p-C₆H₅—C₆H₄; R' = CH₃—	110	294–295 (15)	95				
R = 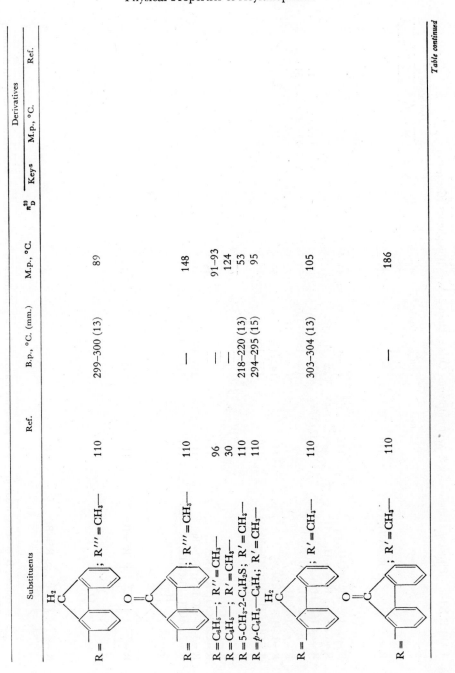; R' = CH₃—	110	303–304 (13)	105				
R = 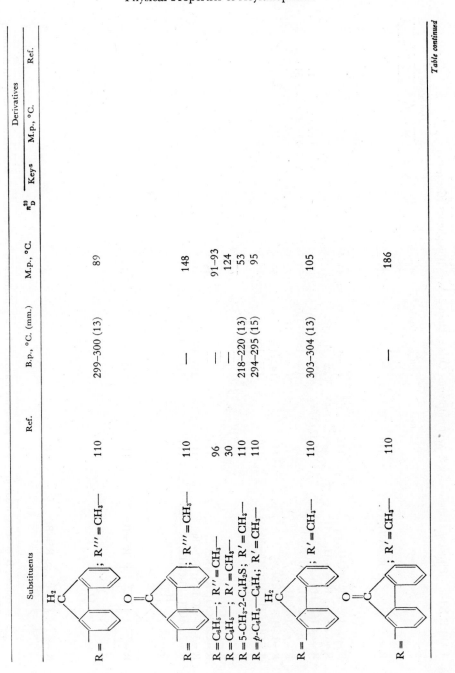; R' = CH₃—	110	—	186				

Table continued

TABLE XI-6.   Physical Constants of 2-Acylthiophenes Other Than 2-Acetylthiophene (*Continued*)

Substituents	Ref.	B.p., °C. (mm.)	M.p., °C.	n_D^{20}	Key[a]	M.p., °C.	Ref.
					Derivatives		
R = [bicyclic N-heterocyclic structure]; R′ = CH₃—	110	—	226–227				
R = C₆H₅—; R′ = C₂H₅—	111	—	44–45				
R = C₆H₅—; R′ = (CH₃)₂CH—	88	209–210 (18)	—				
R = o-CH₃C₆H₄—	31,32a,112	174.5–175 (12)	75–76	—	A	Liquid	112
R = p-CH₃C₆H₄—	31	188–189 (13)	172–173	—	A	77–78	31
R = p-NO₂C₆H₄—	31	—	57				
R = C₂H₅; R′ = Br	110	142 (13)	38–39				
R = CH₃CH₂CH₂; R′ = Br	110	155 (13)	42				
R = CH₃(CH₂)₃CH₂; R′ = Br	110	179–180 (14)	77–79				
R = C₆H₅; R′ = Br	69,110	—	72				
R = C₆H₅CH₂; R′ = Br	110	—	45–46				
R = C₆H₅CO; R′ = Br	110	—	119				
R = 5-Br-2-C₄H₂S; R′ = Br	110	235–239 (13)	69				
R = 2,5-(CH₃)₂-3-C₄HS; R′ = Br	110	211–214 (13)	—				
R = [methylene-bridged fused-ring structure]; R′ = Br	110	280 (13)	113				
R = [oxygen-bridged fused-ring structure]; R′ = Br	110	—	195				

[a] A = oxime; B = semicarbazone; C = phenylhydrazone; D = p-nitrophenylhydrazone; E = 2,4-dinitrophenylhydrazone; F = aminoguanidine.

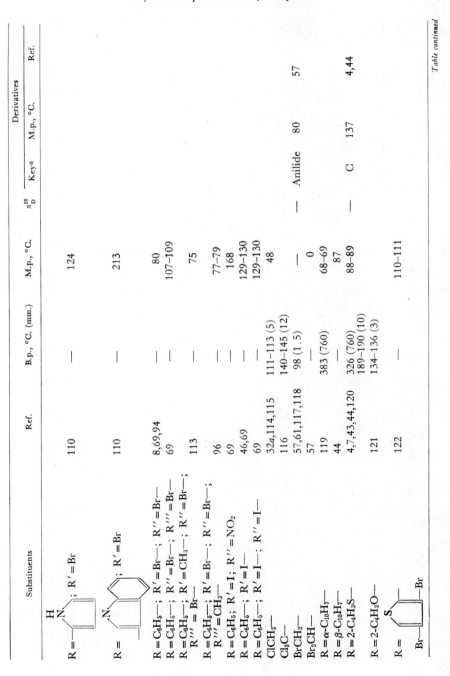

Substituents	Ref.	B.p., °C. (mm.)	M.p., °C.	n_D^{20}	Derivatives		
					Key[a]	M.p., °C.	Ref.
R= (H–N structure); R'=Br	110	—	124				
R= (N–benzo structure); R'=Br	110	—	213				
R=C₆H₅—; R'=Br—; R''=Br—	8,69,94	—	80				
R=C₆H₅—; R''=Br—; R'''=Br—	69	—	107–109				
R=C₆H₅—; R'=CH₃—; R''=Br—; R'''=Br—	113	—	75				
R=C₆H₅—; R'=Br—; R''=Br—; R'''=CH₃	96	—	77–79				
R=C₆H₅; R'=I; R''=NO₂	69	—	168				
R=C₆H₅; R'=I	46,69	—	129–130				
R=C₆H₅; R'=I; R''=I	69	—	129–130				
ClCH₂—	32a,114,115	111–113 (5)	48				
	116	140–145 (12)					
Cl₃C—	57,61,117,118	98 (1.5)	—	—	Anilide	80	57
BrCH₂—	57	—	0				
Br₂CH—	119	383 (760)	68–69				
R=α-C₁₀H₇	44	—	87				
R=β-C₁₀H₇	4,7,43,44,120	326 (760) 189–190 (10)	88–89	—	C	137	4,44
R=2-C₄H₃S—	121	134–136 (3)	110–111				
R=2-C₄H₃O— (thiophene, Br, Br)	122	—					

Table continued

TABLE XI-6.   Physical Constants of 2-Acylthiophenes Other Than 2-Acetylthiophenes (*Continued*)

Substituents	Ref.	B.p., °C. (mm.)	M.p., °C.	n_D^{20}	Derivatives		
					Key[a]	M.p., °C.	Ref.
R=Br—[structure with Br, Br]; R''=Br—; R'''=Br—	122	—	143–144				
R=—CH=CH—	57	—	80				
R=—CHBr—CHBr—	57	—	157				
R=—CO—	72	—	65–65.5	—	A	4 forms	72
"2-Triacetylthiophene"	39	—	177–178				
R=ClCH₂—; R'=Cl—	115	—	80–81				
R=NCCH₂—	115	—	136–137	—	E	160–161	115
R=NCCH₂—; R'=Cl—	115	—	120				
R=NCSCH₂—	115	—	90–91				
R=NCSCH₂—; R'=Cl—	115	—	99				
R=HOCH₂—	117	—	73–74				
R=CH₃COOCH₂—	117	113–114 (3)					
R=C₆H₅COOCH₂—	117	—	95–96				
R=C₆H₅CH=CHCOOCH₂—	117	—	118–120				
R=2-C₄H₃O—COOCH₂—	117	—	93.5				
R=C₆H₅CH₂SCH₂—	118	—	78–79				
R=C₆H₅SCH₂—	118	165–170 (3)					
R=CH₃CH₂CH₂CH₂SCH₂—	118	122–126 (3)					

[a] A = oxime; B = semicarbazone; C = phenylhydrazone; D = p-nitrophenylhydrazone; E = 2,4-dinitrophenylhydrazone; F = aminoguanidine.

TABLE XI-7. Physical Constants of 3-Acylthiophenes Other than 3-Acetylthiophenes

Substituents	Ref.	B.p., °C. (mm.)	M.p., °C.	n_D^{20}	Derivatives		
					Key[a]	M.p., °C.	Ref.
R=C$_2$H$_5$—; R'=R''=CH$_3$—	11	128–134 (15)	—	—	B	178	11
R=C$_3$H$_7$—; R'=R''=CH$_3$—	11	136 (13)	—	—	B	181	11
R=(CH$_3$)$_2$CH—; R'=R''=CH$_3$—	11	128–130 (14)	—	—			
R=C$_4$H$_9$—; R'=R''=CH$_3$—	11	153–155 (16)	—	—	B	135	11
R=(CH$_3$)$_2$CHCH$_2$—; R'=R''=CH$_3$—	11	258–260 (760)	—	—	B	151	11
R=C$_5$H$_{11}$—; R'=R''=CH$_3$—	11	284–285 (760)	—	—			
		160–165 (15)					
R=C$_7$H$_{15}$—; R'=R''=CH$_3$—	11	195–197 (15)	—	—	B	85	11
R=C$_{15}$H$_{31}$—; R'=R''=CH$_3$—	11	255–260 (18)	30	—			
R=C$_{17}$H$_{35}$—; R'=R''=CH$_3$—	11	268–270 (18)	42	—	B	68	11
R=3-C$_4$H$_3$S—	45	—	72–73				
R=H$_3$C⟨ ⟩CH$_3$; R'=R''=CH$_3$—	11	218–222 (13)	79				
R=2-C$_4$H$_3$O—; R'=R''=CH$_3$—	11	180–182 (18)	—	—	B	167	11

Table continued

TABLE XI-7 (Continued)

Substituents	Ref.	B.p., °C. (mm.)	M.p., °C.	n_D^{20}	Derivatives		
					Key[a]	M.p., °C.	Ref.
$R=C_6H_5$—; $R'=R''$—CH_3—	11,123	187–190 (20)	44	—			
$R=C_6H_5CH_2$—; $R'=R''=CH_3$—	11	195–200 (15)	—	—	B	155	11
$R=p\text{-}CH_3C_6H_4$—; $R'=R''=CH_3$—	11	198 (15)	47				
$R=p\text{-}CH_3OC_6H_4$—; $R'=R''=CH_3$—	11	217 (13)	106				
$R=p\text{-}C_2H_5C_6H_4$—; $R'=R''=CH_3$—	11	203–205 (13)					
$R=o\text{-}ClC_6H_4$—; $R'=R''=CH_3$—	11	196 (12)					
$R=\alpha\text{-}C_{10}H_7$—; $R'=R''=CH_3$—	11	236–238 (13)					
$R=\beta\text{-}C_{10}H_7$—; $R'=R''=CH_3$—	11	246–252 (15)	97				
$R=$ [fluorene structure with $\overset{H_2}{C}$]; $R'=R''=CH_3$—	11	295–297 (13)	121				
$R=C_6H_5$—; $R'=R''=CH_3$—; $R'''=Br$—	123	—	85	—	A	176–177	123
$R=2\text{-}C_4H_3SCHOH$—	98	—	116–117				

[a] A = oxime; B = semicarbazone; C = phenylhydrazone; D = p-nitrophenylhydrazone; E = 2,4-dinitrophenylhydrazone; F = aminoguanidine.

TABLE XI-8. Physical Constants of Miscellaneous Acylthiophenes

Formula	Ref.	B.p., °C. (mm.)	M.p., °C.	Derivatives		
				Key[a]	M.p., °C.	Ref.
CH_3CO—[thiophene]—$COCH_3$	32	138–145 (15)	172–173	E	311–312	32
$n\text{-}C_5H_{17}$—[thiophene, CH_3CO]—$COCH_3$	22	Liquid	—	A	58	22
C_2H_5CO—[thiophene]—COC_2H_5	13	—	129–129.2			
C_6H_5CO—[thiophene]—COC_6H_5	46	—	114–115			
$n\text{-}C_9H_{19}CO$—[thiophene]—$CO\text{-}n\text{-}C_9H_{19}$	43	230–250 (8)	109–109.5			
[thiophene]—COCHO	62	92–93 (11)	—	B (mono)	222 (dec.)	62
$(CH_3)_3Si$—[thiophene]—COCHO	62a	89–90 (6)	—	B (mono) Mono-hydrate	221–224 102–109	62a 62a
[thiophene]—COCOOH	See section on Thienylalkanoic acids, Chapter XII					

[a] A = oxime; B = semicarbazone; C = phenylhydrazone; D = p-nitrophenylhydrazone; E = 2,4-dinitrophenylhydrazone; F = aminoguanidine.

Table continued

TABLE XI-8. Physical Constants of Miscellaneous Acylthiophenes (Continued)

Formula	Ref.	B.p., °C. (mm.)	M.p., °C.	Key[a]	M.p., °C.	Ref.
COCH$_2$COOEt	65	150–153 (3)				
COCH$_2$CH$_2$COOH	14,17,18	—	120–120.5			
(thiophene, CH$_3$) COCH$_2$CH$_2$COOH	15	—	111–112			
COCH$_2$CHCOOH, CH$_3$	15a	—	110–111			
CO(CH$_2$)$_3$COOH	16,124,125	224 (11)	92–94	B	202	16
CO(CH$_2$)$_4$COOH	13,17,18, 36,126	—	79–80 / 77	B / —	200–201 / 205	36 / 126
CO(CH$_2$)$_6$COOH	18	—	About 25			
CO(CH$_2$)$_7$COOH	18,126	—	63–65	B	174	126

[a] A = oxime; B = semicarbazone; C = phenylhydrazone; D = p-nitrophenylhydrazone; E = 2,4-dinitrophenylhydrazone; F = aminoguanidine.

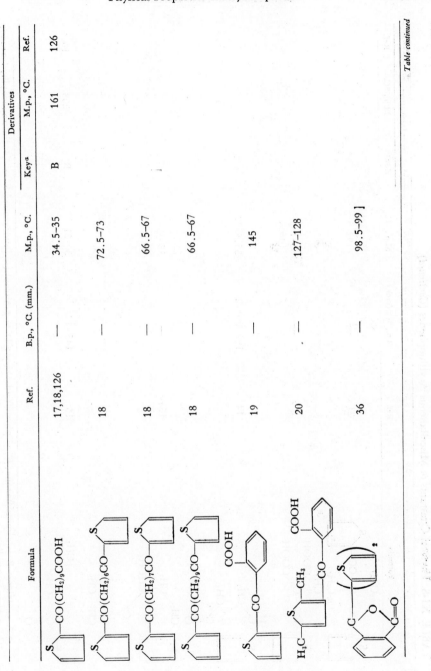

Formula	Ref.	B.p., °C. (mm.)	M.p., °C.	Derivatives Key[a]	Derivatives M.p., °C.	Derivatives Ref.
CO(CH₂)₉COOH	17,18,126	—	34.5–35	B	161	126
CO(CH₂)₆CO	18	—	72.5–73			
CO(CH₂)₇CO	18	—	66.5–67			
CO(CH₂)₉CO	18	—	66.5–67			
COOH	19	—	145			
CH₃, CO, COOH	20	—	127–128			
	36	—	98.5–99]			

Table continued

TABLE XI-8. Physical Constants of Miscellaneous Acylthiophenes (*Continued*)

Formula	Ref.	B.p., °C. (mm.)	M.p., °C.	Derivatives Key[a]	M.p., °C.	Ref.
(thiophene)—CO—C(n-C$_3$H$_7$)—CO—n-C$_3$H$_7$	21	—	192.5			
(thiophene)—CO—C(CH$_3$)(COOH)—COOH	15a	—	165–166 (dec.)			
(thiophene, H$_2$C—CH$_2$—CH$_2$ ring ketone) C=O	14	102–110 (2)	35.5–37			
(thiophene, CH$_2$—CH$_2$—CHCH$_3$ ring ketone) C=O	15a	—	35–36			
(thiophene, CH$_2$—CH$_2$—CH$_2$—CH$_2$ ring ketone) C=O	16	145 (17)	30–31	B	208	16

[a] A = oxime; B = semicarbazone; C = phenylhydrazone; D = *p*-nitrophenylhydrazone; E = 2,4-dinitrophenylhydrazone; F = aminoguanidine.

Formula	Ref.	B.p., °C. (mm.)	M.p., °C.	Derivatives		
				Key[a]	M.p., °C.	Ref.
S—$COCH_2COCH_3$	65a	129–131 (8)	—	Cu^{++} salt	228–230	65a
S—$COCH_2COC_2H_5$	65a	124–126.5 (4)	—	Cu^{++} salt	192–194	65a
S—$COCH_2CO\text{-}n\text{-}C_3H_7$	65a	135–139.5 (4)	—	Cu^{++} salt	140–142	65a
S—$COCH_2COCH(CH_3)_2$	65a	133–136 (5)	—	Cu^{++} salt	159–161	65a
S—$COCH_2CO\text{-}n\text{-}C_5H_{11}$	65a	163–166 (4)	—	Cu^{++} salt	108–109	65a
S—$COCH_2CO$—(phenyl)	65a	198–201 (4)	77–78.5	Cu^{++} salt	276–278	65a
S—$CH\!\!<^{COC_2H_5}_{C_6H_5}$	47a	125–127 (0.5)				
S—$COCH_2CO$—(thienyl)	65a	—	99–100	Cu^{++} salt	259–263	65a

Table continued

TABLE XI-8.   Physical Constants of Miscellaneous Acylthiophenes (*Continued*)

Formula	Ref.	B.p., °C. (mm.)	M.P., °C.	Derivatives		
				Key[a]	M.P., °C.	Ref.
	127	192–195 (6)	54.5–55.5	Cu^{++} salt	272–274	127
$CH_3COCH_2CH_2$ $CH_2CH_2COCH_3$	128	128–130 (0.001)	—	Dioxime	86–87	128
	115	—	88			
	115	—	133–134			
COCHOH	129	—	108–109			
COCO	129	—	81–82			
$COCH_2CH_2N(CH_3)_2 \cdot HCl$	59,59a	—	178–179			

[a] A = oxime; B = semicarbazone; C = phenylhydrazone; D = p-nitrophenylhydrazone; E = 2,4-dinitrophenylhydrazone; F = aminoguanidine.

Formula	Ref.	B.p., °C. (mm.)	M.P., °C.	Derivatives Key[a]	Derivatives M.P., °C.	Derivatives Ref.
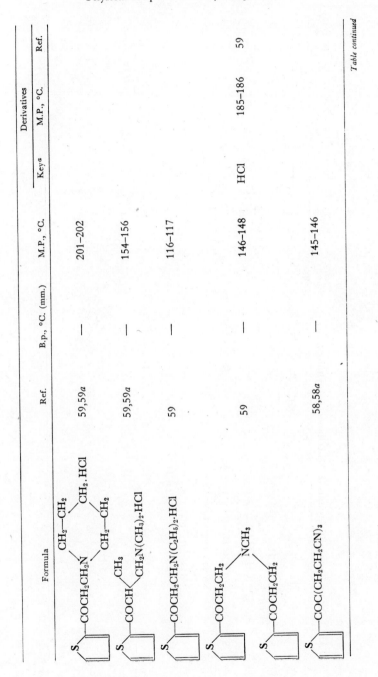	59,59a	—	201–202			
	59,59a	—	154–156			
	59	—	116–117			
	59	—	146–148	HCl	185–186	59
	58,58a	—	145–146			

Table continued

TABLE XI-8. Physical Constants of Miscellaneous Acylthiophenes (*Continued*)

Formula	Ref.	B.p., °C. (mm.)	M.p., °C.	Derivatives		
				Key[a]	M.p., °C.	Ref.
S—COC(COCH₃)(CH₂CH₂CN)₂	58a	—	127–127.5			
S—COC(COOC₂H₅)(CH₂CH₂CN)₂	58a	—	100.5–101			
CH₃CO—[S]—CH₂—[S]—COCH₃	35a	—	124–125			
CH₃CO—[S]—CH(CH₃)—[S]—COCH₃	35a	—	62.5–64			
CH₃CO—[S]—CO—[S]—COCH₃	35a	—	262–263			

[76] Peter, *Ber.*, **17**, 2643 (1884).
[77] Steinkopf and Jaffe, *Ann.*, **413**, 333 (1916).
[78] Demuth, *Ber.*, **18**, 3026 (1885); **19**, 679 (1886).
[79] Gerlach, *Ann.*, **267**, 153 (1892).
[80] Linstead, Noble, and Wright, *J. Chem. Soc.*, **1937**, 911.
[81] Demuth, *Ber.*, **19**, 1859 (1886).
[82] Steinkopf and Schubart, *Ann.*, **424**, 1 (1920).
[83] Chabrier, Tchoubar, and Le Tellier-Dupre, *Bull. soc. chim. France*, **1946**, 332.
[84] Steinkopf, Frömel and Leo, *Ann.*, **546**, 199 (1941).
[85] Schleicher, *Ber.*, **18**, 3015 (1885).
[86] Steinkopf, *Ann.*, **428**, 144 (1921).
[87] Zelinsky, *Ber.*, **20**, 2019 (1887).
[88] Scheibler and Schmidt, *Ber.*, **54**, 139 (1921).
[89] Kutz and Corson, *J. Am. Chem. Soc.*, **68**, 1477 (1946).
[90] Scheibler and Rettig, *Ber.*, **59**, 1194 (1926).
[91] Thiele, *Ann.*, **267**, 134 (1892).
[92] Steinkopf, Merckoll, and Strauch, *Ann.*, **545**, 45 (1940).
[93] Steinkopf, *Ann.*, **430**, 78 (1923).
[94] Steinkopf, Jacob, and Penz, *Ann.*, **512**, 136 (1934).
[95] Steinkopf, *Ann.*, **513**, 281 (1934).
[96] Steinkopf and Jacob, *Ann.*, **515**, 273 (1935).
[97] Johnson, Green, and Pauli, *J. Biol. Chem.*, **153**, 37 (1944).
[98] Campaigne and Le Suer, *J. Am. Chem. Soc.*, **70**, 1555 (1948).
[99] Silberfarb, *J. Russ. Phys.-Chem. Soc.*, **45**, 1938 (1913).
[100] Youtz and Perkin, *J. Am. Chem. Soc.*, **51**, 3511 (1929).
[101] Muhlert, *Ber.*, **19**, 635 (1886).
[102] Product reported in footnote 9 but structure is in doubt; may be 2-acetyl-3,5-di-*tert*-butylthiophene.
[103] Bradsher, Brown, and Grantham, *J. Am. Chem. Soc.*, **71**, 3543 (1949).
[104] Cagniant and Deluzarche, *Compt. rend.*, **225**, 455 (1947).
[105] Campaigne and Diedrich, *J. Am. Chem. Soc.*, **70**, 391 (1948).
[106] Ralston and Christensen, *Ind. Eng. Chem.*, **29**, 194 (1937).
[107] Minnis, *Org. Syntheses*, **12**, 62.
[108] Hantzsch, *Ber.*, **23**, 2332 (1890).
[109] Hantzsch, *Ber.*, **24**, 59 (1891).
[110] Buu-Hoï and Nguyen-Hoan, *Rec. trav. chim.*, **68**, 5 (1949).
[111] Marcusson, *Ber.*, **26**, 2461 (1893).
[112] Ernst, *Ber.*, **19**, 3279 (1886).
[113] Steinkopf, *Ann.*, **513**, 281 (1934).
[114] Peter, *Ber.*, **18**, 540 (1885).
[115] Emerson and Patrick, *J. Org. Chem.*, **13**, 722 (1948).
[116] Houben and Fischer, *J. prakt. Chem.*, [2] **123**, 313 (1929).
[117] Kipnis, Soloway, and Ornfelt, *J. Am. Chem. Soc.*, **71**, 10 (1949).
[118] Kipnis and Ornfelt, *J. Am. Chem. Soc.*, **70**, 3950 (1948).
[119] Scholl and Seer, *Ann.*, **394**, 111 (1912).
[120] Steinkopf and Hempel, *Ann.*, **495**, 162 (1932).
[121] Gilman, Rowe, and Dickey, *Rec. trav. chim.*, [4] **52**, 395 (1933).
[122] Steinkopf and Kohler, *Ann.*, **522**, 27 (1936).
[123] Kitt, *Ber.*, **28**, 1807 (1895).
[124] Cagniant and Deluzarche, *Compt. rend.*, **222**, 1301 (1946).
[125] Melville, Moyer, and duVigneaud, *J. Biol. Chem.*, **146**, 487 (1942).
[126] Cagniant, Cagniant, and Deluzarche, *Bull. soc. chim. France*, **15**, 1083 (1948).
[127] Harris and Levine, *J. Am. Chem. Soc.*, **71**, 1120 (1949).
[128] Griffing and Salisbury, *J. Am. Chem. Soc.*, **70**, 3416 (1948).
[129] Deschamps, King, and Nord, *J. Org. Chem.*, **14**, 184 (1949).

CHAPTER XII

Carboxy Derivatives of Thiophene

I. Thiophenecarboxylic Acids

The preparation of thiophenecarboxylic acids has been difficult in the past and for that reason this interesting field of thiophene chemistry has not been as thoroughly investigated as the preparation of the acyl-thiophenes. This has been particularly true of the 3-thiophenecarboxylic acids and only a few of these are known. The main difficulty has been the disappointing yields obtained by the oxidation of alkylthiophenes. In most cases the yields average only a few percent. Oxidation of the 3,4-dialkylthiophenes is even less satisfactory and no 3,4-thiophenedicarboxylic acid has ever been isolated.

In the past the Grignard reaction has been the only satisfactory method for the preparation of these acids. However, the difficulty in obtaining the halothiophenes necessary for this reaction has greatly limited its application. Two recent general methods will greatly facilitate the preparation of 2-thiophenecarboxylic acids. The first, sodium hypochlorite oxidation of the 2-acetylthiophenes, gives consistently high yields. The second, metalation with sodium, is the most convenient for general laboratory use, since acids can be obtained in high yields by carboxylation with carbon dioxide. The convenience lies in the relatively few hours required to produce the acid directly from the corresponding thiophene without the isolation of intermediates as is necessary in the Grignard and haloform reactions.

For the preparation of 3-thiophenecarboxylic acids recourse to the Grignard reaction is usually necessary. The new synthesis of Campaigne and Le Suer for 3-thenyl bromide offers an attractive intermediate for the preparation of 3-thiophenecarboxylic acids either by conversion to 3-thenyl alcohol or to 3-thiophenealdehyde which can subsequently be oxidized to the acid in high yield.

A.   Preparation of 2-Thiophenecarboxylic Acids

1. Oxidation of Ketones

The oxidation of 2-acetylthiophene to 2-thiophenecarboxylic acid is most conveniently carried out with sodium hypochlorite solution[1] (Eq. 1).

$$\text{S}\!\!-\!\!COCH_3 + 3NaOCl \xrightarrow[95\%]{60-70°} \text{S}\!\!-\!\!COONa + CHCl_3 + 2NaOH \qquad (1)$$

This method has been applied to some ten substituted thiophenes and the yields ranged from 70–90%.   Only a di-*tert*-butylacetylthiophene failed to react.   In general the reaction is very smooth and the final products are obtained in pure form from the reaction mixture.   Recently, it has been demonstrated that 2-propanoyl- and 2-butanoylthiophene can be oxidized to 2-thiophenecarboxylic acid.[1a]   The yields appear to be somewhat lower than with the acetylthiophenes.   The method has also been extended to the preparation of di-(5,5′-dicarboxy-2,2′-dithienyl)methane (21% yield) by oxidation of the 5,5′-diacetyl derivative.[1b]

Oxidation of ketones with potassium permanganate has been rather generally used but the method is better applied to the oxidation of 2-acetylthiophene to 2-thienylglyoxalic acid.[2-4]   Conversion of the latter to 2-thiophenecarboxylic acid can be effected in high yield by further oxidation with hydrogen peroxide.[5]

Demuth[6] does not report the formation of substituted 2-thienylglyoxalic acids from the oxidation of alkyl- and halo-2-acetylthiophenes with alkaline potassium permanganate.   The yields of the substituted thiophenecarboxylic acids by this method seem never to average more than 20–30%.   Permanganate oxidation of 2-propanoylthiophene[7] and 2-isobutanoylthiophene[8] gives 2-thiophenecarboxylic acid in low yields.

2. Oxidation of Aliphatic Side Chains

The oxidation of alkylthiophenes, while giving very low yields, has been widely used in the past.   The main justification for this method was

[1] Hartough and Conley, *J. Am. Chem. Soc.*, **69**, 3096 (1947).
[1a] Farrar and Levine, *J. Am. Chem. Soc.*, **71**, 1496 (1949).
[1b] McKusick, U. S. Pat. 2,467,439 (1949).
[2] V. Meyer, *Ann.*, **236**, 205 (1886); Gattermann, Keiser, and V. Meyer, *Ber.*, **18**, 3005 (1885).
[3] Peter, *Ber.*, **18**, 537 (1885).
[4] Biedermann, *Ber.*, **19**, 637 (1886).
[5] Voermann, *Rec. trav. chim.*, **26**, 293 (1907).
[6] Demuth, *Ber.*, **19**, 679 (1886).
[7] Ernst, *Ber.*, **20**, 518 (1886).
[8] Krekeler, *Ber.*, **19**, 676 (1886).

that alkylthiophenes could be obtained either from coal tar or by a ring closure.   Oxidation of the alkyl group leads to a carboxylic acid group whose position on the nucleus is thus established.   Egli[9] and Schleicher[10] found that alkaline permanganate oxidation of 2-ethylthiophene gave 2-thiophenecarboxylic acid, 2-thienylglyoxalic acid, and 2-acetylthiophene. The isolation of 2-acetylthiophene suggests that the primary attack is on the α-hydrogens of the side chain.   A similar oxidation of 3-ethylthiophene,[11] as well as 3-methylthiophene,[11,12] gives only 3-thiophenecarboxylic acid.   The highest yield reported was 8%.

Oxidation of 2,3-[13,16] and 2,4-dimethylthiophene[14-16] takes place stepwise, with the 2-methyl group being attacked first.   Continued oxidation yields the dicarboxylic acids in still lower yields.[16,17]

The structure of ω-5-dichloro-2-vinylthiophene was deduced by oxidation to 5-chloro-2-thiophenecarboxylic acid.[17a]   The yield was not reported.

Oxidation of the 2-thenylamines[18] or the 2-thenylhydroxylamines[19] gives good yields of the 2-thiophenecarboxylic acids, especially if the technique of Rinkes[19a] is applied (Eq. 2).

$$(2)$$

3. Carbonation of the Thienylmetallo Compounds

Schorigin,[20] in 1910, reported that 2-thiophenecarboxylic acid resulted from the carbonation of a reaction mixture containing thiophene, diethylmercury, and sodium.   The yield was very low.   It was later found that this method, if properly adapted, gave good yields of the acid. The method consists of a transmetalation of thiophene with alkyl- or arylsodiums in the presence of mercury[21] (Eq. 3).   The alkylthiophenes give

[9] Egli, *Ber.*, **18**, 546 (1885).
[10] Schleicher, *Ber.*, **19**, 671 (1886).
[11] Damsky, *Ber.*, **19**, 3284 (1886).
[12] Muhlert, *Ber.*, **18**, 3003 (1885).
[13] Steinkopf and Jacob, *Ann.*, **515**, 273 (1935).
[14] Steinkopf and Hanske, *Ann.*, **527**, 269 (1937).
[15] Zelinsky, *Ber.*, **20**, 2021 (1887).
[16] Rinkes, *Rec. trav. chim.*, [4] **52**, 1052 (1933).
[17] Linstead, Noble, and Wright, *J. Chem. Soc.*, **1937**, 911.
[17a] Emerson and Patrick, *J. Org. Chem.*, **13**, 729 (1948).
[18] Hartough and Meisel, *J. Am. Chem. Soc.*, **70**, 4018 (1948).
[19] Hartough, *J. Am. Chem. Soc.*, **69**, 1355 (1947).
[19a] Rinkes, *Rec. trav. chim.*, [4] **53**, 643 (1934).
[20] Schorigin, *Ber.*, **43**, 1938 (1910).
[21] Schick and Hartough, *J. Am. Chem. Soc.*, **70**, 1645 (1948).

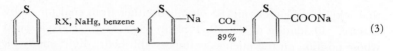

$$(3)$$

yields ranging up to 85% of theory when ethyl chloride is employed in ether solution.[21]

3-Methylthiophene gives a unique reaction with alkyl- or arylsodium in which the substitution takes place exclusively in the 5-position rather than in the expected 2-position. Relatively good yields, 40–50%, of 4-methyl-2-thiophenecarboxylic acid are obtained upon carbonation[21] (Eq. 4).

$$(4)$$

2-Thienylsodium can be prepared directly from any of the 2-halothiophenes if an inert solvent other than diethyl ether is employed[22] (Eq. 5).   However, with sodium or sodium amalgam in ether solvent an

$$(5)$$

entirely unexpected reaction takes place in which the halogen atom is not removed and the sodium replaces the hydrogen in the 5-position[22] (Eq. 6)

$$(6)$$

The general method involving sodium metalation for the preparation of the thiophenecarboxylic acids is applicable to all of the 2-thiophenecarboxylic acids and is, by far, the most convenient laboratory method from the standpoint of time and yields.   There is no method at the present for the preparation of 4-alkyl-2-thiophenecarboxylic acids (except by selective oxidation of a 2,4-dialkylthiophene) other than by the anomalous addition of sodium to the 3-alkylthiophenes.   Since the thienylsodiums appear to undergo typical Grignard reactions, this anomalous addition of sodium to the 3-alkylthiophenes brings a class of compounds, heretofore practically unknown, into easy reach of the synthetic chemist.

Transmetalation of Grignard reagents with thiophene has not been thoroughly investigated, but a reaction somewhat similar to that of the

[22] Schick and Hartough, *J. Am. Chem. Soc.*, **70**, 286 (1948).
[23] Challenger and Gibson, *J. Chem. Soc.*, **1940**, 308.

alkylsodiums has been carried out with ethylmagnesium chloride[23] (Eq. 7). Carbonation of the thiophenemagnesium iodide prepared from 2- or

$$
\text{(thiophene)} \xrightarrow[10\%]{\text{C}_2\text{H}_5\text{MgBr, ether}} \text{C}_2\text{H}_6 + \text{(thiophene)}-\text{MgBr} \xrightarrow{\text{CO}_2} \xrightarrow{\text{H}^+} \text{(thiophene)}-\text{COOH} \tag{7}
$$

3-iodothiophene and magnesium gives excellent yields of the 2- or 3-thiophenecarboxylic acid.[24] The preparation of several isomeric methylthiophenecarboxylic acids from the corresponding methyliodothiophenes through the Grignard reaction is described by Steinkopf and Hanske.[25,26] A thorough discussion of the preparation of the six isomeric methylthiophenecarboxylic acids is given in Chapter V.

4. The Gattermann Synthesis

The Gattermann synthesis has been used to prepare the alkylthiophenecarboxylic acids. Gattermann condensed carbamyl chloride with 3-methylthiophene in the presence of aluminum chloride to produce the 3-methyl-2-thiophenecarboxamide which was subsequently hydrolyzed to the acid[27] (Eq. 8). The method has been successfully applied to the

$$
\text{(thiophene)}-\text{CH}_3 \xrightarrow{\text{ClCONH}_2,\ \text{AlCl}_3} \text{(thiophene)}\begin{matrix}-\text{CONH}_2\\-\text{CH}_3\end{matrix} + \text{HCl} \tag{8}
$$

production of 2,5-dimethyl-3-thiophenecarboxylic acid, 3,5-dimethyl-2-thiophenecarboxylic acid, and 3,4,5-trimethyl-2-thiophenecarboxylic acid.[28] The yields are not reported but they are presumably low.

5. Miscellaneous Methods

The Wurtz synthesis using ethyl chloroformate can be applied in the thiophene series. Nahnsen[29] prepared 2-thiophenecarboxylic acid by condensing ethyl chloroformate with 2-iodothiophene by means of sodium amalgam (Eq. 9). Levi[30] reported that this reaction and the reaction of ethyl chloroformate with alkyliodothiophenes proceeded more easily than in the benzene series.

[24] Schlenk and Ochs, *Ber.*, **48**, 679 (1915).
[25] Steinkopf and Hanske, *Ann.*, **527**, 264 (1937).
[26] Steinkopf and Hanske, *Ann.*, **532**, 236 (1937).
[27] Gattermann, *Ann.*, **244**, 58 (1888).
[28] Kitt, *Ber.*, **28**, 1810 (1895).
[29] Nahnsen, *Ber.*, **17**, 2192 (1884).
[30] Levi, *Ber.*, **19**, 656 (1886).

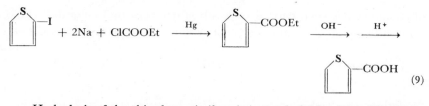

$$\text{(9)}$$

Hydrolysis of the thiophenenitriles gives good yields of the thiophene-carboxylic acids. Unfortunately, there are no good methods for the preparation of the thiophenenitriles. 2-Thiophenenitrile can be prepared as demonstrated in the following ways: equations (10)[31], (11),[32] (12),[33]

$$\text{(10)}$$

$$\text{(11)}$$

$$\text{(12)}$$

$$\text{(12a)}$$

$$\text{(13)}$$

$$\text{(14)}$$

$$\text{(15)}$$

(12a),[33a] (13),[34,35] and (14).[36] An attempt to dehydrate 2-thiophene-carboxamide with P_2O_5 did not yield the expected 2-thiophenenitrile.[33a]

5-Nitro-2-thiophenenitrile is easily prepared by refluxing cuprous cyanide with 5-nitro-2-iodothiophene in pyridine solution[37] (Eq. 15).

[31] V. Meyer and Kreis, *Ber.*, **16**, 2173 (1883).
[32] Rosemund and Struck, *Ber.*, **52**, 1755 (1919); Germ. Pat. 327,049 (1920).
[33] Douglas, *Ber.*, **25**, 1311 (1892).
[33a] Putokhin and Egorova, *J. Gen. Chem. (U. S. S. R.)*, **18**, 1866 (1948); *Chem. Abstr.*, **43**, 3816 (1949).
[34] Karrer, Rebmann, and Zeller, *Helv. Chim. Acta*, **3**, 261 (1920).
[35] Hartough and Dickert, unpublished work, found yield to be approximately 40% with formation of some 2,5-thiophenedinitrile.
[36] Steinkopf and Ohse, *Ann.*, **437**, 14 (1924).
[37] Dann, *Ber.*, **B76**, 419 (1943).

Subsequent hydrolysis and alcoholysis to the ethyl ester and reduction with aluminum scale in ether gave ethyl 5-amino-2-thiophenecarboxylate:

$$O_2N-\text{[thiophene]}-COOEt \xrightarrow{\text{Ether (2\% H}_2\text{O), Al scale}} H_2N-\text{[thiophene]}-COOEt \qquad (16)$$

Mucic acid, when heated with barium sulfide at 200–210°, gives 2-thiophenecarboxylic acid.[38] This preparation is similar to that of 2-furoic acid by heating of mucic acid.

B. Preparation of 3-Thiophenecarboxylic Acids

3-Thiophenecarboxylic acid was first prepared by Muhlert[12] in 1885 by permanganate oxidation of 3-methylthiophene. Oxidation of 3-ethylthiophene also was reported to give 3-thiophenecarboxylic acid.[11]

3-Thiophenecarboxylic acid and chlorinated 3-thiophenecarboxylic acids have been obtained by Voermann[39] by chlorination of 3-methyl-thiophene with phosphorus pentachloride. A low yield of 3-thenal chloride along with nuclear-chlorinated 3-thenal chlorides was obtained. Subsequent hydrolysis to the aldehyde and mild oxidation yielded free acid.

Rinkes[40] prepared 3-thiophenecarboxylic acid from 3-iodo-thiophene

$$\text{[thiophene]}-I \xrightarrow[\text{sealed tube}]{\text{KCN, CuCN,}} \text{[thiophene]}-CN \xrightarrow{\text{H}_2\text{O, alc.}} \text{[thiophene]}-COOH \qquad (17)$$

(Eq. 17). Steinkopf and Schmitt carbonated the Grignard reagent of 3-iodothiophene to obtain the same acid but did not record their yields.[41]

Of more recent date is the synthesis of Campaigne and Le Suer.[42] This method also involves a 4-step reaction starting with 3-methylthio-phene (Eq. 18).

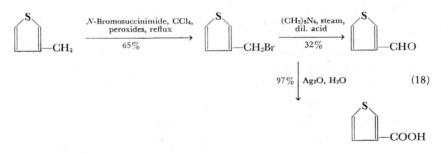

[38] Paal and Tafel, *Ber.*, **18**, 458 (1885).
[39] Voermann, *Rec. trav. chim.*, **26**, 293 (1907).
[40] Rinkes, *Rec. trav. chim.*, [4] **55**, 991 (1936).
[41] Steinkopf and Schmitt, *Ann.*, **533**, 264 (1938).
[42] Campaigne and Le Suer, *J. Am. Chem. Soc.*, **70**, 1555 (1948).

The preparation of the three isomeric methyl-3-thiophenecarboxylic acids is discussed in detail in Chapter V.

4-Amino-3-thiophenecarboxylic acids are prepared by ring closure according to the method of Cheney and Piening.[43,43a] An internal condensation of an α-carboalkoxyalkyl β'-carboalkoxyalkyl sulfide in the presence of an alkali metal oxide produces the intermediate 3-carbethoxy-4-oxo-5-alkylthiolane. This compound is then converted to the thiophene derivative in the following manner:

$$\tag{19}$$

where R is a carboethoxy, alkoxy, aralkoxy, or aryloxy group and n is 1 to 8.

C. Chemical Properties of Thiophenecarboxylic Acids

In general, it can be considered that the —COOH group in thiophenecarboxylic acids is much the same as in any organic compound. It undergoes esterification to give yields almost identical with those with benzoic acid. Acid chlorides are prepared by standard procedures, *i.e.*, with thionyl chloride, etc., and the nucleus is not affected during such reactions. Amide formation is carried out in a manner similar to the preparation of benzamide. However, unlike benzamide, 2-thiophenecarboxamide cannot be pyrolyzed to 2-thiophenenitrile in yields above 10%. The acid chlorides undergo normal reactions and can be employed in Friedel-Crafts reactions; they are lachrymators; they decompose rapidly in contact with water.

A few specific reactions of the thiophenecarboxylic acids are discussed below.

1. Halogenation

Halogenation of 2-thiophenecarboxylic acid gives only the 5-halo-[44] and 4,5-dihalo-2-thiophenecarboxylic acids.[45] Further halogenation cleaves the —COOH group with the formation of polyhalothiophenes.[46]

[43] Cheney and Piening, U. S. Pat. 2,443,598 (1948); *J. Am. Chem. Soc.*, **67**, 729,731 (1945).
[43a] Cheney and Piening, U. S. Pat. 2,466,004 (1949).
[44] Steinkopf, Jacob, and Penz, *Ann.*, **512**, 150 (1934).
[45] Bonz, *Ber.*, **18**, 2308 (1886).
[46] Steinkopf and Kohler, *Ann.*, **532**, 250 (1937).

Bromine or iodine in the 4,5-positions of 2-thiophenecarboxylic acid is replaced by chlorine to yield 4,5-dichloro-2-thiophenecarboxylic acid.[47] Although bromine generally replaces iodine on the thiophene nucleus, 3-iodo-2-thiophenecarboxylic acid brominates normally in the 4,5-positions and the iodine is not lost.[47] The 3,4,5-trihalo-2-thiophenecarboxylic acids are prepared by an indirect method rather than by direct halogenation[44] (Eq. 20).

$$ (20) $$

It is well known that excess sodium hypochlorite must be destroyed in the preparation of thiophenecarboxylic acids, since, upon acidification, chlorination of the thiophene nucleus takes place. Bunnett et al.[47a] investigated this reaction and found that sodium hypochlorite, when acidified in the presence of 2-thiophenecarboxylic acid, gave 5-chloro-2-thiophenecarboxylic acid in 46% yield. A large excess of the hypochlorous acid gave rise to a 14% yield of 4,5-dichloro-2-thiophenecarboxylic acid. The major proportion of the 2-thiophenecarboxylic acid was converted to 2,5-dichlorothiophene by a decarboxylation process.

2. Nitration

Methods for the determination of isomers formed during nitration of 2-thiophenecarboxylic acid and of the methylthiophenecarboxylic acids by Rinkes[19a, 48−50] are classic examples of orientation study in the thiophene series. Although Rinkes did not make the initial study of the nitration of 2-thiophenecarboxylic acid,[51−53] it was he who established irrevocably that the influence of a normally meta-directing group such as carboxyl does not predominate in the thiophene series and that, as a result of such substitution reactions, the major product is a 5-substituted-2-thiophenecarboxylic acid rather than a 4-substituted-2-thiophenecarboxylic acid. 2-Thiophenecarboxylic acid is nitrated as in equation (21)[48] below. The structures (I) and (II) were determined by decarboxylation and

[47] Steinkopf, Schmitt, and Fiedler, Ann., **527**, 237 (1937).
[47a] Bunnett et al., J. Am. Chem. Soc., **71**, 1493 (1949).
[48] Rinkes, Rec. trav. chim., [4] **51**, 1134 (1932).
[49] Rinkes, Rec. trav. chim., [4], **52**, 1052 (1933).
[50] Rinkes, Rec. trav. chim., [4] **52**, 538 (1933).
[51] Römer, Ber., **20**, 116 (1887).
[52] Steinkopf and Müller, Ann., **448**, 210 (1926).
[53] Steinkopf and Höpner, Ann., **501**, 175 (1933).

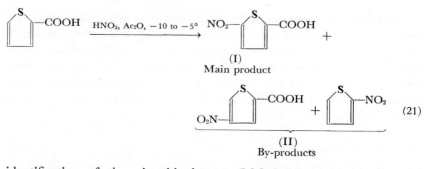

(I)
Main product

(21)

(II)
By-products

identification of the nitrothiophenes. 5-Methyl-2-thiophenecarboxylic acid is nitrated somewhat differently[48] (Eq. 22). (III) was decarboxyl-

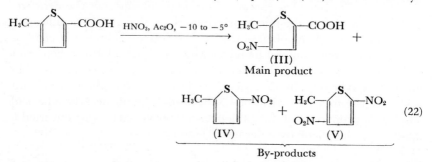

(III)
Main product

(22)

(IV)   (V)

By-products

ated and nitrated again to give (V), a known substance from the nitration of 2-methylthiophene. 4-Methyl-2-thiophenecarboxylic acid is nitrated under similar conditions as might be expected[49] (Eq. 23). VI was de-

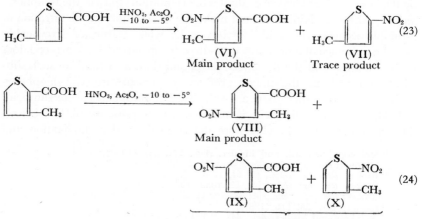

(VI)   (VII)
Main product   Trace product

(23)

(VIII)
Main product

(IX)   (X)

By-products

(24)

carboxylated and nitrated further to 2,5-dinitro-3-methylthiophene. 3-Methyl-2-thiophenecarboxylic acid gave the products shown in equation (24).[49] In the latter case, (VIII) was formed where (IX) would actually be expected. This would appear to demonstrate that the combined forces of the —COOH directing toward the 4-position and the —CH$_3$ group (in the 3-position), also directing toward the 4-position, are now evidently stronger than the directive force of the sulfur.

The nitration of 5-iodo-2-thiophenecarboxylic acid takes place normally, yielding the 4-nitro derivative.[19a]

The nitrothiophenecarboxylic acids are reduced normally to aminothiophenecarboxylic acids.[19a,37,52] The latter are stable compounds and, when diazotized, undergo typical coupling reactions.

3. Decarboxylation

Decarboxylation occurs by direct displacement of the carboxyl by a nitro group according to Rinkes,[19a,48,49] but the reaction never occurs in other than minor degree.

In general, decarboxylation of the thiophenecarboxylic acids can easily be carried out in high yields, and this technique can be conveniently applied to the preparation of certain halogen compounds not easily prepared by direct halogenation (see 3-bromothiophene, Chapter VII).

The most convenient method for the decarboxylation of the halo-2-thiophenecarboxylic acids involves replacement of the carboxyl by a mercuriacetate group[25,26,54] (Eq. 25). Another convenient method for

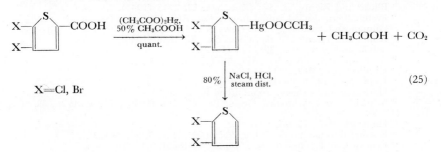

the decarboxylation is the standard copper-quinoline method[48] (Eq. 26).

$$O_2N\!-\!\!\underset{}{\overset{S}{\bigcirc}}\!\!-COOH \xrightarrow[\substack{70\%}]{Cu,\ quinoline,\ 200°} O_2N\!-\!\!\underset{}{\overset{S}{\bigcirc}} + CO_2 \qquad (26)$$

[54] Coonradt, Hartough, and Johnson, J. Am. Chem. Soc., **70**, 2564 (1948).

4-Nitro-2-thiophenecarboxylic acid yields 53% of the theoretical 3-nitro-thiophene.

D. Physical Properties of Thiophenecarboxylic Acids

With the exception of the melting points, and in a few cases the boiling points, very few physical properties of the thiophenecarboxylic acids have been determined. A comparison of the physical properties of 2- and 3-thiophenecarboxylic acids is made in Table XII-1. Table XII-2 lists the physical constants of the derivatives of 2- and 3-thiophenecarboxylic acids. Tables XII-3 and XII-4 list the physical constants of all thiophenecarboxylic acids prepared before October, 1949.

The physiological properties of the thiophenecarboxylic acids and their derivatives have received considerable attention.[37,55-59]

[55] Jaffe and Levy, *Ber.*, **21**, 3458 (1888).
[56] Barger and Easson, *J. Chem. Soc.*, **1938**, 2103.
[57] Johnson, Green, and Pauli, *J. Biol. Chem.*, **153**, 37 (1944).
[58] Steinkopf, Jacob, and Penz, *Ann.*, **512**, 136 (1934).
[59] Campaigne and Le Suer, *J. Am. Chem. Soc.*, **70**, 3498 (1948).
[60] Ostwald, *Z. physik. Chem.*, **3**, 384 (1889).
[61] Boder, *Z. physik. Chem.*, **6**, 313 (1890).
[62] Catlin, *Iowa State College J. Sci.*, **60**, 65 (1935).
[63] Loven, *Z. physik. Chem.*, **19**, 456 (1896).
[64] Stohmann and Kleber, *J. prakt. Chem.*, [2] **43**, 1 (1891).
[65] International Critical Tables, Vol. V, p. 169.
[66] Rojahn and Schulten, *Arch. Pharm.*, **264**, 384 (1926); *Chem. Abstr.*, **20**, 2857 (1926).
[67] Curtuis and Thyssen, *J. prakt. Chem.*, [2] **65**, 1 (1902).
[68] Jones and Hurd, *J. Am. Chem. Soc.*, **43**, 2422 (1921).
[69] Arndt and Eistert, Ger. Pat. 650,706 (1937); *Chem. Abstr.*, **32**, 595 (1938).
[70] Blicke and Zienty, *J. Am. Chem. Soc.*, **63**, 2945 (1941).
[71] Freudenberg, Eichel, and Leutert, *Ber.*, **B65**, 1183 (1932).
[72] Gilman and Pickens, *J. Am. Chem. Soc.*, **47**, 245 (1925).
[73] Kollof and Hunter, *J. Am. Chem. Soc.*, **62**, 1646 (1940).
[74] Scholl and Seer, *Ann.*, **394**, 174 (1912).
[75] Steinkopf and Ohse, *Ann.*, **448**, 205 (1926).
[76] Kindler, *Ber.*, **B69**, 2797 (1936).
[77] Ruffi, *Ber.*, **20**, 1740 (1887).
[78] Hartough and Conley, unpublished work.
[79] Schneider and Wilmanns, Germ. Pat. 629,196 (1936); *Chem. Abstr.*, **30**, 5051 (1936).
[80] Hantzsch, *Ber.*, **22**, 2827 (1889).
[81] Karrer, Rebmann, and Zeller, *Helv. Chim. Acta*, **3**, 261 (1919).
[82] Leuckart and Schmidt, *Ber.*, **18**, 2338 (1885).
[83] Buu-Hoï and Nguyen-Hoan, *Rec. trav. chim.*, **68**, 5 (1949).
[84] Rinkes, *Rec. trav. chim.*, [4] **54**, 940 (1935).
[85] Paal, *Ber.*, **18**, 2253 (1885).
[86] Ernst, *Ber.*, **19**, 3275 (1886).
[87] Grose and Campaigne, *J. Am. Chem. Soc.*, **71**, 3258 (1949).

TABLE XII-1. Physical Properties of 2- and 3-Thiophenecarboxylic Acids

Property	2-COOH	Ref.	3-COOH	Ref.
Melting point, °C.	129–130	1	138.4	40
Dissociation constant ($\times 10^5$) at 25°. . . .	3.02–3.42	39,60–62	7.8	63
Solubility, g./100 g. H_2O at 25°.	0.75	39	0.43	39
Heat of combustion, kcal./mole.	646	64,65	—	—

Tables XII-2 to XII-4 follow on pages 376–381.

[88] Schleicher, *Ber.*, **18**, 3018 (1885).
[89] Steinkopf and Gording, *Biochem. Z.*, **292**, 368 (1937).
[90] Backer and Stevens, *Rec. trav. chim.*, **59**, 423 (1940).
[91] Gattermann and Römer, *Ber.*, **19**, 690 (1886).
[91a] Steinkopf and Eger, *Ann.*, **533**, 270 (1938).
[92] Steinkopf and Nitschke, *Ann.*, **536**, 135 (1938).
[93] Steinkopf, *Ann.*, **513**, 281 (1934).
[94] Steinkopf and Hanske, *Ann.*, **541**, 260 (1939).
[95] Dann and Moller, *Ber.*, **80**, 23 (1947).
[96] Steinkopf, Poulsson, and Herdey, *Ann.*, **536**, 128 (1938).
[97] Justoni, *Gazz. chim. ital.*, **71**, 375 (1941); *Chem. Abstr.*, **36**, 7002 (1942).
[98] Buu-Hoï and Nguyen-Hoan, *Rec. trav. chim.*, **67**, 309 (1948).

TABLE XII-2. Carboxyl Derivatives of 2- and 3-Thiophenecarboxylic Acids

Derivative	2-COOH B.p., °C. (mm.)	2-COOH M.p., °C.	2-COOH Ref.	3-COOH B.p., °C. (mm.)	3-COOH M.p., °C.	3-COOH Ref.
Anhydride	—	62	36,66	—	54.5–56	41
Amide	—	180	2,29,33a	—	179–180	11,42
Amidoxime	—	91–92	2			
Azoimide	—	37	67			
Chloride	190 (760)	0	29,68–75	203–204 (748) 110–111 (36)	51–52	41,42 42
Ethyl ester	218 (760) 115 (25) 96 (18) 94.5 (14)	— — — —	29,68,76–78 67 24 37			
Methyl ester	—	—	—	98 (10)	—	19a
p-Bromophenacyl ester	—	—	79	—	129–130	42
Ethyl orthoester	110–120 (30)	—	79			
Propyl orthoester	140–160 (30)	—	67			
Hydrazide	—	136	68			
Hydroxamic acid	—	123–124.5				
Nitrile	192 (760) 196 (760) 77.5–78 (12)	—	2,31,33,33a,36,80,81			
Phenylurea	—	206	2	—	206	2
Acetylamide	—	135–136	33a			
Methylamide	—	142–145	33a			
Anilide	—	140	82			

Derivative	2-COOH			3-COOH		
	B.p., °C. (mm.)	M.p., °C.	Ref.	B.p., °C. (mm.)	M.p., °C.	Ref.
o-Toluidide	—	132	83			
m-Toluidide	—	105	83			
p-Toluidide	—	168	83			
m-Chloranilide	—	139	83			
p-Chloranilide	—	164	83			
o-Xylidide	—	143	83			
p-Xylidide	—	146	83			
asym-Xylidide	—	132	83			
vic-Xylidide	—	139	83			
o-Diphenylamide	—	80	83			
p-Diphenylamide	—	203	83			
α-Naphthylamide	—	210	83			
β-Naphthylamide	—	194	83			
5-Acenaphthenylamide	—	162	83			
p-Acetanilide amide	—	245	83			
2-Fluorenylamide	—	219	83			
o-Phenylenediamide	—	266	83			
Benzidine diamide	—	>315	83			
m-Tolylenediamide	—	209–210	83			
β-Phenylhydrazamide	—	177–178	83			

TABLE XII-3. Physical Constants of 2-Thiophenecarboxylic Acids

Structure: thiophene ring (S) bearing R and R′ on the ring, substituent R″ and a COOH group.

Substituent	M.p., °C	Ref.	—COOH derivative			
			Compound	B.p., °C	M.p., °C	Ref.
R″ = CH₃	148	1,13,15–18, 26,27,30, 83	chloride	218–220	—	30,83
			methyl ester	216–217	—	26
			amide	—	122–123	15,27,30
			p-diphenylamide	—	150	83
			α-naphthylamide	—	137	83
			β-naphthylamide	—	115	83
			p-toluidide	—	91	83
			p-acetanilide amide	—	185–186	83
			p-aminophenylsulfonamide	—	260–261	83
R′ = CH₃ R = CH₃	120–121 138–138.5	1,13,15,21,84 1,14,19a,21,25, 30,48,50, 85,86	chloride	102 (16)	—	83
			methyl ester	216–217	—	50
			ethyl ester	77–79 (5)	—	87
			n-propyl ester	87–89 (5)	—	87
			isopropyl ester	95–98 (5)	—	87
			n-butyl ester	87–88 (5)	—	87
			isobutyl ester	106.5–108.5 (5)	—	87
			n-amyl ester	102–105 (5)	—	87
			α-naphthylamide	116–118 (5)	192	83
R = C₂H₅	71	88				
R = n-propyl	57	77				
R = tert-butyl	124–125	1,21				
R = tert-amyl	86.5–87.5	1,21				
R = (CH₃CH₂CH₂CH(CH₃)—)	liquid, b.p. 152–155 (11)	1				

Substituent	M.p., °C.	Ref.	Compound	—COOH derivative B.p., °C.	M.p., °C.	Ref.
R = tert-octyl	122–123	21	chloride	—	80	89
R = C₆H₅—	184	89	piperidide	—	103–104	89
R = CH₃CH— / C₆H₅	99.5–101.5	21				
R = R″ = CH₃	171–172	27	amide	—	115–116	27
R′ = R″ = CH₃	207–208	27	amide	—	146–147	27
R′ = R″ = C₆H₅	222–224	90				
R″ = Cl	175–176	46				
R = Cl	146–147	1,22,47a,58,91				
R = R′ = Cl	196–197	46,47a				
R = R′ = R″ = Cl	224	58	methyl ester		83.5–84	92
R = R′ = Cl; R″ = CH₃	197–197.5	92	chloride	126–130 (14)	41–42	83
R″ = Br	190	58	amide	—	163	83
R = Br	141–142	1,22,58,83,91	m-chloroanilide	—	156	83
			p-chloroanilide	—	193	83
			o-xylidide	—	162–163	83
			α-naphthylamide	—	172	83
			β-naphthylamide	—	210	83
			p-diphenylamide	—	235–236	83
			p-acetanilide amide	—	300	83
			β-phenylhydrazamide	—	179	83
R′ = R″ = Br	180–188	58	chloride	—	39.5	45
R = R′ = Br	227–228	9,45,58,91a	methyl ester	—	80.5	45
			amide	—	167	45
R = R′ = R″ = Br	258–259	58	methyl ester	140.5 (12)	61–61.5	92
R′ = Br; R″ = CH₃	187.5–188.5	92				
R = CH₃; R′ = Br	197–198	92,93	methyl ester		—	92
R′ = CH₃; R″ = Br	225–225.5	13,92				
R = R′ = Br; R″ = CH₃	228–229	26	methyl ester		89–90	92
R = R″ = Br; R′ = CH₃	216–217	26,92				
R = CH₃; R′ = R″ = Br	224	85				

Table continued

TABLE XII-3.   Physical Constants of 2-Thiophenecarboxylic Acids (continued)

Substituent	M.p., °C.	Ref.	—COOH derivative Compound	B.p., °C.	M.p., °C.	Ref.
R″ = I	193–195	47				
R = I	133–134	19a,22,91				
R′ = I; R″ = CH₃	208–209	26				
R = CH₃; R″ = I	178.5–179	26	methyl ester	—	84–86	26
R = CH₃; R″ = I	186–188	26				
R = I; R′ = CH₃	172–173	94				
R′ = CH₃; R″ = I	215–218	25,26	methyl ester	—	75.5–76.5	26
R = R′ = I; R″ = CH₃	264.5	26	methyl ester	—	157–158	26
R = R″ = I; R′ = CH₃	240.5–242	26	methyl ester	—	112–112.5	26
R = CH₃; R′ = R″ = I	236	25				
R = CH₃; R′ = Br; R″ = I	267–268	47				
R′ = NO₂	154	48,50	methyl ester	—	100–101	48,50
R = NO₂	158	37,48,57	methyl ester	—	76	48
			nitrile	—	46–47	37
			amide	—	—	57
			ethyl ester	—	63.5–64	37,51
			chloride	146–148 (17)	52–53	37,50
			HCl·Et₂NCH₂CH₂ ester	—	118 (dec.)	37
R″ = NO₂; R″ = CH₃	137	19a	methyl ester	—	56	19a
R = NO₂; R″ = CH₃	208	49				
R = NO₂; R′ = CH₃	182	49				
R = NO₂; R′ = CH₃	180	49				
R = CH₃; R′ = NO₂	181	48	methyl ester	—	79–80	50
R = I; R′ = NO₂	201	19a	methyl ester	—	118	19a
R = C₆H₅—CH=CH, R′ = NO₂	222	50	methyl ester	—	110	50
R = R″ = NO₂	135–136	50	methyl ester	—	50–53	37
R = NH₂	—	52,95	HCl·Et₂N—CH₂CH₂ ester	—	154–157 (dec.)	37
R = CH₃CONH	272–273	37,52	ethyl ester	—	160–162	37
R = HOOC—[thiophene]—CH₂	above 300	1b				

Note: the equations in the formulas render $R'' = I$, $R = I$, $R' = I$; $R'' = CH_3$, etc. The compound $HCl \cdot Et_2NCH_2CH_2$ ester, C_6H_5—CH=CH, $R = NO_2$, $R = NH_2$, CH_3CONH, HOOC, CH_2.

TABLE XII-4. Physical Properties of 3-Thiophenecarboxylic Acids

$$R'' \underset{R'}{\overset{R}{\text{—}}} \text{—COOH}$$

Substituents	M.p., °C.	Ref.	—COOH derivative			
			Derivative	B.p., °C. (mm.)	M.p., °C.	Ref.
$R'' = CH_3$	115–117	13				
$R' = CH_3$	139	17,26				
$R = CH_3$	131–132	25				
$R = R'' = CH_3$	119–120	28,96–98	amide	144–145 (13)	133–134	28
			chloride	—	—	98
$R' = Br$	150–152	58				
$R = R'' = Br$	222	45	chloride	250–270	35.5	45
			amide	—	165.5	45
			methyl ester	—	80	45
$R = R'' = CH_3; R' = Br$	188–189	28				
$R = R'' = Br; R' = CH_3$	178.5–179	26				
$R' = I$	169–170	47				
$R = R'' = CH_3; R' = I$	199	96				
$R = R'' = I; R' = CH_3$	181–183	26				
$R = R'' = Br; R' = I$	182	47				
$R = R' = Cl$	176–177	46				
$R'' = NO_2$	147	19a	methyl ester	—	81	19a
$R'' = NO_2$	155–156	19a				
$R' = NH_2; R = (CH_2)_4COOH$	—		ethyl ester	—	97–97.5	43
$R' = NH_2; R = (CH_2)_4COOEt$	—		ethyl ester	—	43–44	43
$R' = NH_2; R = (CH_2)_3OC_6H_5$	—		ethyl ester	—	56–57	43
$R' = NHCOC_6H_5; R = (CH_2)_4COOH$	—		ethyl ester	—	155.5–157	43
$R' = NHCOC_6H_5; R = (CH_2)_4COOH$			azide	—	126.5–127.5	43a
$R' = NHCOC_6H_5; R = (CH_2)_4COOC_4H_9$			azide	—	99–100 (dec.)	43a
$R' = NH_2 \cdot HCl; R = (CH_2)_3COOH$			ethyl ester	—	99–100 (dec.)	43
$R' = NH_2 \cdot HCl; R = (CH_2)_3COOC_2H_5$			ethyl ester	—	92–94	43
$R' = NH_2 \cdot HCl; R = (CH_2)_3OC_6H_5$			ethyl ester	—	43–44	43
$R' = NH_2 \cdot HCl; R = (CH_2)_3OCH_2C_6H_5$			ethyl ester	—	163.5–164.5	43
$R' = NHCOC_6H_5; R = (CH_2)_4COOH$			ethyl ester	—	121–125	43
$R' = NHCOC_6H_5; R = (CH_2)_4COOH$			hydrazamide	—	141–142	43a
$R' = NHCOC_6H_5; R = (CH_2)_3OC_6H_5$			ethyl ester	—	98–99	43a
$R' = NHCOC_6H_5; R = (CH_2)_3OC_6H_5$			hydrazamide	—	186.5–187.5	43a
$R' = NHCOC_6H_5; R = (CH_2)_3OC_6H_5$			azide	—	108–109 (dec.)	43a
$R' = NHCOC_6H_5; R = (CH_2)_3OCH_2C_6H_5$			ethyl ester	—	65–66	43a
$R' = NHCOC_6H_5; R = (CH_2)_3OCH_2C_6H_5$			hydrazamide	—	116–117	43a
$R' = NHCOC_6H_5; R = (CH_2)_3OCH_2C_6H_5$			azide	—	62–64	43a

II. Thenoylalkanoic and Thienylalkanoic Acids

This hitherto little known class of thiophene compounds has recently received considerable attention as valuable intermediates in the preparation of antispasmodic drugs and in the preparation of thianaphthene by the Fieser method.

The thenoylalkanoic acids are usually obtained by Friedel-Crafts reactions of dibasic acid chlorides with thiophene, only a single acid chloride group reacting. These can be reduced to the thienylalkanoic acids by Clemmensen reduction. The latter are also obtained through typical malonic acid and acetoacetic ester syntheses. Thienylalkenoic acids are prepared by condensation of 2-thiophenealdehydes with malonic acid.

A. Preparation

1. 2-Thienylglyoxylic Acid (2-Thenoylformic Acid)

Peter[1] and Egli[2] prepared this compound in 1885 by alkaline potassium permanganate oxidation of 2-acetylthiophene or 2-ethylthiophene. By careful oxidation in the cold, Biedermann obtained good yields of the acid free from 2-thiophenecarboxylic acid[3] (Eq. 1). Bradley[4] reported later that this method still gave some 2-thiophenecarboxylic acid.

$$\text{COCH}_3 \xrightarrow[50\%]{\text{KOH, KMnO}_4, \text{ cold}} \text{COCOOH} \qquad (1)$$

2-(β-Isonitrosoacetyl)thiophene can be converted to the nitrile of 2-thienylglyoxylic acid in good yield. The free acid can then be obtained by acid hydrolysis of the nitrile[5] (Eq. 2).

$$\text{COCH}{=}\text{NOH} \xrightarrow[70\%]{\text{CH}_3\text{COCl, reflux}} \text{COCN} \xrightarrow[80\%]{\text{H}^+, \text{H}_2\text{O}} \text{COCOOH} \qquad (2)$$

Ruffi[6] prepared the 5-methyl-, 3-methyl-, and 5-propyl-2-thienylglyoxylic acids by oxidation of the corresponding acetyl derivatives. Peter[1] prepared the 5-nitro-2-thienylglyoxylic acid by a similar oxidation.

Fermentation of 2-thienylglyoxal with yeast gives the 2-thienylglyoxylic acid.[7]

[1] Peter, *Ber.*, **18**, 537 (1885).
[2] Egli, *Ber.*, **18**, 547 (1885).
[3] Biedermann, *Ber.*, **19**, 637 (1886).
[4] Bradley, *Ber.*, **19**, 2115 (1886).
[5] Steinkopf, *Ann.*, **540**, 14 (1939).
[6] Ruffi, *Ber.*, **20**, 1745 (1887).
[7] Fujise, *Biochem. Z.*, **236**, 241 (1931); *Chem. Abstr.*, **25**, 4898 (1931).

Another method giving the acid in fair yield employs ethyl oxalyl chloride and aluminum chloride in tetrachloroethane solvent[8-10] (Eq. 3).

$$\text{(thiophene)} + \text{ClCOCOOEt} \xrightarrow[\substack{30-50\%}]{\text{AlCl}_3,\ \text{C}_2\text{H}_2\text{Cl}_4,\ -5\ \text{to}\ 0°} \text{(2-thienyl)}-\text{COCOOEt} + \text{HCl} \qquad (3)$$

Since nitrobenzene gives highly improved yields in the acylation of thiophene with other acyl halides, it is possible that this solvent may give improved yields when employed in reaction (3).

2-Thienylglyoxylic acid crystallizes from aqueous solutions as the monohydrate. The anhydrous acid is easily obtained in a sulfuric acid desiccator.[4]

3-Thienylglyoxylic acid is unknown, but 2,5-dimethyl-3-thienylglyoxylic acid has been prepared by standard procedures.[6]

2. 2-Thenoylalkanoic Acids

A few 2-thenoylalkanoic acids are known. They are prepared by the reaction of succinic or glutaric anhydride with thiophene in the presence of aluminum chloride[11-13] (Eq. 4).

$$\xrightarrow[54\%]{\text{nitrobenzene, AlCl}_3,\ 0-5°} \text{(2-thienyl)}-\text{COCH}_2\text{CH}_2\text{COOH} \qquad (4)$$

The ethyl acyl chlorides may also be employed in the same manner as ethyl oxalyl chloride.[8-10]

The dibasic acyl dihalides are also employed, and the keto acid is formed to the exclusion of the diketone.[10,14] Effective catalysts other than the Friedel-Crafts type are clays[15] and orthophosphoric acid:[16]

$$\text{(thiophene)} + \text{ClCO(CH}_2)_4\text{COCl} \xrightarrow[35\%]{\text{H}_3\text{PO}_4,\ 50-80°,\ 4\ \text{hrs.}} \text{(2-thienyl)}-\text{CO(CH}_2)_4\text{COOH} + \text{HCl} \qquad (5)$$

Phthalyl chloride gives 3,3-bis-(2-thienyl)phthalide rather than a diketone or keto acid[15] (Eq. 6).

[8] Steinkopf and Wolfram, *Ann.*, **437**, 27 (1924).
[9] Blicke and Tsao, *J. Am. Chem. Soc.*, **66**, 1645 (1944).
[10] Papa, Schwenk, and Hankin, *J. Am. Chem. Soc.*, **69**, 3018 (1947).
[11] Feiser and Kennelly, *J. Am. Chem. Soc.*, **57**, 1611 (1935).
[12] Cagniant and Deluzarche, *Compt. rend.*, **222**, 1301 (1946).
[13] Steinkopf, Poulsson, and Herdey, *Ann.*, **536**, 132 (1938).
[14] Billman and Travis, *Proc. Indiana Acad. Sci.*, **54**, 101 (1945).
[15] Hartough, Kosak, and Sardella, *J. Am. Chem. Soc.*, **69**, 1014 (1947).
[16] Hartough and Kosak, *J. Am. Chem. Soc.*, **69**, 3093 (1947).

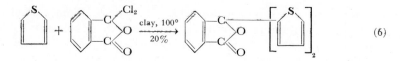

$$(6)$$

While 2-thenoylacetic acid has not been reported, its ethyl ester has been prepared by carbethoxylation of 2-acetylthiophene with diethyl carbonate[17] (Eq. 7).

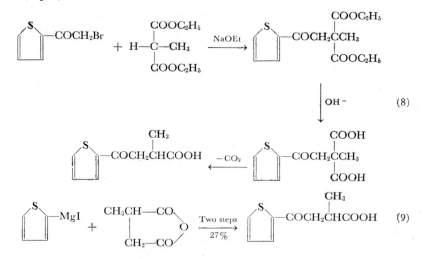

Kitchen and Sandin have prepared branched-chain thenoylalkanoic acids by way of the diethyl malonate synthesis[18] (Eq. 8). The structure of 2-methyl-3-(2-thenoyl)propanoic acid was established by condensation of methylsuccinic anhydride with thiophene by the method of Feiser and Kennelly[11] and by an independent synthesis involving the Grignard reaction (Eq. 9).

3. 2-Thienylacrylic Acid (Thiophene Isolog of Cinnamic Acid)

Two methods are available for the production of 2-thienylacrylic acid. The Perkin synthesis with 2-thiophenealdehyde and sodium acetate gives only moderate yields[19] (Eq. 10). A better method yielding the acid in

[17] Levine and Hauser, *J. Am. Chem. Soc.*, **66**, 1768 (1944).
[18] Kitchen and Sandin, *J. Am. Chem. Soc.*, **67**, 1645 (1945).
[19] Biedermann, *Ber.*, **19**, 1855 (1886).

$$\text{(thiophene)}-CHO + CH_3COONa \xrightarrow[30\%]{(CH_3CO)_2O,\ \text{reflux, 7 hrs.}} \text{(thiophene)}-CH=CHCOONa \quad (10)$$

high yields involves Knoevenagel condensation of 2-thiophenealdehyde and malonic acid in pyridine and piperidine solution[20] (Eq. 11). This

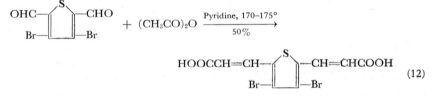

$$\text{(thiophene)}-CHO + H_2C(COOH)_2 \xrightarrow[85\%]{\text{Pyridine solvent,}\ \text{piperidine, }100^\circ} \text{(thiophene)}-CH=CHCOOH + CO_2 \quad (11)$$

synthesis has been extended to the homologs of 2-thiophenealdehyde.[20a]

In a modified Perkin type synthesis acetic anhydride was condensed with 3,4-dibromo-2,5-thiophenedialdehyde to form 3,4-dibromo-2,5-thiophenediacrylic acid[21] (Eq. 12).

$$OHC-\text{(thiophene)}-CHO\ (Br,Br) + (CH_3CO)_2O \xrightarrow[50\%]{\text{Pyridine, }170-175^\circ}$$

$$HOOCCH=CH-\text{(thiophene)}-CH=CHCOOH\ (Br,Br) \quad (12)$$

3-(2-Thienyl)-2-mercaptoacrylic acid (or 2-thienylthiopyruvic acid) is prepared as demonstrated in equation (12a).[21a]

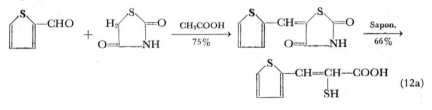

$$\text{(thiophene)}-CH=CH-COOH\ (SH) \quad (12a)$$

4. 2-Thienylalkanoic Acids

This series of acids is most conveniently prepared by the Clemmensen reduction of the corresponding 2-thenoylalkanoic acids or by reduction of the unsaturated 2-thienylalkenoic acids. Barger and Easson[20] obtained a 98% yield of 2-thienylpropanoic acid by reducing 2-thienylacrylic acid with sodium amalgam. Reduction of the 2-thenoylalkanoic acids gave yields of the order of 70%.[11-13,21b]

[20] Barger and Easson, *J. Chem. Soc.*, **1938**, 2103.
[20a] King and Nord, *J. Org. Chem.*, **14**, 405 (1949).
[21] Steinkopf, Leitsmann, Müller, and Wilhelm, *Ann.*, **541**, 260 (1939).
[21a] Libermann, Himbert, and Hengel, *Bull. soc. chim. France*, [5] **15**, 1124 (1948).
[21b] P. Cagniant, D. Cagniant, and Deluzarche, *Bull. soc. chim. France*, [5] **15**, 1083 (1948).

Low yields of a mixture of ethyl 10- and 11-(2-thienyl)undecylate are obtained by the alkylation of thiophene with ethyl undecylenate in carbon disulfide solution with aluminum chloride catalyst.[21c]   2,5-Dimethyl-thiophene also gives a mixture of ethyl 10- and 11-(2,5-dimethyl-3-thi-enyl)undecylate.   Ethyl hydnocarpate with thiophene gives an ethyl 2-thienyldihydrohydnocarpate.

2-Thienylacetic acid and its esters are conveniently prepared from 2-thenyl chloride and sodium cyanide[22,22a] (Eq. 13).   The 3-thienylacetic

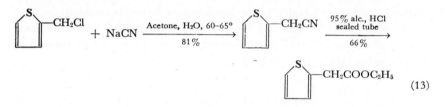

$$\tag{13}$$

acid has been prepared from 3-thenyl bromide in a somewhat similar fashion[23] and 2,5-dimethyl-3-thienylacetic acid has been prepared from the respective 2,5-dimethyl-3-thenyl chloride.[23a]   The preparation of these acids from the corresponding malonic acids is discussed in Section 5.

Phenyl-2-thienylacetic acid has been prepared from 2-benzylthiophene by metalation of the methylene moiety with potassium amide followed by carbonation.[23b]   A subsequent metalation of the corresponding car-bethoxy derivative with potassium amide followed by coupling with chloroalkylamines gives compounds with analgesic activity comparable to pethidine.

2-Thienylcyclopropanecarboxylic acid is prepared from the action of ethyl diazoacetate on 2-vinylthiophene.[23c]   1-(2-Thienyl)cyclohexane-carboxylic acid and 1-(2-thienyl)cyclopentanecarboxylic acid are pre-pared as demonstrated in equation (13a).[23d]   Various alkylaminoesters of these acids have been prepared and tested for analgesic activity.

Ethyl β-methyl-β-(2-thienyl)-glycidate has been synthesized from 2-acetylthiophene and ethyl bromoacetate[23e] (Eq. 13b).

[21c] Buu-Hoï and Xuong, *Bull. soc. chim. France*, [5] **15**, 751 (1948).
[22] Blicke and Leonard, *J. Am. Chem. Soc.*, **68**, 1934 (1946).
[22a] Blicke and Zienty, *J. Am. Chem. Soc.*, **63**, 2945 (1941).
[23] Campaigne and Le Suer, *J. Am. Chem. Soc.*, **70**, 1555 (1948).
[23a] Buu-Hoï and Nguyen-Hoan, *Rec. trav. chim.*, **68**, 5 (1949).
[23b] Brown, Cook, and Heilbron, *J. Chem. Soc.*, **1949**, S 113.
[23c] Burger *et al.*, *J. Am. Chem. Soc.*, **71**, 3307 (1949).

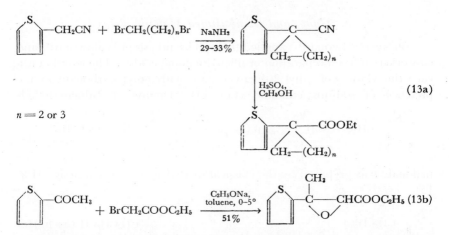

$n = 2$ or 3

(13a)

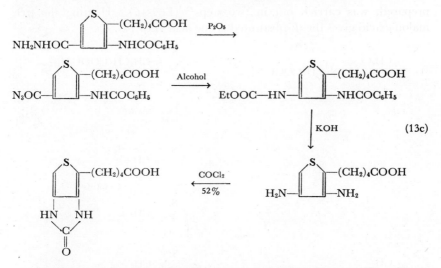

Derivatives of 3,4-diamino-2-thiophenevaleric acid are prepared by the following series of reactions[23f] (Eq. 13c). The last step involves ring closure to give 2'-oxo-3,4-imidazolo-2-thiophenevaleric acid.

(13c)

Syntheses of the thienylalanines are reported in Chapter IX. Their physiological properties are discussed in Chapter II.

[23d] Tilford *et al.*, *J. Am. Chem. Soc.*, **71**, 1705 (1949).
[23e] Kipnis, Levy, and Ornfelt, *J. Am. Chem. Soc.*, **71**, 4265 (1948).
[23f] Cheney and Piening, U. S. Pat. 2,466,004 (1949).

5. Mono- and Disubstituted Malonic Acids

Blicke and Leonard[22] applied the novel synthesis of Wallingford[24] and co-workers to the preparation of thienylmalonic acids.   The reaction is a carbethoxylation of ethyl 2-thienylacetate with ethyl carbonate in the presence of sodium ethoxide (Eq. 14).   Diethyl β-(2-thienyl)ethyl-

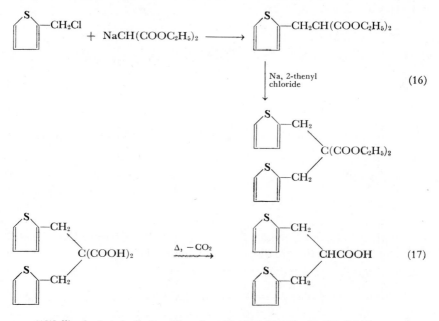

malonate was prepared by the classical diethyl malonate synthesis[22] (Eq. 15).

A further modification, in which diethyl di-(2-thenyl)malonate was prepared, was carried out in two steps[22] (Eq. 16).   Heating the free malonic acid gives the disubstituted acetic acid (Eq. 17).

[24] Wallingford et al., J. Am. Chem. Soc., **63**, 2056 (1941); **64**, 580 (1942).

Bis-2,5-(chloromethyl)thiophene reacts with diethyl malonate in the usual manner to give the disubstituted acids as shown in equation (18) following:[24a]

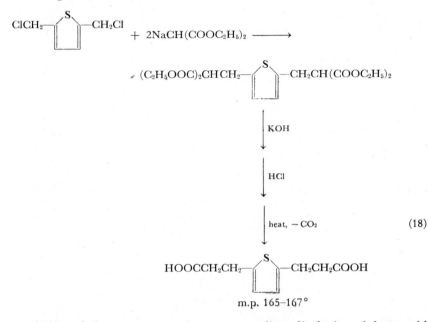

m.p. 165–167°   (18)

With ethyl acetoacetate the corresponding disubstituted keto acid ester is formed (Eq. 19).

CH₃COCHCH₂ ... CH₂CHCOCH₃ (19)

b.p. 158–160° (0.0001 mm.)

dl-2-Thenylsuccinic acid has been synthesized by a modified malonic acid synthesis[24b] (Eq. 19a). The *d*-acid is separated by means of the strychnine salt. The *l*-acid is separated from the *dl*-acid by means of dilute sulfuric acid.

[24a] Griffing and Salisbury, *J. Am. Chem. Soc.*, **70**, 3416 (1948).
[24b] Fredga and Palm, *Arkiv Kemi. Mineral. Geol.*, **A26**, No. 26 (1949); *Chem. Abstr.*, **43**, 6611 (1949).

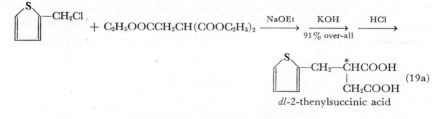

$$dl\text{-2-thenylsuccinic acid} \qquad (19a)$$

B. Chemical Properties

1. 2-Thienylglyoxylic Acid

The reactions of the carboxyl group are similar to those of pyruvic acid, and the esters and amides are formed by standard procedures.[4] The acid chloride is not reported. With phosphorus pentachloride, 2-thiophenecarbonyl chloride is formed[4] (Eq. 20). Mild oxidation with hydrogen peroxide yields 2-thiophenecarboxylic acid.[25]

$$\text{(thiophene)}-COCOOH \xrightarrow{\ PCl_5\ } \text{(thiophene)}-COCl + CO_2 \qquad (20)$$

The reactions of the keto group are complicated by the proximity of the thienyl and acid groups.   While the oxime[1,4] and phenylhydrazone[4] form normally, they decarboxylate on heating to the oxime and phenyl-hydrazone of 2-thiophenealdehyde.[19] This is also characteristic of 2-thienylglyoxylic acid which decarboxylates on being heated in a stream of carbon dioxide to 2-thiophenealdehyde in fair yield (Eq. 21). The oxime

$$\text{(thiophene)}-COCOOH \xrightarrow[50\%]{\ \text{Heat in stream of } CO_2,\ } \text{(thiophene)}-CHO + CO_2 \qquad (21)$$

of 2-thienylglyoxylic acid can be reduced with zinc and hydrochloric acid to 2-thienylglycine[4] (Eq. 22). The oxime can be dehydrated to 2-

$$\text{(thiophene)}-\underset{NOH}{\overset{}{C}}COOH \xrightarrow{\ Zn,\ HCl\ } \text{(thiophene)}-\underset{NH_2\cdot HCl}{\overset{}{C}H}COOH \qquad (22)$$

thiophenenitrile by treatment with acetic anhydride,[26] thus leading Hantzsch to predict that the oxime existed in the *syn* form.

2-Thienylglyoxylic acid gives a number of color reactions.   Egli[2] reports a "thiophene green" obtained by warming the acid with dimethyl-

[25] Holleman, *Rec. trav. chim.*, **23**, 169 (1904).
[26] Hantzsch, *Ber.*, **24**, 48 (1891).

aniline and zinc chloride. When the acid is dissolved in two parts of acetic acid and one part of sulfuric acid, a brown color results changing to blue-green and finally to deep green.[1] Addition of more sulfuric acid gives a color transition starting with violet, changing to red, then to blue, and finally to deep blue. The deep blue appears to be a final color stage and addition of more sulfuric acid causes no further change. With isatin and sulfuric acid this acid gives a blue-green color changing to blue.[27]

Reduction of 2-thienylglyoxylic acid with sodium amalgam in alcohol in the cold gives 2-thienylglycolic acid (thiophene isolog of mandelic acid)[28] (Eq. 23). The 2-thienylglycolic acid can be further reduced to 2-

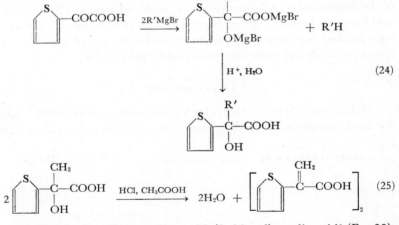

thienylacetic acid with red phosphorus and hydriodic acid. Oxidation of the glycolic acid with manganese dioxide gives 2-thiophenealdehyde.

The 2-thienylglyoxylic acid reacts with Grignard reagents to form di-substituted glycolic acids[8,9] (Eq. 24). When R′ is a methyl group the acid

may be dehydrated easily to a dimer of 2-(2-thienyl)acrylic acid[8] (Eq. 25).

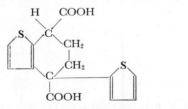

[27] Steinkopf, *Die Chemie des Thiophens.* Steinkopff, Dresden-Leipzig, 1941, p. 90.
[28] Ernst, *Ber.,* **19,** 3280 (1886).

Steinkopf and Wolfram[8] suggest a possible structure for the dimer (Eq.26).

Brubaker[29] has found that 3-(2-thienyl)acrylic acid, when esterified with glycerol or other polyhydric alcohols, gives a product that is suitable as a drying oil due to rapid drying film properties. In ether saturated with hydrogen chloride at −30 to −40° 2-(2-thienyl)acrylic acid dehydrates, and hydrogen chloride adds to the monomeric acid[8] (Eq. 27).

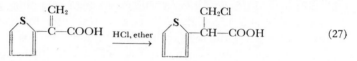

$$(27)$$

With stannous chloride and hydrochloric acid the 2-(2-thienyl)propanoic acid is formed (Eq. 28).

$$(28)$$

Various amino esters of 2-thienylalkanoic acids have been prepared and evaluated as antispasmodics.[9,30] The antispasmodic activity of some of the amino esters of 2-thienylglycolic acid and phenyl-(2-thienyl)acetic acid has been found to be comparable to that of atropine.[30] These esters have marked mydriatic action when applied to the eye of a rabbit. They also depress salivary secretions provoked by pilocarpine.

2. 2-Thienylalkanoic Acids

Only a few reactions of this class of compounds are reported. One of the most important is the ring closure of 4-(2-thienyl)butyric acid to 4-

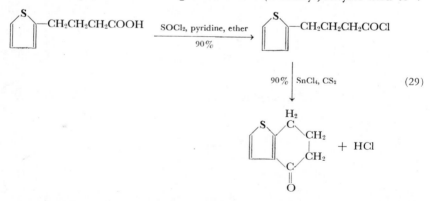

$$(29)$$

[29] Brubaker, U. S. Pat. 2,381,889 (1945).
[30] Lands and Nash, *Proc. Soc. Exptl. Biol. Med.*, **57**, 55 (1944); *Chem. Abstr.*, **39**, 557 (1944).

oxo-4,5,6,7-tetrahydrothianaphthene[11] (Eq. 29). This compound is an intermediate in the preparation of 4-hydroxythianaphthene (Eq. 30).

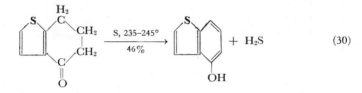

$$\xrightarrow[46\%]{S, \ 235\text{--}245°} \ + \ H_2S \qquad (30)$$

The 2-thienylpentanoic acid can be similarly ring-closed to give the thieno-(2,3-b)-suber-4-one[12] (Eq. 31).

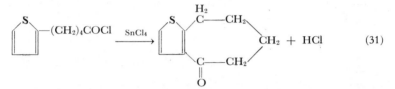

$$\xrightarrow{SnCl_4} \qquad CH_2 \ + \ HCl \qquad (31)$$

C. Physical Properties

No precise physical data other than melting and boiling points are available. Data for the thienylalkanoic and thienylalkenoic acids and

TABLE XII-5. Physical Properties of 2-Thienylglyoxylic Acid and Derivatives

Derivative	B.p., °C. (mm.)	M.p., °C.	Ref.
2-Thienylglyoxylic acid..................	—	91.5–92	1–5,7–9, 25,26
Monohydrate........................	—	52–53	4,5
Methyl ester........................	—	28.5	4
Ethyl ester..........................	264–265 (uncorr.) 115–120 (3)	Below −20	4,8,9
Oxime.............................	—	136–137	1,4,26
Nitrile.............................	95–107 (13)	51.5	5
Amide.............................	—	88	4
Methyl ester, oxime.................	—	104–105	4
Ethyl ester, oxime..................	—	122–123	4
O-Acetate of oxime..................	—	85–87	26
5-Methyl-...........................	—	80	6
3-Methyl-...........................	—	142	6
Oxime.............................	—	104	6
Phenylhydrazone.....................	—	141	6
5-Propyl-...........................	—	Oil	6
5-Nitro-............................	—	92	1
2,5-Dimethyl-3-thienylglyoxylic acid.......	—	Oil	6

TABLE XII-6. Physical Constants of Thienylalkanoic Acids and Their Derivatives

Compound	Ref.	B.p., °C. (mm.)	M.p., °C.	Derivative Compound	B.p., °C. (mm.)	M.p., °C.	Ref.
2-Thienylacetic acid	8,9,22a, 28	—	76	nitrile	115-120 (22)	—	22a
				ethyl ester	119-123 (23)	—	22
3-Thienylacetic acid	23	—	79-80	nitrile	—	—	23
2-Thienylglycolic acid	28	—	115				
2-Thienylglycine	4	—	235-240 (dec.)				
β-Methyl-β-(2-thienyl)glycidic acid	23e	—	—	ethyl ester	122-125 (2)	—	23e
3-(2-Thienyl)propionic acid	20,21b	160 (15.5)	43-45	amide	—	99-100	20
				chloride	121 (15)	—	21b
3-(2,5-Dimethyl-3-thienyl)propionic acid	23a	—	116				
4-(2-Thienyl)butanoic acid	11	130-134(15)	13.5-15				
4-(2,5-Dimethyl-3-thienyl)butanoic acid	13,23a	—	55-56				
5-(2-Thienyl)pentanoic acid	12	178 (14)	36	amide	135 (11)	118-119	12
				chloride	—	103	12
6-(2-Thienyl)hexanoic acid	21b	201 (19)	40	amide	—	83	21b
8-(2-Thienyl)nonanoic acid	21b	219 (17)	15				
11-(2-Thienyl)undecanoic acid	21b	240 (19)	—	amide	—	—	21b
CH_3 S⟨⟩—CH—CH—COOH (CH_2)	23c	—	124-125	amide	—	163-164	23c
				anilide	—	119	23c
				ethyl ester	107 (3)	—	23c
				$(C_2H_5)_2NCH_2CH_2$ ester	161 (2.5)	—	23c
S⟨⟩—C—COOH (H_2)	23d	—	145-147	nitrile	102-103 (1)	—	23d
				$(C_2H_5)NCH_2CH_2 \cdot HCl$ ester	—	140-141	23d

Compound	B.p., °C. (mm.)	M.p., °C.	Ref.	Derivative			
				Compound	B.p., °C. (mm.)	M.p., °C.	Ref.
S ring C—CH_2—CH_2—COOH	—	143–145	23d	nitrile	95–98 (0.3)	—	23d
				$(C_2H_5)NCH_2CH_2 \cdot HCl$ ester	—	118–121	23d
2-C_4H_3S C COOH $CH_2CH_2N(C_2H_5)_2$	—	—	23b	ethyl ester	155–157 (0.1)	—	23b
2-C_4H_3S C COOH C_6H_5							
C_6H_5 C $CH_2CH_2NC_4H_8O$ 2-C_4H_3S	—	—	23b	ethyl ester	185–188 (0.4)	—	23b
				ethyl ester-oxalate	—	144–145	23b
2-C_4H_3S C COOH C_6H_5	—	—	23b	ethyl ester	193–196 (0.3)	—	23b
C_6H_5 C $CHCH_2NC_4H_8O$ CH_3							
dl-2-Thenylsuccinic acid	—	156.5	24b	d-acid	—	156.5	23b
				l-acid	—	156.5	23b

their derivatives are listed in Tables XII-6–XII-9.   The physical properties and the recorded derivatives of 2-thienylglyoxylic acid are recorded in Table XII-5; the physical properties of the 2-thenoylalkanoic acids are listed in Chapter XI, Table XI-8.

TABLE XII-7. Physical Properties of Thienylacrylic Acids

| Compound | M.p., °C. | Derivative | | Ref. |
		Compound	B.p., °C. (mm.)	
2-(2-Thienyl)acrylic acid.........	—	dimer	m. 76–77	8
3-(2-Thienyl)acrylic acid.........	143–145	dimer	m. 216	8,19,20,
		ethyl ester	110–116 (3.5)	20a
3-(3-Methyl-2-thienyl)acrylic acid..	172–173	ethyl ester	121–126 (3)	20a
3-(5-Methyl-2-thienyl)acrylic acid..	165–166	ethyl ester	116–122 (5)	20a
3-(5-Ethyl-2-thienyl)acrylic acid...	102–103	ethyl ester	122–128 (2)	20a
3-(5-Propyl-2-thienyl)acrylic acid..	109–110	ethyl ester	135–140 (2)	20a
3-(5-Chloro-2-thienyl)acrylic acid..	201–203 (dec.)	—	—	a20
3,4-Dibromo-2,5-thiophenediacrylic acid........................	>350	—	—	21
3-(2-Thienyl)-2-mercaptoacrylic acid........................	188	—	—	21a

TABLE XII-8. Substituted 2-Thienylacetic Acids

$$R''—\underset{\underset{R'}{|}}{\overset{\overset{R}{|}}{C}}—COOH^a$$

Substituents	B.p., °C. (mm.)	M.p., °C.	Ref.
R = C_6H_5; R″ = $C_4H_3SCH_2$	196–197 (5)	73–74	22
R = $C_6H_5CH_2$; R″ = $C_4H_3SCH_2$	212–214 (7)	70–71	22
R = $C_6H_5CH_2CH_2$; R″ = $C_4H_3SCH_2$	224–226 (8)	Oil	22
R = 2-C_4H_3S; R″ = $C_4H_3SCH_2$	—	94–95	22
R = 2-$C_4H_3SCH_2$; R″ = $C_4H_3SCH_2$	218–219 (9)	71–72	22
R = 2-$C_4H_3SCH_2CH_2$; R″ = $C_4H_3SCH_2$	232–233 (8)	Oil	22
R = C_6H_{11}[b]; R″ = $C_4H_3SCH_2$	174–176 (3)	62–63	22
R = $C_6H_{11}CH_2$; R″ = $C_4H_3SCH_2$	205–206 (6)	54–56	22
R = $C_6H_{11}CH_2CH_2$; R″ = $C_4H_3SCH_2$	211–212 (5)	Oil	22
R = C_3H_7; R″ = $C_4H_3SCH_2$	159–162 (6)	Oil	22
R = CH_3; R′ = OH; R″ = C_4H_3S	—	111–113	8,9
Acetate	—	Oil	8
Tropinate	—	240–241	8

Table continued

TABLE XII-8 (*Continued*)

Substituents	B.p., °C. (mm.)	M.p., °C.	Ref.
R = C_6H_{11}; R′ = OH; R″ = C_4H_3S	—	125–126	9
R = $C_6H_5CH_2$; R′ = OH; R″ = C_4H_3S	—	140–142	9
R = C_6H_5; R′ = OH; R″ = C_4H_3S	—	123 (dec.)	9
R = p-$C_6H_5C_6H_4$; R′ = OH; R″ = C_4H_3S	—	129–130	9
R = α-$C_{10}H_7$; R′ = OH; R″ = C_4H_3S	—	101–102 (dec.)	9
R = 2-C_4H_3S; R′ = OH; R″ = C_4H_3S	—	93 (dec.)	9
R = C_6H_{11}; R″ = C_4H_3S	—	129–132	9
R = $C_6H_5CH_2$; R″ = C_4H_3S	—	76–78	9
R = C_6H_5; R″ = C_4H_3S	—	115–116	9
R = p-$C_6H_5C_6H_4$; R″ = C_4H_3S	—	137–139	9
R = α-$C_{10}H_7$; R″ = C_4H_3S	—	133–135	9
R = 2-C_4H_3S; R″ = C_4H_3S	—	91–94	9

[a] R″ represents either 2-C_4H_3S or 2-$C_4H_3SCH_2$.
[b] C_6H_{11} represents the cyclohexyl radical.

TABLE XII-9. 2-Thienylmalonic Acids and Their Esters

$$\begin{array}{c} R \\ \diagdown \\ C(COOR'')_2 \\ \diagup \\ R' \end{array}$$

Substituent	B.p., °C. (mm.)	M.p., °C.	Ref.
R = C_4H_3S; R″ = C_2H_5	148–151 (6)	—	22,22a
R = $C_4H_3SCH_2$; R′ = R″ = H	—	138–139	22
R = $C_4H_3SCH_2$; R″ = C_2H_5	149–152 (6)	—	22
R = $C_4H_3SCH_2CH_2$; R′ = R″ = H	—	130–131	22
R = $C_4H_3SCH_2CH_2$; R″ = C_2H_5	150–154 (4)	—	22
R = C_4H_3S; R′ = $C_4H_3SCH_2$; R″ = C_2H_5	219–223 (9)	—	22
R = $C_4H_3SCH_2$; R′ = C_6H_5; R″ = C_2H_5	174–178 (2)	—	22
R = $C_4H_3SCH_2$; R′ = $C_6H_5CH_2$; R″ = H	—	162	22
R = $C_4H_3SCH_2$; R′ = $C_6H_5CH_2$; R″ = C_2H_5	203–206 (5)	—	22
R = $C_4H_3SCH_2$; R′ = $C_6H_5CH_2CH_2$; R″ = H	—	156–157	22
R = $C_4H_3SCH_2$; R′ = $C_6H_5CH_2CH_2$; R″ = C_2H_5	226–228 (8)	—	22
R = R′ = $C_4H_3SCH_2$; R″ = H	—	166	22
R = R′ = $C_4H_3SCH_2$; R″ = C_2H_5	200–203 (3)	—	22
R = $C_4H_3SCH_2$; R′ = $C_4H_3SCH_2CH_2$; R″ = H	—	167–168	22
R = $C_4H_3SCH_2$; R′ = $C_4H_3SCH_2CH_2$; R″ = C_2H_5	203–206 (4)	—	22
R = $C_4H_3SCH_2$; R′ = C_6H_{11}; R″ = C_2H_5	201–204 (8)	—	22
R = $C_4H_3SCH_2$; R′ = $C_6H_{11}CH_2$; R″ = H	—	151–152	22
R = $C_4H_3SCH_2$; R′ = $C_6H_{11}CH_2$; R″ = C_2H_5	204–206 (6)	—	22
R = $C_4H_3SCH_2$; R′ = $C_6H_{11}CH_2CH_2$; R″ = H	—	126–127	22
R = $C_4H_3SCH_2$; R′ = $C_6H_{11}CH_2CH_2$; R″ = C_2H_5	213–214 (6)	—	22
R = $C_4H_3SCH_2$; R′ = C_3H_7; R″ = H	—	130–131	22
R = $C_4H_3SCH_2$; R′ = C_3H_7; R″ = C_2H_5	153–156 (4)	—	22

III. Thiophenepolycarboxylic Acids

This series of thiophene derivatives has received a relatively small amount of attention and there are no good methods for their preparation directly from thiophene.   Only 2,5-thiophenedicarboxylic acid has been prepared directly from thiophene in satisfactory yield.   The other thiophenepolycarboxylic acids are normally obtained in extremely low yields by oxidation of dialkylthiophenes or alkylthiophenecarboxylic acids or by ring closure methods.

The ring closure methods of Bavarian and Hinsberg yield hydroxythiophenecarboxylic acids or hydroxythiophenepolycarboxylic acids. These and other syntheses are the subject of Section IV of this chapter.

A. Preparation of the Thiophenepolycarboxylic Acids

1. Oxidation of Dialkylthiophenes

2,3- and 2,4-Dimethylthiophene have been oxidized to their respective dicarboxylic acids with alkaline permanganate but the yields, while not reported, appear to be quite low (Eq. 1).[1,2]   The oxidation of 2,5-dimethylthiophene is not reported.   3,4-Dimethylthiophene, oxidized

$$\underset{\text{CH}_3}{\overset{\text{S}}{\diagup}}\text{—CH}_3 \quad \xrightarrow{\text{KMnO}_4,\ \text{NaOH}} \quad \underset{\text{COOH}}{\overset{\text{S}}{\diagup}}\text{—COOH} \tag{1}$$

with alkaline permanganate, yields 4-methyl-3-thiophenecarboxylic acid and oxalic acid but no 3,4-thiophenedicarboxylic acid.[3]   Oxidation of thianaphthene with alkaline permanganate yielded no 2,3-thiophenedicarboxylic acid.[3]   Since the thianaphthene could not be recovered, an attempt was made to isolate an organic sulfinic or sulfonic acid.   A positive test for sulfate ion represented the only identifiable portion of the oxidation product.

2. Oxidation of Acetylalkylthiophenes and Diacetylthiophenes

3-Methyl-2-acetylthiophene has been oxidized to 2,3-thiophenedicarboxylic acid by alkaline permanganate in 14% yield.[3,4]   Schleicher oxidized 5-ethyl-2-acetylthiophene and 5-ethyl-2-heptanoylthiophene to 2,5-thiophenedicarboxylic acid by this method.[5]   Permanganate oxida-

[1] Zelinsky, Ber., 20, 2021 (1887).
[2] Grünewald, Ber., 20, 2587 (1887).
[3] Linstead, Noble, and Wright, J. Chem. Soc., 1937, 911.
[4] Gerlach, Ann., 267, 155 (1892).
[5] Schleicher, Ber., 19, 660 (1886).

tion of ⁻5-octyl-2,4-diacetylthiophene gave 5-octyl-2,4-thiophenedicarboxylic acid.[6] Oxidation of 2,5-diacetylthiophene with sodium hypochlorite gives good yields of the corresponding acid.[7] Unfortunately, the highest yield of 2,5-diacetylthiophene reported is 6% of theory.

A thiophenetricarboxylic acid has been obtained by oxidation of a mixture of isomeric dimethylacetylthiophenes.[8] Since its triethyl ester melted sharply it appears to have been a pure product and it is assumed by the present author to be the 2,3,5-isomer. All the isomeric acetylthiophenes formed by the acylation of dimethylthiophenes with the exception of 2-acetyl-3,4-dimethylthiophene, upon oxidation, yield 2,3,5-thiophenetricarboxylic acid.

3. Oxidation of Alkylthiophenecarboxylic Acids

Oxidation of 5-ethyl-2-thiophenecarboxylic acid is reported by Schleicher to give 2,5-thiophenedicarboxylic acid.[9] Yields are not reported, but adaptation of this method in the author's laboratories to the 5-(and 3-)methyl-2-thiophenecarboxylic acids has given yields averaging 30%.

Oxidation of 5-hydroxymethyl-2-thiophenecarboxylic acid gives 2,5-thiophenedicarboxylic acid.[10]

4. Wurtz and Grignard Syntheses

Bonz prepared diethyl 2,5-thiophenedicarboxylate from the reaction of ethyl chloroformate and 2,5-dibromothiophene in the presence of sodium[11] (Eq. 2).

2,5-Dichloro-3,4-thiophenedicarboxylic acid has been prepared in low yield (Eq. 3).[12] A similar reaction with 2,3,5-triiodo-4-methyl-

[6] von Schweinitz, *Ber.*, **19**, 646 (1886).
[7] Hartough and Kosak, *J. Am. Chem. Soc.*, **69**, 1012 (1947).
[8] Messinger, *Ber.*, **18**, 2302 (1885).
[9] Schleicher, *Ber.*, **18**, 3020 (1885).
[10] Cinneide, *Proc. Roy. Irish Acad.*, **B42**, 359 (1935); *Chem. Abstr.*, **29**, 7326 (1935). Cinneide lists this compound as 2,4-thiophenedicarboxylic acid, but this conclusion is extremely unlikely, since subsequent orientation studies indicate that substitution of 2-thiophenecarboxylic acid gives 5-substitution predominantly. Cinneide, however, claims the melting point of the dimethyl and diethyl esters checked those obtained in footnote 1. The original article was not consulted.
[11] Bonz, *Ber.*, **18**, 2305 (1885).
[12] Steinkopf and Kohler, *Ann.*, **532**, 250 (1937).

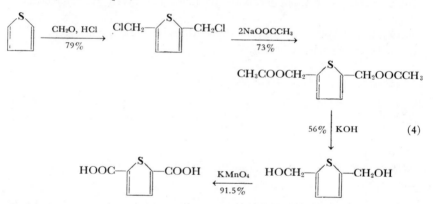

$$(3)$$

thiophene gave 3-iodo-4-methyl-2,5-thiophenedicarboxylic acid and some 3-iodo-4-methyl-2-thiophenecarboxylic acid.[13]

5. Miscellaneous Methods

Fusion of the potassium salt of 2,5-thiophenedisulfonic acid with potassium cyanide gives low yields of the 2,5-thiophenedicarbonitrile, which was hydrolyzed to the dicarboxylic acid.[14]

Exhaustive bromination of 2,5-dimethylthiophene gives 2,5-(dibromomethyl)-3,4-dibromothiophene. Hydrolysis of this compound gives the 2,5-dialdehyde, which can be subsequently oxidized to 3,4-dibromo-2,5-thiophenedicarboxylic acid.[12]

2,5-Thiophenedicarboxylic acid is prepared from thiophene in 29% over-all yield[15] (Eq. 4).

Permanganate oxidation of the polymeric amines from the reaction of thiophene, hydroxylamine salts, and formaldehyde gives high yields of 2,5-thiophenedicarboxylic acid.[16]

The tetraethyl ester of thiophenetetracarboxylic acid has been prepared by boiling diethyl acetylenedicarboxylate with sulfur.[17] The yield was not reported, but the impression is created that it is quite good (Eq. 5).

[13] Steinkopf and Hanske, *Ann.*, **532**, 243 (1937).
[14] Jaekel, *Ber.*, **19**, 190 (1886).
[15] Griffing and Salisbury, *J. Am. Chem. Soc.*, **70**, 3416 (1948).
[16] Hartough, *J. Am. Chem. Soc.*, **69**, 1355 (1947).
[17] Michael, *Ber.*, **28**, 1634 (1895).

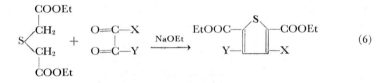

$$\begin{array}{c} \text{EtOOC—C} \\ \text{EtOOC—C} \end{array} + \begin{array}{c} \text{C—COOEt} \\ \text{C—COOEt} \end{array} \xrightarrow[\text{150–155°, 20 hrs.}]{} \quad \text{EtOOC} \begin{array}{c} \text{—COOEt} \\ \text{—COOEt} \end{array} \qquad (5)$$

The tetramethyl ester of thiophenetetracarboxylic acid was prepared in an identical fashion.

The most versatile ring closure is that of Hinsberg.[18,19] This method involves the ring closure of diethyl thiodiglycolate and an α-diketone:

$$\begin{array}{c} \text{COOEt} \\ | \\ \text{CH}_2 \\ S \\ \text{CH}_2 \\ | \\ \text{COOEt} \end{array} + \begin{array}{c} \text{O=C—X} \\ | \\ \text{O=C—Y} \end{array} \xrightarrow{\text{NaOEt}} \quad \text{EtOOC} \begin{array}{c} \text{—COOEt} \\ \text{Y——X} \end{array} \qquad (6)$$

where X and Y may be hydrogen (from glyoxal), C_6H_5 (from benzil), or parts of a fused phenanthro system (from phenanthroquinone). This method will be discussed in more detail in Section IV, since X and/or Y may also be hydroxy groups when oxalic acid, pyruvic acid, or another keto acid of this type is employed. This method has been used to prepare 3,4-diphenyl-2,5-thiophenedicarboxylic acid,[18–20] 3-methyl-4-phenyl-2,5-thiophenedicarboxylic acid,[21] 3,4-di-p-tolyl-2,5-thiophenedicarboxylic acid,[21] 3,4-di-(2-furyl)-2,5-thiophenedicarboxylic acid,[21] and 3,4-di-methoxy-2,5-thiophenedicarboxylic acid.[22]

B. Chemical Properties of the Thiophenepolycarboxylic Acids

Perhaps the lack of attempts to obtain nuclear substitution products of the polycarboxylic acids is due to the difficulties encountered in preparation. Linstead, Noble, and Wright[3] reported that 2,3-thiophenedicarboxylic acid easily formed the anhydride on treatment with acetic anhydride. It formed the diamide, imide, amic acid, the dimethyl ester, and the diethyl ester normally, but the dinitrile could be obtained only in very low yield by a method which gives a high yield of o-phthalonitrile. Esters of the thiophenepolycarboxylic acids are prepared by the action of alkyl iodides on silver salts[1] or by the action of diazomethane on acids.[3,15] Thionyl chloride gives good yields of the corresponding acid chlorides.[3,15]

[18] Hinsberg, *Ber.*, **43**, 901 (1910).
[19] Hinsberg, *Ber.*, **45**, 2413 (1912).
[20] Backer and Stevens, *Rec. trav. chim.*, **59**, 423 (1940).
[21] Backer and Stevens, *Rec. trav. chim.*, **59**, 899 (1940).
[22] Fager, *J. Am. Chem. Soc.*, **67**, 2217 (1945).

TABLE XII-10. Physical Constants of the Thiophenepolycarboxylic Acids

Compound	Ref.	M.p., °C.	Derivative	M.p., °C.	Ref.
2,3-Thiophenedicarboxylic acid............	2,3,4	270	di-Me ester	59.5	2,3
			diamide	228	3
			imide	204	3
			amic acid	238	3
			dinitrile	140	3
			anhydride	140	3
2,4-Thiophenedicarboxylic acid............	1,3,10(?)	280	di-Me ester	120	1,3
			di-Et ester	35–36	1
2,5-Thiophenedicarboxylic acid............	4,5,7,9,10, 11,14–16, 18	358.5–359.5 (dec.)	di-Me ester	148.5–149.5	5,15
			di-Et ester	50–51	5
			di-chloride	45–46	15
			di-phenyl ester	136–137	15
5-Octyl-2,4-thiophenedicarboxylic acid...........	6	185			
5-Bromo-2,4-thiophenedicarboxylic acid...........	4	240 (dec.)			
3,4-Dichloro-2,5-thiophenedicarboxylic acid........	12	314–315			
3,4-Dibromo-2,5-thiophenedicarboxylic acid........	12	317–318			

Compound	Ref.	M.p., °C.	Derivative	M.p., °C.	Ref.
2,5-Dichloro-3,4-thiophenedicarboxylic acid..........	12	subl. above 200	di-Me ester	156.5–158	13
3-Iodo-4-methyl-2,5-thiophenedicarboxylic acid......	13	—	di-Et ester	141.5–142.5	20
3,4-Diphenyl-2,5-thiophenedicarboxylic acid.........	18,20	341 (dec.)	mono-Et ester	225–226	20
			mono-Me ester	268	20
3-Methyl-4-phenyl-2,5-thiophenedicarboxylic acid...	21	190 (dec.)	di-Me ester	134.5–135	21
			di-Et ester	60.5–61.5	21
3,4-Di-(p-tolyl)-2,5-thiophenedicarboxylic acid.......	21	313 (dec.)	di-Me ester	211–212	21
3,4-Di-(2-furyl)-2,5-thiophenedicarboxylic acid.......	21	295 (dec.)	di-Me ester	128–128.5	21
3,4-Dimethoxy-2,5-thiophenecarboxylic acid..........	22	decomp. above 250	di-Me ester	180–180.5	22
3,4-Diphenylene-2,5-thiophenedicarboxylic acid......	18	decomp. above 270			
2,3,5-Thiophenetricarboxylic acid....................	8	—	tri-Me ester	118	8
2,3,4,5-Thiophenetetracarboxylic acid................	17	—	tetra-Me ester	—	17
			tetra-Et ester	126–128	—

2,3-Thiophenedicarbonitrile, when heated at 230–250° for ten min-utes with cuprous chloride, gives copper tetrathieno-[2,3-b]-porphyra-zine.[3]   The pigment is greenish blue with a faint purple luster.   It is greener than free phthalocyanine and resembles zinc phthalocyanine hydrochloride in color.   This compound can also be formed with metallic copper, but no pigment formation was noted when the dinitrile was heated with sodium amylate, litharge, or magnesium.

3,4-Disubstituted-2,5-thiophenedicarboxylic acids are easily decar-boxylated to the corresponding 3,4-disubstituted thiophenes by heating above 300°.[20,21]

C. Physical Properties of the Thiophenepolycarboxylic Acids

The melting points of these acids and their reported derivatives are in Table XII-10 on pp. 402–403.   Little else is known of their physical properties save that they are insoluble in benzene and can usually be separated from alkylthiophenecarboxylic acids in this manner.

IV. The Hydroxythiophenecarboxylic Acids

Very little is known about this class of thiophene compounds.   Their preparations usually involve quite complex ring closures.   They appear to be quite reactive compounds and for that reason their chemistry is very interesting.   Benary and Hinsberg are the chief investigators in this field. Their work constitutes the basis for most of the material in this chapter. The nomenclature of this class is so complex that structural formulas have been used generously and a section with the chemical names of the compounds listed has been given to simplify the material for the reader.

A. Hydroxythiophenecarboxylic Acids

1. Preparation by Ring Closure of Benary[1-3]

This method involves the ring closure of 2-chloroacetyl-3-amino-crotonic acid esters with potassium hydrosulfide (Eq. 1).   Saponification

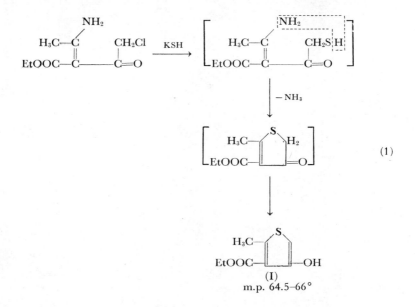

$$(1)$$

(I)
m.p. 64.5–66°

yields the free acid, m. 135°.   The reactions of this compound are given in equations (2) and (3) following.

[1] Benary, *Ber.*, **43,** 1943 (1910).
[2] Benary, Germ. Pat. 282,914 (1913).
[3] Benary and Baravian, *Ber.*, **48,** 593 (1915).

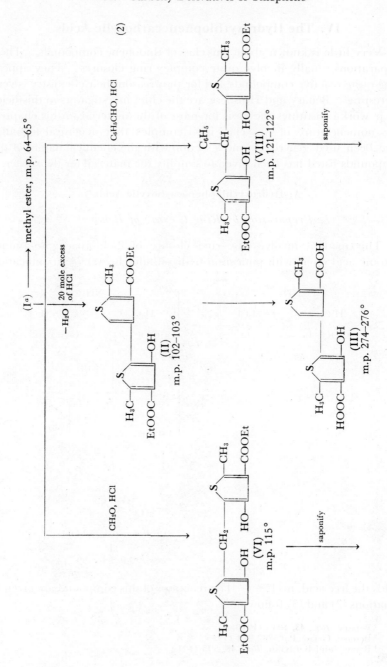

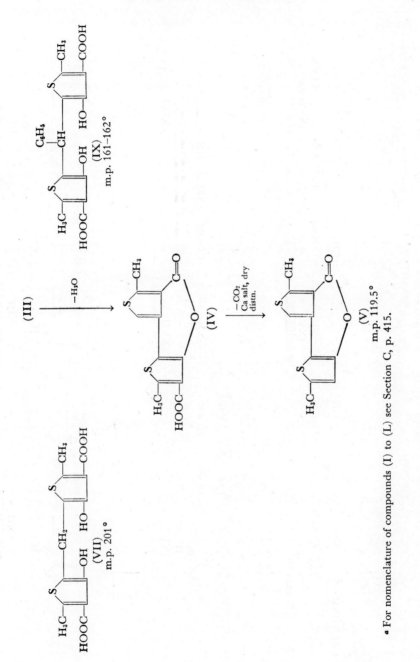

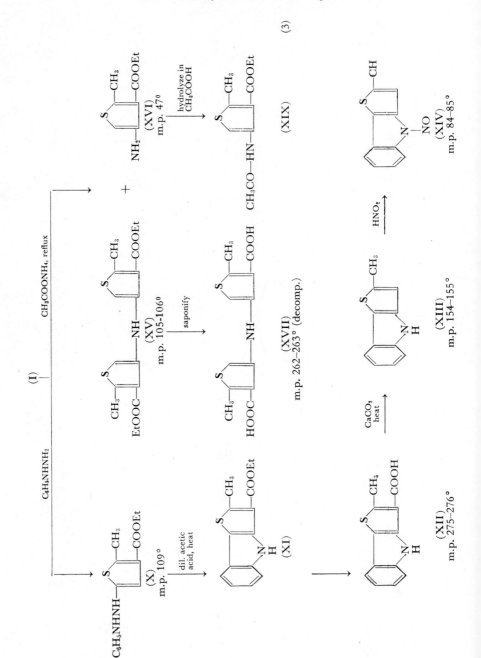

(3)

By a similar method, Benary and Silberstrom[4] prepared α-acetylthio-tetronic acid amide (XX), m.p. 233°. Saponification yielded the α-acetylthiotetronic acid (XXI), m.p. 88–89° (Eq. 4). Further studies of

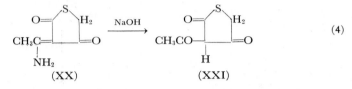

$$\text{(4)}$$

the reactions of (I) were reported by Benary and Silberstrom.[4] These are shown in the form of equations (5).

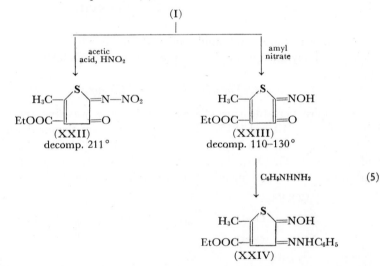

$$\text{(5)}$$

Benary and Kerckhoff[5] prepared similar derivatives by treating α-chloroacetyl-β-aminocrotonanilide with potassium hydrosulfide (Eq. 6).

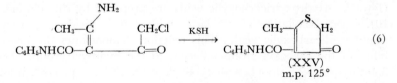

$$\text{(6)}$$

When treated with nitrous acid, (XXV) forms the anilide of ((XXII), m.p. 235° (dec.).

With ethyl chloroacetylcyanoacetate and potassium hydrosulfide a nitrile is formed which in turn reacts with benzaldehyde to give the characteristic benzylidine derivative[1] (Eq. 7).

[4] Benary and Silberstrom, *Ber.*, **52**, 1605 (1919).
[5] Benary and Kerckhoff, *Ber.*, **B59**, 2548 (1926).

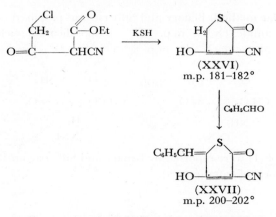

(XXVI)
m.p. 181–182°

(7)

(XXVII)
m.p. 200–202°

An intermediate compound believed to be ethyl 4-oxo-2-imino-3-thiolanecarboxylate appeared to be the precursor of (XXVI).

2. The Hinsberg Ring Closure

The most versatile ring closure of this series was first reported by Hinsberg[6,7] in 1910 and 1912.   This method involves the condensation of thiodiglycollic acid with a system represented by X—COCO—Y, where X and Y may be H, OH, alkyl, OR, phenyl, or carboxyl groups.   Condensation is effected by means of sodium ethoxide (Eq. 8).   Phenanthra-

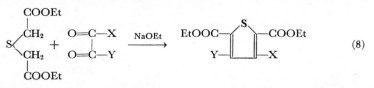

(8)

quinone has also been used in this reaction.   Ethyl pyruvate condenses to give (XXVIII), which in turn is readily decarbethoxylated to (XXIX) (Eq. 9).   Hydroxytricarboxylic acids are prepared by ring closure (Eq. 10).   Decarboxylation of the latter with caustic yields 4-hydroxy-2,3-thiophenedicarboxylic acid.   This reaction demonstrates the lower stability of the carboxyl group adjacent to the hydroxyl group.   Diethyl 3,4-dihydroxy-2,5-thiophenedicarboxylate (XXXI), m.p. 178°, is formed

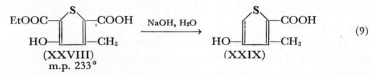

(XXVIII)
m.p. 233°

(XXIX)

(9)

⁶ Hinsberg, *Ber.*, **43**, 901 (1910).
⁷ Hinsberg, *Ber.*, **45**, 2413 (1912).

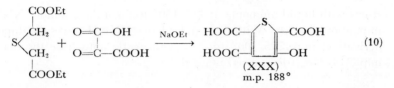

$$(10)$$

(XXX)
m.p. 188°

by this method from oxalic acid and thiodiglycollic acid.[6-10]   (XXXI) is rather difficult to saponify without decarboxylation and the best method[10] is fusion of the product with sodium acetate trihydrate at 120°.   The free acid (XXXII) melts with decomposition at 190°.

When the disodium salt of (XXXI) is treated with ethylene bromide a second ring closure can be effected in low yield[8] (Eq. 11).

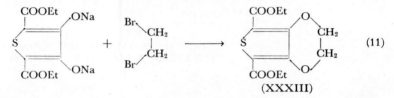

$$(11)$$

(XXXIII)

With aniline at 170° (XXXI) forms the dianilide; the latter can then be ring-closed to produce a quinoline derivative[9] (Eq. 12).   (XXXII)

$$(XXXI) + 2C_6H_5NH_2 \xrightarrow{170°}$$

$$(12)$$

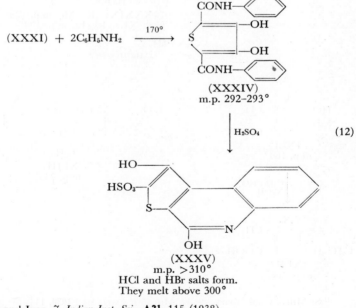

(XXXIV)
m.p. 292–293°

(XXXV)
m.p. >310°
HCl and HBr salts form.
They melt above 300°

[8] Guha and Iyer, *J. Indian Inst. Sci.*, **A21,** 115 (1938).
[9] Ghosh, *J. Indian Chem. Soc.*, **14,** 713 (1937).
[10] Turnbull, U. S. Pat. 2,453,102 (1948).

reacts with liquid ammonia at 115–130° to form the diamide (**XXXVI**), m.p. above 250°.[10]   With dimethyl sulfate (**XXXII**) gives the dimethoxy derivative, m.p. 295–300° (dec.);   with acetic anhydride the diacetate, m.p. 314–315° (dec.), was obtained.[10]

3. *Mitra-Chakrabarty-Mitra Ring Closure*[11]

Another novel method of ring closure is the reaction of diethyl acetylsuccinate with hydrogen sulfide and hydrogen chloride.   Alkoxy thiophenecarboxylic acids are obtained.   (See equations 13 and 14.)

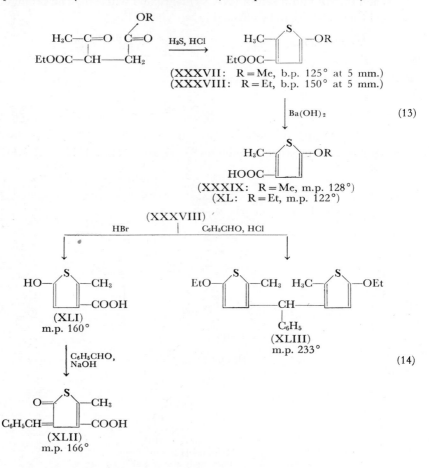

(**XXXVII**: R = Me, b.p. 125° at 5 mm.)
(**XXXVIII**: R = Et, b.p. 150° at 5 mm.)

(13)

(**XXXIX**: R = Me, m.p. 128°)
(**XL**: R = Et, m.p. 122°)

(**XLI**)
m.p. 160°

(**XLIII**)
m.p. 233°

(14)

(**XLII**)
m.p. 166°

[11] S. Mitra, Chakrabarty, S. K. Mitra, *J. Chem. Soc.*, **1939**, 1116.

4. Color Reactions

Hydroxythiophenecarboxylic acids give characteristic phenol colors with ferric chloride. This is a further indication that the enolic form of the hydroxyl group is predominant. With sulfuric acid (I) and (II) give a blue-green fluorescence. Ferric chloride gives a green coloration with (II) and with (XXV) gives a blue color reminiscent of resorcinol rather than catechol (*o*-dihydroxybenzene).

B. Hydroxylalkyl- and Hydroxyarylthiophenecarboxylic Acids

Heating of 2,5-di-(dibromomethyl)-3,4-dichlorothiophene with an excess of aqueous sodium hydroxide simultaneously effects hydrolysis and an internal Cannizzaro reaction, and 3,4-dichloro-5-(hydroxymethyl)-2-thiophenecarboxylic acid is obtained[12] (Eq. 15).

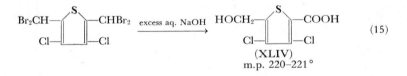

$$(15)$$

Cinneide[13] describes the preparation of the compound, "4-(hydroxy-methyl)-2-thiophenecarboxylic acid," by the procedure in which 2-thio-phenecarboxylic acid is condensed with methylolchloroacetamide (Eq. 16, p. 414). It appears that assigning the 4-position to —CH$_2$OH in (XLVIII) is not justified since it has been pointed out that the primary directive influence in 2-thiophenecarboxylic acid is toward the 5-position with only secondary direction toward the 4-position. And too from the melting point of (XLVII) it would appear that the acid is rather 2,5-thiophenedicarboxylic acid (m.p. 358.5–359.5°[14]), since the melting point of the 2,4-acid is reported to be 280°.[15]

Sawlewicz[16,17] obtained a lactone of 2,5-(*o*-hydroxyphenyl)-3,4-thiophenedicarboxylic acids by the treatment of coumarin with sulfur (Eq. 17). This author lists other derivatives of (L).

[12] Steinkopf and Kohler, *Ann.*, **532**, 279 (1937).
[13] Cinneide, *Proc. Royal Irish Acad.*, **B42**, 359 (1935); *Chem. Abstr.*, **29**, 7326 (1935).
[14] Hartough and Kosak, *J. Am. Chem. Soc.*, **69**, 1012 (1947).
[15] Linstead, Noble, and Wright, *J. Chem. Soc.*, **1937**, 911.
[16] Sawlewicz, *Roczniki Chem.*, **16**, 470 (1936); *Chem. Abstr.*, **31**, 2186 (1937).
[17] Szperl and Chmielnicka, *Roczniki Chem.*, **16**, 101 (1936); *Chem. Abstr.*, **31**, 2186 (1937).

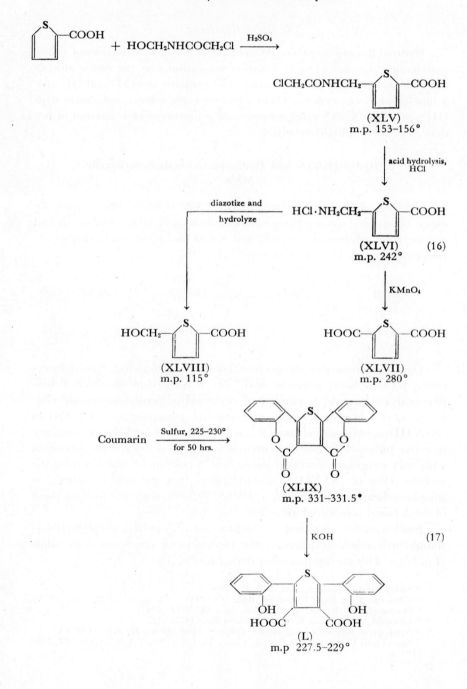

$$\text{[thiophene]}\text{—COOH} + HOCH_2NHCOCH_2Cl \xrightarrow{H_2SO_4}$$

$$ClCH_2CONHCH_2\text{—[thiophene]}\text{—COOH}$$

(XLV)
m.p. 153–156°

acid hydrolysis, HCl

$$HCl\cdot NH_2CH_2\text{—[thiophene]}\text{—COOH}$$

(XLVI)   (16)
m.p. 242°

diazotize and hydrolyze

KMnO₄

$$HOCH_2\text{—[thiophene]}\text{—COOH}$$

(XLVIII)
m.p. 115°

$$HOOC\text{—[thiophene]}\text{—COOH}$$

(XLVII)
m.p. 280°

Coumarin $\xrightarrow[\text{for 50 hrs.}]{\text{Sulfur, 225–230°}}$

(XLIX)
m.p. 331–331.5°

KOH   (17)

(L)
m.p 227.5–229°

C. Chemical Names of the Compounds Listed

(I)	Ethyl 2-methyl-4-hydroxy-3-thiophenecarboxylate.
(II)	2,3'-(3-Hydroxy-4,4'-dicarbethoxy-5,5'-dimethyl)bithiophene.
(III)	Free acid of (II).
(IV)	Lactone of (III).
(V)	Lactone of 2,3'-(3-hydroxy-4'-carboxy-5,5'-dimethyl)bithiophene.
(VI)	Bis-2,2'-(3-hydroxy-4-carbethoxy-5-methylthienyl)methane.
(VII)	Free acid of (VI).
(VIII)	Phenyl-di-(3-hydroxy-4-carbethoxy-5-methyl-2-thienyl)methane.
(IX)	Free acid of (VIII).
(X)	2-Methyl-3-carboethoxy-4-thiophenephenylhydrazine.
(XI)	4-Carbethoxy-5-methylthieno[3,2-b]indole.
(XII)	Free acid of (XI).
(XIII)	5-Methylthieno[3,2-b]indole.
(XIV)	N-Nitroso-5-methylthieno[3,2-b]indole.
(XV)	Di-(4-carbethoxy-5-methyl-3-thienyl)amine.
(XVI)	3-Amino-4-carbethoxy-5-methylthiophene.
(XVII)	Free acid of (XV).
(XIX)	3-Acetamido-4-carbethoxy-5-methylthiophene.
(XX)	α-Acetylthiotetronic acid amide.
(XXI)	α-Acetylthiotetronic acid.
(XXII)	2-Methyl-3-carbethoxy-4-oxo-5-imidonitro-2-thiolene.
(XXIII)	2-Methyl-3-carbethoxy-4-oxo-5-isonitroso-2-thiolene.
(XXIV)	2-Methyl-3-carbethoxy-4-phenylhydrazino-5-isonitroso-2-thiolene.
(XXV)	2-Methyl-3-carbanilido-4-oxo-2-thiolene.
(XXVI)	2-Oxo-3-cyano-4-hydroxy-3-thiolene.
(XXVII)	2-Oxo-3-cyano-4-hydroxy-5-benzylideno-3-thiolene.
(XXVIII)	3-Methyl-4-hydroxy-5-carbethoxy-2-thiophenecarboxylic acid.
(XXIX)	3-Methyl-4-hydroxy-2-thiophenecarboxylic acid.
(XXX)	4-Hydroxy-2,3,5-thiophenetricarboxylic acid.
(XXXI)	Diethyl 3,4-dihydroxy-2,5-thiophenedicarboxylate.
(XXXII)	Free acid of (XXXI).
(XXXIII)	2,5-Dicarbethoxythieno[3,4-b]-1,4-dioxane.
(XXXIV)	Dianilide of (XXXII).
(XXXV)	1,4-Dihydroxythieno[2,3-c]quinoline-2-sulfonic acid.
(XXXVI)	Diamide of (XXXII).
(XXXVII)	2-Methoxy-4-carbethoxy-5-methylthiophene.
(XXXVIII)	2-Ethoxy-4-carbethoxy-5-methylthiophene.
(XXXIX)	Free acid of (XXXVII).
(XL)	Free acid of (XXXVIII).
(XLI)	5-Hydroxy-2-methyl-3-thiophenecarboxylic acid.
(XLII)	2-Methyl-3-carboxy-4-benzylideno-5-oxo-2-thiolene.
(XLIII)	Phenyldi-(2-methyl-5-ethoxy-3-thienyl)methane.
(XLIV)	3,4-Dichloro-5-hydroxymethyl-2-thiophenecarboxylic acid.
(XLV)	5-(Chloroacetamidomethyl)-2-thiophenecarboxylic acid.
(XLVI)	5-(Aminomethyl)-2-thiophenecarboxylic acid hydrochloride.

(XLVII)   2,5-Thiophenedicarboxylic acid.
(XLVIII)   5-(Hydroxymethyl)-2-thiophenecarboxylic acid.
(XLIX)   2,5-Bis(2'-hydroxyphenyl)-3,4-thiophenedicarboxylic γ,γ-dilactone.
(L)   2,5-Bis(2'-hydroxyphenyl)-3,4-thiophenedicarboxylic acid.

CHAPTER XIII

Sulfur Derivatives of Thiophene

Victor Meyer first isolated thiophene from coal tar benzene by selective sulfonation. The sulfonic acid was converted to its lead salt and on dry distillation yielded thiophene. Since that time, only abbreviated studies have been made of the sulfonation, probably because thiophene is rapidly polymerized by the sulfonating medium if due precautions are not exercised. Methods producing good yields of thiophenesulfonic acids require either inert solvents or careful control of reaction temperatures.

While secondary substitution of 2-thiophenesulfonic acid appears to give mostly 5-substituted acid with a minor amount of the 4-substituted isomer, substitution of 2-thiophenesulfonyl chloride gives 4-substitution predominantly. In the case of the nitration of 2-thiophenesulfonyl chloride, about 73% of the nitro derivative is 4-nitro-2-thiophenesulfonyl chloride. Removal of the chlorosulfonyl group hydrolytically gives high yields of pure 3-nitrothiophene. It should be pointed out that this is the only proved case where 4-substitution occurs to a major extent in thiophene substituted by a typical *meta*-directing group as recognized in the benzene series. Thus, the chlorosulfonyl group is so strongly electronegative it overcomes the strong directional influence of the heterocyclic sulfur.

Work with thiophene compounds containing additional sulfur has been concentrated in relatively narrow fields by specific interests. For example, the bacteriostatic action of various nitrothienyl sulfides has led Otto Dann to a thorough study of this field. The recent availability of 3-thiophenethiol as a by-product in the thiophene synthesis has caused increased interest in a relatively new field of thiophene chemistry. The tables in this chapter, compiling the derivatives of 3-thiophenethiol, represent principally unpublished work of J. W. Brooks of the Socony-Vacuum Laboratories. Sulfones of thiophene are of recent origin and only a few references are listed below.

I. Preparation of Thiophenesulfonic Acids

1. 2-Thiophenesulfonic Acid

As mentioned above, Victor Meyer prepared thiophenesulfonic acid, in 1883, by treating coal tar benzene with 96% sulfuric acid.[1] Modifications of this procedure with pure thiophene involve the use of various inert diluents, such as the petroleum naphthas, and careful control of reaction temperatures.[2-4] Weitz prepared 2-thiophenesulfonic acid by the method of Meyer, characterized various metal salts, and studied some of the reaction variables.[5]

The simplest laboratory procedure that appears to give consistently high yields and to hold polymerization to a minimum is described by Steinkopf and Ohse.[6] Thiophene (30 g.) is added over a period of three to four minutes to 200 g. of 95% sulfuric acid previously warmed to 30°. The temperature is controlled below 40° during the thiophene addition. The reaction mixture is then quenched in ice water and the 2-thiophene-sulfonic acid is converted to its calcium salt. Calcium sulfate is filtered off. The solution is evaporated almost to dryness in order to precipitate impurities, treated with charcoal, and extracted finally with ether. The filtered and purified solution of the calcium salt is converted to the sodium salt by treatment with sodium carbonate. The yield is 69–76% of theory. The acid is best analyzed as its lead salt. Derivatives are usually prepared directly from the sodium salt. During a subsequent investigation, a small amount of 3-thiophenesulfonic acid was isolated from the mother liquors.[7]

2-Thiophenesulfonyl chloride is prepared in high yield by treatment of sodium 2-thiophenesulfonate with phosphorus pentachloride.[5,8] It can be prepared directly from thiophene with chlorosulfonic acid.[7,9,10] Treatment of the 2-thiophenesulfonyl chloride with ammonium fluoride gives 2-thiophenesulfonyl fluoride, a stable compound, b.p. 94–96° (20 mm.).[7] Fluorosulfonic acid, thionyl chloride, and thiophene give a blue solid whose analyses indicate an empirical formula of $C_{24}H_{12}S_8$.[7]

Removal of the thiophenes from coal tar aromatics or sulfur-containing petroleum stocks by V. Meyer's method[1] is still one of the most

[1] V. Meyer, *Ber.*, **16**, 1472 (1883).
[2] Biedermann, *Ber.*, **19**, 1615 (1886).
[3] Tohl, *Ber.*, **27**, 665 (1894).
[4] Hessle, U. S. Pat. 1,996,334 (1935).
[5] Weitz, *Ber.*, **17**, 792 (1884).
[6] Steinkopf and Ohse, *Ann.*, **437**, 14 (1924).
[7] Steinkopf and Höpner, *Ann.*, **501**, 174 (1933).
[8] V. Meyer and Kreis, *Ber.*, **16**, 2172 (1883).
[9] Steinkopf, Jacob, and Penz, *Ann.*, **512**, 136 (1934).
[10] Burton and Davy, *J. Chem. Soc.*, **1948**, 525.

widely employed techniques of the present day. A comparison of methods by Woods and co-workers is recommended reading.[11,12] (See also section on "Removal of Thiophene from Coal Tar and Petroleum Stocks," Chapter I.)

2. 3-Thiophenesulfonic Acid

Langer[13] first prepared this isomer by sulfonation of 2,5-dibromo-thiophene with pyrosulfuric acid. Although it is formed along with 2,5-dibromo-3,4-thiophenedisulfonic acid, the 2,5-dibromo-3-thiophene-sulfonic acid can be separated in the pure state. Subsequent reduction with 5% sodium amalgam removes the bromine groups (Eqs. 1 and 2).

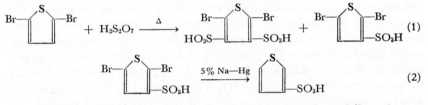

(1)

(2)

3-Thiophenesulfonyl chloride has been prepared as follows:[9]

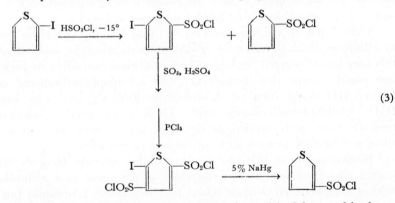

(3)

The same series of reactions was carried out with 2-bromothiophene but no cleavage of the bromine was noted.

3. Di- and Trithienylsulfonic Acids

Only two references to this field are to be found. No orientation studies have been carried out and no attempt will be made by the author to assign structures to the sulfonic acids prepared.

[11] Woods, Lowy, and Faragher, *Ind. Eng. Chem.*, **16**, 1116 (1924).
[12] Woods, Shelby, and Trusty, *Ind. Eng. Chem.*, **18**, 169 (1926).
[13] Langer, *Ber.*, **17**, 1566 (1884).

A 2,2'-dithienylsulfonic acid has been obtained by reacting 2,2'-dithienyl with twenty times its weight of concentrated sulfuric acid and warming one hour on the steam bath.[14]   Distillation of its potassium salt in the presence of ammonium chloride regenerates the original 2,2'-dithienyl.

A trithienyl, described by Renard[15] and prepared from benzene and sulfur, gave a trisulfonic acid, but the structure was not established.

4. Thiophenedisulfonic Acids

Of the four possible isomeric thiophenedisulfonic acids, it would appear that at least three are known.   So much confusion exists in the literature that it is almost impossible, without repeating portions of the experiments, to adjudge the experimental data of the various research workers.   While the work was carefully done in most cases, the investigators failed to consider the possibility of rearrangements of the halogen substituents on the thiophene nucleus, although this was indeed shown to occur in one case (see Step III, Table XIII-1).   There are several general methods for the preparation of the three known isomeric disulfonic acids.   In order to give the reader a clearer picture, a graphic outline is presented in Table XIII-1 on pages 422–423.

Were it not for the disconcerting fact that Isomer (I) was converted to a dinitrile which in turn gave 2,5-thiophenedicarboxylic acid, although this may have occurred through a rearrangement according to Jaekel,[16] one could assume that Isomer (I) was 2,4-thiophenedisulfonic acid. Isomer (II) could then be 2,5-thiophenedisulfonic acid and Isomer (III) 3,4-thiophenedisulfonic acid.   Until more precise orientation methods have been applied, it does not appear that one can assign structures to these isomers with any degree of certainty.

Kazitsyna found that the pyridine-sulfur trioxide complex when heated with thiophene at 100° for eight to ten hours gave a disulfonic acid of thiophene (Kazitsyna stated that it was the 2,4-isomer, but no proof was given).[18]

It is unfortunate that Steinkopf and co-workers[9] did not reduce their 3,4-dibromo-2,5-thiophenedisulfonic acid to an authentic 2,5-thiophenedisulfonic acid and prepare an authentic dichloride and diamide.

[14] Nahnsen, *Ber.*, **17**, 2197 (1884).
[15] Renard, *Compt. rend.*, **112**, 49 (1891).
[16] Jaekel, *Ber.*, **19**, 184 (1886).
[17] Langer, *Ber.*, **18**, 553, 1114 (1885).
[18] Kazitsyna, *Vestnik Moskov. Univ.*, **1947**, No. 3, 109–111;   *Chem. Abstr.*, **42**, 3751 (1948).

There would be less likelihood in this case, than in any other of the sulfonations in steps III and IV, for rearrangement of the halo atoms.

Only isomer (IIIA) can be nitrated; the other two isomeric disulfonyl-chlorides do not react with nitric acid.[7]

5. Sulfonation of Alkyl- and Arylthiophenes

The alkylthiophenes may be sulfonated directly and the methods used for thiophene are applicable. 3-Methylthiophene has been sulfonated recently[18a] by the method of Steinkopf and Hopner.[7] The 3-methylthiophenesulfonic acid is presumably the 2-isomer, but the structure was not verified. 5-Methyl-2-thiophenesulfonic acid was prepared by replacement of the acetyl group in 2-acetyl-5-methylthiophene by the sulfonic acid group[18b] (see following section). The 2,4- and 2,5-dimethylthiophenes form mono- and disulfonic acids with sulfuric acid.[9,19]

Renard reported that a disulfonic acid of a phenylthiophene could be obtained by warming the parent compound with sulfuric acid at 50-60°.[20] Nahke[20a] reported that dithienylphenylmethane could be sulfonated to give a trisulfonic acid, but the structure of the product was not determined.

6. Sulfonation of Acylthiophenes

Krekeler,[21,22] Schleicher,[23] and Muhlert[18b] observed independently and almost simultaneously, that replacement of an acyl group by the sulfonic acid group was a standard reaction (Eq. 4). When R was an

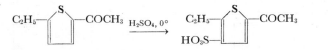

$$R\text{—}\underset{S}{\fbox{ }}\text{—COCH}_3 \quad \xrightarrow{\text{H}_2\text{SO}_4,\ \text{heat}} \quad R\text{—}\underset{S}{\fbox{ }}\text{—SO}_3\text{H} + \text{CH}_3\text{COOH} \qquad (4)$$

ethyl group disulfonic acids were formed.[23] The reaction, if carried out in the cold, will also give nuclear sulfonation without cleavage of the acyl group[23] (Eq. 5).

$$\text{C}_2\text{H}_5\text{—}\underset{S}{\fbox{ }}\text{—COCH}_3 \quad \xrightarrow{\text{H}_2\text{SO}_4,\ 0°} \quad \text{C}_2\text{H}_5\text{—}\underset{\text{HO}_3\text{S}}{\underset{S}{\fbox{ }}}\text{—COCH}_3 \qquad (5)$$

[18a] Challenger, Miller, and Gibson, J. Chem. Soc., **1948,** 769.
[18b] Muhlert, Ber., **19,** 1620 (1886).
[19] Keiser, Ber., **29,** 2560 (1896).
[20] Renard, Compt. rend., **109,** 699 (1889).
[20a] Nahke, Ber., **30,** 2033 (1897).
[21] Krekeler, Ber., **19,** 676 (1886).
[22] Krekeler, Ber., **19,** 2627 (1886).
[23] Schleicher, Ber., **19,** 660 (1886).

TABLE XIII-1. Formation of Three Isomeric Thiophenedisulfonic Acids

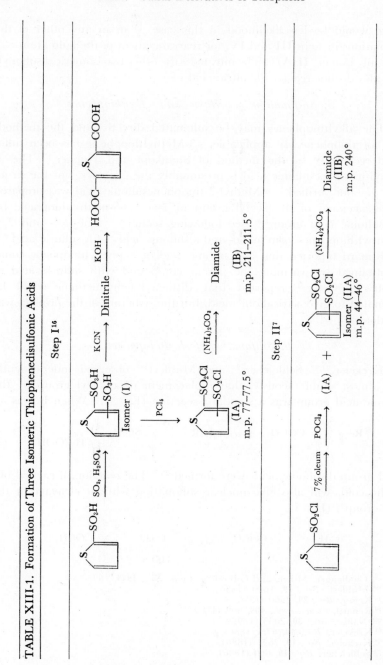

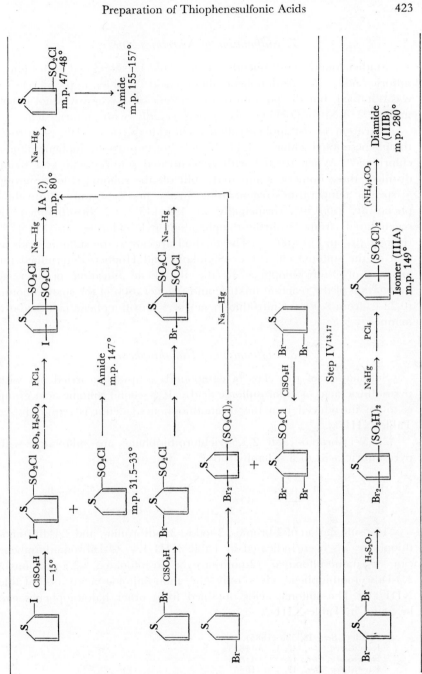

7. Sulfonation of Nitrothiophenes

Stadler found that 2-nitrothiophene could be sulfonated with fuming sulfuric acid.   2-Nitrothiophenesulfonic acid (amide, m.p. 172–173°) was obtained, but the position of the sulfonic acid group was not determined.[24] 3-Nitrothiophene also reacts rapidly with sulfuric acid.[7]

Nitration of 2-thiophenesulfonyl chloride gives 64–73% 4-nitro-2-thiophenesulfonyl chloride and 27–36% of 5-nitro-2-thiophenesulfonyl chloride.[7, 10] When treated with concentrated sulfuric acid and steam distilled, these isomeric compounds split off the sulfonyl chloride group at specific temperatures regenerating, in the first case, pure 3-nitrothiophene at 130–150° (principally at 135–145°). 2-Nitrothiophene is regenerated from 5-nitro-2-thiophenesulfonyl chloride at 150–175° (principally at 150–160°).   The method applies to the sulfonic acids as well as the sulfonyl chlorides. Steinkopf and Höpner[7] determined the amount of 3-nitrothiophene in the thiophene nitration product by sulfonation of the reaction mixture and regeneration of the small amount (0.22 g. from 8.0 g. of nitrothiophene) of 3-nitrothiophene in the above manner.

8. Sulfonation of Halothiophenes

Sulfonation of this class of compounds is usually carried out with pyrosulfuric acid or chlorosulfonic acid.   If a second sulfonic acid group is to be introduced into the bromothiophenes, oleum is required (see Table XIII-1).

2,3,5-Tribromo- and 2,3,5-trichlorothiophene are sulfonated with pyrosulfuric acid to a sulfanhydride[25–27] (Eq. 6).

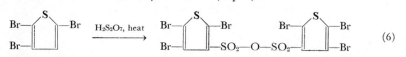

$$(6)$$

The sulfonation of 2-bromo-, 2-iodo-, 2,5-dibromo-, and 2,4-dibromo-thiophene has been indicated in Table XIII-1.   3,4-Dibromothiophene can be monosulfonated (2-position) or disulfonated (2,5-positions).[9] 2,3-Dibromothiophene gives only the monosulfonic acid[9] (see Table XIII-1).   The sulfonic acids obtained from other halothiophenes can be found in Table XIII-2.

[24] Stadler, *Ber.*, **18,** 536 (1885).
[25] Rosenberg, *Ber.*, **18,** 1773 (1885).
[26] Rosenberg, *Ber.*, **18,** 3027 (1885).
[27] Rosenberg, *Ber.*, **19,** 650 (1886).

Tohl and Schultz[28] studied the effect of concentrated and fuming sulfuric acid on various bromothiophenes. The results are given in equations (7)–(11).

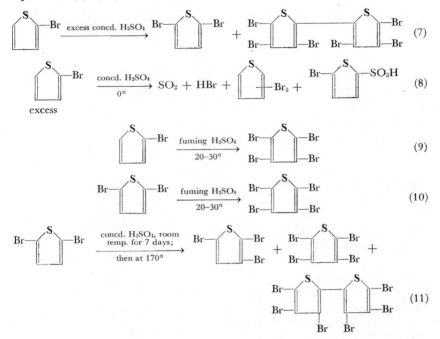

$$(7)$$

$$(8)$$

$$(9)$$

$$(10)$$

$$(11)$$

3-Methyl-2-bromothiophene is normally sulfonated in the 5-position with chlorosulfonic acid.[29]

Replacement of halogen atoms by the sulfonic acid group in the 2-acetamidothiophene series has been established recently[30] (Eq. 12).

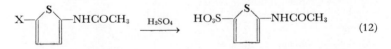

$$(12)$$

II. Properties of Thiophenesulfonic Acids

In general, not much is known about the chemical reactions of the thiophenesulfonic acids. They are best converted to the sulfonyl chlorides by the action of phosphorus oxychloride or phosphorus penta-

[28] Tohl and Schultz, *Ber.*, **27**, 2834 (1894).
[29] Steinkopf and Jacob, *Ann.*, **515**, 273 (1935).
[30] Hurd and Priestley, *J. Am. Chem. Soc.*, **69**, 859 (1947).

TABLE XIII-2. Physical Constants of the Derivatives of Thiophenesulfonic Acids

Compound	Sulfonyl chloride, m.p., °C.	Ref.	Amide, m.p., °C.	Ref.
2-Thiophenesulfonic acid..............	32–33 b.p. 123–125 (14 mm.) Sulfonyl fluoride b.p. 94–96 (20 mm.)	5,7,10, 11	141–142, 147 Methylamide 71–72	8,9,13 7
5-Chloro-2-thiophenesulfonic acid......	28	33		
4,5-Dichloro-2-thiophenesulfonic acid...	55–56	33		
3,4,5-Trichloro-2-thiophenesulfonic acid.	55–57	33		
3-Bromo-2-thiophenesulfonic acid......	—	—	163–164	34
5-Bromo-2-thiophenesulfonic acid......	44–46	9	144	9
3,4-Dibromo-2-thiophenesulfonic acid..	118	9		
4,5-Dibromo-2-thiophenesulfonic acid..	80	9	146–147	9
5-Iodo-2-thiophenesulfonic acid........	51–52	9	165	9
4-Nitro-2-thiophenesulfonic acid........	48 b.p. 147–152 (2 mm.)	10 7	164	10
5-Nitro-2-thiophenesulfonic acid........	Liquid, b.p. 130–134 (0.9 mm.)	10	136	10
2-Nitro-x-thiophenesulfonic acid........	—	—	172–173	24
5-Amino-2-thiophenesulfonic acid......	—	—	133 (dec.)	10
5-Acetamido-2-thiophenesulfonic acid...	—	—	—	30
3-Thiophenesulfonic acid..............	43, 47–48	9,13	148, 155–157	9,13
2,5-Dibromo-3-thiophenesulfonic acid..	32–33	27	146.5–147	17
2,4,5-Tribromo-3-thiophenesulfonic acid	126	27		
Thiophenedisulfonic acids (Table XIII-1)				
Isomer (I)......................	77–77.5, 80	7,9,16	211–211.5	7,16
Isomer (II)......................	44–46	7	240	7
Isomer (III)......................	149	13,17	280	13,17
3,4-Dibromo-2,5-thiophenedisulfonic acid............................	169	9		
2,4-Dibromo-3,5-thiophenedisulfonic acid............................	157	9		
2,5-Dibromo-3,4-thiophenedisulfonic acid............................	219–220	17,27	>270 Dianilide 198–200	9,13, 17 9
5,-Iodo-2,4-thiophenedisulfonic acid....	87–88	9		
2-Nitro-3,4-thiophenedisulfonic acid....	148	7		
3-Methyl-2(?)-thiophenesulfonic acid...	Liquid, b.p. 98–99 (0.5 mm.)	18a	146	18a
5-Methyl-2-thiophenesulfonic acid......	Liquid	18b	78–80	18b
4,5-Dimethyl-2-thiophenesulfonic acid..	—	—	137–139	9
2,5-Dimethyl-3-thiophenesulfonic acid..	—	—	135	17
4-Bromo-5-methyl-2-thiophenesulfonic acid............................	—	—	150–151	35
5-Bromo-4-methyl-2-thiophenesulfonic acid............................	—	—	142	29
2-Methyl-3,4-thiophenedisulfonic acid..	138–139	35		
2,5-Dimethyl-3,4-thiophenedisulfonic acid............................	146	9		
2,4-Dimethyl-3,5-thiophenedisulfonic acid............................	74	9		
5-Bromo-2-methyl-3,4-thiophenedisulfonic acid	174 (syn form) 189 (anti form)	35 35	300 dec.(syn) 300 dec.(anti)	35 35

chloride on the respective alkali salts.   They form derivatives in the manner of their benzene isologs.   The free acids are very deliquescent, have an acrid odor, and are highly corrosive.

The thiophenesulfonyl chlorides, like benzenesulfonyl chloride, are capable of undergoing Friedel-Crafts reactions, giving thienyl-sulfones with aromatic compounds.[10]   (See Section VIII below.)   With phenylmagnesium bromide, 2-thiophenesulfonyl chloride yields di-phenylsulfoxide instead of the expected 2-thienylphenylsulfone.[31]

The 4- and 5-nitro-2-thiophenesulfonamides are reduced catalytically with Raney nickel to give the respective aminothiophenesulfonamides.[10] Apparently, the molecule is stable enough when substituted with the sulfonic acid group to prevent poisoning of the Raney nickel (Eq. 13).

$$O_2N-\underset{}{\overset{S}{\bigcirc}}-SO_2NH_2 \xrightarrow[\text{hydrogen, no pressure}]{\text{Raney nickel, 20–30°,}} H_2N-\underset{}{\overset{S}{\bigcirc}}-SO_2NH_2 \tag{13}$$

Meyer and Stadler[32] were unable chemically to reduce nitrothiophene-sulfonic acid to the aminothiophenesulfonic acid with ammonium sulfide. A transient fuchsin red color was observed during the reductions.

The physical properties of the derivatives of the thiophenesulfonic acids are listed in Table XIII-2.

III. 2-Thiophenesulfinic Acid

2-Thiophenesulfinic acid, the only known member of this series, has been prepared by the action of zinc dust in water or alcohol[2,36] or of sodium sulfite[10,37] on 2-thiophenesulfonyl chloride.   The product is very deliquescent and is obtained in a crystalline form, m.p. 72–73°, in a vacuum desiccator.   It is unstable and decomposes slowly when stored at room temperature.

IV. 2-Thiophenesulfenyl Chloride

Burton and Davy[10] attempted to prepare this compound by the action of chlorine on 2,2′-dithienyl disulfide in chloroform.   The product obtained could not be condensed with resorcinol to obtain derivatives similar to those obtained with benzenesulfenyl chloride and the authors considered it doubtful that the preparation had succeeded.

[31] Burton and Hu, *J. Chem. Soc.*, **1949**, 258.
[32] Meyer and Stadler, *Ber.*, **17**, 2778 (1884).
[33] Steinkopf and Kohler, *Ann.*, **532**, 250 (1937).
[34] Steinkopf, *Ann.*, **543**, 128 (1940).
[35] Steinkopf, *Ann.*, **513**, 281 (1934).
[36] Weitz, *Ber.*, **17**, 800 (1884).
[37] Cymerman and Lowe, *J. Chem. Soc.*, **1949**, 1666.

V. Thiophenethiols

2-Thiophenethiol was discovered by V. Meyer and Neure in the alkali-soluble portion resulting from the preparation of thiophene from succinic acid and phosphorus pentasulfide.[38] Biedermann[2] prepared the same compound by zinc dust reduction of 2-thiophenesulfonic acid. It forms the acetate with acetyl chloride, the 2,2'-dithienyl disulfide, and the methyl-2-thienyl thioether with methyl iodide in the presence of alkali.[38]

3-Thiophenethiol occurs in the tars produced by the reaction of sulfur and butane in the current semicommercial thiophene process.[39] Its formation apparently results from a primary reaction of the C_4 unit at the 2-carbon. Subsequent ring closure is then effected, leaving a compound containing a C—S— linkage at 3-carbon of thiophene. The hypothesis that thiophenethiol formed in a primary reaction was established when thiophene failed to react with sulfur or hydrogen sulfide under conditions simulating those for the preparation of thiophene from butane and sulfur.[40] There are many possible mechanisms for the reaction. One of the more likely is presented in equation (14).

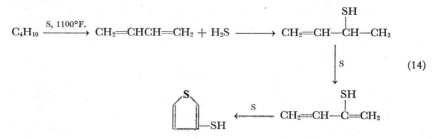

The properties of 2- and 3-thiophenethiol are quite similar. They have equally bad odors. They polymerize on storage to dimeric substances which, in the case of the 3-isomer, can be pyrolyzed in part to give the original material. They decompose on distillation, even *in vacuo*, and are best purified by steam distillation.

Caesar[41] prepared an authentic sample of 3-thiophenethiol by adding sulfur to the Grignard reagent (Eq. 15). Caesar[41] also studied

[38] Meyer and Neure, *Ber.*, **20,** 1756 (1887).
[39] Rasmussen, Hansford, and Sachanen, *Ind. Eng. Chem.*, **38,** 376 (1946).
[40] Rasmussen, Socony-Vacuum Laboratories, unpublished work.
[41] Caesar, Socony-Vacuum Laboratories, unpublished work.

the properties of the compound and found it to exist in both the thione and thiol forms (compare with the hydroxythiophenes, Chapter X). In neutral and basic solutions the thiol form predominates, but in acid the thione form is present in large amount.

Derivatives of 3-thiophenethiol, prepared by Brooks,[42] are listed in Tables XIII-3 and XIII-4. In general, these compounds were prepared by the standard procedures used with mercaptans. Tables XIII-3 and XIII-4 summarize this work and give the catalysts, yields, and the physical constants of many of the derivatives. Caesar[41] found that 3-thiophenethiol could be polymerized with formaldehyde in the presence of a basic catalyst such as sodium hydroxide to give a Bakelite-type resin. Otherwise, ring substitution is very difficult, as would be predicted from the properties of thiophenol. With formaldehyde, ammonium chloride or hydroxylamine hydrochloride, and 3-thiophenethiol, white crystalline amine hydrochlorides separate from the reaction mixture.[45] The structure of these products was not established other than to ascertain that ring substitution had not occurred.

Although the preparation and physical constants of 2-thenylthiol has not been reported, Kipnis and Ornfelt[46] have described its reaction with D-glucose to give D-glucose-2-thenylmercaptal (m.p. 130–131°). These same authors describe the conversion of 2-thenyl chloride to the 2-thenylisothiouronium chloride (m.p. 160–161°) and conversion of this material to 2-(thiophene-2′-methylthio)-4-methyl-6-hydroxypyrimidine:[47]

$$\text{(15a)}$$

[42] J. W. Brooks, Socony-Vacuum Laboratories, unpublished work.
[43] Unpublished work of J. W. Brooks, Socony-Vacuum Laboratories, Paulsboro, New Jersey.
[43a] This compound was originally prepared by E. E. Reid of the Johns Hopkins University.
[44] Condensation in each case was catalyzed by anhydrous hydrogen chloride. Uncatalyzed, the reaction gave only hemiketals and hemiacetals.
[45] Hartough and Schick, unpublished work.
[46] Kipnis and Ornfelt, *J. Am. Chem. Soc.*, **71**, 2270 (1949).
[47] Kipnis and Ornfelt, *J. Am. Chem. Soc.*, **71**, 2271 (1949).

TABLE XIII-3. 3-Thienyl Sulfides and Thioesters from 3-Thiophenethiol[43]

R	3-Thiophenethiol Condensed with	Condensing agent	% yield	B.p., °C. (mm.)	M.p., °C.	n_D^{25}	d_4^{20}
$(CH_3)_2CH-$	$(CH_3)_2CHCl$	KOH	79	65–66 (3)	—	1.5532	1.0742
$(CH_3)_3C-$	$(CH_3)_2C=CH_2$	BF₃-etherate	78	65–67 (1)	—		
$CH_3(CH_2)_5CH(CH_3)-$	1-Octene	Activated clays	—	108–111 (1)			
$(CH_3)_3C-CH_2-C(CH_3)_2-$	Diisobutylene	BF₃-etherate	76	102–110 (1.5)	—	1.5356	1.0140
Nonyl-	Mixed nonenes	BF₃-etherate	52	105–110 (1)	—	1.5403	1.0261
Dodecyl-	Triisobutylenes	BF₃-etherate	60	174–176 (8)	—	1.5343	
$CH_3(CH_2)_{13}-$	$CH_3(CH_2)_{13}-Cl$	KOH	80	—	44–45		
$CH_2=CH-CH_2$	$CH_2=CH-CH_2Cl$	KOH	86	50–54 (0.4)	—	1.5964	1.1541
α-Pinyl-	α-Pinene	BF₃-etherate	55	118–122 (0.7)	—	1.5720	1.0923
$C_6H_5CH_2CH(CH_3)-$	$C_6H_5CH_2CH_2Cl$	KOH	81	—	37–38		
$C_6H_5CH(CH_3)-$	Styrene	None	67	120–122 (0.5)	—	1.6168	1.1591
$2,4-(NO_2)_2-C_6H_3-$	2,4-Dinitrophenyl chloride	KOH	Good	—	133		
$-CH_2COOH$	$ClCH_2COOH$	KOH	61	—	51.5–52.5 (56[18a,38])		
$-(CH_2)_{10}COOH$[43a]	$CH_2=CH-(CH_2)_8-COOH$	None	—	—	84		

R	3-Thiophenethiol Condensed with	Condensing agent	% yield	B.p., °C. (mm.)	M.p., °C.	n_D^{25}	d_4^{20}
—CHCOOH —CH₂COOH CH₃	Maleic anhydride	None	72	—	130–131		
—CH—CH₂CHO	Crotonaldehyde	None	63	122 (0.8)	—		
—CH₂COCH₃	Chloroacetone	KOH	71	100 (0.3)	—		
—CH₂CH₂OH	ClCH₂CH₂OH	KOH	72	125 (1)	—		
—CH₂CH₂—S—3-C₄H₃S	ClCH₂CH₂Cl	KOH	97	—	54–55		
—(CH₂)₄—S—3-C₄H₃S	Cl(CH₂)₄Cl	KOH	87	—	62–63		
—CH₂OCH₂—S—3-C₄H₃S	ClCH₂OCH₂Cl	KOH	85	—	40–41		
—(CH₂)₂O(CH₂)₂—S—3-C₄H₃S	(ClCH₂CH₂)₂O	KOH	82	191–193 (0.5)	33		
—(CH₂)₂S(CH₂)₂—S—3-C₄H₃S	(ClCH₂CH₂)₂S	KOH	—	—	53–55		
—CH₂—CHOCH₂CH₃ S—3-C₄H₃S	ClCH₂CHClOCH₂CH₃	KOH	—	—	Liquid		
—CH₂CH₂OC₆H₅	ClCH₂CH₂OC₆H₅	KOH	93	—	47–48		
—COCH₃	CH₃COCl	None	78	84–86 (1)	41.5–43		
—COC₆H₅	C₆H₅COCl	Pyridine	—	—	69–70		
—CO—2-C₄H₃O	2-C₄H₃OCOCl	Pyridine	70	—	51–52		
—P(S—3-C₄H₃S)₂	PCl₃	KOH	51	—	71.5–73		
—PS(S—3-C₄H₃S)₂	PSCl₃	KOH	61	—	76.5–78		
—PO(S—3-C₄H₃S)₂	POCl₃	KOH	51	—	Solid		
—S—3-C₄H₃S	I₂	—	84	—	Liquid		
—S—S—3-C₄H₃S	SCl₂	KOH	71.5	—	Liquid		
—S—S—S—3-C₄H₃S	S₂Cl₂	KOH	93.7	—	Liquid		

3-(2-Thienyl)-2-mercaptoacrylic acid has been prepared by the saponification of 5-(2-thenal)-thiazolone.[48] The compound appeared to exist in both the enol and the keto form (3-(2-thienyl)-thiopyruvic acid).   It melts at 188°.

Another derivative somewhat related to this class of compounds, 5-(2-thienyl)-2-imino-1,3-oxathiolane (m.p. 140–141°), is prepared from 2-vinylthiophene[49] (Eq. 15b).   5-(5-Chloro-2-thienyl)-2-imino-1,3-oxa-thiolane (m.p. 145°) was also prepared from 5-chloro-2-vinylthiophene.

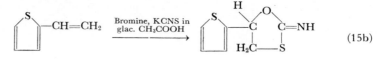

$$(15b)$$

TABLE XIII-4. 3-Thienyl Mercaptals and Mercaptols[43, 44]

Compound, mercaptal or mercaptol of	% yield	B.p., °C. (mm.)	M.p., °C.
Butyraldehyde	58	173–176 (2)	—
Furfuraldehyde	80	—	Liquid
Benzaldehyde	73	—	Liquid
Hydrocinnamaldehyde	70	—	Liquid
Acetone	84	148–153 (1)	—
2-Acetylthiophene	79	—	85–86
Benzophenone	80	—	152

Pyrolysis of the "thiophene tars" from the commercial process[39] gives a compound, $C_4H_4S_3$, 3-thiophenethiol and thiophene. $C_4H_4S_3$ is believed from infrared spectrogram studies to be a 3,4-substituted thiophene, but no mercapto groups could be detected.   It can be reduced to 3-thiophenethiol with zinc dust and hydrochloric acid.[41]   The compound forms a dipotassium mercaptide slowly in alcohol but shows no mercapto groups in the standard silver nitrate method (acidic medium) for determination of mercaptans and does not display any acidity in electrometric titration.   The compound can thus be considered to exist in the tautomeric forms of 3,4-thiophenedithiol and 3,4-thiolanedithione, the latter structure accounting almost exclusively for the neutral material (Eq. 16).   This compound could form by a mechanism similar to that

$$(16)$$

[48] Liberman, Himbert, and Hengl, *Bull. soc. chim. France*, [5] **15**, 1124 (1948).
[49] Emerson and Patrick, *J. Org. Chem.*, **13**, 729 (1948).

postulated for the formation of 3-thiophenethiol.   However, it is to be remembered that thiophenethiols dimerize upon standing and that the 3-thiophenethiol dimer can be pyrolyzed to give some thiophene and the 3-thiophenethiol.   The "thiophene tars"[39] are fairly consistent in analyzing for $(C_4H_4S_2)_2$, the empirical formula of the 3-thiophenethiol dimer. Pyrolysis of these tars gives thiophene, 3-thiophenethiol, and 3,4-thiolane-dithione.   It is likely then that the dimer is one of the major constituents of the "thiophene tars," is an "inter-dimer," and pyrolyzes into the three above-mentioned compounds by loss of the central ring (Eq. 17).

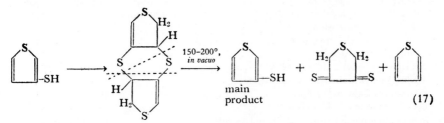

$$(17)$$

Challenger and Harrison have reduced thieno[3,2-b]-thiophene to 2-ethyl-3-thiophenethiol with sodium in alcohol[50] (Eq. 18).   This is the only alkylthiophenethiol listed in the literature.

$$(18)$$

VI. Thienyl and Thenyl Sulfides

Sulfides of thiophene were originally observed as by-products in the ring closure of the dialkyl esters of succinic acid with phosphorus tri-sulfide[51] (Eq. 19).   Alkyl thienyl sulfides are formed by treatment of the

$$(19)$$

sodium mercaptides with alkyl iodides,[38] or by the action of olefins on thiophenethiol in the presence of boron trifluoride etherate or activated clays.[42]   (See Table XIII-3.)   Some very reactive olefins such as styrene react with 3-thiophenethiol to give the sulfides in the absence of catalysts.[41]

[50] Challenger and Harrison, *J. Inst. Petroleum Technol.*, **21**, 135 (1935).
[51] Steinkopf and Leonhardt, *Ann.*, **495**, 166 (1932).

TABLE XIII-5. Thiophenethiols and Miscellaneous Derivatives[62]

Compound	B.p., °C.	M.p., °C.	Ref.
2-Thiophenethiol	166	—	38
2,2'-Dithienyl disulfide	—	55–56	18a,38, 41
Methyl 2-thienyl sulfide	186	—	38,51
Ethyl 2-thienyl sulfide	196–197	—	51
Phenyl 2-thienyl sulfide	155–157	—	10
2-Thienyl thioacetate	230–232	—	38
2-Thienylthioacetic acid	—	61–62	18a
Ethyl 2-thienylthioacetate	138 (20 mm.)	—	18a
2-Thienylthioacetamide	—	92–93	18a
o-Carboxyphenyl 2-thienyl sulfide	—	195–197	61
4-Nitrophenyl 2-thienyl sulfide	—	62	10
2,4-Dinitrophenyl 2-thienyl sulfide	—	119	52
4-Nitrophenyl 5-nitro-2-thienyl sulfide	—	130–133	53
Bis-(5-nitro-2-thienyl) sulfide	—	104–106	54
Bis-(5-acetamido-2-thienyl) sulfide	—	248–252	54
4-Acetamidophenyl 5-nitro-2-thienyl sulfide	—	174–176	53
4-Aminophenyl 5-nitro-2-thienyl sulfide	—	98–100	53
Bis-(3,5-dinitro-2-thienyl) sulfide	—	196–198	53
Bis-(5-acetamido-2-thienyl) disulfide	—	218–221 (dec.)	54
3-Thiophenethiol	171.1 (760)	—	43,55
2-Ethyl-3-thiophenethiol	195–197 (760)	—	50
3-Thienylthioacetic acid	—	50.5–51	18a
3-Thienylthioacetamide	—	115.5–116	18a
3-Thienylthioacetanilide	—	118–118.5	18a
o-Carboxyphenyl 3-thienyl sulfide	—	191	56
o-Carboxyphenyl 2,5-dimethyl-3-thienyl sulfide	—	198	57
2,4-Dinitrophenyl 3-thienyl sulfide	—	133	41
3,4(?)-Thiolanedithione	121–123 (2)	—	43,58
Ethyl 2-thenyl sulfide	66–69 (3)	—	59
Isobutyl 2-thenyl sulfide	89–91 (3.5)	—	59
n-Hexyl 2-thenyl sulfide	106–109 (2)	—	59
Benzyl 2-thenyl sulfide	120–121 (1.5)	—	59
Di-(2-thenyl) sulfide	129–131 (1.5)	—	59
Ethyl 3-(2-thenylmercapto)propionate	126 (1)	—	59
Cyanoethyl 2-thenyl sulfide	127–130 (2.5)	—	59
2-Thenyl thioacetate	56–60 (2)	—	60
2-Thenyl thiopropionate	79–83 (2)	—	60
2-Thenyl thiobenzoate	155 (2.5)	—	60
2-Thenyl 2'-thiofuroate	—	55	60

[52] Bost, Turner, and Norton, *J. Am. Chem. Soc.*, **54**, 1985 (1932).
[53] Dann and Moller, *Chem. Ber.*, **82**, 76 (1949).
[54] Dann and Moller, *Chem. Ber.*, **80**, 23 (1947).
[55] 3-Thiophenethiol is a straw-colored liquid, $d_{25}^{25} = 1.251$, $n_D^{20} = 1.6157$.

The most convenient method of characterizing 2- and 3-thiophenethiols is the reaction of the respective sodium mercaptides with 2,4-dinitrochlorobenzene.[41,52] The melting points of the isomers are listed in Table XIII-5. The monoiodothiophenes and 2,5-diiodothiophene react with the sodium mercaptide of thiosalicyclic acid to give thienyl thioethers.[56,57,61] Burton and Davy[10] reported that 2-iodothiophene failed to react with sodium 2,4-dimethoxyphenyl mercaptide. Dann and Moller[54] reported that 5-nitro-2-iodothiophene reacted with thiourea to form 5,5'-dinitro-2,2'-dithienyl sulfide (Eq. 20). This reaction also took place to a lesser extent with potassium thiocyanate. 5,5'-Diacetamido-

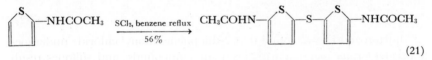

$$O_2N-\underset{\quad}{\overset{S}{\bigcirc}}-I \xrightarrow[57\%]{\text{thiourea, acetone, reflux}} O_2N-\underset{\quad}{\overset{S}{\bigcirc}}-S-\underset{\quad}{\overset{S}{\bigcirc}}-NO_2 \tag{20}$$

2,2'-dithienyl sulfide is formed by boiling 2-acetamidothiophene with sulfur dichloride in benzene solvent.[54] 5,5'-Diacetamido-2,2'-dithienyl disulfide is formed in a similar reaction with sulfur monochloride (S_2Cl_2):

$$\underset{\quad}{\overset{S}{\bigcirc}}-NHCOCH_3 \xrightarrow[56\%]{SCl_2, \text{ benzene reflux}} CH_3COHN-\underset{\quad}{\overset{S}{\bigcirc}}-S-\underset{\quad}{\overset{S}{\bigcirc}}-NHCOCH_3 \tag{21}$$

The physical constants of thienyl sulfides and the thiophenethiols are listed in Table XIII-5. In addition to this heterogeneous compilation, Tables XIII-3 and XIII-4 deal specifically with some unpublished work on 3-thiophenethiol.[43]

Thenyl sulfides are prepared by the interaction of thenyl chloride and sodium mercaptides.[59] 2-Thenyl 2-cyanoethyl sulfide and 2-thenyl ethyl crotonyl sulfide are prepared by the addition of 2-thenyl sodium mercaptide to acrylonitrile and ethyl acrylate, respectively.[59] 2-Thenyl mercaptan reacts with acyl halides in pyridine solution to give high yields of 2-thenyl thioesters.[60]

VII. Thienyl Disulfides

2,2'-Dithienyl disulfide was first reported by Meyer and Neure[38] as a by-product from the ring closure of succinic acid with the sulfides of

[56] Steinkopf and Schmitt, *Ann.*, **533**, 264 (1938).
[57] Steinkopf, Poulsson, and Herdey, *Ann.*, **536**, 128 (1938).
[58] 3,4-Thiolanedithione; $d_{25}^{25} = 1.446$, $n_D^{30} = >1.70$. It is a deep red liquid.
[59] Kipnis and Ornfelt, *J. Am. Chem. Soc.*, **71**, 3571 (1949).
[60] Kipnis, Levy, and Ornfelt, *J. Am. Chem. Soc.*, **71**, 3570 (1949).
[61] Steinkopf, Schmitt, and Fiedler, *Ann.*, **527**, 237 (1937).
[62] Tables **XIII-3** and **XIII-4** list additional derivatives of 3-thiophenethiol.

phosphorus. When 2-thiophenesulfonyl chloride is reduced stepwise first with hydriodic acid in glacial acetic acid and then with sodium thiosulfate, 2,2′-dithienyl disulfide is produced in 60–70% yield.[18a] Impure 3,3′-dithienyl disulfide has also been prepared by this method[18a] and by the action of iodine on 3-thiophenethiol[42] (see Table XIII-4). Subsequent reduction of these disulfides gave the respective 2- and 3-thiophenethiols which were not isolated but used in basic solution for further reaction.[18a]

VIII. Thienyl Sulfones and Sulfoxides

Dann and Moller prepared 5,5′-dinitro-2,2′-dithienyl sulfone by oxidizing the corresponding sulfide with potassium permanganate[53,54] (Eq. 22). Other sulfones prepared by this method are listed in Table XIII-6.

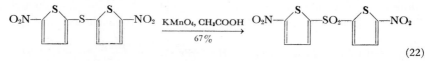

$$\text{(22)}$$

Burton and Davy[10] found that 2-thiophenesulfonyl chloride undergoes a Friedel-Crafts reaction with aromatic compounds, and sulfones result directly (Eq. 23).

$$\text{(23)}$$

A series of alkyl 2-thienyl sulfones have been synthesized by reacting sodium 2-thiophenesulfinate with alkyl halides.[37] The 4-nitrobenzyl 2-thienyl sulfone was also prepared by this method.

Phenyl 2-thienyl sulfoxide, m.p. 69–70°, has been prepared by the oxidation of phenyl 2-thienyl sulfide with 30% hydrogen peroxide at ordinary temperatures in acetic acid[10] (Eq. 24).

$$\text{(24)}$$

2-Thiophenesulfinic acid has been reduced to di-(2-thienyl) di-sulfoxide (m.p. 46–47°) by means of hydrogen iodide[37] (Eq. 25).

$$\text{(25)}$$

TABLE XIII-6. Thienyl Sulfones

Compound	B.p., °C. (mm.)	M.p., °C.	Ref.
Methyl 2-thienyl sulfone....................	—	47	10,37
Ethyl 2-thienyl sulfone......................	120.5 (2.5)	—	37
n-Propyl 2-thienyl sulfone...................	153–154 (6.5)	—	37
n-Butyl 2-thienyl sulfone....................	163–165 (3)	—	37
n-Pentyl 2-thienyl sulfone...................	162–163 (2)	—	37
n-Hexyl 2-thienyl sulfone....................	160 (2)	—	37
Phenyl 2-thienyl sulfone.....................	—	123	10
2,4-Dimethoxyphenyl 2-thienyl sulfone........	—	128–129	10
2,5-Dihydroxyphenyl 2-thienyl sulfone........	—	186	10
4-Nitrophenyl 2-thienyl sulfone..............	—	139	10
4-Nitrobenzyl 2-thienyl sulfone..............	—	177	37
Bis-(5-nitro-2-thienyl) sulfone...............	—	158–159	54
4-Nitrophenyl 5-nitro-2-thienyl sulfone........	—	193–195	53
4-Acetamidophenyl 5-nitro-2-thienyl sulfone...	—	190–191.5	53
4-Aminophenyl 5-nitro-2-thienyl sulfone.......	—	158–159	53

IX. Mercaptals and Mercaptols of Thiophene

Table XIII-4 lists various mercaptals and mercaptols derived from 3-thiophenethiol. These were prepared by standard procedures with gaseous hydrogen chloride as catalyst.

2-Acetylthiophene condenses with ethylene mercaptan with considerable heat evolution to give high yields of 2-methyl-2-(2′-thienyl)-1,3-dithiacyclopentane[63] (Eq. 26). 2-Phenyl-2-(2′-thienyl)-1,3-dithia-

$$(26)$$

cyclopentane, m.p. 52–53°, was prepared similarly.[63]

[63] Meisel, Hartough, and Reid, unpublished work. 2-Methyl- and 2-phenyl-2-(2′-thienyl)-1,3-dithiacyclopentane were prepared by condensing ethylene mercaptan with 2-acetylthiophene and 2-benzoylthiophene, respectively, with gaseous hydrogen chloride.

CHAPTER XIV

Metal and Miscellaneous Metalloid Derivatives of Thiophene

Introduction

A considerable amount of research has been carried out with this class of thiophene compounds. For the most part, interest in these compounds has been in intermediates, and the thienylmagnesium halides, the thienylsodiums, and the thienylmercuric salts have been widely used for this purpose. Most of this work has been concentrated on thiophene mercury salts of which Steinkopf has been the foremost investigator. A major portion of the work on the mercurial and arsenical derivatives of thiophene has been directed toward an extensive study of fungicidal, bactericidal, and bacteriostatic properties. To summarize generally, activity of these compounds in these respects does not differ markedly from that of their benzene isologs.

While the Grignard derivatives have received the widest attention in synthetic thiophene chemistry, it is predicted that lithium and particularly sodium will eventually replace magnesium compounds. Magnesium derivatives require the isolation of an intermediate bromo- or iodothiophene. In some cases, a considerable amount of research or a multiple synthesis is required prior to the preparation of the Grignard reagent. Transmetalation with Grignard agents is known but has not been studied to any extent. Transmetalations with alkyllithium and alkyl- and arylsodiums are established reactions and are very convenient from a synthetic standpoint. A thorough study of the transmetalation reaction with Grignard reagents would be a worthy contribution to synthetic thiophene chemistry.

In this chapter, all metals and nonmetallic elements such as phosphorus, tellurium, silicon, etc. (with the single exception of sulfur which appears in the previous chapter), are included. Typical nonmetals such as the halogens and nitrogen are dealt with separately under specific chapter headings.

439

I. Derivatives of Thiophene Containing Alkali Metals

A. Lithium

Lithium does not react with 2-chlorothiophene in ether to produce 5-chloro-2-thienyllithium under conditions that produce high yields of 5-chloro-2-thienylsodium.[1] Nor does it react with 2-chlorothiophene in benzene to form 2-thienyllithium. However, it can be formed in high yield[2] (Eq. 1). This compound can be carbonated to 2-thiophenecar-

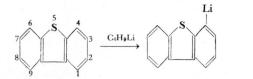

$$\text{(1)}$$

boxylic acid or it can react with trimethylchlorosilane to produce 2-thienyltrimethylsilane in 75% yield.[2] (See silane derivatives below.)

Butyllithium reacts anomalously with dibenzothiophene to give the 4-substituted derivative rather than the anticipated 2-substituted derivative[3] (Eq. 2). Carbon dioxide gives 4-dibenzothiophenecarboxylic acid.

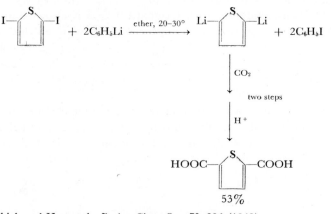

$$\text{(2)}$$

When the 4-lithium derivative is treated with ethylmagnesium halide and oxygen, a 33% yield of the 4-hydroxydibenzothiophene is obtained.

In the presence of phenyllithium, 2-iodo- and 2,5-diiodothiophene undergo a lithium-iodine exchange[4] (Eq. 3). 2-Thiophenecarboxylic

$$\text{(3)}$$

53%

[1] Schick and Hartough, *J. Am. Chem. Soc.*, **70**, 286 (1948).
[2] Benkeser and Currie, *J. Am. Chem. Soc.*, **70**, 1780 (1948).
[3] Gilman and Jacoby, *J. Org. Chem.*, **3**, 108 (1938).
[4] Campaigne and Foye, *J. Am. Chem. Soc.*, **70**, 3941 (1948).

acid is obtained in 58% yield (admixed with some benzoic acid) when 2-iodothiophene is employed. Campaigne and Foye[4] cite a private communication from G. B. Bachmann reporting that butyllithium causes replacement by lithium of at least one α-chlorine in 2,5-dichloro- and 2,3,4,5-tetrachlorothiophene.

B. Sodium

Schorigin first produced low yields of 2-thienylsodium in 1910 by the reaction of thiophene with sodium and diethylmercury.[5] Later, Gilman and Breuer[6] were able to prepare 2-thienylsodium and 5-methyl-2-thienylsodium by the action of sodium on thiophene or 2-methylthiophene in the presence of difurylmercury or dibenzylmercury, but the yields showed no marked improvement over those of Schorigin.[5]

Recently, it has been found that 2-thienylsodiums are easily prepared by a transmetalation procedure which consists of adding an alkyl or aryl halide, e.g., ethyl chloride or bromobenzene, to a mixture of sodium amalgam and thiophene or an alkylthiophene[7,8] (Eq. 4). Sodium

$$R-\underset{S}{\text{(thiophene)}} \xrightarrow[\substack{60-85\%}]{\text{NaHg, RX, ether reflux}} R-\underset{S}{\text{(thiophene)}}-Na \; + \; RH \qquad (4)$$

amalgam was required in the case of thiophene (R = H) but in other cases was unnecessary (R = CH_3 or tert-butyl). Its use, however, improved the yields about 20%. With 3-methylthiophene an anomalous substitution occurred and only the derivatives of 4-methyl-2-thienyl-sodium were obtained[7] (Eq. 5).

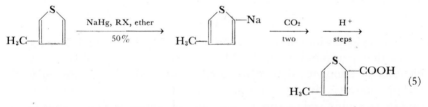

$$H_3C-\underset{S}{\text{(thiophene)}} \xrightarrow[50\%]{\text{NaHg, RX, ether}} H_3C-\underset{S}{\text{(thiophene)}}-Na \xrightarrow[\text{two}]{CO_2} \xrightarrow[\text{steps}]{H^+} \quad H_3C-\underset{S}{\text{(thiophene)}}-COOH \qquad (5)$$

In benzene and other inert solvents, except diethyl ether, the direct reaction of sodium and 2-chlorothiophene takes place at temperatures above 60° with the formation of 2-thienylsodium in yields above 80%

$$\underset{S}{\text{(thiophene)}}-Cl \; + \; 2Na \xrightarrow[84\%]{\text{benzene, 60-80°}} \underset{S}{\text{(thiophene)}}-Na \; + \; NaCl \qquad (6)$$

[5] Schorigin, Ber., **43**, 1938 (1910).
[6] Gilman and Breuer, J. Am. Chem. Soc., **56**, 1123 (1934).
[7] Schick and Hartough, J. Am. Chem. Soc., **70**, 1645 (1948).
[8] Schick and Hartough, J. Am. Chem. Soc., **70**, 1646 (1948).

of theory[1] (Eq. 6). The high yields are effected by use of 20–50% sodium amalgam as a dust. A convenient preparation of sodium amalgam sand is described in the Appendix.

The most surprising reaction of sodium or sodium amalgam with thiophene compounds takes place with the 2-halothiophenes in ether.[1] The hydrogen at the 5-position appears to be sufficiently acidic to react vigorously with the sodium to produce a 2-halo-5-thienylsodium. Sodium amalgam raises the yield from 70 to 92% of theory when 2-chlorothiophene is employed (Eq. 7). Carbonation of these compounds produces

$$X-\underset{S}{\text{[thiophene]}}-H + Na(NaHg) \xrightarrow{\text{ether, 35–39°}} X-\underset{S}{\text{[thiophene]}}-Na + \tfrac{1}{2}H_2 \quad (7)$$

the 5-halo-2-thiophenecarboxylic acids. 2-Chloro-5-thienylsodium reacts with ethylene oxide to produce 5-chloro-2-thienylethanol and appears to undergo typical Grignard reactions, although the reactions have not been generally studied.

Carbonation of thienylsodiums appears to be a nearly quantitative reaction and, to date, this method is the most convenient known for the production of 2-thiophenecarboxylic acids.

The thienylsodiums are ether-insoluble, brown to black solids. They are oxidized rapidly by air with evolution of light and heat much as is Raney nickel. They do not, however, burst into flame spontaneously. They appear to undergo typical Grignard reactions with ketones, aldehydes, ethylene oxide,[7] alkyl halides, and carbon dioxide or carbon disulfide to give the characteristic products anticipated from the thienylmagnesium halides.

C. Potassium

Thienylpotassium has not been reported. Schick and Hartough[1] found that potassium reacted with 2-chlorothiophene in ether, but no identifiable thiophene derivative could be isolated upon treatment with carbon dioxide. Instead, a product resembling an unsaturated mercaptan was obtained. This compound was unstable and polymerized upon contact with air. Apparently potassium caused ring scission, probably by attachment at the sulfur rather than at the 5-carbon.

II. Magnesium Derivatives of Thiophene

Magnesium forms typical Grignard reagents with 2-iodothiophene and 2-bromothiophene. 2-Chlorothiophene reacts slowly or not at all. 3-Bromothiophene in its lack of reactivity is similar to 2-chlorothiophene, but 3-iodothiophene readily undergoes the reaction. Transmetalation with other Grignard reagents apparently takes place, since a carbonated mixture of thiophene and ethylmagnesium bromide gives only 2-thiophenecarboxylic acid.[9] The yield was not reported (Eq. 8).

$$\text{(thiophene)} + C_2H_5MgBr \longrightarrow \text{(thiophene)}-MgBr + C_2H_6 \tag{8}$$

The reactivity of 3-substituted halothiophenes is enhanced by the addition of molecular amounts of methyl iodide, methyl bromide, or ethyl bromide.[10,11] Under these conditions, 3-bromothiophene reacts smoothly with magnesium. Presumably there is a halogen-magnesium exchange of the type of lithium-halogen exchange reported by Campaigne and Foye.[4] This method has been used extensively by Steinkopf and co-workers[12-16] for the preparation of many halothiophenes difficult

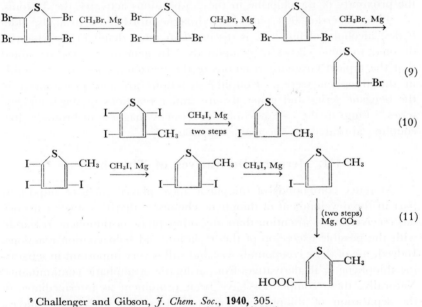

[9] Challenger and Gibson, *J. Chem. Soc.*, **1940**, 305.
[10] Steinkopf, Jacob, and Penz, *Ann.*, **512**, 136 (1934).
[11] Grignard, *Compt. rend.*, **198**, 625 (1934).
[12] Steinkopf, *Ann.*, **513**, 281 (1934).
[13] Steinkopf, Schmitt, and Fiedler, *Ann.*, **527**, 237 (1937).
[14] Steinkopf and Jacob, *Ann.*, **515**, 273 (1935).
[15] Steinkopf and Hanske, *Ann.*, **527**, 264 (1937).
[16] Steinkopf and Hanske, *Ann.*, **532**, 236 (1937).

or impossible to prepare by direct halogenation (for specific details, see chapters on chlorination, bromination, and iodination). The two-step equations (9–11), *i.e.*, the Grignard reaction and subsequent hydrolysis, illustrate the general method.

Formation of two —MgX groups in a single organic molecule is considered to be quite difficult, but surprisingly enough 2,5-dichloro-3,4-diiodothiophene reacts as shown in equation (12).[17] Since 3,4-diiodo-

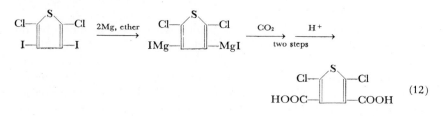

$$\tag{12}$$

thiophene will not undergo a similar reaction, it must be assumed that the proximity of the chlorine in the 2,5-positions activates the I atoms.

The conversion of typical thienylmagnesium halides to acids, aldehydes, alcohols, olefins, etc. is discussed in more detail in the chapters devoted to these classes of compounds. In general, it may be stated that the typical Grignard reactions of the benzene series are applicable in the thiophene series. Coupling reactions are not pronounced in the benzene series and generally are minor reactions in the thiophene series. Only in the case of 5-phenyl-2-thienylmagnesium bromide does coupling appear to be the major reaction.[18]

III. Mercury Derivatives of Thiophene

Mercury compounds of thiophene have played such an important part in the development of thiophene chemistry that this single category has received more attention than any other phase of thiophene research, with the possible exception of the acylation and halogenation reactions. Indeed, use of these compounds was and still is very important in separating thiophene or its derivatives from aromatic or aliphatic contaminants. Naturally, these compounds have been prominent as intermediates in the separation of thiophenes from coal tars and petroleum sources. Steinkopf[18a] has made a comprehensive survey of the mercury compounds and their chemistry which the present author will not try to improve.

For the sake of convenience, the present treatment of the subject is separated into two sections, the mercurihalides and the mercuriacetates of thiophene.

[17] Steinkopf and Kohler, *Ann.*, **532**, 250 (1937).
[18] Steinkopf, Petersdorff, and Gording, *Ann.*, **527**, 278 (1937).

A. Mercurihalides of Thiophene and Its Derivatives

Volhard,[19] in 1892, found that thiophene reacted with mercuric chloride in dilute alcoholic solution to produce 2-thiophenemercurichloride and small amounts of 2,5-thiophenedimercurichloride (Eq. 13).

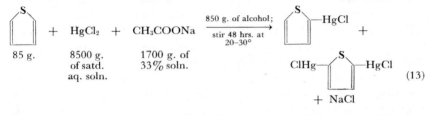

(13)

The insoluble white salt is collected and separated by recrystallization from alcohol; the dimercurichloride derivative is totally insoluble. The yield is quantitative. Higher yields of 2,5-thiophenedimercurichloride are obtained at the boiling point of the mixture.

No tri- or tetramercurihalides of thiophene have been reported from direct mercuration and apparently the 3- and 4-positions are inactive toward mercuric chloride. Preparation of thiophenetetramercurichloride by an indirect method is described below. Reaction does occur in the 3- and 4-positions when the 2-position or both the 2- and 5-positions are blocked with typical electropositive groups (electron-donating groups), e.g., alkyl, ethoxy,[20] or —SR.[20] When thiophene is substituted with strong electronegative groups (electron-withdrawing groups), e.g., carboxyl and nitro, mercuration with mercuric chloride proceeds slowly or not at all.[20a] 2-Nitrothiophene does not form a mercurichloride derivative. It is reported that dialkylthiophenes, e.g., 2,5-dimethyl- and 2,4-dimethylthiophene, form addition complexes such as:

$$H_3C- \overset{S}{\underset{}{\triangle}} \overset{CH_3}{\underset{OH}{\underset{HgCl}{\underset{H}{}}}} \quad \text{and} \quad H_3C- \overset{S}{\underset{}{\triangle}} \overset{H}{\underset{HgCl}{\underset{OH}{\underset{CH_3}{}}}} \qquad (14)$$

These materials are unstable and on recrystallization from alcohol lose water to give the normal substitution products, 2,5-dimethyl-3-thiophenemercurichloride and 2,4-dimethyl-5-thiophenemercurichloride.[21-23] In this respect, these thiophene homologs behave like olefins.[24,25]

[18a] Steinkopf, Die Chemie des Thiophens. Steinkopff, Dresden, 1941, pp. 108–122.
[19] Volhard, Ann., 267, 172 (1892).
[20] Steinkopf and Leonhardt, Ann., 495, 166 (1932).
[20a] Steinkopf, Ann., 413, 310 (1916).
[21] Steinkopf and Bauermeister, Ann., 403, 50 (1914).
[22] Steinkopf, Ann., 430, 78 (1923).
[23] Steinkopf, Ann., 424, 23 (1920).
[24] Hofmann and Sand, Ber., 33, 1340, 1358, 2962 (1900).
[25] Sand, Ann., 329, 135 (1903).

Under similar conditions, benzene and its homologs are unreactive toward mercuric chloride and the above method is of particular value in recovering small amounts of thiophene, methylthiophenes, and dimethyl-thiophenes from their respective coal tar fractions or from dilute solutions in hydrocarbons.

Mercurihalide derivatives of the halothiophenes are listed in Table XIV-2 with appropriate references. In general, mercurihalide deriva-tives of halothiophenes form only if the 2- or 5-position is unsubstituted. Only in the case of Steinkopf's "2,3,5-trichloro-4-thiophenemercuri-chloride," which was later shown to be the 2,3,4-trichloro-5-thiophene-mercurichloride (see section on trichlorothiophenes), and in the case of 2,3,5-tribromo-4-thiophenemercurichloride   has β-substitution   been reported.   It seems likely in the latter case, as in the first, that the "2,3,5-tribromothiophene" was actually 2,3,4-tribromothiophene.

Thiolane forms a molecular addition complex with mercuric chloride, $C_4H_8S \cdot HgCl_2$.[26,27]

Reactions of Thiophenemercurichlorides

Steam distillation of the thiophenemercurichlorides in the presence of hydrochloric acid regenerates the original thiophene or thiophene derivative in quantitative yield. Usually a second mercurichloride precipitation followed by regeneration gives products of high purity.

Mercuribromides, iodides, and thiocyanates are prepared from the mercurichlorides by an ion-exchange procedure with the corresponding sodium salts[23] (Eq. 15). In boiling acetone, another reaction takes

$$\text{\includegraphics{thiophene}}\text{—HgCl} + \text{NaBr(—I or —CNS)} \xrightarrow{\text{acetone,} \atop \text{20–30°}} \text{\includegraphics{thiophene}}\text{—HgBr(—I or —CNS)} +$$

$$\text{NaCl} \quad (15)$$

place (Eq. 16). Reconversion to the original 2-thiophenemercuri-

$$\text{\includegraphics{thiophene}}\text{—HgCl} + \text{NaBr} \xrightarrow{\text{acetone, 60–70°}} \text{\includegraphics{thiophene}}\text{—Hg—}\text{\includegraphics{thiophene}} + \text{NaBr} \cdot \text{HgCl}_2 \quad (16)$$

chloride is accomplished by boiling 2,2'-dithienylmercury with fresh mercuric chloride in acetone.

[26] Grischkewitsch-Trokhimovskii, J. Russ. Phys.-Chem. Soc., 48, 901 (1916).
[27] Mozingo et al., J. Am. Chem. Soc., 67, 2093 (1945).

Thiophenedimercurichlorides may be converted to cyclic mercurials (Eqs. 17 and 18).[28-30] In the former case, no proof has been presented

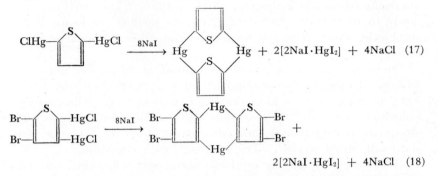

$$+ \ 2[2\text{NaI} \cdot \text{HgI}_2] \ + \ 4\text{NaCl} \quad (17)$$

$$2[2\text{NaI} \cdot \text{HgI}_2] \ + \ 4\text{NaCl} \quad (18)$$

that these materials are not open chain polymers rather than macro-ring systems, since they were too insoluble in all solvents for molecular weight determinations. In the latter case, the formation of the simple six-membered ring seems plausible.

The cleavage of these ring systems with potassium triiodide leading to various diiodothiophene derivatives is discussed in more detail in the chapter on iodothiophenes.

The use of 2-thiophenemercurichlorides as catalysts for the acylation of thiophene, and the preparation of acylthiophenes by direct replacement of the mercurichloride group, are discussed in Chapter XI.

B. The Mercuriacetates of Thiophene and Its Derivatives

Mercuric acetate reacts rapidly with thiophene and its derivatives to form polymercuriacetates[15,16,30a,31-34] (Eq. 19). If the 2,5-positions

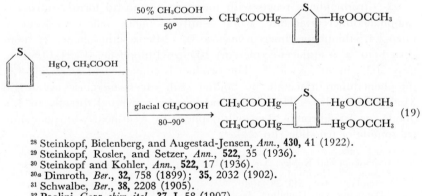

$$(19)$$

[28] Steinkopf, Bielenberg, and Augestad-Jensen, *Ann.*, **430**, 41 (1922).
[29] Steinkopf, Rosler, and Setzer, *Ann.*, **522**, 35 (1936).
[30] Steinkopf and Kohler, *Ann.*, **522**, 17 (1936).
[30a] Dimroth, *Ber.*, **32**, 758 (1899); **35**, 2032 (1902).
[31] Schwalbe, *Ber.*, **38**, 2208 (1905).
[32] Paolini, *Gazz. chim. ital.*, **37**, I, 58 (1907).
[33] Briscoe, Peel, and Young, *J. Chem. Soc.*, **1929**, 2589.
[34] Steinkopf and Killingstad, *Ann.*, **532**, 288 (1937).

are blocked, the 3,4-dimercuriacetate is formed with 50% acetic acid. In general, the method employing glacial acetic acid will replace all unsubstituted nuclear hydrogens.   Since benzene is converted only very slowly to mercuric acetate derivatives, the method employing glacial acetic acid is one of the best for the determination of thiophene in coal tar benzene.[32]

Steinkopf[18] lists a convenient preparation of thiophenetetramercuriacetate.   To the filtered solution of 285 g. of mercuric oxide dissolved in 550 g. of glacial acetic acid is added 25 g. of thiophene.   The mixture is heated on a water bath for two hours and then diluted with water.   The precipitate is collected, washed with water, dried on a porous plate, and finally dried at 130°.   The yield is 315.5 g. (quantitative).

When mercuric acetate in glacial acetic acid is warmed with halogenated 2-thiophenecarboxylic acids, decarboxylation takes place[15,16] (Eq. 20).   This reaction appears to be generally applicable and has been

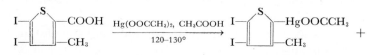

$$CO_2 + CH_3COOH \quad (20)$$

used to prepare 2,3-dibromothiophene[35] and 2,3-dichlorothiophene[35,36] by mercuric acetate decarboxylation of 4,5-dihalo-2-thiophenecarboxylic acid.   2,3-Dihalothiophenes are generated by treating the mercuriacetate with sodium chloride to prepare the mercurichloride, which, in turn, is steam distilled in the presence of hydrochloric acid.   High yields of the 2,3-dihalothiophene are collected in the distillate.

2-Nitrothiophene reacts with mercuric acetate to form 2-nitro-4,5-thiophenedimercuriacetate, while 3-nitrothiophene reacts to form 3-nitro-2,4,5-thiophenetrimercuriacetate.[37]   2-Benzoylthiophene is converted to a sesquiacetoxymercuri-2-benzoylthiophene, $C_{28}H_{22}O_8S_2Hg_3$, m.p. 202°, in 90% yield.[38]   The product is converted to 2-benzoyl-4,5-thiophenedimercuriacetate by boiling with excess mercuric acetate in Methyl Cellosolve.   This compound can be converted directly to 4,5-diiodo- or 4,5-dibromo-2-benzoylthiophene by treatment with potassium tribromide or triiodide (Eq. 21).

[35] Steinkopf and Kohler, *Ann.*, **532,** 281 (1937).
[36] Coonradt, Hartough, and Johnson, *J. Am. Chem. Soc.*, **70,** 2564 (1948).
[37] Steinkopf, *Ann.*, **545,** 38 (1940).
[38] Weitkamp and Hamilton, *J. Am. Chem. Soc.*, **59,** 2700 (1937).

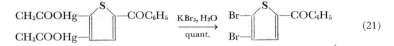

$$(21)$$

Further references on less important reactions of the mercury derivatives of thiophene are listed below.[39-44]

Table XIV-1 lists the melting points of all mercury compounds of thiophene and its homologs reported in the literature. Certain polymercuri derivatives of thiophene,[39,45] thiophthene,[42] dithienyls,[30] nitrothiophenes,[46,47] halothiophenes,[29,35,46] and 2-methylthiophene,[15] having no melting points, are not listed. The melting point of 2-hydroxymethyl-5-thiophenemercurichloride[48] is listed as 183–185° dec. No melting point is given for the 5-mercurichloro-2-thiophenecarboxylic acid,[20a,47] nor for the product obtained from mercuric acetate and 2-thiophenecarboxylic acid.[47]

C. Dithienyl Mercury Compounds

The general methods of preparation of these compounds have been discussed in section III-1-A. The preparation of 2,4-diphenyl-5-thienylphenylmercury is accomplished as shown in equation (22).[49] In a

$$(22)$$

similar reaction carried out with thiophene, 2-thienylphenylmercury was prepared.[50]

Table XIV-3 lists the melting points of the dithienyl mercury compounds found in the literature.

[39] Paolini and Silbermann, *Gazz. chim. ital.*, **37**, 58 (1907).
[40] Steinkopf, *Ann.*, **428**, 123 (1921).
[41] Steinkopf and Nitschke, *Arch. Pharm.*, **278**, 360 (1940).
[42] Challenger and Harrison, *J. Inst. Petroleum Technol.*, **21**, 135 (1935).
[43] I. G. Farbenindustrie, Ger. Pat. 519,488 (1930).
[44] Kharasch, U. S. Pat. 1,934,803 (1933).
[45] Steinkopf and Boetius, *Ann.*, **546**, 208 (1941).
[46] Steinkopf, *Ann.*, **543**, 128 (1940); *Ann.*, **545**, 38 (1940).
[47] Rhodehamel and Degering, *J. Am. Pharm. Assoc.*, **31**, 281 (1942).
[48] Dunn and Dittmer, *J. Am. Chem. Soc.*, **68**, 2561 (1946).
[49] Andersen, U. S. Pat. 2,085,065 (1937).
[50] Kharasch and Flenner, *J. Am. Chem. Soc.*, **54**, 674 (1932).

TABLE XIV-1. Mercury Derivatives of Thiophene and Its Homologs

Parent compound	Mercury derivative and position on nucleus	M.p., °C.	Ref.
Thiophene...................	2-HgCl	182–183	19,20a,23,33, 47,50–52
	2-HgBr	169–170	20a,23
	2-HgI	116–117	20a,21,23
	2-HgSCN	196–197	23
	2-HgC$_6$H$_5$	80–120	28,50
	2,5-HgCl	no m.p.	19,33,34,47
2-Methylthiophene..............	5-HgCl	204	19,21,23
	5-HgBr	179–180	23
	5-HgI	111–112	23
	5-HgSCN	202–204	23
	5-HgOOCCH$_3$	133	34
3-Methylthiophene..............	2-HgCl	128–129	19,23
	2-HgSCN	169 (dec.)	23
	2,5-HgOOCCH$_3$	dec. above 240°	34
2-Ethylthiophene...............	5-HgCl	147–148	23
	5-HgI	96–97	23
	5-HgSCN	167.5–169	23
3-Ethylthiophene..............	2-HgCl	67–68	40
	2,5-HgCl	295–297 (dec.)	40
2,3-Dimethylthiophene...........	5-HgCl	218.5–219.5	23,52,53
	5-HgI	184–184.5	41
	5-HgSCN	200–202	23,40,52
	4,5-HgOOCCH$_3$	237–240	41
2,4-Dimethylthiophene...........	5-HgCl	138–139	23
	5-HgI	137–139	23
	5-HgSCN	173–175	23
2,5-Dimethylthiophene...........	3-HgCl	156–157	20a,21,23
	3-HgI	175	20a,23
	3-HgSCN	177–177.5	23
	3,4-HgOOCCH$_3$	dec. above 290	34
3,4-Dimethylthiophene...........	2-HgCl	139–140.5	21,21a,23,52
	2-HgBr	152	21a
	2-HgI	142	20a,23,52
	2-HgSCN	178–179	23
	2,5-HgCl	no m.p.	21,23
2-Propylthiophene..............	5-HgCl	155	23
	5-HgSCN	169–169.5	23
3-Isopropylthiophene............	5-HgCl	137	19,23
2-Methyl-3-ethylthiophene........	5-HgCl	150–151	54
	5-HgBr	165–166.5	54
	5-HgI	157.5–158	54
2-Ethyl-3-methylthiophene........	5-HgCl	172–173	54
	5-HgI	156–157	54
	4,5-HgOOCCH$_3$	248–250 (dec.)	54
Trimethylthiophene..............	x-HgCl	160–161	55
3,4-Diethylthiophene.............	2-HgCl	118	56
2-Isoamylthiophene.............	5-HgCl	171.5–172	23
	5-HgSCN	199–200	23

Table continued

TABLE XIV-1 (*Continued*)

Parent compound	Mercury derivative and position on nucleus	M.p., °C.	Ref.
2-Phenylthiophene...............	5-HgCl	234	21,23,57
	5-HgI	265	20a
2-Benzylthiophene...............	5-HgCl	189–191	23
2,4-Diphenylthiophene	5-HgCl	223	58
	5-HgC₆H₅	114	49
2,5-Diphenylthiophene............	3-HgCl	221–222	23
	3-HgSCN	dec. above 200	23
2-Methyl-3-phenylthiophene.......	5-HgOOCCH₃	126.5–129	57
2-Methyl-4-phenylthiophene.......	5-HgOOCCH₃	113.3–113.5	57
Thianaphthene..................	2-HgCl	179–182	59
	2,3-HgCl	no m.p.	59
2,2'-Dithienyl..................	5,5'-HgCl	no m.p.	30
2,2'-Dithienyl..................	3,4,5,3',4',5'-HgCl	no m.p.	30
5-Methyl-2,2'-dithienyl...........	5'-HgCl	Sinters at 225 and decomposes	60
2,5,2',5'-Tetramethyl-3,3'-dithienyl	4,4'-HgOOCCH₃	233–234	61
5,5'-Dimethyl-3,3'-diethyl-2,2'-dithienyl......................	4,4'-HgOOCCH₃	225–230 (dec.)	54

TABLE XIV-2. Mercury Derivatives of Halogenated Thiophenes

Compound	Position and type of mercury derivative	M.p., °C.	Ref.
2-Chlorothiophene................	5-HgCl	218–219	21,21a,23
	5-HgBr	191	20a,23
	5-HgI	126–126.5	20a,23
	5-HgSCN	187–188	23
2-Bromothiophene................	5-HgCl	225	21,21a,23
	5-HgBr	197–197.5	20a,23
	5-HgI	119	20a,23
	5-HgSCN	187–188	23
	5-HgOOCCH₃	134–135	34

Table continued

[51] Johnson, Van Campen, and Grummitt, *J. Am. Chem. Soc.*, **60**, 111 (1938).
[52] Shepard, Henne, and Midgley, *J. Am. Chem. Soc.*, **56**, 1355 (1934).
[53] Shepard, *J. Am. Chem. Soc.*, **54**, 2951 (1932).
[54] Steinkopf, Merckoll, and Strauch, *Ann.*, **545**, 45 (1940).
[55] Weissgerber, *Ber.*, **B61**, 2111 (1928).
[56] Steinkopf, Frömmel, and Leo, *Ann.*, **546**, 199 (1941).
[57] Broun and Vornokov, *Doklady Akad. Nauk, U. S. S. R.*, **59**, 1293 (1941); *Chem. Abstr.*, **43**, 2614 (1949).
[58] Bogert and Herrera, *J. Am. Chem. Soc.*, **45**, 238 (1923).
[59] Challenger and Miller, *J. Chem. Soc.*, **1939**, 1005.
[60] Steinkopf, Leitsmann, and Hofmann, *Ann.*, **546**, 180 (1941).
[61] Steinkopf, Barlog, and von Petersdorff, *Ann.*, **540**, 7 (1939).

TABLE XIV-2. Mercury Derivatives of Halogenated Thiophenes (*Continued*)

Compound	Position and type of mercury derivative	M.p., °C.	Ref.
2-Iodothiophene	5-HgCl	225	21,21*a*,23
	5-HgBr	190 (dec.)	21*a*,23
	5-HgI	141–142	21*a*,23
	5-HgSCN	174	23
3-Chlorothiophene	2-HgCl	137–138	35
3-Bromothiophene	2-HgCl	120.5–123	62
3-Iodothiophene	2-HgCl	138–139	63
2,3-Dichlorothiophene	5-HgCl	269–270	35
2,3-Dibromothiophene	5-HgCl	240 (dec.)	62
2,3-Diiodothiophene	5-HgCl	228 (dec.)	63
3,4-Dichlorothiophene	2-HgCl	206–207	35
3,4-Dibromothiophene	2-HgCl	191	62
3,4-Diiodothiophene	2-HgCl	178–180	63
2,4-Dibromothiophene	5-HgCl	184–187	62
2,3,4-Trichlorothiophene	5-HgCl	211	35
	5-HgBr	207	35
2,3,4-Tribromothiophene	5-HgCl	236	29
2,3,4-Triiodothiophene	5-HgCl	235 (dec.)	63
2,3,5-Tribromothiophene	4-HgCl	270	29,62
2-Methyl-3-bromothiophene	5-HgCl	237–239	64
2-Methyl-3-iodothiophene	5-HgCl	dec. above 200	15
2-Methyl-4-bromothiophene	5-HgCl	165–166	64
2-Methyl-4-iodothiophene	5-HgCl	201.5–203	15
2-Methyl-3,4-diiodothiophene	5-HgCl	216.5–218	15
3-Methyl-5-bromothiophene	2-HgCl	217–222	65
3-Methyl-5-iodothiophene	2-HgCl	217 and 282	16
3-Methyl-2-bromothiophene	5-HgCl	251	65
3-Methyl-2-iodothiophene	5-HgCl	208–209	16
3-Methyl-4-bromothiophene	2(5)-HgCl	no mp.	65
	2,5-HgOOCCH$_3$	dec. above 270	
3-Methyl-4,5-dichlorothiophene	2-HgCl	230.5–231	66
3-Methyl-2,4-dibromothiophene	2-HgCl	208–209	66
3-Methyl-4,5-dibromothiophene	2-HgCl	240–241	65
3-Methyl-2,4-diiodothiophene	5-HgCl	228–229	16
2,5-Dichlorothiophene	3,4-HgCl	314–315	35
2,3-Dibromothiophene	4,5-HgCl	300	29
2,5-Dibromothiophene	3,4-HgCl	300–305	29
3,4-Dibromothiophene	2,5-HgCl	317	29
2,5-Diiodothiophene	3,4-HgCl	no m.p.	29
2-Bromothiophene	3,4,5-HgCl	no m.p.	29
2-Iodothiophene	3,4,5-HgCl	290 (dec.)	29
3-Iodothiophene	2,5-HgCl	245–247 (dec.)	63

[62] Steinkopf, Jacob, and Penz, *Ann.*, **512**, 136 (1934).
[63] Steinkopf, Schmitt, and Fiedler, *Ann.*, **527**, 237 (1937).
[64] Steinkopf, *Ann.*, **513**, 281 (1934).
[65] Steinkopf and Jacob, *Ann.*, **515**, 273 (1935).
[66] Steinkopf and Nitschke, *Ann.*, **536**, 135 (1938).

TABLE XIV-3. Dithienylmercury Derivatives, R_2Hg

R—	M.p., °C.	Ref.
2-Thienyl	198–199	20a,21,23,28
5-Methyl-2-thienyl	162–162.5	23
3-Ethyl-2-thienyl	68	40
4,5-Dimethyl-2-thienyl	169.5–170	41
3,5-Dimethyl-2-thienyl	160–161	23
3,4-Dimethyl-2-thienyl	155–156	20a,23,52
5-Propyl-2-thienyl	57–58	23
5-Ethyl-4-methyl-2-thienyl	99–100	54
5-Methyl-4-ethyl-2-thienyl	85–85.5	54
3,4-Diethyl-2-thienyl	93	56
5-Isoamyl-2-thienyl	55–57	23
5-Benzyl-2-thienyl	209–210	23
3-Chloro-2-thienyl	174–175	35
5-Chloro-2-thienyl	155	20a,23
3,4,5-Trichloro-2-thienyl	242–243	35
3-Bromo-2-thienyl	154	62
5-Bromo-2-thienyl	183	20a,23
3,5-Dibromo-2-thienyl	195–200	62
4,5-Dibromo-2-thienyl	No m.p.	62
3,4,5-Tribromo-2-thienyl	291	29
5-Methyl-4-bromo-2-thienyl	266	64
3-Iodo-2-thienyl	165	63
5-Iodo-2-thienyl	245	20a,23
4,5-Diiodo-3-methyl-2-thienyl	290 (dec.)	16
2,5-Dimethyl-3-thienyl	144–145	20a,23
2,5-Diphenyl-3-thienyl	260–261	23
2,5-Dichloro-4-iodo-3-thienyl	238	35
4,5-Dichloro-2-bromo-3-thienyl	238–239	35
3-Thianaphthenyl	322	59

IV. Miscellaneous Metalloid and Metal Derivatives of Thiophene

A considerable number of nonmetal and metal derivatives of thiophene other than those mentioned above have been prepared, generally from the thienylmagnesium halides or the thiophenemercurihalides by the action of the respective nonmetal or metal halides (Eq. 23). Thus

$$\text{—MgX(HgX)} \xrightarrow{MCl_3} \text{—MCl_2} + MgClX(HgClX) \qquad (23)$$

[67] Finzi, *Gazz. chim. ital.*, **45**, II, 280 (1915).
[68] Finzi and Furlotti, *Gazz. chim. ital.*, **45**, II, 290 (1915).
[69] Steinkopf and Bauermeister, *Ann.*, **413**, 330 (1916).
[70] Finzi, *Gazz. chim. ital.*, **55**, 824 (1925).

arsenic,[38,67−72] lead,[73−75] thallium,[74] bismuth,[75,76] tellurium,[75] germanium,[76] antimony,[76] and boron[76] derivatives have been prepared. Silicon compounds are prepared in this manner[75] and from direct coupling of the 2-thienyllithium with trimethylchlorosilane.[77]

Tri-(2-thienyl)arsine was prepared by a modified Wurtz-Fittig reaction[70] (Eq. 24). An attempt to prepare thienylarsines from 2-amino-

$$3 \quad \text{[thienyl]}{-}Br \;+\; 6Na \;+\; AsCl_3 \;\xrightarrow{\text{ether}}\; \left(\text{[thienyl]}\right)_3{-}As \;+\; 3NaBr \;+\; 3NaCl \qquad (24)$$

thiophene by diazotization and coupling with arsenic halides gave no traces of the expected arsine.[67,68] Although the di-(5-nitro-2-thienyl)-arsinic acid is difficult to reduce to the amine, sodium amalgam being required, the corresponding amine diazotizes well and can be coupled with a variety of materials.[68]

The phosphorus derivatives have been studied to a limited extent. 2-Thiophenedichlorophosphine (2-thiophenephosphorus dichloride) has been prepared only in low yield from the action of phosphorus trichloride on thiophene in the presence of aluminum chloride.[78] Better yields are obtained thermally, by passing thiophene and phosphorus trichloride over pumice in a glass tube at red heat (Eq. 25). 2-Thiophenedichloro-

$$\text{[thiophene]} \;+\; PCl_3 \;\longrightarrow\; \text{[thiophene]}{-}PCl_2 \;+\; HCl \qquad (25)$$

phosphine is hydrolyzed to the acid, $C_4H_3S{-}PO_2H_2$, by the action of water. It is converted by the action of chlorine to $C_4H_3S{-}PCl_4$, which, in turn, yields 2-thiophenephosphonic acid with water. Zinc diethyl gives 2-thiophenediethylphosphine; methyl iodide gives a phosphonium iodide with the latter. Sulfur dioxide oxidizes the dichlorophosphine to the 2-thienylphosphorus oxydichloride, $C_4H_3S{-}POCl_2$.[78]

[71] Finzi, *Gazz. chim. ital.*, **60**, 159 (1930).
[72] Finzi, *Gazz. chim. ital.*, **62**, 244 (1932).
[73] Krause and Renwanz, *Ber.*, **B60**, 1582 (1927).
[74] Gilman and Towne, *Rec. trav. chim.*, **51**, 1054 (1932).
[75] Krause and Renwanz, *Ber.*, **B62**, 1710 (1929).
[76] Krause and Renwanz, *Ber.*, **B65**, 777 (1932).
[77] Benkeser and Currie, *J. Am. Chem. Soc.*, **70**, 1780 (1948).
[78] Sachs, *Ber.*, **25**, 1514 (1892).

More recently, 2-thenylphosphonic acid has been prepared[79] (Eq. 26).

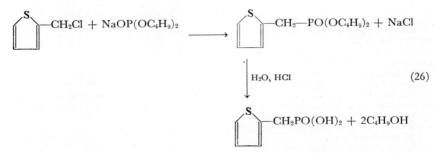

$$H_2O, HCl \qquad\qquad (26)$$

Gilman and Towne[74] studied the cleavage rates of mixed thienyl-phenyllead and thienylfuryllead. With hydrogen chloride, furan is split before thiophene (Eq. 27). Similarly, thiophene was split from di-2-

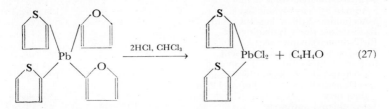

$$(27)$$

thienyldiphenyllead. Gilman and Towne were thus able to show that the order of reactivity was furan > thiophene > benzene > ethane. From this work grew the concept of "super-aromaticity" of these hetero-cyclics. This same relationship was found to exist in the cleavage rates of 2-trimethylsilyl- and 2-triphenylsilylthiophene with hydrochloric acid.[80]

The physical constants of these thiophene derivatives are listed in Table XIV-4 following.

[79] Kosolapoff, *J. Am. Chem. Soc.*, **69**, 2248 (1947).
[80] Gilman and Marshall, *J. Am. Chem. Soc.*, **71**, 2066 (1949).
[81] Tischtschenko and Smirnow, *J. Applied Chem.* (*U. S. S. R.*), **3**, 1041 (1930); *Chem. Zentr.*, **1931**, I, 2375.
[82] Benkeser and Landesman, *J. Am. Chem. Soc.*, **71**, 2493 (1949).
[83] Gilman and Plunkett, *J. Am. Chem. Soc.*, **71**, 1117 (1949).
[84] Bobaschinskaja and Kotscheschkow, *J. Gen. Chem.* (*U. S. S. R.*), **8**, 1850 (1938).

TABLE XIV-4. Physical Constants of Thiophene Derivatives of Metals and Metalloids

Compound	B.p., °C. (mm.)	M.p., °C.	Ref.
2-Thienyldichloroarsine	118–122 (11)	—	67,69
Di-(2-thienyl)chloroarsine	219–232 (13)	—	69
Tri-(2-thienyl)arsine	199–200.5 (0.5)	—	69
5-Benzoyl-2-thienyldichloroarsine	—	113	38
2-Thienylarsenious oxide	—	115–116	72
5-Bromo-2-thienylarsenious oxide	—	191	72
5-Iodo-2-thienylarsenious oxide	—	233–234	72
5-Nitro-2-thienylarsenious oxide	—	171–172	72
5-Nitro-2-thienylarsenious sequisulfide	—	60–80	72
5-Iodo-4(3)-nitro-2-thienylarsenious oxide	—	157	72
2-Thienylarsonic acid	—	135.5	72
5-Methyl-2-thienylarsonic acid	—	132	71
5-Methyl-4(3)-nitro-2-thienylarsonic acid	—	270 (dec.)	71
5-Methyl-4(3)-amino-2-thienylarsonic acid	—	270 (dec.)	71
5-Methyl-4(3)-acetamido-2-thienylarsonic acid	—	above 260	71
5-Benzoyl-2-thienylarsonic acid	—	360	38
5-Bromo-4(3)-nitro-2-thienylarsonic acid	—	288–290	72
5-Nitro-2-thienylarsonic acid	—	194	68
5-Amino-2-thienylarsonic acid	—	194 (dec.)	68
5-Acetamido-2-thienylarsonic acid	—	134 (dec.)	68
Bis(5-iodo-2-thienyl)arsinic acid	—	184	72
Bis(2-thienyl)arsinic acid	—	172	67
Bis(5-nitro-2-thienyl)arsinic acid	—	287 (dec.)	68
Bis(5-acetamido-2-thienyl)arsinic acid	—	134 (dec.)	68
5,5'-Dimethyl-2,2'-arsenothiophene	—	125–130	71
5,5'-Dimethyl-3,3'(4,4')-dinitro-2,2'-arsenothiophene	—	225 (dec.)	71
Tri-(2-thienyl)antimony	197–198 (2.5)	49–49.5	76
Tri-(2-thienyl)antimony dichloride	—	229	76
Tri-(2-thienyl)antimony dibromide	—	182.5 and 230 (dec.)	76
Tri-(2-thienyl)antimony oxide	—	217	76
Tri-(2-thienyl)bismuth	—	137.5	75,76
2-Thienylboronic acid, monohydrate	—	134	51,76
Tetra-(2-thienyl)germanium	—	149–150	76
2-Thienylgold	—	not given	81
Tetra-(2-thienyl)lead	—	154.5	73
Diphenyl-di-(2-thienyl)lead	—	184–185	74
Triphenyl-2-thienyllead	—	208	74,75
Di-(2-thienyl)lead dichloride	—	202 (dec.)	74
Di-(2-furyl)-di-(2-thienyl)lead	—	117–119	74
2-Thienyldichlorophosphine	218 (760)	—	78
2-Thienyltetrachlorophosphine	—	not given	78
2-Thienylphosphorus oxydichloride	258–260 (760)	—	78
2-Thienylphosphinic acid	—	70	78
2-Thienylphosphonic acid	—	159	78
2-Thienyldiethylphosphine	225 (760)	—	78
2-Thienyldiethylmethylphosphonium iodide	—	122	78
Dibutyl-2-thenylphosphonate	147–150 (3)	—	79
2-Thenylphosphonic acid	—	108–109	79
Tetra-(2-thienyl)silane	—	135.5	75
2-Thienyltrimethylsilane	159–160 (748)	—	77
5-Acetyl-2-thienyltrimethylsilane	104–105 (4)	—	77
5-Acetyl-2-thienyltrimethylsilane, semicarbazone	—	217–220	77

Table continued

TABLE XIV-4 (*Continued*)

Compound	B.p., °C. (mm.)	M.p., °C.	Ref.
5-Trimethylsilyl-2-thiophenecarboxylic acid....	—	134–135	77
5-Trimethylsilyl-2-thiopheneglyoxal............	89–90 (6)	—	82
5-Trimethylsilyl-2-thiopheneglyoxal, mono-hydrate...................................	—	102–109	82
2-(5-Trimethylsilyl-2-thienyl)quinoxaline.......	—	99–100	82
2-(5-Triphenylsilyl-2-thienyl)quinoline.........	—	168–170	83
2-(5-Triphenylsilyl-2-thienyl)-6-methoxy-quinoline.................................	—	227–228	83
2-(5-Triphenylsilyl-2-thienyl)-4,7-dichloro-quinoline.................................	—	200–203	83
Di-(2-thienyl)thallium bromide...............	—	270 (dec.)	75
Di-(2-thienyl)tellurium......................	—	50.5	75,76
Di-(2-thienyl)tellurium dichloride.............	—	189.5	75
Di-(2-thienyl)tellurium dibromide............	—	195	75
Di-(2-thienyl)tellurium diiodide..............	—	126.5	75
Tri-(2-thienyl)telluroniumbromide.............	—	253	75
Tetra-(2-thienyl)tin (stannane)................	—	156	73
Triphenyl-(2-thienyl)tin (stannane)............	—	206	75
Diphenyl-di-(2-thienyl)tin (stannane)..........	—	202–210	84
Di-α-naphthyl-di-(2-thienyl)tin (stannane)......	—	145–146	84
Di-p-anisyl-di-(2-thienyl)tin (stannane)........	—	89–93	84

CHAPTER XV

Synthesis and Properties of Di- and Polythienyls and Arylthiophenes

I. The Di- and Polythienyls

The chemistry of the di- and polythienyls has not been studied extensively but it has been established that they substitute in the α-positions (*i.e.*, 5,5'-positions). Subsequent substitution is believed to take place at the 3,3'- and finally at the 4,4'-positions. The methods for preparing these compounds are very ineffectual unless the coupling is carried out with compounds in which the 5,5'-positions are blocked. Indeed, methods are such that the compounds, particularly the polythienyls, are no more than laboratory curiosities which occur in many cases as by-products in standard reactions.

The nomenclature of this class of compounds is very unsettled and the author has compromised in the usage made in this chapter. It is an attempt to combine the commonly used systems into a readable form of nomenclature not requiring a great number of structural formulas to clarify the terms used. The nomenclature used by *Chemical Abstracts* (see Chapter I) is cumbersome when one tries to name a compound such as α-sexithienyl and its derivatives; the *Chemical Abstracts* systematic nomenclature for this compound is 2,2',5',2'',5'',2''',5''',2'''',5'''',2'''''-sexithiophene. Numbering and naming of derivatives then becomes even more confusing. Use of the system of nomenclature proposed by *Chemical Abstracts* will be more necessary when a polythienyl is synthesized in which the coupling is varied between the 2- and 3-positions.

A. Dithienyls

1. 2,2'-Dithienyls

Preparation

There are two methods of producing 2,2'-dithienyl, but in general the methods are poor, and only in special cases can yields up to 50% of theory be anticipated. In most cases, yields of 20% are the best obtainable. The two general methods are coupling of halothiophenes with

metals and coupling of the Grignard reagents. The first, and most
widely practiced, involves coupling of 2-iodothiophene by means of
metallic silver[1] or copper–bronze[2,3] (Eq. 1). The polythienyls, ter-

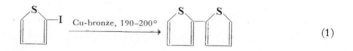

$$(1)$$

thienyl, quaterthienyl, and quinquethienyl, are also isolated from this
reaction. The other reaction involves the coupling of the 2-thienyl
magnesium bromide by means of cupric chloride.[4,5]

Miscellaneous methods of producing 2,2′-dithienyl from thiophene
involve passage of thiophene through a glowing tube,[6,7] whereby a mixture
of 2,2′- and 3,3′-dithienyl is produced, and the treatment of thiophene
with sulfuric acid.[8]

Homologs of 2,2′-dithienyl are conveniently prepared by the copper–
bronze coupling method. For example, 5,5′-dimethyl-2,2′-dithienyl
is prepared from 5-methyl-2-iodothiophene in 75–81% yield by treatment
with copper–bronze at 190–200° for thirty minutes.[9] 5,5′-Dibenzyl-
2,2′-dithienyl is prepared similarly[2] and by the Grignard-CuCl₂ method.[5]
5-Methyl-2,2′-dithienyl[2,3] or 5-benzyl-2,2′-dithienyl[2] results by inter-
reaction of 2-iodothiophene and the 5-methyl- or 5-benzyl-2-iodothio-
phene (Eq. 2). 2,2′-Dithienyl and 5,5′-dimethyl-2,2′-dithienyl are also

$$(2)$$

isolated from the reaction mixture. Minnis prepared 5,5′-di-(triphenyl-
methyl)-2,2′-dithienyl from the corresponding 2-iodothiophene by the
copper–bronze method.[10]

Derivatives of 2,2′-dithienyl are prepared in a novel manner from
thienylmagnesium halides and diethyl mesoxalate[11] (Eq. 3).

[1] Eberhard, *Ber.*, **27**, 2919 (1894).
[2] Steinkopf, Leitsmann, and Hofmann, *Ann.*, **546**, 180 (1941).
[3] Sease and Zechmeister, *J. Am. Chem. Soc.*, **69**, 270 (1947).
[4] Steinkopf and Roch, *Ann.*, **482**, 260 (1930).
[5] Steinkopf, Petersdorff, and Gording, *Ann.*, **527**, 272 (1937).
[6] Nahnsen, *Ber.*, **17**, 789 (1884).
[7] Auwers and Bredt, *Ber.*, **27**, 2919 (1894).
[8] Tohl, *Ber.*, **27**, 665 (1894).
[9] Steinkopf, Leitsmann, Müller, and Wilhelm, *Ann.*, **541**, 271 (1939).
[10] Minnis, *J. Am. Chem. Soc.*, **51**, 2143 (1939).
[11] Steinkopf and Hanske, *Ann.*, **541**, 238 (1939).

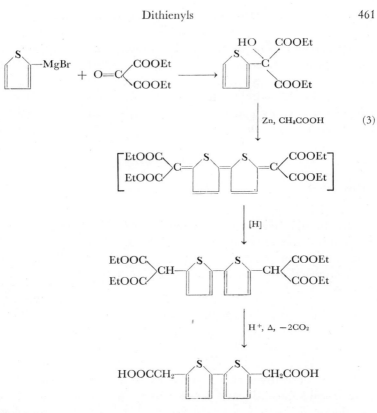

(3)

Reactions

2,2'-Dithienyl can be acylated to give a mixture of 5-acetyl-2,2'-dithienyl and 5,5'-diacetyl-2,2'-dithienyl[12] (Eq. 4). 5,5'-Dibenzoyl-2,2'-dithienyl is similarly prepared.[11]

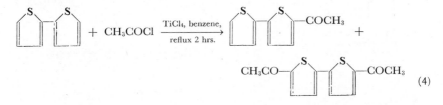

(4)

2,2'-Dithienyl will undergo the following reactions: chlorination and bromination,[13] nitration,[14] mercuration,[2,14] and sulfonation.[13]

[12] Steinkopf and Petersdorff, *Ann.*, **543**, 119 (1940).
[13] Nahnsen, *Ber.*, **17**, 2197 (1884).
[14] Steinkopf, *Ann.*, **545**, 38 (1940).

2,2'-Dithienyl can be regenerated by fusion of the potassium salt of the sulfonic acid with ammonium chloride.[13]   5,5'-Dimethyl-2,2'-dithienyl cannot be mercurated with mercuric chloride.[2]

5-Methyl-2,2'-dithienyl can be iodinated to give the 5'-iodo derivative which is easily converted to 5-methyl-5'-carboxy-2,2'-dithienyl by the Grignard reaction.[2]

2. 3,3'-Dithienyls

Preparation

3,3'-Dithienyl is formed with 2,2'-dithienyl when thiophene is passed through a glass tube at red heat.[6,7]   3,3'-Dithienyl is prepared by treating the tetrasodium salt of 1,2,3,4-butanetetracarboxylic acid with phosphorus trisulfide (Eq. 5).   No other authentic preparations of this compound are reported.

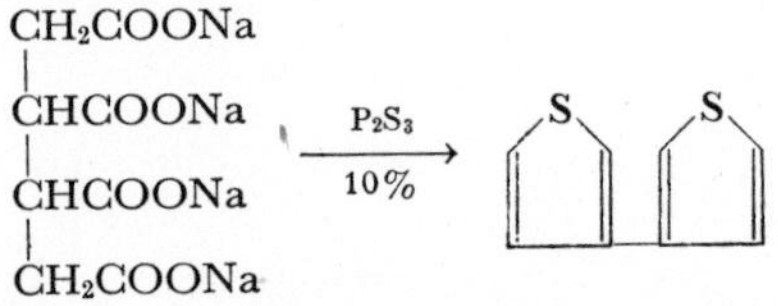

$$
\begin{array}{l}
\text{CH}_2\text{COONa} \\
|\\
\text{CHCOONa} \\
|\\
\text{CHCOONa} \\
|\\
\text{CH}_2\text{COONa}
\end{array}
\quad \xrightarrow[10\%]{\text{P}_2\text{S}_3} \quad
\text{[structure]}
\tag{5}
$$

Three derivatives of 3,3'-dithienyl have been prepared.   2,2',5,5'-Tetramethyl-3,3'-dithienyl is prepared by coupling 2,5-dimethyl-3-iodothiophene with copper–bronze.[15]   The tetraethyl homolog is obtained as a side product in the Wolff-Kishner reaction with the phenyl-hydrazone of 5-ethyl-2-acetylthiophene[16] (Eq. 6).   5-Methyl-2-hydroxy-

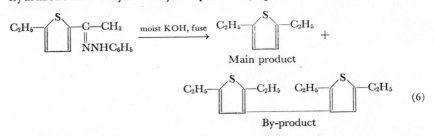

(6)

thiophene in its keto form is oxidized with ferric chloride to 2,2'-dimethyl-5,5'-diketo-$\Delta^{4,4'}$-dithienyl (Eq. 7).[17]   For further details see pages 292–294.

[15] Steinkopf, Barlag, and Petersdorff, *Ann.*, **540**, 7 (1939).
[16] Steinkopf, Frommel, and Leo, *Ann.*, **546**, 199 (1941).
[17] Steinkopf and Thormann, *Ann.*, **540**, 1 (1939).

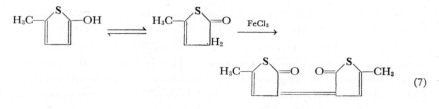

$$(7)$$

Reactions

The only reaction of 3,3'-dithienyl studied is bromination. It was found that a tetrabromo derivative could be prepared in acetic acid.[7] An excess of bromine yielded hexabromo-3,3'-dithienyl.

Acetylation of 2,2',5,5'-tetramethyl-3,3'-dithienyl with acetyl chloride in the presence of titanium tetrachloride yields the 4,4'-diacetyl derivative.[12] Mercuric acetate gives the 4,4'-diacetoxymercury derivative.[12]

3. 2,3'-Dithienyls

2,3'-Dithienyl is unknown but several of its more complex derivatives have been prepared. 2,4-Di-(2-thienyl)thiolane has been obtained from the polymerization of thiophene with montmorillonite clay or ortho-phosphoric acid catalysts.[18] This reaction is discussed in detail in Chapter VI (Sect. III). 5,5'-Dimethyl-4,4'-dicarbethoxy-3-hydroxy-2,3'-dithienyl and its derivatives have been prepared by condensing 3-hydroxy-4-carbethoxy-5-methylthiophene with hydrochloric acid at room temperature.[19] These compounds are discussed in more detail in Chapter XII (Sect. IV).

4. Halogenated Dithienyls

Tohl and Eberhard[20] noted that the exothermic reaction of thiophene, sulfuryl chloride, and a little aluminum chloride gave a mixture of dichloro- and trichloro dithienyl. These investigators also found that treatment of 2-chlorothiophene with a fivefold excess of concentrated sulfuric acid gave 5-chloro-2,2'-dithienyl.[21] Tohl and Schultz[22] studied the action of sulfuric acid on the brominated thiophenes and found that hexabromo-2,2'-dithienyl resulted from this reaction with 2,5-dibromo-thiophene.

[18] Meisel, Hartough, and Johnson, *J. Am. Chem. Soc.*, **72**, 1910 (1950).
[19] Benary and Bavarian, *Ber.*, **48**, 593 (1915).
[20] Tohl and Eberhard, *Ber.*, **26**, 2945 (1893).
[21] Tohl and Eberhard, *Ber.*, **26**, 2947 (1893).
[22] Tohl and Schultz, *Ber.*, **27**, 2834 (1894).

The halogenated dithienyls can be formed by direct halogenation; 5-halo-, 2,5-dihalo-, and polyhalo-2,2′-dithienyls result.[2,3,8,20-22]

Tohl and Schultz[22] reported that hexabromo-2,2′-dithienyl is formed in the direct bromination of thiophene.   This reaction is also reported in the chlorination of thiophene where hexachloro-2,2′-dithienyl results.[23] The yields of the respective hexahalo-2,2′-dithienyls are very low and usually do not exceed 1 or 2% of theory.

The iododithienyls are formed by direct iodination with iodine in the presence of mercuric oxide,[2,3,24] or by replacement of the —HgOOC-CH_3 group by iodine through the use of potassium triiodide.[14]

5-Chloro-2-thienylmagnesium bromide has been noted to give a 5% yield of 5,5′-dichloro-2,2′-dithienyl,[25] although such coupling reactions are not common in the thiophene series.   Various polyhalo di- and polythienyls have been prepared by the coupling action of cupric chloride on a thienylmagnesium halide[5,24] (Eq. 8).

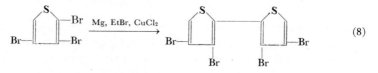

$$(8)$$

Exhaustive bromination or chlorination of 5,5′-dimethyl-2,2′-dithienyl gives side chain halogenation and the octachloro-5,5′-dimethyl-2,2′-dithienyl thus obtained by the action of chlorine can be hydrolyzed to the corresponding 5,5′-diformyl-3,3′,4,4′-tetrachloro-2,2′-dithienyl[9] (Eq. 9).

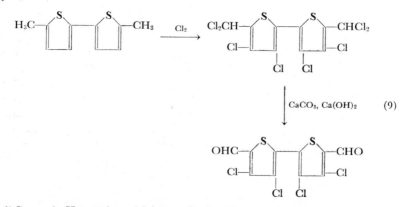

$$(9)$$

[23] Coonradt, Hartough, and Johnson, *J. Am. Chem. Soc.*, **70,** 2564 (1948).
[24] Steinkopf and Kohler, *Ann.*, **522,** 17 (1936).
[25] Bachman and Heisey, *J. Am. Chem. Soc.*, **70,** 2380 (1948).

A very complex reaction takes place between tetraiodothiophene and chlorosulfonic acid.[2] From the products a tetrachlorohexaiodo-α-quaterthienyl can be isolated. Hexabromo-2,2'-dithienyl gives a deca-bromo-α-quaterdithienyl when treated with chlorosulfonic acid.[2]

B. Polythienyls

Various α-polythienyls have been isolated from the lemon variety of the common yellow marigold.[26] As pointed out previously, the reaction of copper-bronze on 2-iodothiophene gave polythienyls from α-terthienyl to α-septathienyl[2,3,9,24] as by-products in the reaction. Steinkopf[27] explained the reaction thus: "2-Iodothiophene reacts with copper to give 2,2'-dithienyl and cupric iodide. The latter decomposes into cuprous iodide and iodine. This forms 5-iodo-2,2'-dithienyl with the 2,2'-dithienyl, which then reacts with copper and 2-iodothiophene to give α-terthienyl and more cupric iodide. Through further decomposition of the latter, iodination of α-terthienyl to form a 2-iodo-α-terthienyl and condensation with 2-iodothiophene occur to give α-quaterthienyl, etc." Separation of the individual compounds was effected by sublimation[2] or by chromatographic adsorption on alumina from petroleum ether or carbon disulfide.[3]

Renard[28] reported a "dithienylthiophene," m.p. 147°, b.p. 357°, from passage of benzene and sulfur through a tube heated at bright red heat. Since the melting point of this compound does not correspond to that of α-terthienyl it is either a β-terthienyl or a mixture of the two isomers. Renard also reported that the material could be brominated to give an unstable, black, powdery hexabromo derivative and that it could be sulfonated to give a trisulfonic acid. Lanfry[29] reported that this compound on reaction with hydrogen peroxide gave two compounds, $C_{12}H_8S_2O_2$, m.p. 231–233°, and $C_{12}H_8S_2O_4$, m.p. 312–313°.

The polythienyls can be brominated or mercurated in the same manner as the dithienyls. The polythienyls are colored, in contrast to the colorless dithienyls. α-Terthienyl is yellowish-green; α-quaterthienyl is chrome yellow; α-quinquethienyl is orange; α-sexithienyl is bright red; and α-septithienyl is wine-red. Polyxenyl isologs are all colorless, while the mixed polyphenylpolythienyls are colored, although less so than the polythienyls. The phenylthienyl derivatives are prepared

[26] Zechmeister and Sease, *J. Am. Chem. Soc.*, **69**, 273 (1947).
[27] Steinkopf, *Die Chemie des Thiophens*. Steinkopff, Dresden, 1941, p. 149.
[28] Renard, *Compt. rend.*, **112**, 49 (1891).
[29] Lanfry, *Compt. rend.*, **155**, 46 (1912).

TABLE XV-1. Physical Constants of the Dithienyls

Compound	M.p., °C.	Ref.
2,2'-Dithienyl	33	1,2,3,6
5-Methyl-2,2'-dithienyl	Liquid, b.p. 145–146 (17 mm.)	2
5,5'-Dimethyl-2,2'-dithienyl	67	9
5,5'-Dimethyl-4,4'-diethyl-2,2'-dithienyl	48.8–49.4	30
5-Phenyl-2,2'-dithienyl	119	2
5,5'-Diphenyl-2,2'-dithienyl	247	2
5,5'-Dibenzyl-2,2'-dithienyl	96.5–97.5	11
5,5'-Di-(triphenylmethyl)-2,2'-dithienyl	277	10
5-Chloro-2,2'-dithienyl	40	20
5,5'-Dichloro-2,2'-dithienyl	107–109 109–110	25 20
3,5,5'-Trichloro-2,2'-dithienyl	103	20
3,3',5,5'-Tetrachloro-2,2'-dithienyl	126–127	31
3,3',4,4',5,5'-Hexachloro-2,2'-dithienyl	189.5–190	23,31
5,5'-Dibromo-2,2'-dithienyl	143	4,7
3,3'-Dibromo-2,2'-dithienyl	96–97	5
3,3',4,4'-Tetrabromo-2,2'-dithienyl	110	24
3,3',5,5'-Tetrabromo-2,2'-dithienyl	139–140	5
4,4',5,5'-Tetrabromo-2,2'-dithienyl	110	24
3,3',4,4',5,5'-Hexabromo-2,2'-dithienyl	257	8,13,22
5-Iodo-2,2'-dithienyl	—	2,3
5,5'-Diiodo-2,2'-dithienyl	164	24
3,3',4,4',5,5'-Hexaiodo-2,2'-dithienyl	284–285	24
5,5'-Dichloro-3,3',4,4'-tetrabromo-2,2'-dithienyl	221–222	20
3,3',5,5'-Tetrachloro-4,4'-dibromo-2,2'-dithienyl	211.5–212.5	31
3',5,5'-Trichloro-3,4,4'-tribromo-2,2'-dithienyl	214–215	20
5-Chloro-3,3',4,4',5'-pentabromo-2,2'-dithienyl	238–240	21
3,3'-Dibromo-4,4',5,5'-tetraiodo-2,2'-dithienyl	273–274	5

Table continued

by coupling of 5-phenyl-2-iodothiophenes or 5-phenyl-5'-iodo-2,2'-dithienyl by standard methods.[2] Yields range as high as 60%.

The nomenclature of the polythienyls is so complex that it seems worth while to discuss it briefly. The author has chosen for the sake of simplicity to use α-terthienyl, α-quaterthienyl, etc. for the following structures:

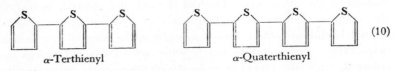

α-Terthienyl   α-Quaterthienyl   (10)

The simplest method of nomenclature and numbering, suggested by Steinkopf and Kohler,[24] follows:

[30] Steinkopf, Merckoll, and Strauch, *Ann.*, **545**, 45 (1940).
[31] Eberhard, *Ber.*, **28**, 2385, 3302 (1895).

TABLE XV-1 *(Continued)*

Compound	M.p., °C.	Ref.
5-Methyl-3,3',4,4',5'-pentachloro-2,2'-dithienyl............	111–112	2
5-Methyl-3,3',4,4',5'-pentabromo-2,2'-dithienyl............	170–171	2
5-(Bromomethyl)-3,3',4,4',5'-pentabromo-2,2'-dithienyl....	264	2
5-Iodo-5'-methyl-2,2'-dithienyl.........................	85–86	2,3
5,5'-Dimethyl-3,3',4,4'-tetrachloro-2,2'-dithienyl..........	201	9
5,5'-Di-(dichloromethyl)-3,3',4,4'-tetrachloro-2,2'-dithienyl.	119–120	9
5,5'-Dimethyl-3,3',4,4'-tetrabromo-2,2'-dithienyl..........	225	9
5,5'-Di-(dibromomethyl)-3,3',4,4'-tetrabromo-2,2'-dithienyl.	210	9
5-Acetyl-2,2'-dithienyl.................................	114.5–115.5	12
5,5'-Diacetyl-2,2'-dithienyl.............................	231–232	12
5,5'-Dibenzoyl-2,2'-dithienyl............................	250–252	11
5,5'-Dimethyl-3,3'-diacetyl-2,2'-dithienyl.................	109–111	12
5,5'-Dibenzoyl-3,3'-dibromo-2,2'-dithienyl...............	195–197	11
5-Methyl-5'-carboxy-2,2'-dithienyl......................	197–198	2
2,2'-Dithienyl-5,5'-diacetic acid.........................	217	11
2,2'-Dithienyl-5,5'-dimalonic acid, tetraethyl ester........	111.5–112.5	11
5,5'-Dicarboxaldehyde-3,3',4,4'-tetrachloro-2,2'-dithienyl...	179	9
5-Nitro-2,2'-dithienyl.................................	109	24
5-Nitro-3,3',5'-triiodo-2,2'-dithienyl....................	187–189	14
2,2'-Dithienyl-5-sulfonic acid..........................	Not given	13
3,3'-Dithienyl...	132	7
2,2',5,5'-Tetramethyl-3,3'-dithienyl....................	Liquid, b.p. 148–152 (12 mm.); 142–144 (9)	15
2,2',5,5'-Tetraethyl-3,3'-dithienyl.....................	Liquid, b.p. 195 (14 mm.)	16
2,2',5,5'-Tetrabromo-3,3'-dithienyl....................	137–138	7
2,2',4,4',5,5'-Hexabromo-3,3'-dithienyl..................	183	7
2,2',5,5'-Tetramethyl-4,4'-diacetyl-3,3'-dithienyl..........	90–91	12

α,α-Terthienyl   α,α,α-Quaterthienyl   (11)

C. Physical Properties

No physical constants of the di- and polythienyls other than melting and boiling points are recorded in the literature. Steinkopf has compared the colors of the polythienyls and the polyphenyls as well as the polyphenylpolythienyl compounds.[27]

Tables XV-1 and XV-2 list the physical properties of the known di- and polythienyls and their derivatives. The nomenclature used for the polythienyls is that of Steinkopf and Kohler[24] (see Section B above).

TABLE XV-2. Physical Constants of the Polythienyls

Compound	M.p., °C.	Ref.
α-Terthienyl	94–95	2,3
α-Quaterthienyl	210–211	2,3,5
α-Quinquethienyl	253	2,3
α-Sexithienyl	304	2,3
α-Septithienyl	326–328	2
1-Methyl-α,α-terthienyl	93–94.5	2,3
1,8-Dimethyl-α,α-terthienyl	100–101	2,3
1,8-Diphenyl-α,α-terthienyl	273	2
1,10-Dimethyl-α,α,α-quaterthienyl	184–185	2
	172–173.5	3
1,10-Diphenyl-α,α,α-quaterthienyl	317	2
1,8-Dibromo-α,α-terthienyl	155–156	2
	160–161	3
1,2,3,4,5,6,7,8-Octabromo-α,α-terthienyl	268–269	2
1-Iodo-α,α-terthienyl	146–148	2
1,8-Diiodo-α,α-terthienyl	198–200	2
1,10-Dibromo-α,α,α-quaterthienyl	251	3
1,3,4,7,8,10-Hexabromo-α,α,α-quaterthienyl	256–258	2,5,24
Octabromo-α,α,α-quaterthienyl	297–299	24
1 to 10-Decachloro-α,α,α-quaterthienyl	246–247	2
1 to 10-Decabromo-α,α,α-quaterthienyl	326–328	2,5
Tetrachlorohexaiodo-α,α,α-quaterthienyl	218–220	2
1 to 12-Duodecabromo-α,α,α,α-quinquethienyl	337–338	2
1 to 14-Tetradecabromo-α,α,α,α,α-sexithienyl	368–379	2

II. The Arylthiophenes

Thiophene chemistry actually had its origin in the synthesis of thionessal (tetraphenylthiophene) by Laurent, in 1844, but this compound was not recognized as a thiophene compound until nearly a half century later.

The synthesis of arylthiophenes has received considerable attention, but their chemistry has not been investigated to any great extent.   A few substitution reactions of the phenylthiophenes such as halogenation, mercuration, nitration, and acetylation have been carried out.   In most cases the position of the entering group was not proved.   Some of the more interesting theoretical studies have not been undertaken.   Among these would be a comparison of the reactivity of the hydrogens on the respective phenyl and thienyl radicals with subsequent determination of the orientation of entering groups.   Specifically, one could compare the reactivity of thienyl hydrogens in the 3,4-position with the phenyl hydrogen in 2,5-diphenylthiophene by some simple reaction such as nitration and the position of the nitro group could be determined by destructive oxidation of the thiophene nucleus.   If the nitro group entered the thiophene ring, benzoic acid would be obtained.   If it nitrated the phenyl radical, then a nitrobenzoic acid would be isolated. Similar studies could be carried out with other isomeric diphenylthiophenes to obtain a complete comparison of reactivities.

A. Preparation and Reactions of the Phenylthiophenes

1. 2-Phenylthiophenes

2-Phenylthiophene is prepared by standard ring closure of a β-keto-acid with a phosphorus sulfide.[1,2] Thus, Kues and Paal[1] prepared this compound from benzoylpropionic acid and phosphorus trisulfide (Eq. 1).

$$C_6H_5COCH_2CH_2COONa \xrightarrow[30\%]{P_2S_3} \text{(thiophene)}-C_6H_5 \tag{1}$$

Benzenediazonium chloride and thiophene react in the presence of aluminum chloride to give a phenylthiophene (m.p. 56–57°) that may be a mixture of 2- and 3-phenylthiophene, since the melting point lies between those of the respective isomers.[3]

Gomberg and Bachmann[4] later found that aryldiazonium chlorides reacted with thiophene in the presence of a two per cent excess of caustic to give 2-arylthiophenes. Aniline gave 2-phenylthiophene in 11% yield. Similar reactions may be applied to prepare substituted 2-phenylthiophenes. Thus, Gomberg and Bachmann[4] observed that: p-bromoaniline gave 2-(p-bromophenyl)thiophene (20%); p-chloroaniline gave 2-(p-chlorophenyl)thiophene (24%); p-nitroaniline gave 2-(p-nitrophenyl)-thiophene (23%); and m-cyanoaniline gave 2-(m-cyanophenyl)thiophene (15%). 2-(p-Tolyl)thiophene was prepared by ring closure from p-toluylpropionic acid and phosphorus trisulfide.[2] When acetophenone, acetone, and phosphorus pentasulfide were heated in a sealed tube at 120° for fifteen minutes, 5-methyl 2-phenylthiophene was obtained in 60–70% yield.[5] 2-Phenylthiophene has been prepared from the action of sulfur on phenylbutane (5%), 1-phenylbutenes (25–35%), and 1-phenylbutadiene (8%).[5a] Similarly, 4-methyl-2-phenylthiophene is obtained from isoamylbenzene and sulfur.

[1] Kues and Paal, *Ber.*, **19**, 3141 (1886).
[2] Chrzaszczewska, *Roczniki Chem.*, **5**, 1, 33 (1925).
[3] Mohlau and Berger, *Ber.*, **26**, 1994 (1893).
[4] Gomberg and Bachmann, *J. Am. Chem. Soc.*, **46**, 2339 (1924).
[5] Paal, *Ber.*, **18**, 367 (1885).
[5a] Broun and Voronkov, *Doklady Akad. Nauk (U. S. S. R.)*, **59**, 1293 (1941); *Chem. Abstr.*, **43**, 2614 (1949).

2-Phenylthiophene may be iodinated,[2] nitrated,[2] mercurated,[5a] and acylated[6] in the 5-position. Exhaustive bromination of 2-phenylthiophene yields a tetrabromo-2-phenylthiophene, presumably the 2-(p-bromophenyl)-3,4,5-tribromothiophene.[1] Other substitution reactions are not reported.

2. 3-Phenylthiophenes

3-Phenylthiophene is prepared by ring closure of phenylsuccinic acid with phosphorus pentasulfide.[2] The yield was 59% of theory. Bamberger reported that the violent reaction of N-nitrosoacetanilide and thiophene produced 3-phenylthiophene.[7] The violence of the reaction was abated by use of a solvent. Bamberger was also able to show that the product of Mohlau and Berger,[3] m.p. 56–57°, contained 3-phenylthiophene. Ring closure of 2-phenyl-2-butene with sulfur yielded 3-phenylthiophene[8,9] (Eq. 2). In a like manner, 2-methyl-4-phenylthiophene and 2-methyl-3-phenylthiophene have been prepared from 2-phenyl-2-pentene and 3-phenyl-2-pentene, respectively.[5a]

$$
\underset{\underset{C_6H_5-C=CHCH_3}{|}}{CH_3} \quad \xrightarrow[44\%]{\text{S, reflux 7 hrs. at 205°}} \quad \text{(structure)} \qquad (2)
$$

Similar reactions can be used for the preparation of substituted 3-phenylthiophenes. 3-Phenyl-4-methylthiophene was obtained in 36% yield from the reaction of sulfur with 2-methyl-3-phenyl-2-butene.[8] Paal and Puschel[10] prepared 3-phenyl-5-methylthiophene (2-methyl-4-phenylthiophene) from sodium α-phenyllevulinate and phosphorus trisulfide (Eq. 3). 3-(p-Anisyl)thiophene and 3-(p-tolyl)thiophene have been prepared by ring closure of the appropriate succinic acids.[2]

$$
CH_3COCH_2CH(C_6H_5)COONa \quad \xrightarrow{P_2S_3} \quad \text{(structure)} \qquad (3)
$$

3-Phenylthiophene can be nitrated to produce a mononitro derivative which in turn can be reduced to an amino-3-phenylthiophene.[2] Presumably, the thiophene is substituted in the 2-position.

[6] Steinkopf and Petersdorff, *Ann.*, **543**, 119 (1940).
[7] Bamberger, *Ber.*, **30**, 366 (1897).
[8] Broun and Voronkov, *Chem. Abstr.*, **42**, 1591 (1948); *J. Gen. Chem. (U. S. S. R.)*, **17**, 1162 (1947).
[9] Broun, Voronkov, and Shlyakhter, *Chem. Abstr.*, **43**, 5392 (1949); *Nauch. Byull. Leningrad. Gosudarst. Univ.*, No. **18**, 11 (1947); No. **20**, 6 (1948).
[10] Paal and Puschel, *Ber.*, **20**, 2557 (1887).

3. 2,4-Diphenylthiophene

The 2,4-diphenylthiophenes are prepared by several general types of ring closure. Baumann and Fromm[11] first reported that a mixture of 2,4- and 2,5-diphenylthiophene resulted from treating cinnamic acid with sulfur at 240°. Since styrene also gives these products when treated with sulfur, it is likely that styrene is an intermediate in the ring closure of cinnamic acid. These same investigators[12] also reported that acetophenone when treated with hydrogen sulfide and hydrogen chloride gave a variety of products including 2,4-diphenylthiophene. Campaigne[13] reinvestigated this reaction and improved the yield by isolating an intermediate, $C_{24}H_{22}S_2$, which gave the thiophene derivative (Eq. 4).

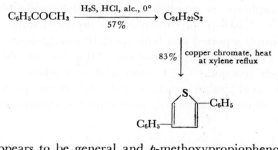

$$C_6H_5COCH_3 \xrightarrow[57\%]{H_2S, HCl, alc., 0°} C_{24}H_{22}S_2$$

$$83\% \Bigg\downarrow \begin{array}{c} \text{copper chromate, heat} \\ \text{at xylene reflux} \end{array} \qquad (4)$$

The reaction appears to be general and p-methoxypropiophenone gives 3,5-dimethyl-2,4-di-(p-anisyl)thiophene in 66% yield.[13] The latter compound can be demethylated and the phenol derivative isolated.

Another general method involves fusing the anils of phenyl alkyl ketones with sulfur at 240°. For example, acetophenone anil gives 2,4-diphenylthiophene,[14] while propiophenone anil yields 3,5-dimethyl-2,4-diphenylthiophene and butyrophenone anil yields 3,5-diethyl-2,4-diphenylthiophene[15] (Eq. 5).

$$\begin{array}{c} R—CH_2 \\ | \\ C_6H_5C=N—C_6H_5 \end{array} \xrightarrow[20-30\%]{S, 240°} \begin{array}{c} \text{thiophene} \end{array} \qquad (5)$$

Glass and Reid[16] have prepared 2,4-diphenylthiophene in 18% yield simply by heating ethylbenzene with sulfur at 340–350° in a pressure reactor. Styrene was isolated from this reaction.

[11] Baumann and Fromm, *Ber.*, **28**, 890 (1895).
[12] Baumann and Fromm, *Ber.*, **28**, 895 (1895).
[13] Campaigne, *J. Am. Chem. Soc.*, **66**, 684 (1944).
[14] Bogert and Herrera, *J. Am. Chem. Soc.*, **45**, 238 (1923).
[15] Bogert and Andersen, *J. Am. Chem. Soc.*, **48**, 223 (1926).
[16] Glass and Reid, *J. Am. Chem. Soc.*, **51**, 3428 (1929).

Willgerodt and co-workers noted the presence of both 2,4- and 2,5-diphenyl- and di-(p-tolyl)thiophenes in the Willgerodt reaction when aliphatic-aromatic ketones were treated with ammonium sulfide.[17-19]

2,4-Diphenylthiophene forms a 5-mercurichloride derivative.[13,14] It is nitrated by acetyl nitrate to give a mixture of nitro compounds difficult to separate.   According to Andersen,[20] this compound reacted with phenylmercurihydroxide to produce 2,4-diphenyl-5-thienylphenylmercury.

4. 2,5-Diphenylthiophenes

Diphenacyl, $C_6H_5COCH_2CH_2COC_6H_5$, when heated at 160–170° with phosphorus pentasulfide gives 2,5-diphenylthiophene in 60–70% yields.[21,22] 2,5-Di-(p-tolyl)thiophene is prepared similarly.[22a] Baumann and Fromm[11] reported that both the 2,4- and 2,5-isomers are formed by heating cinnamic acid and sulfur.   Mixtures are also formed in the Willgerodt reaction.[17-19] Fromm and co-workers[23] reinvestigated the cinnamic acid – sulfur reaction and studied the reactions of the two isomeric diphenylthiophenes, producing tetrabromo and polynitro derivatives.

5. 3,4-Diphenylthiophenes

3,4-Diphenylthiophene has been prepared by decarboxylating 3,4-diphenyl-2,5-thiophenedicarboxylic acid (see ring closure method of Hinsberg, Chapter XII, Sections III and IV, by gentle heating at its melting point (360°).[24-26] 3,4-Di-(p-tolyl)thiophene has also been prepared by this method.[27]

Hinsberg[24] studied some of the oxidation reactions of 3,4-diphenylthiophene and found that it gave a sulfone.   A similar product has also been obtained by Backer and Stevens.[28]   No other reactions are reported.

[17] Willgerodt and Merk, *J. prakt. Chem.*, [2] **80**, 192 (1909).
[18] Willgerodt and Hambrecht, *J. prakt. Chem.*, [2] **81**, 74 (1910).
[19] Willgerodt and Scholtz, *J. prakt. Chem.*, [2] **81**, 382 (1910).
[20] Andersen, U. S. Pat. 2,085,065 (1937).
[21] Kapf and Paal, *Ber.*, **21**, 3053 (1888).
[22] Bohme, Pfeifer, and Schneider, *Ber.*, **B75**, 900 (1942).
[22a] Hollemann, *Rec. trav. chim.*, **6**, 60 (1887).
[23] Fromm, Fantl, and Leibsohn, *Ann.*, **457**, 267 (1927).
[24] Hinsberg, *Ber.*, **48**, 1611 (1915).
[25] Backer, Bult, and Stevens, *Rec. trav. chim.*, **56**, 1063 (1937).
[26] Backer and Stevens, *Rec. trav. chim.*, **59**, 423 (1940).
[27] Backer and Stevens, *Rec. trav. chim.*, **59**, 899 (1940).
[28] Backer, Stevens, and van der Bij, *Rec. trav. chim.*, **59**, 1141 (1940).

6. 2,3,5-Triphenylthiophene

When desylacetophenone, $C_6H_5COCH(C_6H_5)CH_2COC_6H_5$, is heated with phosphorus pentasulfide at 150°, 2,3,5-triphenylthiophene results.[29] The same compound is reported to form from dibenzoylstyrene, hydrogen sulfide, and hydrogen chloride, but the melting points of the compounds from the two procedures do not agree.[30]

7. 2,3,4,5-Tetraphenylthiophene (Thionessal)

2,3,4,5-Tetraphenylthiophene was the first synthetic thiophene compound reported in the literature. Laurent,[31] in 1844, found that a compound containing sulfur and melting at 178° was formed when polymeric thiobenzaldehyde was destructively distilled, but no structure for this compound was proposed, although Laurent noted that it formed nitro and dibromo derivatives. In 1889, Renard[32] described a "phenylthiophene," m.p. 170°, b.p. 300°, that obtained by passing toluene and sulfur through a hot tube. It was suggested by Magnanini and Angeli the same year that Laurent's compound might be a thiophene derivative,[33] and in 1891 this was shown to be true when Baumann and Fromm synthesized the material from stilbene and sulfur.[34] This preparation is described by Baumann and Klett[35] as giving tetraphenylthiophene in good yields (Eq. 6).

$$C_6H_5\text{---CH} \quad HC\text{---}C_6H_5 \atop C_6H_5\text{---CH} \quad HC\text{---}C_6H_5 \; + \; 3S \; \xrightarrow[60-70\%]{250°} \; 2H_2S \; + \; C_6H_5\text{---}\overset{S}{\diagup\diagdown}\text{---}C_6H_5 \atop C_6H_5\text{---}\underset{\quad}{\diagdown\diagup}\text{---}C_6H_5 \tag{6}$$

Adaptations of this method for the preparation of tetraphenylthiophene involve ring closures by heating toluene,[32,36] phenylacetic acid[37] or its barium salt,[38] desoxybenzoin,[37] benzyl alcohol,[39] or thiobenzanilide[40] with sulfur. A somewhat similar synthesis effects ring closure by heating

[29] Smith, J. Chem. Soc., 57, 643 (1890).
[30] Mitra, J. Indian Chem. Soc., 15, 59 (1938).
[31] Laurent, Ann., 52, 348 (1844).
[32] Renard, Compt. rend., 109, 699 (1889).
[33] Magnanini and Angeli, Ber., 22, 856 (1889).
[34] Baumann and Fromm, Ber., 24, 1456 (1891).
[35] Baumann and Klett, Ber., 24, 3307 (1891).
[36] Aronstein and van Nierop, Rec. trav. chim., 21, 448 (1903).
[37] Ziegler, Ber., 23, 2472 (1890).
[38] Forst, Ann., 178, 370 (1875).
[39] Szperl and Wierusz-Kowalski, Chemik Polski, 15, 19 (1917).
[40] Chapman, J. Chem. Soc., 1928, 1894.

1,2,3,4-tetraphenylbutadiene at 250° with sulfur.[41] Another synthesis of tetraphenylthiophene involves heating benzyl sulfide[38,42] or benzyl disulfide[42,43] at the reflux temperature. Dry distillation of sodium benzylsulfonate[44] or sodium thiobenzoate[45] gives tetraphenylthiophene. According to Fromm and Klinger,[46] dry distillation of benzoyl disulfide, benzoyl sulfide, and thiobenzoic acid yields a material of unknown structure, m.p. 172°, which when treated with ammonium sulfide forms tetraphenylthiophene. Bulmer and Mann[47] indicated that benzoyl disulfide, $C_6H_5CO-SS-COC_6H_5$, distils to give a 2,3,4,5-tetraphenylthiophene nonasulfide, m.p. 165.5–166°. Ammonium sulfide or potassium permanganate in acetone converts the nonasulfide to tetraphenylthiophene. Bigelow has reported the formation of tetraphenylthiophene along with several other products, by heating benzalaniline at 230° with carbon disulfide.[48]

Tolantetrasulfide is described by Fromm and Schmoldt[45] as being converted quantitatively to tetraphenylthiophene merely by boiling the compound with alcoholic potassium hydroxide (Eq. 7). Distillation

$$2 \quad C_6H_5-\overset{S-S}{\underset{S-S}{C-C}}-C_6H_5 \xrightarrow[\text{quant.}]{\text{alc. KOH, reflux}} \quad \tag{7}$$

over copper powder or chemical reduction of the tolantetrasulfide also produces tetraphenylthiophene.[45] In a somewhat similar category is the reaction of diphenylthiadiazole, which, when heated alone or in an aromatic solvent, gives tetraphenylthiophene[49] (Eq. 8).

$$2 \quad \overset{C_6H_5-C-N}{\underset{C_6H_5-C-S}{}}\!\!\diagdown N \longrightarrow 2N_2 + S + \tag{8}$$

Dilthey and co-workers[50–53] have described a novel synthesis of tetraphenylthiophene by replacement of the carbonyl group of tetraphenylcyclopentadienone by sulfur (Eq. 9).

[41] Smith and Hoehn, *J. Am. Chem. Soc.*, **63**, 1184 (1941).
[42] Fromm and Achert, *Ber.*, **36**, 534 (1903).
[43] Marcker, *Ann.*, **136**, 75 (1865).
[44] Fromm and de Seixas Palma, *Ber.*, **39**, 3308 (1906).
[45] Fromm and Schmoldt, *Ber.*, **40**, 2861 (1907).
[46] Fromm and Klinger, *Ann.*, **394**, 342 (1912).
[47] Bulmer and Mann, *J. Chem. Soc.*, **1945**, 677.
[48] Bigelow, *J. Am. Chem. Soc.*, **47**, 193 (1925).
[49] Staudinger and Siegwart, *Ber.*, **49**, 1918 (1916).
[50] Dilthey, Schommer, Hoschen, and Dierichs, *Ber.*, **B68**, 1159 (1935).
[51] Dilthey, Ger. Pat. 628,954 (1936).
[52] Dilthey, Graef, Dierichs, and Josten, *J. prakt. Chem.*, [2] **151**, 185 (1938).
[53] Dilthey and Graef, *J. prakt. Chem.*, [2] **151**, 257 (1938).

$$C_6H_5 - \overset{\displaystyle O}{\underset{C_6H_5}{||}} - C_6H_5 \quad \xrightarrow{S, \ 350°} \quad C_6H_5 - \overset{\displaystyle S}{\underset{C_6H_5}{}} - C_6H_5 \tag{9}$$

The derivatives of tetraphenylthiophene in which the positions of substituted phenyl groups are known, are difficult to prepare other than by ring closure. A 2-(p-anisyl)-3,4,5-triphenylthiophene is reported from the reaction of 2-amyl[anisyl?]-3,4,5-triphenylcyclopentadienone and sulfur.[52] Polymeric o-methoxythiobenzaldehyde is converted by Laurent's method[31] to tetra-o-anisylthiophene.[54] The p-anisyl isomer is prepared by the action of sulfur on p,p'-dimethoxystilbene.[10,54] A dichloro and a tetrachloro derivative of tetraphenylthiophene[42] have been obtained by chlorination with phosphorus pentachloride at 150–165°. Bromine yields a variety of bromo derivatives.[55,56] Nitration yields a mixture of nitro derivatives ranging from the mono to the hexanitro derivative.[53] The fact that isomeric dinitrotetraphenylthiophenes could be obtained indicated a random substitution of the phenyl radicals although these investigators, as well as Steinkopf,[57] attempted to assign structural formulas to the products obtained. The mono- and dinitro derivatives could be reduced to the respective amines and diazotized.

Tetraphenylthiophene appears to be the most stable of the thiophene derivatives. It boils without decomposition at about 460° and can be passed over iron or copper powder in a tube at dull red heat with only a small amount of decomposition.[58]

Tetraphenylthiophene can be oxidized to the sulfone with hydrogen peroxide.[53] More vigorous oxidation with hydrochloric acid and potassium chlorate gives cis-α,α'-dibenzoylstilbene.[55] Reduction to 1,2,3,4-tetraphenylbutane can be effected with tin and hydrochloric acid.[56] Steinkopf produced a polynuclear ring system by treating tetraphenylthiophene with aluminum chloride at 120°.[59] The two compounds isolated were alleged to have these structures:

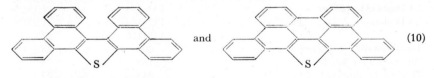

and   (10)

[54] Kopp, Ber., **25**, 600 (1892).
[55] Fleischer, Ann., **144**, 195 (1867).
[56] Berlin, Ann., **153**, 130 (1870).
[57] Steinkopf, Die Chemie des Thiophens. Steinkopff, Dresden, 1941, p. 137.
[58] Dorn, Ann., **153**, 350 (1870).
[59] Steinkopf, Ann., **519**, 297 (1935).

B. Miscellaneous Arylthiophenes

Steinkopf and Kuhnel[60] have prepared 2-(5-phenyl-2-thienyl)cincho-ninic acid by condensation of 2-acetyl-5-phenylthiophene with isatin in the Pfitzinger reaction. The acid was decarboxylated to 2-(2-quinolyl)-5-phenylthiophene, m.p. 144–145.5°. 3,4-Di-(2-furyl)thiophene has been prepared by decarboxylating the 3,4-di-(2-furyl)-2,5-thiophene-dicarboxylic acid at its melting point.[27]

2-Thienylpyridines such as 2,6-diphenyl-4-(2-thienyl)pyridine (m.p. 157°), 2,6-di-(2-thienyl)-4-phenylpyridine (m.p. 126°), and 2,4,6-tri-(2-thienyl)pyridine (m.p. 132°) have been reported.[61] 2,3,4,5-Tetra-(4-pyridyl)thiophene (m.p. 251.8–252.6°) has been prepared by the action of sulfur on 4-picoline.[62] The 2-thienylquinolines are discussed in Chapter IX.

C. Physical Properties of the Arylthiophenes

The melting points and a few boiling points of the arylthiophenes are listed in Table XV-3. Since no studies on the orientation of entering substituents in substitution reactions have been made, compounds of uncertain structure are omitted from the table and the reader is referred to the original literature for these compounds. In some instances pertinent melting points have been included in the text. Very little is known about this series of compounds despite the numerous references

TABLE XV-3. Physical Constants of the Arylthiophenes

Derivative	M.p., °C.	Ref.
2,4-Diphenyl-3,5-dimethyl-...................	163.8	15
2,4-Diphenyl-3,5-diethyl-......................	286	15
2,4-Di-(p-anisyl)-3,5-dimethyl-.................	112.3–112.8	13
2,4-Di-(p-hydroxyphenyl)-3,5-dimethyl-..........	194–196	13
2,4-Di-(p-acetoxyphenyl)-3,5-dimethyl-..........	125.9–126.9	13
2,4-Diphenyl-5-mercurichloride................	223	13,14
Tetrabromo-diphenyl-........................	150	23
2,4-Diphenyl-, picrate.......................	133–134	11,13,23
2,5-Diphenyl-...............................	152–153	21,23
	155–156	22
Tetrabromo-2,5-diphenyl-.....................	203	23
Dinitro-2,5-diphenyl-........................	189	23
Trinitro-2,5-diphenyl-.......................	243	23
2,5-Di-(p-tolyl)-.............................	171	18,22a

Table continued

[60] Steinkopf and Kuhnel, Ann., **545**, 33 (1940).
[61] Steinkopf and Popp, Ann., **540**, 24 (1939).
[62] Thayer and Corson, J. Am. Chem. Soc., **70**, 2230 (1948).

TABLE XV-3 (*Continued*)

Derivative	M.p., °C.	Ref.
3,4-Diphenyl-	114	24–26
3,4-Di-(*p*-tolyl)-	86–87.5	27
3,4-Di-(2-furyl)-	Liquid, b.p. 172–173 (17)	27
2,3,5-Triphenyl-	127	29
	157	30
2,3,4,5-Tetraphenyl-	184	31–59
2,3,4,5-Tetra-(*o*-anisyl)-	136	54
2,3,4,5-Tetra-(*p*-anisyl)-	217	11,54
2-Phenyl-	42–43	1,2,4
	34–34.5	5a
	b.p. 256.1 (760)	5a
2-Phenyl-4-methyl-	17.2	5a
	b.p. 278.6 (764)	5a
2-(*p*-Tolyl)-	63–64	2
2-(*p*-Bromophenyl)-	100	4
2-(*p*-Chlorophenyl)-	83	4
2-(*p*-Nitrophenyl)-	137–138	4
2-(*m*-Cyanophenyl)-	53–54	4
2-Phenyl-5-methyl-	49–51	5
2-Phenyl-5-nitro-	74	2
2-Phenyl-5-iodo-	76–77	2
2-Phenyl-5-acetyl-	115–118	6
2-Phenyl-dibromo-	55–56	1
2-(*p*-Bromophenyl)-3,4,5-tribromo-	145–146	1
2-Phenyl-5-(2-quinolyl)-	144–145.5	60
3-Phenyl-	91–92	2,7,8
	b.p. 254–256 (758)	8
2-Methyl-4-phenyl-	73.5–73.7	5a,9,10
	b.p. 272–274 (750)	5a
2-Methyl-3-phenyl-	−.5 to −.2	5a,9
	b.p. 258.8–260 (760)	
	b.p. 136–136.5 (16)	
	b.p. 86.7–87.2 (1)	
3-Phenyl-4-methyl-	Liquid at −26, b.p. 110–110.5 (3)	8,9
2-Ethyl-3-phenyl-5-methyl-	b.p. 258.5–260	9
3-(*p*-Anisyl)-	129	2
3-(*p*-Tolyl)-	111–112	2
3-Phenyl-2-nitro-	141	2
3-Phenyl-2-amino-(HCl)-	Not reported	2
2,4-Diphenyl-	120.6–121.5	13
	119.5–120.5	11,16
	122.5	14
	119–124	23

given.   No precise measurements of physical constants have been made on any of the compounds in this series.   A precise molecular weight determination of tetraphenylthiophene to an accuracy of $\pm 0.5\%$ has been described.   The method employs the Cottrell boiling point apparatus and employs benzene as the solvent.[63]

[63] Swietoslawski, Waszkosienrenski, and Romei, *Bull. soc. chim.*, **35**, 542 (1924).

CHAPTER XVI

Selenophene, Tetrahydroselenophene, Tellurophene, and Tetrahydrotellurophene

Introduction

Selenophene and tetrahydroselenophene are relatively well known, but their chemistry is not well defined. Selenophene differs from thiophene in degree of reactivity but it appears to undergo the same type of reactions as thiophene, albeit in somewhat lower yields. The selenium hetero-atom in selenophene does not appear to exercise as great a directing influence on entering groups as the sulfur atom in thiophene, since it has been shown that electron-withdrawing groups such as the nitro group direct the entering group toward the *meta* position. Thus, the nitration of 2-nitroselenophene yields 2,4-dinitroselenophene, rather than the 2,5-dinitro isomer that would be expected by analogy with the nitration of 2-nitrothiophene. It will be an interesting comparison to examine the orientation of entering groups in the heterocyclic series of furan, thiophene, selenophene, and tellurophene and to establish with some certainty the exact directing abilities of the heavier atoms on substitution in the heterocyclic nucleus. No other series of compounds enabling equal resonance and containing elements from a periodic group is known in all of organic chemistry. It would appear that a considerable amount of fundamental knowledge could be obtained by an extended study on this field.

Tellurophene appears to have been isolated in one instance, but no reactions of the compound were reported. Tetrahydrotellurophene has been synthesized and its physical properties and a few of its reactions determined.

Nomenclature

The nomenclature of selenophene compounds will be based entirely on that of thiophene compounds (see Chapter I). In general, since only the simpler derivatives are known, the nomenclature illustrated below is not complex, but it is suggested that the terms for the selenophene radicals be selenienyl for C_4H_3Se—, selenenyl for $C_4H_3SeCH_2$—, and selenenylidene (or selenenal) for $C_4H_3SeCH=$.   The nomenclature for the hydrogenated and aromatic forms will then be the same as for thiophene, *i.e.*, selenolane, 2- or 3-selenolene, and selenophene.

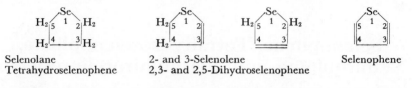

Selenolane
Tetrahydroselenophene

2- and 3-Selenolene
2,3- and 2,5-Dihydroselenophene

Selenophene

The nomenclature of tellurophene compounds has not been established, since no ring-substituted derivatives other than 1,1-derivatives of tellurophene and tetrahydrotellurophene (tellurolane) are known.

I. Selenophene and Its Derivatives

A. Preparation

1. Selenophene

Selenophene itself was not the first selenophene type compound prepared (see *2,5-dimethylselenophene* below).   Its synthesis was first reported in 1909 by Ida Foa,[1] who believed she had prepared this compound by the standard ring-closure procedure used in the thiophene series, *i.e.*, heating disodium succinate with phosphorus triselenide.   The product was described as a yellow mobile liquid, boiling at 147–149° at 250 mm. of mercury.   It was reported to give the Laubenheimer reaction and a dark carmine-red color with isatin and sulfuric acid.   It is unlikely that Foa produced selenophene, since the boiling point recorded in her publication is far too high for selenophene.

Selenophene was synthesized in 1927 by Mazza and Solazzo[2] from acetylene and selenium;   they reported that pure, dry acetylene reacted with selenium at 250–300° with evolution of flame to produce both selenophene and selenonaphthene.   Briscoe and collaborators[3,4] independently confirmed this synthesis and found better means of controlling the reaction.   Yields as high as 15% of selenophene, based on selenium, were reported.   Suginome and Umezawa[5] obtained a 35% yield of selenophene (based on selenium used) by modifying the method of

[1] Foa, *Gazz. chim. ital.*, **39**, II, 527 (1909).
[2] Mazza and Solazzo, *Rend. accad. sci. Napoli*, [3] **33**, 236 (1927).
[3] Briscoe and Peel, *J. Chem. Soc.*, **1928**, 1741.
[4] Briscoe, Peel, and Robinson, *J. Chem. Soc.*, **1928**, 2628.
[5] Suginome and Umezawa, *Chem. Abstr.*, **30**, 5981 (1936); *Bull. Chem. Soc. Japan* **11**, 157 (1936).

Briscoe *et al.*[3,4] Because of the relative unavailability of this article, a rough translation of the modification of Suginome and Umezawa[5] for the preparation of selenophene is included:

"Pure acetylene is allowed to react at 350–370° with 20 g. of selenium contained in a porcelain boat in a porcelain tube. After the reaction is complete a black, tarry substance remains in the (selenium) boat. This residue, as Briscoe and co-workers already have noticed, acts as a catalyst and, indeed, we have found that the yield of selenophene is increased by mixing fresh selenium with this catalyst. Further, the yield depends upon the velocity of the gas (acetylene); for that reason the reaction must be completed in about twenty-four hours. By repetition of this process [apparently the process was carried out nine times] one receives a dark brown oil (sp. gr. = 1.47) with some unchanged selenium. The raw oil is fractionated twice through a Ladenburg flask, whereby the portion obtained at 110° represents 110 g. of pure selenophene that was obtained from 192 g. of crude oil. The yield of selenophene calculates 57% of crude liquid and 35% of the selenium."

In 1933, another improvement of this process[3,4] was announced, wherein the selenium or aluminum selenide, Al_2Se_3, was deposited on roasted bauxite before contacting with acetylene.[6] While the yield was reported to be only 15%, operating difficulties appear to have been reduced.

Selenophene has been prepared from furan by passing the latter over alumina at 450° in a current of hydrogen selenide. The yield of selenophene was 23%.[7]

2. Alkyl- and Arylselenophenes

2,5-Dimethylselenophene was prepared in 1885 by Paal.[8] The synthesis comprised heating hydrogen selenide with acetonylacetone in a sealed tube at 180° (Eq. 1). Bogert and Andersen[9] were not able to

$$CH_3COCH_2CH_2COCH_3 \xrightarrow{\text{H}_2\text{Se, }180°} H_3C \underset{\text{Se}}{\bigcirc} CH_3 + H_2O \qquad (1)$$

isolate 2-methylselenophene from the reaction of levulinic acid and phosphorus triselenide. They were successful, however, in cyclizing acetonylacetone to 2,5-dimethylselenophene with phosphorus penta-selenide in 26% yield.

[6] McMahon, Pearson, and Robinson, *J. Chem. Soc.*, **1933**, 1644.
[7] Yur'ev, *Chem. Abstr.*, **41**, 1654 (1947); *J. Gen. Chem. (U. S. S. R.)*, **16**, 851 (1946).
[8] Paal, *Ber.*, **18**, 2255 (1885).
[9] Bogert and Andersen, *J. Am. Chem. Soc.*, **48**, 223 (1926).

Bogert and Herrera[10] and Bogert and Andersen[9] have prepared 2,4-diphenylselenophene by fusion of acetophenone anil with selenium (Eq. 2).   2,4-Di-(p-tolyl)selenophene was prepared in the same manner

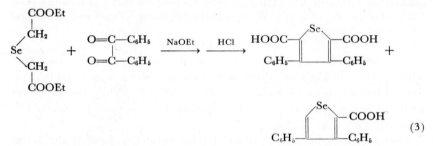

$$\tag{2}$$

in somewhat lower yield (20.5%).

Backer and Stevens applied the Hinsberg ring-closure (see Chapter XII, Sect. IV) to selenodiglycolic acid and benzil and obtained a mixture of 3,4-diphenyl-2,5-selenophenedicarboxylic acid and 3,4-diphenyl-2-selenophenecarboxylic acid[11] (Eq. 3).   Decarboxylation of the above

$$\tag{3}$$

acids yields 3,4-diphenylselenophene.

Tetraphenylcyclopentadienone when fused with sulfur or selenium is reported to give the corresponding tetraphenylthiophene and tetraphenylselenophene.[12]

B. Chemical Reactions

Briscoe and Peel[3] were the first investigators to study the chemistry of selenophene. They reported it to be unaffected by boiling water, sodium hydroxide, or concentrated hydrochloric acid.   It did not form a picrate or a methiodide.   Unlike, thiophene, the compound is not affected by potassium permanganate in acetone solution.   It is not reduced by zinc and hydrochloric acid, nor is it hydrogenated with nickel on pumice at 250° in a stream of hydrogen.   Sulfuric acid causes selenophene to resinify to a green-black mass.   Selenophene gives the indophenine test (see Chapter I) with isatin and sulfuric acid.   It appears

[10] Bogert and Herrera, *J. Am. Chem. Soc.*, **45**, 238 (1923).
[11] Backer and Stevens, *Rec. trav. chim.*, **59**, 423 (1940).
[12] Dilthey, Ger. Pat. 628,954 (1936).

to sulfonate in acetic anhydride and sulfuric acid. With nitric acid, it reacts rapidly to give a red tar, but no pure nitro derivative could be separated. With bromine in carbon disulfide, it gives tetrabromo-selenophene in 70% yield but fails to give an iodo compound under similar conditions. With chlorine in carbon disulfide, an unstable tetrachloro derivative was obtained which the investigators called tetrachloro-selenophene, but this is apparently the chlorine-addition product obtained by Suginome and Umezawa[5] at a later date. Selenophene forms an addition compound (m.p. 57°) with triphenylmethane.[6]

Umezawa has undertaken the only organized studies of the chemistry of selenophene. His work makes it appear that thiophene and seleno-phene are comparable in chemical behavior. If one can base relative reactivity on yields obtained in similar reactions, then one observes that thiophene is more reactive than selenophene. One outstanding difference is in the further substitution of the selenophene ring when it is substituted with an electron-withdrawing group, *i.e.*, the nitro group. In the thio-phene series the sulfur atom still controls further substitution and 2-nitro-thiophene nitrates to give predominantly 2,5-dinitrothiophene. In the case of 2-nitroselenophene, only 2,4-dinitroselenophene is obtained.

Umezawa has not reported attempts to alkylate selenophene but he has reported that acetyl chloride reacts with selenophene in benzene or carbon disulfide solvent in the presence of stannic chloride to produce a 42% yield of 2-acetylselenophene.[13] Propionyl chloride gives 2-pro-pionylselenophene. 2-Benzoylselenophene is prepared in 7% yield through the action of benzoyl chloride on selenophene in the presence of phosphorus pentoxide. Bogert and Andersen[9] also obtained a 7% yield of 3-(*o*-carboxybenzoyl)-2,5-dimethylselenophene from the reaction of 2,5-dimethylselenophene, phthalic anhydride, and aluminum chloride in a carbon disulfide solvent (Eq. 4).

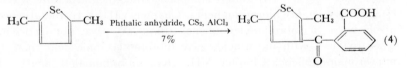

$$\text{(4)}$$

2-Acetylselenophene can be oxidized to 2-selenophenecarboxylic acid with strong alkaline permanganate.[13] In dilute alkali with potas-sium permanganate, it yields 2-selenienylglyoxylic acid. 2-Acetylseleno-phene condenses with benzaldehyde in the conventional manner to produce 2-cinnamoylselenophene (Eq. 5).

[13] Umezawa, *Chem. Abstr.*, **33**, 6303 (1939); *Bull. Chem. Soc. Japan*, **14**, 155 (1939).

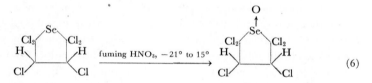

$$\text{—COCH}_3 \xrightarrow{\text{C}_6\text{H}_5\text{CHO, heat}} \text{—COCH=CH—C}_6\text{H}_5 + \text{H}_2\text{O} \tag{5}$$

Chlorination of selenophene at 50–60° gives a mixture of 2-chloro-and 2,5-dichloroselenophene. Exhaustive chlorination gives 2,2,3,4,5,5-hexachloroselenolane.[5] At −15° in carbon disulfide solution, 2,3,4,5-tetrachloroselenolane is obtained by the action of chlorine on selenophene. This compound, when heated, is reported to lose two moles of hydrogen chloride and yield 2,5-dichloroselenophene and a compound considered to be 2,2,5,5-tetrachloroselenolane. In view of the work on compounds of this type in the thiophene series, neither the 2,5-dichloro-isomer nor the 2,2,5,5-tetrachloroselenolane would be expected from pyrolysis (see Chapter VII). In the latter case, the compound designated as 2,2,5,5-tetrachloroselenolane[5] probably is one of the six geometric isomers of 2,3,4,5-tetrachloroselenolane. The chlorinated addition products react with fuming nitric acid at −21 to 15° to give the 1-oxide derivative[5] (Eq. 6). Bromination of selenophene in carbon disulfide solution at

$$\text{fuming HNO}_3, \ -21° \text{ to } 15° \tag{6}$$

−15° yields a compound referred to as "1,1,2,2,5,5-hexabromoseleno-phene" (m.p. 152°) which when washed with water yields "2,2,5,5-tetrabromoselenophene" (m.p. 97°).[5] Nitric acid gives a 1-oxide deriva-tive (m.p. 128.5–130°). At higher temperatures, bromine gives 2-bromo-, 2,5-dibromo-, and a tribromoselenophene [Suginome and Umezawa report this as 2,3,5-tribromoselenophene but the structure was not established (see Trichlorothiophenes, Chapter VII)]. In the absence of a solvent, a "tetrabromoselenophene" (m.p. 102°) was obtained which, when oxidized with nitric acid, gave dibromosuccinnic acid (note that tetrabromothiophene, Chapter VII, gives dibromomaleic acid). The formation of this acid rather than dibromomaleic acid indicates the product of bromination of selenophene in the absence of a solvent (in this work,[5] as well as by Briscoe and Peel[3] who obtained the same product) to be a bromine addition product, i.e., 2,3,4,5-tetrabromoselenolane rather than 2,3,4,5-tetrabromoselenophene. Briscoe, Peel, and Young[14]

[14] Briscoe, Peel, and Young, *J. Chem. Soc.*, **1929**, 2589.

have obtained this same "tetrabromoselenophene" from the action of bromine-water on the 2,5-dimercuriacetate of selenophene.

2,5-Diiodoselenophene is prepared from the action of potassium triiodide in acetone on the 2,5-dimercuriacetate of selenophene[14] (Eq. 7).

$$\text{(7)}$$

Exhaustive chlorination of 2,5-dibromoselenophene does not give tetrachloroselenophene as might be expected from analogy to the exhaustive chlorination of 2,5-dibromothiophene but, rather, it gives the chlorine addition product, 2,5-dibromo-2,3,4,5-tetrachloroselenolane[5] (Eq. 8).

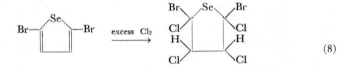

$$\text{(8)}$$

Bogert and Andersen found that 2,4-diphenylselenophene was converted by bromine in glacial acetic acid to 3,5-dibromo-2,4-diphenylselenophene in 80% yield.[9]   In the same solvent, an excess of bromine yielded a tribromo derivative (36%, m.p. 126.7°).   A tetrabromo derivative (m.p. 176.5°) of 2,4-diphenylselenophene is obtained when the compound reacts with liquid bromine in the sunlight without solvent.

Briscoe and Peel[3] reported that nitric acid and selenophene gave a red tar from which no nitroselenophene could be isolated.   Umezawa[15] confirms this in reporting that selenophene and nitric acid give an explosive reaction.   Acetyl nitrate, however, gives a 15% yield of 2-nitroselenophene.   This compound can be nitrated by nitric and sulfuric acids to 2,4-dinitroselenophene.   The structure of this compound was established in the following manner[16] (Eq. 9).   3-Nitroselenophene can be brominated to give a tribromo derivative.   This same tribromo derivative can be detected from bromination of the crude nitroselenophene, indicating that both 2- and 3-nitroselenophene are formed in the original nitration.   3-Nitroselenophene does not appear to be formed in amounts greater than in the thiophene series.   2,4-Dinitroselenophene forms with naphthalene a complex that melts at 53–55°.

[15] Umezawa, *Chem. Abstr.*, **31**, 2211 (1937); *Bull. Soc. Chem. Japan*, **11**, 775 (1936).
[16] Umezawa, *Chem. Abstr.*, **31**, 3913 (1937); *Bull. Chem. Soc. Japan*, **12**, 4 (1937).

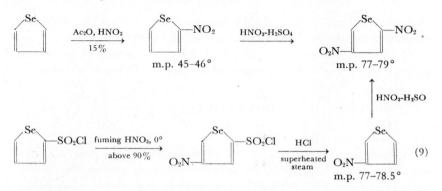

2-Bromoselenophene is converted to 2-bromo-5-nitroselenophene by the action of acetyl nitrate.[15]   Further nitration to 2-bromo-3,5-dinitroselenophene is effected by fuming nitric acid.   2-Chloroselenophene is nitrated directly to 2-chloro-3,5-dinitroselenophene by the action of fuming nitric acid.[15]   2,5-Dibromoselenophene gives 2,5-dibromo-3-nitroselenophene on reaction with fuming nitric acid.   (*Note:*   Under similar nitrating conditions 2,5-dibromothiophene gives 2,5-dibromo-3,4-dinitrothiophene and only a trace of the mononitro derivative.)

Selenophene is sulfonated with sulfuric acid (*d.* 1.84) at the temperature of ice to give 2-selenophenesulfonic acid (95%).[15]   This material was isolated as in the thiophene series, as the barium salt, and converted in that form to 2-selenophenesulfonyl chloride by the action of phosphorus pentachloride.   Sulfonation of selenophene in acetic anhydride at room temperature yields 2,4-selenophenedisulfonic acid.   This is converted to the disulfonyl chloride in the usual manner and to the diamide by interaction of ammonium carbonate with the disulfonyl chloride.[15]   Bogert and Andersen[9] found that 2,4-diphenylselenophene gave a low yield of a tetrasulfonic acid when treated with chlorosulfonic acid.

Umezawa[13]   prepared 2-selenophenemercurichloride from selenophene and mercuric chloride in the presence of sodium acetate.   Bogert and Andersen[9] prepared 2,4-diphenyl-5-selenophenemercurichloride in the same manner.   Briscoe, Peel, and Young[14] prepared 2,5-selenophenedimercuriacetate from selenophene and mercuric acetate in dilute acetic acid.   When treated with bromine-water, this dimercuriacetate is converted to the usual tetrabromoselenophene (m.p. 102°).   With potassium triiodide in acetone, the dimercuriacetate is converted to 2,5-diiodoselenophene and, with aqueous sodium chloride, the 2,5-selenophenedimercurichloride is formed.   It is converted to the dimercurihydroxide with aqueous potassium hydroxide.   This compound decomposes explosively on heating. Chlorine water causes ring oxidation of the 2,5-selenophenedimercuriacetate and selenium tetrachloride can be obtained. Sulfurous acid converts the dimercuriacetate to elementary selenium. Selenophene reacts with mercuric sulfate to give a cream-colored solid, but the structure of the product was not investigated. Bogert and Andersen[9] converted 2,4-diphenyl-5-selenophenemercuri-chloride to the 5-mercuricyanide derivative in 50% yields through the action of sodium cyanide. An attempt to convert the 5-mercurichloride derivative to the 5-mercuriiodide compound gave a diselenienylmercury derivative (Eq. 10). The same compound can be obtained in 65% yield from the 5-mercuribromide derivative in boiling toluene.[9]

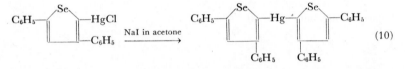

$$\text{(10)}$$

C. Physical Properties

While selenophene and its derivatives appear quite similar to corresponding thiophene compounds in their chemical nature, a much wider difference is noted in the physical properties. Selenophene has a disagreeable odor in contrast to thiophene. The biggest physical difference lies in the densities and refractive indices. Selenophene has a density greater than 1.5, a rather striking figure in comparison with that of thiophene at 1.06, furan at 0.94, and benzene at 0.88. As a general rule, the selenophene derivatives melt within a few degrees of their thiophene isologs. Steinkopf[17] and Steinkopf and Kohler[18] have pointed out that the melting point of 2-nitrothiophene (m.p. 46°) is not depressed by 2-nitroselenophene (m.p. 45–46°). Similarly, 3-nitrothiophene (m.p. 76–77.5°) admixed with 3-nitroselenophene (m.p. 77–78.5°) melts at 76–77° and 2-thiophenesulfonyl chloride (m.p. 31.5–33°) admixed with 2-selenophenesulfonyl chloride (m.p. 31–32.5°) melts at 31–32°.

The physical properties of selenophene are recorded in Table XVI-1. Table XVI-2 lists the physical properties of the derivatives of selenophene when the structure appears well enough established to assign definite positions to entering groups. In other cases, where structures have not been assigned by the investigators, or where the present author has questioned the structure assigned, the physical constants appear in the text where the compound was first mentioned.

[17] Steinkopf, *Die Chemie des Thiophens.* Steinkopff, Dresden, 1941, p. 19.
[18] Steinkopf and Kohler, *Ann.,* **532**, 250 (1937).

TABLE XVI-1. Physical Properties of Selenophene

		Reference
Boiling point, °C. (mm.)	109.9–110.1 (752.1)	3
	110.3–111.2 (754.2)	19
	110–110.7 (760)	7
	110.2–110.8 (762)	20
Freezing point, °C.	−38°	3
Density, d_4^t, $t = 15°$C.	1.5307	3,5
20	1.5232	3,7
25	1.5156	3
30	1.5078	3
40	1.4943	3
50	1.4763	3
Vapor pressure, mm. of Hg, at 25°C.	46.5	3
35	66	
50	112	
75	259	
85	356	
Surface tension, dynes/cm., at 15°C.	36.49	3
25	36.05	19
35.1	34.63	19
56.4	31.96	19
63.6	31.02	19
77.5	28.92	19
94.5	26.95	19
110.2	25.12	19
Critical temp., °K. (calcd.)	624.3	19
Parachor	200.6	19
	210.6 (15°)	3
Dipole moment, $u \times 10^{-18}$	0.41	20
	0.78 (in benzene)	19
	0.77 (in hexane)	19
Refractive indices		
n_D	1.568 (15°)	3,5
	1.56243 (20°)	20
	1.5642 (20°)	7
n_C^{20}	1.55708	20
n_F^{20}	1.57517	20
Diamagnetic susceptibility, per mole	$−66.82 \times 10^{-6}$	21,22

[19] Tamamusi, Akiyama, and Umezawa, *Chem. Abstr.*, **33**, 9064 (1939); *Bull. Chem. Soc. Japan*, **14**, 310 (1939).
[20] Robles, *Rec. trav. chim.*, **58**, 111 (1939).
[21] Hazato, *Chem. Abstr.*, **41**, 3334 (1947); *J. Chem. Soc. Japan*, **63**, 1685 (1942).
[22] Hazato, *Chem. Abstr.*, **41**, 3334 (1947); *J. Chem. Soc. Japan*, **64**, 622 (1943); *ibid.*, 1291 (1943).

TABLE XVI-2. Physical Constants of Selenophene Derivatives

Derivative	M.p., °C.	n_D (°C.)	d_4 (°C.)	Ref.
2,5-Dimethyl..........................	Liquid, b.p. 153–155	—	—	8,9
2,4-Diphenyl..........................	112.3	—	—	9,10
3,4-Diphenyl..........................	109.5–110.5	—	—	11
2-Chloro.............................	Liquid, b.p. 42 (14.5 mm.)	1.594 (20)	1.6621 (14)	5
2,5-Dichloro.........................	Liquid, b.p. 67 (12 mm.)	1.606 (14)	1.8372 (14)	5
2,2,3,4,5,5-Hexachloroselenolane.........	55	—	—	5
2,2,3,4,5,5-Hexachloroselenolane-1-oxide..	172–172.5 (dec.)	—	—	5
2,3,4,5-Tetrachloroselenolane............	97	—	—	3,5
2-Bromo..............................	Liquid, b.p. 59 (13 mm.)	1.635 (20)	2.1003 (20)	5
2,5-Dibromo..........................	Liquid, b.p. 42 (0.02 mm.)	1.667 (20)	2.5005 (20)	5
2,5,-Dibromo-2,3,4,5-tetrachloroselenolane	70–72	—	—	5
2,5-Diiodo............................	45	—	—	14
2-Nitro...............................	45–46	—	—	15
3-Nitro...............................	77–78.5	—	—	16
2,4-Dinitro...........................	76–78	—	—	16
2-Chloro-3,5-dinitro...................	119	—	—	15
2-Bromo-5-nitro.......................	57–59	—	—	15
2-Bromo-3,5-dinitro....................	126–128	—	—	15
2,5-Dibromo-3-nitro...................	83–85	—	—	15
2,3,5-Tribromo-3-nitro.................	100.3–102	—	—	16
2-Sulfonyl chloride....................	31–32.5	—	—	15
2-Sulfonamide........................	157–159	—	—	15
2,4-Disulfonyl chloride.................	70–72	—	—	15
2,4-Disulfonamide.....................	237–239	—	—	15
2-Sulfonyl chloride-4-nitro..............	71–73.5	—	—	16
2-Acetyl, phenylhydrazone of...........	114–116	—	—	13
2-Propionyl, semicarbazone of...........	175–176	—	—	13
2-Benzoyl............................	57–58	—	—	13
2-Cinnamoyl..........................	81–82.5	—	—	13
2-Cinnamoyl, dibromide of.............	155.5–156	—	—	13
2-Carboxylic acid.....................	122–124	—	—	13
2-Glyoxylic acid......................	92–94	—	—	13
2-Glyoxylic acid, semicarbazone of.......	192–193	—	—	13
2-HgCl...............................	201–202	—	—	13
2,5-HgOOCCH₃........................	Not listed	—	—	14
5-HgCl-2,4-diphenyl...................	224	—	—	9,10
5-HgBr-2,4-diphenyl...................	215	—	—	9
5-HgI-2,4-diphenyl....................	176	—	—	9
5-HgCN-2,4-diphenyl..................	256.4	—	—	9
2,5-Dibromo-3,4-diphenyl..............	86.7	—	—	9
3,4-Diphenyl-2-selenophenecarboxylic acid	220 (dec.)	—	—	11
3,4-Diphenyl-2-carbethoxy..............	87.5–88	—	—	11
3,4-Diphenyl-2-carbomethoxy............	133.5–134	—	—	11
3,4-Diphenyl-2,5-selenophenedicarboxylic acid...............................	343 (dec.)	—	—	11
3,4-Diphenyl-2,5-dicarbethoxy...........	160–161	—	—	11
3,4-Diphenyl-2,5-dicarbomethoxy........	185–187	—	—	11

II. Tetrahydroselenophene (Selenolane)

Selenolane is conveniently prepared in high yield by the action of sodium selenide on tetramethylenedibromide[23] (Eq. 11).   Morgan and

$$BrCH_2CH_2CH_2CH_2Br \xrightarrow[75\%]{Na_2Se,\ H_2O,\ heat} \text{[selenolane ring]} + 2NaBr \qquad (11)$$

Burstall[23] report that the compound is decomposed when oxidized with nitric acid or potassium permanganate.   It forms a mercurichloride (m.p. 146°) with mercuric chloride and sodium acetate.   With methyl iodide, a methiodide is formed.   This methiodide sublimes; its melting point in a sealed tube is 174°.   Selenolane, when chlorinated in carbon tetrachloride, gives 1,1-dichloroselenolane (Eq. 12 below).   In a similar

$$\text{[selenolane]} \xrightarrow{CCl_4,\ Cl_2} \text{[1,1-dichloroselenolane]} \qquad (12)$$

m.p. 88–89°

manner, 1,1-dibromoselenolane (m.p. 92°) and 1,1-diiodoselenolane (m.p. 99–100°) are obtained.[23]   With an excess of bromine, selenolane gives a perbromo-1,1-dibromoselenolane, $C_4H_8SeBr_2 \cdot Br_5$.   This unstable compound decomposes slowly into the 1,1-dibromo derivative.   Treatment of 1,1-dibromoselenolane with silver oxide gives the 1,1-dihydroxy-selenolane, a liquid neutral to litmus paper.   This compound is easily converted to the original 1,1-dibromo derivative by the action of hydrogen bromide.   Although the 1,1-dihydroxyselenolane is neutral to litmus, the 1-hydroxy-1-bromoselenolane (m.p. 99–100°), prepared by the action of an equivalent amount of silver oxide on the 1,1-dibromo derivative, is strongly acid in aqueous solution.   1-Hydroxy-1-chloroselenolane [m.p. 116° (dec.)] is prepared in the same manner.[23]   1,1-Dichloro-selenolane gives a crystalline chloroplatinate [m.p. 179° (dec.)] when treated with chloroplatinic acid.[23]

$$\begin{array}{c} COOH \\ | \\ H_2C-CHBr \\ | \\ H_2C-CHBr \\ | \\ COOH \end{array} + K_2Se \xrightarrow[80\%]{acetone,\ cool} \text{[selenolane-2,5-dicarboxylic acid]} \qquad (13)$$

Fredga[24] has prepared the 2,5-selenolanedicarboxylic acid from α,α'-dibromoadipic acid and potassium selenide (Eq. 13). The compound exists in *cis* and *trans* forms. *meso*-α,α'-Dibromoadipic acid gives the *cis* acid (m.p. 173°). *dl*-α,α'-Dibromoadipic acid gives the *trans* acid (m.p. 195°). Fredga determined the ionization constants of these acids as follows: *cis* acid, K (25°) = 2.7 × 10^{-4}; *trans* acid, K = 3.4 × 10^{-4}. Fredga[25-27] studied methods of separating the *cis* and *trans* isomers by means of the brucine salts, and determined miscellaneous physical properties of these acids.

Robles[20,28] studied various physical properties of selenolane which are listed in Table XVI-3 along with the physical properties determined by Morgan and Burstall.[23] Robles[20] found the dipole moment of selenolane to be 1.79, μ × 10^{-18}, and later discussed the ring configuration of selenolane, which he is inclined to believe does not exist in an entirely planar form.[28] A shallow tub form appears to be the most probable configuration of the ring.

TABLE XVI-3. Physical Constants of Selenolane (Tetrahydroselenophene)

		Reference
B.p., °C. (mm.)	90–91 (172)	23
	140.2–140.4 (760)	20
	135–136 (770)	23
Density, d_4^{15}	1.484	23
d_4^{20}	1.4789	20
Parachor	229.5	23
Surface tension, γ (dynes/cm.)		23
10°C	41.28	
15	40.40	
20	39.53	
30	38.07	
40	37.14	
Refractive indices		
n_D^{18}	1.5510	23
n_D^{20}	1.54956	20
n_C^{20}	1.54540	20
n_F^{20}	1.56015	20

[23] Morgan and Burstall, *J. Chem. Soc.*, **1929**, 1096.
[24] Fredga, *J. prakt. Chem.*, **127**, 103 (1930).
[25] Fredga, *J. prakt. Chem.*, **130**, 180 (1931).
[26] Fredga, *Uppsala Univ. Arsskrift*, **1935**, No. 5, 232 pp.
[27] Fredga, *J. prakt. Chem.*, **150**, 124 (1938).
[28] Robles, *Rec. trav. chim.*, **59**, 184 (1940).

III.   Tellurophene and Tetrahydrotellurophene
(Tellurolane)

Tellurophene is all but unknown.   McMahon, Pearson, and Robinson[29] believed that the product boiling between 120–150° obtained by passing acetylene over aluminum telluride, Al_2Te_3, deposited on roasted bauxite, was tellurophene (calc. b.p. 136°).   They also attempted to prepare this material from acetylene and tellurium by the method used for selenophene, but failed.

Morgan and Burstall[30] prepared tellurolane (tetrahydrotellurophene) by reacting tetramethylene diiodide with amorphous tellurium and reducing the 1,1-diiodotellurolane with sulfur dioxide (Eq. 14).   Farrar

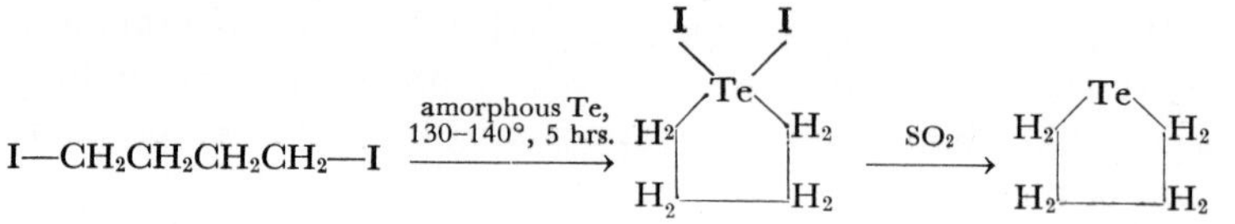

$$I—CH_2CH_2CH_2CH_2—I \xrightarrow[\text{130–140°, 5 hrs.}]{\text{amorphous Te,}} \quad \xrightarrow{\text{SO}_2} \qquad (14)$$

b.p.   105–106   (122   mm.)
b.p.   166–167   (761   mm.)
n_D^{18} 1.6175

and Gulland[31] took a somewhat similar approach in preparing tellurolane from tetramethylene dibromide (Eq. 15).

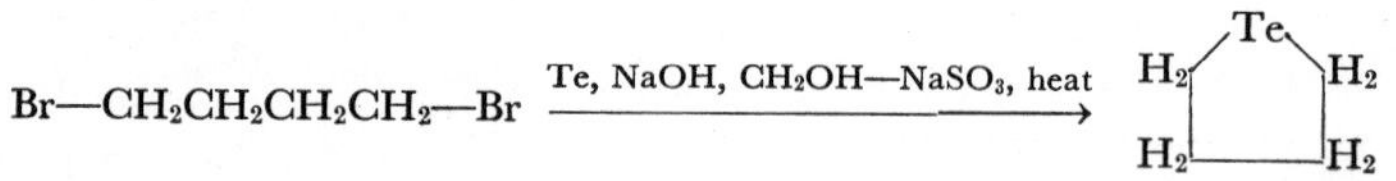

$$Br—CH_2CH_2CH_2CH_2—Br \xrightarrow{\text{Te, NaOH, CH}_2\text{OH—NaSO}_3\text{, heat}} \qquad (15)$$

Tellurolane reacts explosively with concentrated nitric acid and gives a red color with sulfuric acid.   It forms a mercuric chloride complex, m.p. 146–147°.[30]   With chlorine or bromine, it forms a 1,1-dichloro-(m.p. 111–112°) or a 1,1-dibromotellurolane (m.p. 130°).[30,31]   It forms a methiodide that sublimes at 240°.[30]   The 1,1-dibromotellurolane reacts with sodium carbonate solution to form an oxide (Eq. 16).[30]

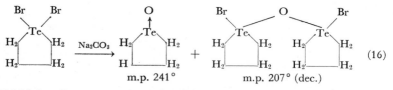

m.p. 241°   m.p. 207° (dec.)

[29] McMahon, Pearson, and Robinson, *J. Chem. Soc.*, **1933**, 1644.
[30] Morgan and Burstall, *J. Chem. Soc.*, **1931**, 180.
[31] Farrar and Gulland, *J. Chem. Soc.*, **1945**, 11.

When aluminum telluride and 1,4-dibromobutane are heated together at 125° the following series of reactions is observed.[30] Heat dissociates the resultant telluronium compounds to tellurolane.

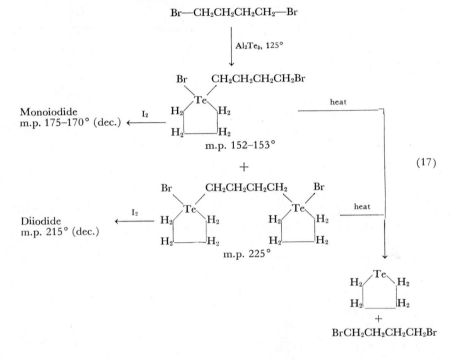

$$(17)$$

Laboratory Preparations of Thiophene Compounds

This section is designed primarily for the research chemist who will need intermediate thiophene derivatives in synthesis of a given thiophene compound. It supplements the theoretical discussions of Chapter V, where new syntheses are suggested and where the syntheses of the isomeric methylthiophenecarboxylic acids suggest the methods which could be applied to other isomeric disubstituted thiophene compounds.

The more important syntheses were chosen, first, to obtain the compounds as intermediates, and, second, to describe general methods by which many other derivatives could be prepared. In nearly all cases, procedures have been checked and adapted to larger scale preparations than originally outlined in the literature. In a number of cases, the yields have been substantially improved in this adaptation.

The apparatus for the following series of preparations, unless specifically described, is a 4-necked, round-bottom flask. The necks of the flask are provided with ground-glass joints into which are fitted a motor-driven glass paddle-stirrer, a thermometer, and a reflux condenser. On occasion, the fourth neck is used to introduce reactants through a dropping funnel, but normally it is closed with a ground-glass stopper.

2-Methylthiophene

Materials required to produce 116 g. (41%).

Sodium levulinate (2.9 moles).........................	400 g.
Phosphorus trisulfide (6.3 moles)......................	1000 g.
Sand...	200 g.

Procedure. The above reactants are mixed thoroughly and heated in a retort or in an apparatus as described by Steinkopf (*Die Chemie des Thiophens*, page 9). The distillate from this reaction is washed with caustic to remove 5-methyl-2-hydroxythiophene, and the organic layer is steam distilled. The crude 2-methylthiophene is dried over sodium sulfate or calcium sulfate, and then distilled from sodium, b.p. 113°.

Reference. Original method of Kues and Paal as described and modified by Steinkopf, *Die Chemie des Thiophens*, Steinkopff, 1941, page 34. Steinkopf lists the yield as 116 g. (48%). Calculation of the yield from the reactants listed indicates a 41% yield. This method is also applicable to production of 3-methylthiophene from pyrotartaric acid.

2,5-Dimethylthiophene

Materials required to produce 80–85 g. (68–72%).

Acetonylacetone (1.05 moles)............................120 g.
Phosphorus trisulfide (1.6 moles)......................250 g.

Procedure. The acetonylacetone and finely divided phosphorus trisulfide are heated cautiously until a spontaneous reaction begins to take place. After this reaction ceases the mixture is boiled under reflux for ten to fifteen minutes and then distilled until crystals begin to form in the condenser. The distillate is washed with aqueous sodium hydroxide and water, dried, and the 2,5-dimethylthiophene is distilled twice, b.p. 135.5–136°

Reference. Buu-Hoï and Nguyen-Hoan, *Rec. trav. chim.*, **67,** 309 (1948). Modification of the method of Paal, Ber., **18,** 2252 (1885).

2,3-Dimethylthiophene

Materials required to produce 11.6 g. (60%).

Semicarbazone of 3-methyl-2-thiophenealdehyde (0.17 mole)....35 g.
Potassium hydroxide (0.9 mole)............................50 g.
Water.. 5 ml.

Procedure. The semicarbazone and powdered potassium hydroxide are intimately mixed in a distilling flask and the water is added. The mixture is shaken for a few minutes and then prepared for distillation using a stream of nitrogen gas, the inlet for which is in the top of the distilling flask. The mixture is heated rapidly. When the temperature reaches 100–110° (the source of heat is temporarily removed), a vigorous evolution of gas, water, and product begins to take place and the temperature rises rapidly to about 150° before beginning to fall. The mixture is then heated to 250° and held there as long as liquid product distils. The organic layer of the distillate is separated from the aqueous layer and the former is steam distilled, dried over calcium sulfate, and distilled through a 12-plate fractionating column; b. p. 142.5°.

Reference. The above procedure is the author's modification of the procedure described by Shepard, *J. Am. Chem. Soc.*, **54**, 2952 (1932), for the preparation of 2-methyl-5-ethylthiophene in 40% yield. The method has been used for the preparation of 2,5-dimethylthiophene by the author; an 80% yield of distilled product was obtained. Steinkopf, Frommel, and Leo, *Ann.*, **546**, 199 (1941) used another modification of this method involving the phenylhydrazone of 2-ethyl-5-acetylthiophene to prepare 2,5-diethylthiophene in 50% yield.

2- and 3-*tert*-Butylthiophene and Di-*tert*-butylthiophene

Materials required to produce 160–180 g. (58–65%) of 2- and 3-tert-butyl-thiophene and 85–95 g. of di-tert-butylthiophene.

Thiophene (2 moles)...................................168 g.
Isobutylene (2.1 moles)...............................116 g.
75% Sulfuric acid.................................... 15 g.

Procedure. Isobutylene (gaseous) is introduced in a rapid stream to the well-stirred mixture of thiophene and sulfuric acid over a period of about one hour. The temperature is raised to 60–70° before addition of the isobutylene and maintained in that range throughout the addition by means of a water bath. The organic layer is decanted from the catalyst layer and washed with dilute alkali (KOH or NaOH), dried over calcium chloride, and distilled in a 10-plate fractionating column. The cut boiling between 162 and 170° is a mixture of 2- and 3-*tert*-butyl-thiophene. These isomers are best separated in a 60-plate column by a double fractionation. Pure 2-*tert*-butylthiophene boils at 163.9°, n_D^{20} 1.4979, while the 3-*tert*-butylthiophene boils at 168.9°, n_D^{20} 1.5015. In the reaction product, the proportion of 2-*tert*-butylthiophene varies from 50 to 60%. The material boiling between 220 and 225° (10-plate column), n_D^{20} 1.493, is a mixture of isomeric di-*tert*-butylthiophenes.

References. The above preparation of these materials is an adaptation of the procedure described by Caesar, *J. Am. Chem. Soc.*, **70**, 3623 (1948). Meisel and Hartough fractionated Caesar's products by the procedure described above [for original separation of 2- and 3-*tert*-butylthiophene see Appleby *et al.*, *J. Am. Chem. Soc.*, **70**, 1553 (1948)].

Scope of Reaction. This procedure can be adapted to the preparation of amyl-, *tert*-octyl, and hexadecylthiophenes. Caesar (see above reference) describes various catalysts applicable to these reactions. The choice of catalyst depends upon whether a higher or lower proportion of monoalkyl derivatives to dialkyl derivatives is desired.

2-Chloro-, 2,5-Dichlorothiophene and Other Isomeric Chlorothiophenes

Materials required to produce 1080–1100 g. of 2-chlorothiophene and 500–520 g. of 2,5-dichlorothiophene.

Thiophene (25 moles)................................2100 g.	
Chlorine (25 moles).................................1775 g.	

Procedure. Chlorine is bubbled into the thiophene (hood) at ambient temperature, and the temperature is controlled at 50° by means of an ice bath. The chlorine is usually introduced over a three- to four-hour period. After chlorine addition is complete, the temperature is raised to 80°, a vigorous stream of nitrogen gas is bubbled through for ten minutes, and then 240 g. of potassium hydroxide pellets are added cautiously over a period of two hours. Sodium hydroxide (300 g.) is cautiously added and the mixture boiled under reflux for sixteen hours to remove all traces of the chlorine addition compounds of thiophene. The mixture is filtered and the filtrate is charged to an efficient fractionating column. Unreacted thiophene, 295 g., is recovered. 2-Chlorothiophene is collected at 128–130° and 2,5-dichlorothiophene at 161–162.5°. The residue from this distillation or products boiling above 162.5° are distilled in a 90- to 95-plate fractionating column and the following compounds are collected: 2,4-dichlorothiophene (60–65 g.), b.p. 167.6°; 2,3-dichlorothiophene (60–65 g.), b.p. 172.7°; 3,4-dichlorothiophene (110–115 g.), b.p. 182.0°; a trace of 2,3,5-trichlorothiophene, b.p. 198.7°; and 2,3,4-trichlorothiophene (115–120 g.), b.p. 209.6°.

Reference. Coonradt, Hartough, and Johnson, *J. Am. Chem. Soc.*, **70**, 2564 (1948). The procedure has not been checked outside the author's laboratory. Separation of the chlorine addition products of thiophene is effected by cooling the above reaction mixture in a Dry-Ice–acetone bath and collecting the crystalline product; other addition products are present [see Coonradt and Hartough, *J. Am. Chem. Soc.*, **70**, 1158 (1948)].

2-Bromo- and 2,5-Dibromothiophene

Materials required to produce 150–160 g. of 2-bromothiophene and 300–320 g. of 2,5-dibromothiophene.

Thiophene (4 moles)......................... 336 g.	
Bromine (6.3 moles)...........................1007 g. (323 ml.)	
Glacial acetic acid...........................3200 ml.	

Procedure. The thiophene is mixed with 1600 ml. of acetic acid and cooled to 10°. The bromine is mixed with the remaining acetic acid, cooled to 10°, and added slowly to the thiophene-acetic acid solution. The cooling bath is removed and the mixture stirred until the solution is light brown in color (requires 5–8 hours). Addition products are best destroyed by adding an equal volume of water to the reaction mixture and extracting the brominated thiophenes with ether. This extract is washed with 10% sodium hydroxide to remove acetic acid, dried, and evaporated, and the brominated thiophenes are charged to a flask. The mixture is warmed to 80° and 200 g. of potassium hydroxide pellets is cautiously added to the well-stirred mixture over a period of one to two hours. The mixture is boiled for eight to twelve hours, filtered, and distilled in a 10–12-plate fractionating column. The 2-bromothiophene is collected at 149–152° and the 2,5-dibromothiophene at 210–212°. The other isomeric di- and tribromothiophenes probably can be separated in a manner similar to that used for the separation of the chlorine isologs described above.

Reference. This method is an adaptation of various methods practiced in the literature, see Chapter VII, which has been used in the author's laboratory by A. I. Kosak and L. G. Conley.

2,3-Dibromothiophene

Materials required to produce 78–86 g. (79–87%).

4,5-Dibromo-2-thiophenecarboxylic acid (0.41 mole)	115 g.
Mercuric acetate (0.9 mole)	286 g.
Glacial acetic acid	1000 ml.

Procedure. The above materials are mixed and heated with stirring for four hours at the reflux temperature. Carbon dioxide is evolved during the first hour of heating. The mercuriacetate derivative is obtained by cooling the reaction mixture and filtering. The solid is then transferred to a flask and boiled under reflux for one hour with a excess of aqueous sodium chloride (one liter, 20% concentration) and then treated with 100 ml. of concentrated hydrohcloric acid. The mixture is steam distilled. 2,3-Dibromothiophene is collected in the distillate, dried, and fractionated, b.p. 212–213°.

Reference. The above procedure is a modification of the method of Steinkopf and Kohler, *Ann.*, **532**, 250 (1937), and Steinkopf, Jacob, and Penz, *Ann.*, **512**, 136 (1934), adapted by Caesar, Socony-Vacuum Laboratories.

3-Bromothiophene

Materials required to produce 25 g. (72%).

2,3-Dibromothiophene (0.21 mole)	52 g.
Magnesium	9.0 g.
Ether (dried over sodium wire)	500 ml.
Ethyl bromide	15 g.

Procedure. The above reactants are mixed, a few crystals of iodine are added, and the mixture is boiled for thirty-six hours. Water (200 ml.) is added slowly at first, then rapidly. The ether layer is decanted, dried, and the ether distilled off. The product, 3-bromothiophene, distils at 155–160° from a Vigreaux-modified Claisen flask. It boils at 157–158° through a 12-plate column, n_D^{20} 1.5860.

References. This procedure is a modification of the method of Steinkopf, Jacob, and Penz, *Ann.*, **512**, 136 (1934), adapted by Caesar at the Socony-Vacuum Laboratories.

2-Iodothiophene

Materials required to produce 63–66 g. (72–75%).

Thiophene (0.42 mole)................................... 35 g.
Benzene.. 50 ml.
Mercuric oxide (0.35 mole)............................. 75 g.
Iodine (0.43 mole).....................................109 g.

Procedure. To the vigorously stirred mixture of thiophene and benzene, cooled to 0° in an ice bath, the mercuric oxide and iodine are added alternately in small amounts during a period of fifteen to twenty minutes. The yellow mercuric oxide changes to crimson mercuric iodide. The mixture is filtered by suction and the residue is washed with three 25 ml. portions of ether. The ether-benzene filtrate is shaken with a 5% solution of sodium thiosulfate to remove excess iodine and then dried over 5 g. of calcium chloride and filtered. The ether and benzene are removed by distillation and the residue is fractionally distilled *in vacuo.* 2-Iodothiophene distils at 73° at 15 mm.; 80–81° at 20 mm.; 90–94° at 34–38 mm. If the 2-iodothiophene is still colored by traces of iodine, the color may be removed by shaking with a small amount of mercuric oxide and drying again over calcium chloride.

Reference. The above procedure is essentially that described by Minnis, *Organic Syntheses,* **12**, 44 (1932). Larger preparations made in the author's laboratories have given yields above 80%.

3-Iodothiophene

Materials required to produce 87 g. (60% based on thiophene).

Tetraiodothiophene (0.69 mole)........................ 402 g.
Aluminum amalgam...................................... 400 g.
Water... 50 g.
Alcohol (95%)...1000 ml.
Ether...1500 ml.

Procedure. The tetraiodothiophene is suspended in the ether-alcohol mixture and a 20-g. portion of the aluminum amalgam is introduced. The water is then added cautiously from a dropping funnel. The rest of the aluminum amalgam is added cautiously in portions. The tetra-iodothiophene gradually dissolves in the mixture. When solution is complete and the mixture takes on a metallic appearance, it is warmed gently for one to two hours. Insoluble material is filtered off; 1 l. water is added and the ether distilled off. The residue is steam distilled. The distillate is extracted with ether, dried, and the ether and product distilled. 3-Iodothiophene distils at 77° (11 mm.). The residues from the distillation and steam distillation contain 3,4-diiodothiophene.

Reference. The method was developed in the Socony-Vacuum Laboratories from the method of Rinkes, *Rec. trav. chim.*, **53**, 648 (1934); **55**, 991 (1936). See Chapter VII for other references.

Tetraiodothiophene

Materials required to produce 400–450 g. (68–77%).

Thiophene (1 mole)................................. 84 g.
Mercuric oxide (6 moles)...........................1300 g.
Glacial acetic acid.................................1700 ml.
Iodine (8.1 gram atoms)............................1030 g.

Procedure. The thiophene, mercuric oxide, and glacial acetic acid are mixed together and heated quickly to reflux and the iodine is added in small portions to the mixture at such a rate that the color of iodine has disappeared before the next portion is added. After the last portion of the iodine has been introduced, the mixture is cooled and the contents of the reaction flask are diluted with 2 liters of water. The insoluble product and mercuric iodide are collected by suction filtration. The mixture is digested with carbon disulfide to remove the tetraiodothiophene. The latter is recrystallized once from dioxane, m.p. 198–199°.

Reference. This procedure is a modification of the method of Steinkopf and Hanske, *Ann.*, **527**, 247 (1937), used in the Socony-Vacuum Laboratories. See also Steinkopf, *Die Chemie des Thiophens*, page 43, for a modification of a method to introduce the iodine evenly to the reaction mixture.

2-Thenyl Chloride

Materials required to produce 25 g. (40%).

Thiophene (0.47 mole)................................40 g.
Concd. hydrochloric acid............................20 ml.
Formaldehyde (40%)..................................50 ml.
Stream of hydrogen chloride.

Procedure. The thiophene and concentrated hydrochloric acid are mixed and cooled to 0–5° and a vigorous stream of hydrogen chloride is introduced. During the course of one hour the formaldehyde is added. The hydrogen chloride stream is stopped and the mixture is extracted with ether. The extract is washed with water and then with sodium carbonate solution, dried, and the solvent removed. The product boils at 80–81° at 18 mm. In addition, there may also be obtained 16 g. of di-(2-thienyl)methane, b.p. 125–129° at 9 mm., m.p. 45–47°.

2-Thenyl chloride is a lachrymator and, in addition, has a tendency to decompose violently in tightly stoppered bottles. It can be stored for a considerable period, in an ice chest without decomposition, but it is best to use the material as soon as possible after distillation.

References. Blicke and Burckhalter, *J. Am. Chem. Soc.*, **64**, 478 (1942). The method has been checked in the Socony-Vacuum Laboratories. In cases where di-(2-thienyl)methane can be conveniently separated from the end-products, the crude reaction mixture can be conveniently utilized without resorting to distillation of the 2-thenyl chloride. Over-all yields normally are improved in this manner. The author has found that it is convenient to prepare this compound using equimolar quantities of hydrochloric acid, thiophene, and formaldehyde, omitting the use of hydrogen chloride. The yields are comparable when the above procedure is employed.

Very recently, methods of stabilizing 2-thenyl chloride under storage conditions have been reported. Zienty, U. S. Pats. 2,457,079–081, describes the addition of about 0.5% of a heterocyclic amine such as alkylpyrrolidines, morpholines, or a tertiary amine such as *N*-alkyldicyclohexylamine in order to stabilize the material toward polymerization on storage.

3-Thenyl Bromide

Materials required to produce 57 g. (66%).

3-Methylthiophene (0.56 mole)	55 g.
N-Bromosuccinimide (0.50 mole)	88.5 g.
Carbon tetrachloride	150 ml.
Benzoyl peroxide	0.4 g.

Procedure. Half the benzoyl peroxide is added to a solution of the other reactants. The mixture is shaken vigorously and then heated. During the first ten minutes an additional 0.2 g. of benzoyl peroxide is added. The flask and contents are shaken frequently during the first hour, boiled for five additional hours, then cooled in an ice bath. The succinimide is removed by filtration and washed with an additional 50 ml. of carbon tetrachloride. The carbon tetrachloride is removed under reduced pressure. The remaining highly lachrymatory oil is collected at 70–100° at 2 mm. This product is unstable and darkens slowly. The material, contaminated with a small amount of 3-methyl-2-bromothiophene, can be redistilled to higher purity; b.p. 75–78° at 1 mm., d_4^{20} 1.635, n_D^{20} 1.604.

Reference. This procedure is described by Campaigne and Le Suer, *J. Am. Chem. Soc.*, **70**, 1556 (1948). Dittmer, Martin, Herz, and Cristol, *J. Am. Chem. Soc.*, **71**, 1201 (1949) describe similar results.

2-Acetylthiophene

Materials required to produce 107–118 g.

    Thiophene (3 moles)...................................252 g.
    Acetic anhydride (95%) (1.1 moles).....................117 g.
    Orthophosphoric acid (85%)........................... 10 g.

Procedure. The thiophene and acetic anhydride are mixed, stirred, and heated to 70° and the orthophosphoric acid is added. The temperature rises rapidly to 90° (it is sometimes necessary to cool at this point with a water bath). The mixture is then boiled under reflux (temp. 96–97°) for two hours and cooled to 50°. Water (200 ml.) is added and the mixture thoroughly stirred for five minutes. The water is separated and the organic layer is washed with 200 ml. of 10% sodium carbonate solution, or until the wash water shows a pH of 10 to Hydrion paper. It is not necessary to dry the product, since thiophene and water form a constant boiling mixture at 68°. The washed organic layer is transferred to a Claisen flask and the excess thiophene (160–175 g.) recovered by distillation. The product may be distilled from the Claisen flask or through a 12-plate fractionating column. It boils at 77° at 4 mm. pressure; n_D^{20} 1.5666. The product, if stored in a brown bottle, will remain water white for several months.

Reference. Hartough and Kosak, *J. Am. Chem. Soc.*, **69**, 3093 (1948). See also, Kosak and Hartough, *Organic Syntheses*, **28**, 1 (1948). This reaction has been checked by L. G. Conley, Socony-Vacuum Laboratories. It has been successfully extended to the preparation of 2-propanoyl- and 2-butanoylthiophene without modification. The yields are in the range of 85–95% of theory.

3-Methyl- and 4-Methyl-2-acetylthiophene

Materials required to produce 988 g. of 3-methyl-2-acetylthiophene and 216 g. of 4-methyl-2-acetylthiophene.

    3-Methylthiophene (10 moles)......................... 980 g.
    Acetic anhydride (95%) (11.2 moles)...................1200 g.
    Orthophosphoric acid (85%)........................... 50 g.

Procedure. The 3-methylthiophene and acetic anhydride are stirred together in a five-liter flask and heated to 70°. The orthophosphoric acid is added in one portion and the temperature is controlled at 70–80° by means of an ice bath. The mixture is then warmed at 110° for two hours (reaction is essentially over in about 15 minutes and a longer heating period increases the yield by only a few per cent). The mixture is cooled and diluted with two liters of water. The heavy oil is washed three times with water and then with 10% Na_2CO_3 until the aqueous layer remains basic. The oil is dried over sodium sulfate, filtered, and distilled from a 12-plate fractionating column. A few grams of 3-methylthiophene are recovered in the forerun. The 2-acetyl-3-methylthiophene distilling at 68–72° at 3 mm. is about 93% pure and the 2-acetyl-4-methylthiophene boiling at 83–85° at 3 mm. is 90% pure. A second distillation of the individual products from the first distillation achieves purity higher than 98%.

Reference. Hartough and Kosak, *J. Am. Chem. Soc.*, **69**, 3093 (1947), and Hartough and Conley, *ibid.*, **69**, 3096 (1947). This has been checked by L. G. Conley and D. J. Crowley, Socony-Vacuum Laboratories.

Scope of the Reaction. The above procedure has been used to obtain 1168–1220 g. of 2-acetyl-5-methylthiophene from 2-methylthiophene, b.p. 84.5° at 2 mm., m.p. 27–28°. The reaction gives yields of the same high order if carried out with one or two moles of 2- or 3-methylthiophene.

2-Acetyl-5-chlorothiophene

Materials required to produce 300–337 g. (65–70%).

2-Chlorothiophene (3 moles)..........................355.5 g.
Acetic anhydride (95%) (3.5 moles)....................377 g.
Orthophosphoric acid (85%)........................... 35 g.

Procedure. The three materials are stirred together and boiled under reflux (130°) for three hours. After cooling to 50°, 500 ml. of water is added and the mixture is steam distilled to recover 42 g. of 2-chlorothiophene. The heavy oil may be worked up, as in the case of 2-acetylthiophene, by washing with water and 10% sodium carbonate. Benzene may be used as a solvent if desired. The product is distilled from a Claisen flask, b.p. 88° at 4 mm., whereupon it crystallizes. An analytical sample is prepared by recrystallization from water and alcohol, m.p. 46.5–47°.

Reference. Hartough and Conley, *J. Am. Chem. Soc.*, **69**, 3096 (1947). The procedure has been checked by H. E. Rasmussen, Socony-Vacuum Laboratories, on semipilot-plant scale operations in a 30-gal. Pfaudler kettle. The yields are slightly improved on larger scale production.

3-Acetyl-2,5-dichlorothiophene

Materials required to produce 286 g. (73%).

2,5-Dichlorothiophene (2 moles)	306 g.
Acetyl chloride (3.8 moles)	300 g.
Aluminum chloride, anhydrous	300 g.
Petroleum ether	1500 ml.

Procedure. The 2,5-dichlorothiophene, acetyl chloride, and petroleum ether are mixed and the well-stirred mixture is cooled to 15°. The aluminum chloride is added slowly to the mixture over a fifteen-minute period. In about fifteen minutes, a precipitate begins to form and hydrogen chloride evolution becomes vigorous. After maintaining the temperature at 15° for two hours, the temperature of the mixture is allowed to rise slowly to room temperature and, after an additional three and a half hours, the mixture is boiled thirty minutes at 40°. The reaction mixture is cooled and poured into two liters of ice. The petroleum ether layer is separated and washed three times with water and the solvent removed on the steam bath. The residue is transferred to a Claisen flask and distilled *in vacuo* in an apparatus suitable for distillation of crystalline material. It boils at 87° at 3 mm. and melts at 38–38.5° after one recrystallization from dilute alcohol.

Reference. Steinkopf and Kohler, *Ann.*, **532**, 265 (1937), list the original preparation but obtained a yield of only 16%. The modification described above is from Hartough and Conley, *J. Am. Chem. Soc.*, **69**, 3096 (1947). Bachman and Heisey, *J. Am. Chem. Soc.*, **70**, 2378 (1948), reported an 84% yield when carbon disulfide was employed as a solvent.

2-Thiophenecarboxylic Acid

Materials required to produce 110–122 g. (86–95%).

2-Acetylthiophene (1 mole)	126 g.
Sodium hydroxide (11 moles)	440 g.
Chlorine (4.5 moles)	322 g.
Ice	2500 g.

Procedure. The sodium hydroxide is dissolved in 600 ml. of water, cooled, charged to a 5-liter flask and the chipped ice is weighed in directly. A chlorine inlet-tube is extended to the bottom of the flask. The flask is placed upon a balance, tared, and the chlorine is introduced as rapidly as possible (about fifteen minutes are required for the addition). The sodium hypochlorite solution is transferred to a steam bath and warmed to 55–60°. The flask is then transferred to a cooling bath and the 2-acetylthiophene addition is begun cautiously from a dropping funnel. Addition of the 2-acetylthiophene is carried out at such a rate that the temperature can be maintained between 60 and 70° by means of the cooling bath. After addition of the ketone is complete, stirring is continued until the temperature falls to 25–30° without aid of the cooling bath. Sodium bisulfite, 100 g. in 200 ml. of water, is added to remove excess sodium hypochlorite. The product is then poured into two 4-liter beakers and cautiously acidified with concentrated hydrochloric acid. The product is collected and recrystallized from 1200 ml. of hot water, m.p. 128–129°. The yield of pure product varies with the precautions taken in recrystallization. The higher yield figure quoted above is obtained by concentration of the mother liquors at a pH of 8 or above, subsequent acidification and extraction with ether. The ether layer contains 8–11 g. of acid. 2-Thiophenecarboxylic acid is highly volatile with steam and prolonged boiling during the recrystallization should be avoided.

Reference. Modification of method of Hartough and Conley, *J. Am. Chem. Soc.*, **69**, 3096 (1947). The method has been checked by G. C. Johnson, Socony-Vacuum Laboratories.

2-Thiophenecarboxylic Acid from 2-Chlorothiophene

Materials required to produce 105–108 g. (82–84%)

2-Chlorothiophene (1 mole)............................	118 g.
Sodium (2.17 gram atoms)............................	50 g.
Mercury...	29 g.
Benzene...	1000 ml.

Procedure:

Preparation of Sodium Amalgam Sand

To 750 ml. of toluene in a 3-liter flask are added the mercury and then the sodium. This mixture is warmed rapidly to 95° and then more cautiously until the sodium melts and amalgamates with a puff of smoke at about 100–103°. The toluene boils vigorously for 30–90 seconds. When the toluene reflux stops, the mixture is stirred vigorously until the temperature falls to 50° at most, preferably to 35°. The flask is then fitted with a glass wool filter plug in one of the side arms and the toluene is decanted off. The glass wool plug is pushed into the flask and the sodium amalgam is blanketed with the solvent to be used in the next step.

Preparation of 2-Thienylsodium

The sodium amalgam is blanketed with 1000 ml. of benzene and the 2-chlorothiophene is added. The mixture is heated at 80–82° for four hours.   As the reaction proceeds a gray to black powdery cast develops in the flask.

Carbonation of 2-Thienylsodium

The mixture described just above is cooled to 5–10° and carbonated with freshly crushed Dry Ice.   A temperature rise usually accompanies carbonation.   Completion of the carbonation reaction is indicated by a decrease of the temperature to 0–5°.   Alcohol (100 ml.) is cautiously added to the mixture, accompanied by vigorous stirring, to consume any unreacted sodium.   Water (350 ml.) is then added and the aqueous phase is separated, filtered, and acidulated with 230 ml. of concentrated hydrochloric acid, and cooled.   The 2-thiophenecarboxylic acid is filtered off, and after one recrystallization from water melts at 126–128°.

Reference.   Method of Schick and Hartough, *J. Am. Chem. Soc.*, **70**, 287 (1948)· This method has not been checked outside the author's laboratory.

4-Methyl-2-Thiophenecarboxylic Acid

Materials required to produce 58–62 g. (81–86%).

3-Methylthiophene (1 mole)	98 g.
Sodium (1 gram atom)	23 g.
Mercury	15 g.
Ethyl chloride (0.5 mole)	32 g.
Ethyl ether	600 ml.

Procedure.   The sodium amalgam is prepared as described above (see Preparation of Sodium Amalgam Sand of 2-thiophenecarboxylic acid), blanketed with 200 ml. of ether, and the 3-methylthiophene is added.   Ethyl chloride is condensed from a cylinder into a tared flask cooled in an ice bath, poured into 400 ml. of ice cold ether, and added rapidly to the reaction flask maintained at 10–20°.   The mixture is stirred for two hours at room temperature.   Carbonation is then carried out as described above under 2-thiophenecarboxylic acid and the product is purified in the same manner (one-half the amount of water and acid being required).   The white crystalline needles melt at 119–121°.

Yields are somewhat improved by the use of n-butyl bromide or bromobenzene instead of the ethyl chloride.   With these materials, the reaction mixture can be heated under reflux to complete the reaction in the two-hour stirring period.

The excess 3-methylthiophene is recovered from the ether layer.

Reference.   Method of Schick and Hartough, *J. Am. Chem. Soc.*, **70**, 1645 (1948). This method has not been checked outside of the author's laboratory.

Scope of the Reaction. This method has been successfully applied to the preparation of 5-methyl-, *tert*-butyl-, *tert*-amyl-, *tert*-octyl-, and 5-(1-phenylethyl)-2-thiophenecarboxylic acids in yields ranging from 46–85% of theory.

5-Chloro-2-thiophenecarboxylic Acid from 5-Chloro-2-thienylsodium

Materials required to produce 150 g. (92%) of crude acid.

2-Chlorothiophene (1 mole)	118 g.
Sodium (1.5 gram atoms)	35 g.
Mercury	25 g.
Ether (anhydrous)	1000 ml.

Procedure:

Preparation of 5-Chloro-2-thienylsodium

The sodium amalgam prepared as described under 2-thiophenecarboxylic acid above is blanketed with 700 ml. of ether. The 2-chlorothiophene in 300 ml. of anhydrous ether is added from a dropping funnel to the sodium amalgam sand at the reflux temperature (36–39°). A typical Grignard apparatus is employed, the system being kept under a slight nitrogen pressure. The addition of the 2-chlorothiophene is carried out over a four-hour period. The surface of the sodium amalgam darkens immediately and in a short time the ether solution takes on a gray to black cast. The mixture is refluxed an additional two hours. The 5-chloro-2-thienylsodium is gray to black and is essentially insoluble in the ether solution. It is capable of undergoing standard Grignard reactions in this state.

Preparation of 5-Chloro-2-thiophenecarboxylic Acid

The reaction mixture described above is cooled to 25° and carbonated by adding freshly crushed Dry Ice. The temperature falls rapidly when carbonation is complete. Ethanol (100 ml.) is added dropwise (and cautiously) to destroy unreacted sodium after which 350 ml. of distilled water is added, also cautiously. The aqueous solution is separated in a separatory funnel, filtered and acidulated with 230 ml. of concentrated hydrochloric acid. The gray crystalline solid, 150 g., is filtered off, taken up in hot water, treated with decolorizing charcoal, filtered, and allowed to recrystallize as long white needles, m.p. 153–153.5°. This acid is not very soluble in hot water and is usually recrystallized batchwise from 2500 ml. of water in a 4-liter beaker. The mother liquor is recycled.

The product can be recrystallized from benzene with less difficulty than from water.

Reference. This method is described by Schick and Hartough, *J. Am. Chem. Soc.*, **70**, 287 (1948), and has not been checked outside the author's laboratory, although it has been repeated many times by Dr. Schick.

Scope of the Preparation. This preparation can be used generally for the preparation of the 5-halo-2-thienylsodiums, the corresponding acids and in the preparation of alcohols by addition of ethylene oxide.

4,5-Dibromo-2-thiophenecarboxylic Acid

Materials required to produce 250–260 g. (90–92%).

2-Thiophenecarboxylic acid (1 mole)....................128 g.
Bromine (6 moles).....................................960 g.

Procedure. The 2-thiophenecarboxylic acid is added to the bromine with stirring. After standing until most of the excess bromine has evaporated the mixture is dissolved in excess ammonium carbonate solution. This treatment removes the last traces of bromine from the mixture. The aqueous solution is acidulated with hydrochloric acid and the product filtered off, dried, and recrystallized once from alcohol, m.p. 225–227°.

Reference. This is a modification of the method of Steinkopf, Jacob, and Penz, *Ann.*, **512**, 136 (1934), adapted by Caesar, Socony-Vacuum Laboratories.

2-Thiophenealdehyde

Materials required to produce 19 g. (68%).

Thiophene (0.25 mole).................................21 g.
Phosphorus oxychloride (0.31 mole)....................48 g.
N-Methylformanilide (0.32 mole).......................45 g.

Procedure. The above reactants are mixed together in a one-necked, 500-ml. round-bottom flask fitted through a ground glass joint to a condenser. The reaction is exothermic, and, if the mixture is allowed to stand for some time, the temperature will slowly rise. To reduce the time interval the mixture is heated until hydrogen chloride evolution commences. Heating is immediately discontinued and cooling applied to prevent excessive decomposition. When larger experiments are made, considerable care must be exercised in the cooling, as insufficient cooling will lower the yield considerably. After the initial reaction has subsided, the reaction mixture is heated for twenty minutes on a steam bath to complete the reaction.   After cooling, the contents of the flask are carefully neutralized with excess aqueous sodium acetate.   The mixture is steam distilled and the 2-thiophenealdehyde is extracted from the distillate with ether.   After drying over sodium sulfate the extract is freed of ether and the product distilled; b.p. 66–67° at 4 mm.

> *Reference.* King and Nord, *J. Org. Chem.*, **13**, 635 (1948). A recent modification of this method is said to give improved yields; see Weston and Michaels, *J. Am. Chem. Soc.*, **72**, 1422 (1950).

2-Thenylamine or 2-Thiophenealdehyde

Materials required to produce 250–335 g. of 2-thenylamine or 196–232 g. of 2-thiophenealdehyde.

Thiophene (5 moles).................................. 420 g.
Formaldehyde(36%) (20 moles)...................... 1700 g.
Ammonium chloride (10 moles)...................... 535 g.

Procedure

Step A.   The well-stirred mixture of the above reactants is warmed to 65 degrees and the temperature is controlled at 65–67° degrees by means of an ice bath.   (*Caution:* it is essential that this temperature not be exceeded, since the intermediate N-(2-thenyl)formaldimine hydrochloride undergoes secondary reactions above this temperature.   Vigorous stirring is required to effect distribution of the thiophene in the aqueous layer.)   When the temperature falls to 55°, the stirring is stopped.   If the reaction has proceeded properly, no thiophene layer separates.   If thiophene remains, it can be separated in a separatory funnel.   [Caustic neutralization of this reaction mixture gives dimeric N,N'-di-(2-thenyl)tetrahydro-1,3-diazocyclobutane, see Hartough *et al.*, *J. Am. Chem. Soc.*, **70**, 4013 (1948).]

Step B.   To the aqueous reaction mixture described under *Step A* is added 1000–1500 ml. of methanol and the mixture is allowed to stand at room temperature for three hours.   The dimethylal and methanol are then distilled out, distillation being stopped when the temperature of the residue reaches 90°.   The mixture is cooled and treated with 10 moles of 40% sodium hydroxide.   The amine layer is taken up in ether and the aqueous layer extracted three times with 300 ml. of ether.   The ether extract is dried over anhydrous calcium sulfate and the ether is then removed by distillation.   Distillation of the amine is carried out from a Claisen flask, b.p. 82° at 17 mm., n_D^{20} 1.5615.   Further purification can be effected by distillation through a 12-plate fractionating column.

If *Step A* is carried out with polymeric formaldehyde (300 g.) and 100 g. of acetic acid, the yield of 2-thenylamine is 110 g. and about 195 g. of di-(2-thenyl)amine can be distilled from the reaction, b.p. 162–165° at 5 mm.

References. Hartough, Meisel, Schick, and Koft, *J. Am. Chem. Soc.*, **70**, 4013 (1948). Hartough and Meisel, *ibid.*, **70**, 4018 (1948). The method has been checked by H. E. Rasmussen, Socony-Vacuum Laboratories, on a semipilot plant scale.

Step C (Preparation of 2-Thiophenealdehyde). To the reaction mixture described under *Step A* is added enough 10% sodium hydroxide to raise the *p*H of the mixture to 5–6.5, preferably 6.0–6.5 (as determined by Hydrion Paper). The mixture is then steam distilled; any material (unreacted thiophene) coming over below 100° is discarded. The 2-thiophenealdehyde is collected in the distillate. Steam distillation is continued until all odor (oil of bitter almonds) of 2-thiophenealdehyde disappears. If the distillate is basic, it is acidified with hydrochloric acid to a *p*H of 2–4. The product is taken up in ether and the aqueous layer extracted twice more with ether. The ether solution is dried over calcium sulfate, the ether is removed by distillation, and the product is distilled from a Claisen flask, b.p. 72.5° at 7 mm., n_D^{20} 1.5920.

Reference. Hartough and Dickert, *J. Am. Chem. Soc.*, **71**, 3922 (1949). This preparation has not been checked outside of the author's laboratory but it has been carried out more than fifty times with repeated success.

Scope of the Reactions. These processes are applicable to the preparation of 5-methyl-, 3-methyl-, and 5-chloro-2-thiophenealdehydes and 5-methyl-, 3-methyl-, and 5-chloro-2-thenylamines. The yields are not as high with the 2-chlorothiophene derivatives and the reaction must be carried out with polymeric formaldehyde.

3-Thiophenealdehyde

Materials required to produce 36 g. (49%).

```
3-Thenyl bromide (0.65 mole)..........................114 g.
Hexamethylenetetramine (0.65 mole)....................  90 g.
Chloroform............................................ 200 ml.
```

Procedure. The 3-thenyl bromide is dissolved in the chloroform and the hexamethylenetetramine is added. The mixture is boiled for one hour, cooled, and the salt filtered off. The dry salt is dissolved in 500 ml. of hot water and the mixture steam distilled until one liter of distillate is collected. The distillate is acidified with dilute hydrochloric acid and extracted three times with ether. The extract is dried over calcium sulfate, the ether evaporated on a steam bath and the aldehyde distilled, b.p. 195–199° at 744 mm., d_4^{24} 1.2800, n_D^{20} 1.5860. The phenylhydrazone melts at 136–137°; the 2,4-dinitrophenylhydrazone melts at 236–237°; the semicarbazone melts at 233–234°.

Reference. This procedure is described by Campaigne and Le Suer, *J. Am. Chem. Soc.*, **70**, 1557 (1948). It has not been checked by outside workers but has been used extensively by the above investigators.

2-Nitrothiophene

Materials required to produce 90–110 g. (70–85%).

Thiophene (1 mole)	84 g.
Nitric acid (fuming, sp. g. 1.51) (1.2 moles)	80 g.
Acetic acid (glacial)	600 ml.
Acetic anhydride	340 ml.

Procedure. The thiophene is dissolved in the acetic anhydride and the nitric acid is dissolved in the acetic acid. Each solution is divided into two equal parts. One-half of the nitric acid solution is introduced into a 2-liter reaction flask and the mixture cooled to 10°. Then, with moderate stirring, one-half of the thiophene solution is introduced drop by drop, and at such a rate as to prevent the heating of the reaction mixture above ambient temperatures. Care should be taken to prevent a temperature rise above 25–27°. If such occurs, cool again to 10°. After addition of the first half of the thiophene, the temperature is again reduced to 10° and the remainder of the nitric acid solution is added rapidly to the flask. Nitration is continued by gradual addition of the remaining thiophene. After addition of the thiophene, the mixture is allowed to remain at room temperature for two hours. It is then poured into an equal weight of finely crushed ice and rapidly shaken. The mixture is stored in an ice chest overnight and filtered on a Büchner funnel, washed thoroughly with ice water and dried in a desiccator in the dark. The product is recrystallized from petroleum ether, m.p. 44–45°.

A small amount of additional 2-nitrothiophene and some 3-nitrothiophene can be obtained by steam distillation of the acid filtrate of the original reaction mixture. *Caution:* This compound is a vesicant—remove from exposed skin surfaces by washing with alcohol. Store in a brown bottle.

Reference. This procedure is an adaptation of the method of Babasinian, *Organic Syntheses*, **14**, 76 (1934), used in the author's laboratory. Steinkopf and Hopner, *Ann.*, **501**, 174 (1933), indicate the presence of 3-nitrothiophene as a contaminant in 2-nitrothiophene obtained by Babasinian's method; see *J. Am. Chem. Soc.*, **50**, 2748 (1928).

2-Aminothiophene Hydrochloride Stannic Chloride Double Salt

Materials required to produce 56–59 g. (68–72%).

2-Nitrothiophene (0.31 mole) .... 40 g.
Tin (16–60 mesh) .... 68 g.
Hydrochloric acid (concd.) .... 680 ml.

Procedure. The 2-nitrothiophene and hydrochloric acid are warmed together with vigorous stirring at 40–45° and the tin is added portionwise over a period of fifteen minutes. The temperature is maintained at 40–45° by means of an ice bath during the addition. The ice bath is removed and the remainder of the tin is dissolved without cooling. The white crystalline material is collected, washed with a little alcohol, and then with ether. The product, $(C_4H_3S \cdot NH_2 \cdot HCl)_2 \cdot SnCl_4$, is a white crystalline solid and can be used for further reactions of the 2-amino-thiophene described in Chapter VIII. It turns dark gray on standing and should be stored in a brown bottle. *Caution:* Avoid contact of skin with this material, since it produces a violet skin coloration. Airborne dust from pouring this compound has turned skin of workers to mottled violet where dust contacted moist wrists. Coloration disappears in a few hours to a few days without noticeable after affects.

Reference. Steinkopf, *Die Chemie des Thiophens*, Steinkopff, Dresden, 1941, p. 59
The procedure was checked by the author and A. I. Kosak.

Sodium 2-Thiophenesulfonate or 2-Thiophenesulfonyl Chloride

Materials required to produce 38 g. of the sodium sulfonate (67%)

Thiophene (0.3 mole) .... 25 g.
Chlorosulfonic acid (0.86 mole) .... 100 g.

Procedure. The chlorosulfonic acid in a beaker is cooled to −15°. The thiophene is added, with stirring (manual stirring rod) over a period of eight minutes, during which time the temperature rises to −5°. This mixture is immediately poured into 100 g. of crushed ice and the temperature of the quenched mixture is held below 30° by means of external cooling. The mixture is then neutralized with 325 ml. of 20% sodium hydroxide solution at a temperature below 40°. The aqueous solution is extracted three times with petroleum ether and then evaporated to dryness on a drum drier. The residue is extracted with boiling anhydrous methanol to remove the product from sodium sulfate and the alcoholic solution is dried on the drum drier (or the alcohol is evaporated and the product dried in a vacuum desiccator). The product is a white hygroscopic solid. In this form it may be treated with phosphorus penta-chloride and the resultant 2-thiophenesulfonyl chloride extracted from the reaction mixture by means of carbon tetrachloride. The sulfonyl chloride boils at 123–125° at 14 mm. and melts at 31.5–33° after crystal-lization from petroleum ether.

References. The procedure above is a modification of the method of Steinkopf and Hopner, *Ann.*, **501**, 174 (1933), adapted by R. Smith, Socony-Vacuum Labora-tories. Burton and Davy, *J. Chem. Soc.*, **1948**, 525, obtained a 50% yield of 2-thiophene-sulfonyl chloride by Steinkopf and Hopner's method.

2,3,4,5-Tetraacetoxymercurithiophene

Materials required to produce 336 g. (quantitative yield).

Thiophene (0.30 mole)............................... 25 g.
Mercuric oxide (1.32 moles)...........................285 g.
Acetic acid (glacial).................................550 ml.

Procedure. The mercuric oxide is dissolved in warm acetic acid and the mixture is filtered and placed on a steam bath. The thiophene is added and the mixture heated for two hours. One liter of water is then added to the mixture and the solid derivative is filtered off. After being washed thoroughly with water, the product is dried at 120° in an oven.

Reference. Paolini and Silbermann, *Gazz. chim. ital.*, **55**, 388 (1915). The method has been checked by Rinkes, *Rec. trav. chim.*, **53**, 648 (1934); Steinkopf and the present author.

SUBJECT INDEX

A

515

C

M

Magnesium derivs. of thiophene, 442–4
Malonic acid synthesis, 388–390
Mannich reaction, 310–1, 355
Mass spectral data for
  2,3-dimethylthiophene, 133–140
  2,4-dimethylthiophene, 133
  2,5-dimethylthiophene, 133–140
  3,4-dimethylthiophene, 133–140
  2-methylthiophene, 133–140
  3-methylthiophene, 133–140
  substit. thiophenes, 132–141
  thiolane, 132–140
  thiophene, 132–134
  2-thiophenethiol, 133–140
Meerwein-Pondorff-Verley reaction, 298
Mercaptals of thiophene, 437
Mercaptols of thiophene, 437
2-Mercapto-4-(2-thienyl)thiazole, 256
Mercury acetate derivs., 447–449
Mercury derivs. of thiophene, 444–453
  phys. prop., 449–453
  prepn., 444–9
Mercury halide derivs., 444–7
Mercury halide derivs. of alkylthiophenes,
  450–1
Mercury halide derivs. of halothiophenes,
  451–2
Methadon, see Amidone
2-Methoxy-4-carboxy-5-methylthiophene,
  415
  ethyl ester, 415
2-Methoxy-3,5-dinitrothiophene, 300–301
2-Methoxythiophene, 300
3-Methyl-2-bromothiophene, 425
2 - Methyl - 3 - carbanilido - 4 - oxo - 2-
  thiolene, 415
2 - Methyl - 3 - carbethoxy - 4 - oxo - 5-
  imidonitro-2-thiolene, 415
2 - Methyl - 3 - carbethoxy - 4 - oxo - 5-
  isonitroso-2-thiolene, 415
2 - Methyl - 3 - carbethoxy - 4 - phenyl-
  hydrazino - 5 - isonitrosothiophene,
  415
2 - Methyl - 3 - carbethoxy - 4 - thio-
  phenephenylhydrazine, 415
2 - Methyl - 3 - carboxy - 4 - benzylideno-
  5-oxo-2-thiolene, 415

5-Methyl-5′-carboxy-2,2′-dithienyl, 462
5-Methyl-2,2′-dithienyl, 460, 462
3 - Methyl - 4 - hydroxy - 5 - carbethoxy-
  2-thiophenecarboxylic acid, 415
5-Methyl-2-hydroxythiophene, 313, 462
  prepn., 289
  reactions, 293
2 - Methyl - 4 - hydroxy - 3 - thiophenecarboxylic acid
  ethyl ester, 415
3 - Methyl - 4 - hydroxy - 2 - thiophenecarboxylic acid, 415
5-Methyl-2-iodothiophene, 460
2-Methyl-3-phenylthiophene, 470
2-Methyl-4-phenylthiophene, 470
4-Methyl-2-phenylthiophene, 469
5-Methyl-2-phenylthiophene, 469
3 - Methyl - 4 - phenyl - 2,5 - thiophene-
  dicarboxylic acid, 401
N-Methyl-2-thenaldimine, 206
2-Methyl-3-(2-thenoyl)propanoic acid,
  384
N-Methyl-2-thenylamine, 246, 252, 265
3-Methyl-2-thenylamine, 264
5-Methyl-2-thenylamine, 265
3 - Methyl - 2 - thenylaminomethylsulfonic acid, 249
3 - Methyl - 5 - thenylaminomethylsulfonic acid, 249
5-Methyl-2-thenylbromide, 186, 190, 301
5-Methyl-2-thenyl cyanide, 301
2 - (5 - Methyl - 2 - thenyl) - 4,5 - di-
  hydroimidazole, 44
5-Methyl-2-thenyl ethyl ether, 301
N - (5 - Methyl - 2 - thenyl)formaldimine
  hydrochloride, 244
2-Methylthienylcinchoninic acid, 30
2 - Methyl - 2 - (2′ - thienyl) - 1,3 - di-
  thiacyclopentane, 437
1 - Methyl - 4 - (2 - thienylphenylmethyl)-
  piperazine, 259
2 - (5 - Methyl - 2 - thienyl)quinoline - 4-
  carboxylic acid, 39–40
4-Methyl-2-thienylsodium, 441
5-Methyl-2-thienylsodium, 441
4-Methyl-3-thiolene-2-carboxylic acid,
  155

N

O

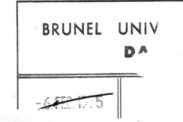